A
HISTORY OF SCIENCE
AND ITS RELATIONS WITH
PHILOSOPHY & RELIGION

New York
The Macmillan Co.

London
The
Cambridge University Press

Bombay, Calcutta and Madras
Macmillan and Co., Ltd.

Toronto
The Macmillan Co. of
Canada, Ltd.

A

HISTORY OF SCIENCE

AND ITS RELATIONS WITH
PHILOSOPHY & RELIGION

By

SIR WILLIAM DAMPIER
M.A., F.R.S.

Fellow and sometime Senior Tutor of Trinity College, Cambridge
Fellow of Winchester College

NEW YORK: THE MACMILLAN COMPANY
CAMBRIDGE, ENGLAND: AT THE UNIVERSITY PRESS
1932

REPRINTED, NOVEMBER, 1930
REPRINTED,   JANUARY, 1931
REPRINTED,   FEBRUARY, 1931
REPRINTED,   MARCH, 1932

REPRODUCED AND PRINTED IN THE UNITED STATES OF AMERICA
BY THE NATIONAL PROCESS COMPANY, NEW YORK CITY.

Contents

"Natura enim non nisi parendo vincitur."

At first men try with magic charm
To fertilize the earth,
To keep their flocks and herds from harm
And bring new young to birth.

Then to capricious gods they turn
To save from fire or flood;
Their smoking sacrifices burn
On altars red with blood.

Next bold philosopher and sage
A settled plan decree,
And prove by thought or sacred page
What Nature ought to be.

But Nature smiles—a Sphinx-like smile—
Watching their little day
She waits in patience for a while—
Their plans dissolve away.

Then come those humbler men of heart
With no completed scheme,
Content to play a modest part,
To test, observe, and dream,

Till out of chaos come in sight
Clear fragments of a Whole;
Man, learning Nature's ways aright,
Obeying, can control.

The great Design now glows afar;
But yet its changing Scenes
Reveal not what the Pieces are
Nor what the Puzzle means.

And Nature smiles—still unconfessed
The secret thought she thinks—
Inscrutable she guards unguessed
The Riddle of the Sphinx.

Hilfield, Dorset;
September, 1929.

Preface

THE vast and imposing structure of modern science is perhaps the greatest triumph of the human mind. But the story of its origin, its development and its achievements is one of the least known parts of history, and has hardly yet found its way into general literature. Historians treat of war, of politics, of economics; but of the growth of those activities which have revealed the individual atom and opened to our vision the depths of space, which have revolutionized philosophic thought and given us the means of advancing our material welfare to a level beyond the dreams of former ages, most of them tell us little or nothing.

To the Greeks, philosophy and science were one, and, in the Middle Ages, both were bound up with theology. The experimental method of studying nature, developed after the Renaissance, led to a separation; for, while natural philosophy came to be based on Newtonian dynamics, the followers of Kant and Hegel led idealist philosophy away from contemporary science, which, in turn, soon learned to ignore metaphysics. But evolutionary biology and modern mathematics and physics on the one hand have deepened scientific thought, and on the other have again forced philosophers to take account of science, which has now once more a meaning for philosophy, for theology, and for religion. Meanwhile physics, which for so long sought and found mechanical models of the phenomena observed, seems at last to be in touch with concepts where such models fail, with fundamental things which, in Newton's phrase, "certainly are not mechanical".

Men of science, most of whom used naïvely to assume that they were dealing with ultimate reality, are coming to see more clearly the true nature of their work. The methods of science are primarily analytic, and lead, as far as may be, to the explanation of phenomena in mathematical form and in terms of physical concepts. But the fundamental concepts of physical science, it is now understood, are abstractions, framed by our minds so as to bring order and simplicity into an apparent chaos of phenomena. The approach to reality

b

through science, therefore, gives only aspects of reality, pictures drawn on simplified lines, but not reality itself. Nevertheless, even philosophers are coming to see that, in a metaphysical study of reality, the methods and results of science are the best available evidence, and that a new realism, if possible at all, must be built up by their means.

Simultaneously, a renewed interest in the history of science and its interactions with other modes of thought has grown up. The first publication in Belgium of the periodical *Isis* in 1913, and later the foundation of the History of Science Society, an international organization with its centre in America, mark an epoch in the development of the subject. Probably the philosophic and historical revivals are connected, for, while the mathematician or the experimentalist engaged on some specific problem needs only a knowledge of the work of his immediate predecessors, he who studies the deeper meaning of science in general, and its bearing on other realms of thought, must understand something of how it has come to be.

It is nearly a hundred years since Whewell wrote his books on the history and philosophy of the inductive sciences, but his careful and well-balanced judgments are still of use and value. Since Whewell's day, not only has there been a mighty growth of scientific knowledge, but many specialized studies have thrown new light on the past. The time has come for another attempt to tell the general story of science on Whewell's lines, to present, not a detailed study of any one period or subject, but a complete outline of the development of scientific thought. I believe that such a history of science has much to teach both about the inner meaning of science itself and about its bearing on philosophy and on religion.

The humanists of the Renaissance revived the study of Greek not solely for the sake of the language and literature, but also because the best knowledge of nature available was to be found in the works of the Greek philosophers. Thus a classical education then comprised all natural knowledge. That has long ceased to be true, and nowadays a culture based on the languages of two thousand years ago represents very inadequately the true Greek spirit, unless, from a simultaneous study of the methods and achievements of science in the past and the present, it looks forward joyously to an increasing knowledge of nature in the future.

The general plan of this book is based on that of a sketch of the subject by my wife and myself published by Messrs Longmans in 1912, under the name of *Science and the Human Mind*. I have also used and extended ideas which appear in some of my other writings, especially in the following: *The Recent Development of Physical Science* (Murray, 5 editions, 1904 to 1924); the chapter on "The Scientific Age" in Volume XII of the *Cambridge Modern History* (1910); the article "Science" in the eleventh edition of the *Encyclopædia Britannica* (1911); the collection of scientific classics in the volume of *Cambridge Readings in the Literature of Science*, 1924 and 1929; a Presidential Address to the Devonshire Association in 1927 on the Newtonian Epoch; and the chapter on "The Birth of Modern Science" in Harmsworth's *Universal History* (1928). Acknowledgment is due to the respective Publishers of these works.

It is of course quite impossible to specify all the sources from which the following chapters have been derived. But I must make mention of the help I have obtained from the historical work of Dr George Sarton, and the scientific and philosophic writings of my friends Dr A. N. Whitehead and Professor Eddington. The first volume of Dr Sarton's monumental *Introduction to the History of Science* appeared in 1927, so that I was able to use his wonderful collection of material for my account of ancient times and the early mediaeval period. His other volumes will be awaited with interest.

I am also deeply grateful for much personal help from friends who have criticized parts of the manuscript or the proof sheets. Professor D. S. Robertson read the first chapter on "Science in the Ancient World", Dr H. F. Stewart that on "The Middle Ages", Sir Ernest Rutherford the account of "The New Era in Physics", Professor Eddington the sections on relativity and astro-physics and also the last chapter, on "Scientific Philosophy and its Outlook", while my daughter Margaret, Mrs Bruce Anderson, read the parts dealing with biology and the introductory matter. Miss Christine Elliott did most of the secretarial work; she copied and recopied the manuscript on an average about five times, and made innumerable criticisms and suggestions. My sister and my daughter Edith shared in the tedious task of preparing the index. I offer them all my cordial thanks; to their help is due much of any value the book may possess.

I began the studies of which this volume is the outcome in an attempt to clarify my own ideas on the all-important subjects with which it deals. I have written the book chiefly for my own satisfaction and amusement, but I hope that some of my readers may find my labours useful to themselves.

W. C. D. D.-W.

Cambridge
August, 1929

The need for a new edition of this book, coming as it does within a few months of publication, shows that the subjects with which it deals are of interest not only to men of science but also to a wider circle of readers.

No story is more fascinating than that of the development of scientific thought—man's age-long effort to understand the world in which he finds himself. Moreover, the story is of special interest now, when we see one of the historic syntheses of knowledge taking place under our eyes, and feel that we are on the eve of great events. I have a firm belief in science as a fit subject for history and a basis for literature, and, if I have done something to instil that belief into others, I am content.

I wish to thank those several reviewers and correspondents who have offered instructed criticism of specific points in the first edition. If I have not adopted all their suggestions, I have at least given to them careful consideration. In particular I must acknowledge gratefully the help I have received from my friends Sir James Jeans and Professor E. D. Adrian.

W. C. D. D.-W.

Cambridge
March, 1930

Introduction

THE Latin *scientia* (*scire*, to learn, to know), in its widest sense, means learning or knowledge. But the English word "science" is used as a shortened term for natural science, though the nearest German equivalent, *Wissenschaft*, still includes all systematic study, not only of what we call science, but also of history, philology or philosophy. To us, then, science may be defined as ordered knowledge of natural phenomena and the rational study of the relations between the concepts in which those phenomena are expressed.

The origin of physical science can be traced in the observation of natural occurrences, such as the apparent movements of the heavenly bodies, and in the invention of rude implements, by the help of which men strove to increase the safety and comfort of their lives. Similarly, biological science must have begun with the observation of plants and animals, and with primitive medicine and surgery.

But, at an early stage, men almost universally took a wrong path. Led by the idea that like produces like, they tried by imitating nature in rites of sympathetic magic to bring rain or sunshine, or fertility to the teeming earth. Some of them, not satisfied by the results achieved, passed to another stage, to the animistic belief that nature must be under the sway of beings, capricious like themselves, but more powerful. The Sun became the flaming chariot of Phoebus; thunder and lightning were the weapons of Zeus or Thor. Men sought to propitiate such beings, perhaps by rites which were the same as, or developed from, those which had arisen in the more primitive stage. Other men, watching the steady motion of the stars, or the wanderings of the planets, conceived the idea of an immutable Fate controlling human destinies, which might be read in the sky. Magic, religion and astrology are clearly three forerunners of science, though their exact historical relations with science and with each other are uncertain.

Some order in empirical knowledge appears in the records of ancient Egypt and Babylon—units and rules of measurement, simple arithmetic, a calendar of the year, the recognition of the periodicity of astronomic events, even of eclipses. But the first to submit such knowledge to rational examination, to try to trace causal relations among its parts, in fact the first to create science, were the Greek nature-philosophers of Ionia. The earliest and most successful of such attempts was the conversion of the empirical rules for land surveying, mostly derived from Egypt, into the deductive science of geometry, the beginnings of which are traditionally assigned to Thales of Miletus and Pythagoras of Samos, while the final formulation in ancient times was made by Euclid of Alexandria three hundred years later.

The nature-philosophers sought reality in matter, and slowly developed a theory of a primary element, culminating in the atomism of Leucippus and Democritus. On the other hand, the more mystical Pythagoreans of South Italy saw reality, not in matter, but in form and number. Though their own discovery that the side and diagonal of a square were incommensurable in finite units was difficult to reconcile with the idea that integral numbers are the fundamental entities of existence, that idea survived and reappeared from time to time throughout the ages.

With the rise of the Athenian School of Socrates and Plato, the Ionian nature-philosophy was superseded by metaphysics. The Greek mind became entranced with its own operations, and turned from the study of nature to look within. The Pythagorean doctrine of form was developed into the view that ideas alone possess full reality, which is denied to the objects of sense. Aristotle in his biology returned to observation and experiment, but in physics and astronomy he followed too closely the introspective methods of his master Plato.

The conquests of Alexander carried Hellenistic civilization to the East, and founded a new intellectual centre at Alexandria. Here, and simultaneously in Sicily and South Italy, a new method appeared. Instead of complete philosophic schemes, Aristarchus, Archimedes and Hipparchus set out specific and limited problems, and solved them by scientific processes like those of modern times. Even astronomy showed the change. To the Egyptians and Babylonians the Universe was a box, the Earth being the floor. The Ionians realized the Earth as floating free in space; the Pythagoreans as a sphere moving round a central fire. Aristarchus, considering the definite geometrical problem of the Sun, Earth and Moon, saw that it was simpler to imagine the central fire to be the Sun, and from his geometry made an estimate of its size. But this theory was unacceptable to most, and Hipparchus returned to the belief in a central Earth, with the heavenly bodies moving round it in a complex system of cycles and epicycles, a system handed on to the Middle Ages in the writings of Ptolemy.

The Romans, with all their genius as soldiers, lawyers and administrators, had little original philosophic power, and even before Rome fell, science had ceased to advance. Meanwhile, the Early Fathers of the Church welded together Christian doctrines, Neo-Platonic philosophy, and elements derived from oriental Mystery Religions, into the first great Christian synthesis, predominantly Platonic and Augustinian. Through the Dark Ages, Greek learning was only known to the West in abstracts and commentaries, though an Arabic school arose which, deriving its original impulse from Greek sources, itself made some additions to natural knowledge.

In the thirteenth century the full works of Aristotle were rediscovered and translated into Latin, first from Arabic versions and then directly from the Greek. A new and alternative synthesis arose in the scholasticism of St Thomas Aquinas, who built up a complete, rational scheme of knowledge, in which Christian doctrines were blended with Aristotelian philosophy and science.

As the survival of Roman Law kept alive the ideal of order through the time of chaos and through the Middle Ages, so Scholasticism upheld the supremacy of reason, teaching that God and the Universe can be apprehended, even partially understood, by the mind of man. In this it prepared the way for science, which has to assume that nature is intelligible. The men of the Renaissance, when they founded modern science, owed this assumption to the Scholastics.

Yet the essence of the new experimental method was an appeal from a completely rational system to the tribunal of brute facts—facts which bore no relation to any philosophic synthesis then possible. Natural science may use deductive reasoning at an intermediate stage of its enquiries, and inductive theories are an essential part of its procedure, but primarily it is empirical, and its ultimate appeal is to observation and experiment; it does not, like mediaeval Scholasticism, accept a philosophic system on authority and then argue from the system what the facts ought to be. Contrary to an opinion sometimes held, mediaeval philosophy and theology made full use of reason, being deduced by logical methods from what were accepted as authoritative and certain premises, the scriptures as interpreted by the Church, and the works of Plato and Aristotle. Science, on the other hand, depends on experience, and uses methods somewhat like those employed in fitting together the pieces or words of a puzzle. Reason is used to solve the definite problems of the puzzle, and to form the limited syntheses and theories which alone are possible; but observation or experiment is the starting point of the investigation and the final arbiter.

Scholasticism as interpreted by Thomas Aquinas preserved a belief in the intelligibility of nature, amid the welter of magic, astrology and superstition, mostly relics of Paganism, which enmeshed the mediaeval mind. But Thomist philosophy included the geocentric astronomy of Ptolemy, and the anthropomorphic physics of Aristotle with his many erroneous ideas—for instance, that motion implies the continual exertion of force, and again that things are essentially heavy or light and seek their natural places. Hence the Scholastics opposed the theory of Copernicus, refused to look through the telescope of Galileo, and denied that things heavy and light could fall to the ground at the same rate, even when Galileo had demonstrated that fact from the leaning Tower of Pisa.

And an even deeper divergence lay behind these differences. To Aquinas and his contemporaries, as to Aristotle, the real world was that disclosed by the senses: a world of colour, sound and warmth; of beauty, goodness and truth, or sometimes perhaps of ugliness, evil and error. Under the analysis of Galileo, colour, sound and warmth vanished into mere sensations, and the real world appeared to be but particles of matter in motion, which apparently had nothing to do with the beautiful, the good, the true, or their opposites. The perplexities of the theory of knowledge, the difficulties which underlie the apprehension of matter in motion by a non-material and non-extended mind, appeared for the first time.

The work begun by Galileo was consummated by Newton, who showed that the hypothesis of masses moving under their

mutual forces was sufficient to explain all the majestic motion
of the solar system. Thus the first great physical synthesis
was put together, though Newton himself pointed out that
the cause of the gravitational force remained unknown. His
disciples, however, especially the French philosophers of the
eighteenth century, ignoring his wise spirit of caution, converted Newton's science into a mechanical philosophy, in
which the whole of the past and future was theoretically
calculable and man became a machine.

Some clear-thinking minds realized that science did not
necessarily reveal reality, while others, with practical wisdom,
accepted determinism as a convenient working hypothesis for
science—indeed the only hypothesis possible—but treated man
as a free and responsible agent in ordinary life, and continued
to practise their religion unperturbed. The whole of existence
is too great a thing to yield its secrets when studied in one
aspect only. Another line of escape from mechanism was taken
by the followers of Kant and Hegel, who, in German idealism,
built up a philosophy ultimately derived from Plato, a philosophy which became almost completely separated from contemporary science.

In spite of these reactions, Newtonian dynamics reinforced
both crude materialism and the philosophy of determinism.
To minds more logical than profound the inference from science
to philosophy seemed inevitable, an inference strengthened
with every advance in physical science. Lavoisier extended
the proof of the persistence of matter to cover chemical transformations, Dalton finally established the atomic theory, and
Joule proved the principle of the conservation of energy. The
motion of each individual molecule, it is true, was still indeterminate, but statistically the behaviour of the myriad
molecules which make up a finite quantity of matter could be
calculated and predicted.

In the second half of the nineteenth century it seemed to
some men that the mechanical outlook was extending to
biology. Darwin gained credence for the old theory of evolution by marshalling the facts of geology and variation, and
framing the hypothesis of natural selection. Man, who, a little
lower than the Angels, had surveyed creation from the Earth
its centre, became a mere link in the chain of organic development on a small and casual planet circling round one of a

myriad stars—a puny being, the plaything of blind, irresistible forces, which bore no relation to his desires or his welfare.

Physiology, too, began to expand the field of research within which physical and chemical principles could be used to explain the functions of the living organism. In some biological problems the organism must be treated as a whole, and this fact is of philosophic importance. But science is by its nature analytical and abstract, and is forced to express as much of its knowledge as possible in terms of physics, the most fundamental and abstract of all the natural sciences. When it was found that more and more could be so expressed, confidence was gained in the method, and there arose a belief that a complete physical or mechanical explanation of all existence is theoretically possible.

Supreme importance is thus given to those physical concepts which, at any given time, are the most fundamental yet reached, though philosophers have sometimes been rather too late in adopting them. The German materialists of the nineteenth century based their philosophy on *Kraft und Stoff* just when physicists were realizing that force was but an anthropomorphic aspect of mass-acceleration, and matter was being sublimated from the hard, massy particles of Democritus and Newton into vortex atoms or kinks in an aethereal medium. Light, explained by Young and Fresnel in terms of mechanical waves in a semi-rigid, material aether, was converted by Maxwell into electro-magnetic undulations in something unknown —a simplification to the mathematician, but a loss of intelligibility to the experimentalist.

In spite of these indications, most men of science, and especially biologists, at that time held a common-sense materialism, and believed that physical science revealed the reality of things. They did not read idealist philosophy, and in any case would not have been convinced thereby. But in 1887 Mach, speaking in language with which they were familiar, revived the old theory that science only gives information about phenomena as apprehended by the senses, and that the ultimate nature of reality is beyond the reach of our intelligence. Others upheld the view, that, while this phenomenalism is as far as the scientific evidence can carry us, yet the fact that science has put together a consistent model of natural phenomena is a valid *metaphysical* argument that some reality, corresponding to the model, lies beneath. But the different sciences are only analogous to plane diagrams from which the model can be constructed, so that, for instance, the determinism indicated by mechanics is but an effect of our procedure and of the definitions which underlie that science. Similarly, principles such as the persistence of matter and the conservation of energy are inevitable, for, in constructing a science of nature from the welter of phenomena, the mind, unconsciously and as a matter of convenience, picks out those quantities which remain constant, and builds its model round them. Then, later on, the experimentalist rediscovers their constancy.

But few nineteenth century men of science were interested in philosophy, even in that of Mach. Most of them assumed that they themselves were dealing with realities, and that the main lines of possible scientific enquiry had been laid down once for all. It seemed that all that remained for the physicist to do was to make measurements to an increasing order of accuracy, and invent an intelligible mechanism which would explain the nature of the luminiferous aether.

Meanwhile biology had accepted Darwinian natural selection as an adequate explanation of the origin of species and had turned to other problems. It was only with the rediscovery in 1900 of Mendel's forgotten work that the question was reopened, and Darwin's experimental method once more used. While the broad facts which point to evolution in past geological ages are conclusive, it has become increasingly doubtful whether natural selection alone is a sufficient cause.

Then, from 1895 onwards, there came the new revelation in physics. Atoms were resolved by J. J. Thomson into more minute corpuscles, and these in turn into electrical units, the mass of which was explained as being merely one factor in electro-magnetic momentum. It began to look as though "electricity" were to be the last and sufficient word in physical science. Rutherford explained radio-activity in terms of atomic disintegration, and pictured the atom as a positive nucleus with negative electrons circling round it. Matter, instead of being dense, closely-packed stuff, became an open structure, in which the material, even as disembodied electric charges, was almost negligible in size compared with the empty spaces. Furthermore, the statistical principles of atomic disintegration were discovered. It became possible to calculate how many atoms in a milligram of radium will explode in a second, though we cannot yet tell when the life of any given atom will end.

If waves of light are electrical, they must start from electric charges in motion, and at first it seemed that in our new-found electron, moving in accordance with Newtonian dynamics, we had a satisfactory electrical theory of matter. But, if electrons swing round the nucleus of the atom as planets circle round the Sun, they should give out radiation of all wave-lengths, the energy increasing in a calculable way as the wave-length shortens. This does not happen, and, to explain the facts, Planck was led to suppose that radiation is emitted and absorbed in definite units or quanta, each quantum being a fixed amount of "action", a quantity equivalent to energy multiplied by time. This theory was greatly strengthened by its success in fields of physics other than that which saw its birth; yet it cannot, like the classical theory of continuous waves, explain easily and naturally the facts of diffraction, and other phenomena due to the interference of light. We have to be content to use the classical theory for some purposes and the quantum theory for others, though they seem inconsistent with each other, a compromise unusual to the physicist, whose subject has hitherto been the most completely consistent and rationalized of all experimental sciences.

Another difficulty, the constancy of the measured velocity of light irrespective of the motion of the observer, was cleared up when Einstein pointed out that neither space nor time are absolute quantities, but are always relative to some one who measures them. This principle of relativity, when its consequences are followed out, means a revolution not only in physical theories, but in the implicit assumptions of older physical thought. It explains matter and gravitation as the necessary consequences of something analogous to curvature in a four-dimensional continuum of space-time. The curvature even sets bounds to space, and light travelling onwards may, after millions of years, return to its starting point.

Not only have the hard, massy particles of matter disappeared, but philosophically it will be seen that the old metaphysical concept of matter, as that which is extended in space and persistent in time, is destroyed, now that neither space nor time are absolute, but are figments of the imagination, and a particle is a mere series of events in space-time. Relativity reinforces the conclusions of atomic physics.

Rutherford's conception of the atom was developed on the lines of the quantum theory by Bohr, who explained many of the facts by supposing that the single electron in the hydrogen atom can only circulate in four definite orbits, and only radiate at the moments when it leaps suddenly from one orbit to another. This, like the quantum theory itself, is inconsistent with Newtonian dynamics, as long, at all events, as the electron is regarded as a simple particle.

For a time Bohr's atom, developed in detail by himself and others, seemed a most convincing model of atomic structure, but in 1925 it definitely failed to account for some of the finer lines in the hydrogen spectrum. In the next year a new chapter in physics was opened by the work of Heisenberg, who pointed out that any theory of electronic orbits went beyond what the facts warranted. We can only study atoms by observing what goes into them or what comes out— radiation, electrons, and sometimes radio-active particles; we cannot tell what happens at other times. Orbits are an unconscious and unjustified assumption, founded on the analogy of Newtonian dynamics. Heisenberg therefore left his theory of atomic structure in terms of differential equations, with no attempt at a physical explanation.

Then Schrödinger, taking up de Broglie's wave-mechanics, developed a new theory, on which an electron has some of the properties of a particle and some of a wavelet, an idea since supported by experimental evidence. Schrödinger's theory is expressed by equations which are equivalent to those of Heisenberg, so that mathematically the two theories are identical. It is impossible to frame a physical model on Heisenberg's theory, and difficult to do so on that of Schrödinger. Indeed, a principle of uncertainty has appeared, which indicates that we cannot specify both the position and the velocity of an electron. Physical science has successively found many ultimates—gravitating particles, atoms, electrons—and in each case has gone farther and invented models which explained those ultimates in terms of something yet more fundamental. But, in the quantum of "action" and in the equations of the indeterminate particle and wavelet, we see concepts which the mind finds it difficult to picture. Perhaps a new atomic model may be framed successfully once more, but possibly we are approaching fundamental things, which cannot be expressed in mechanical terms.

After a period of separation, with crude materialism on one side and somewhat hazy German idealism on the other, science and philosophy once more came into touch, first in various forms of evolutionary thought, and then, through a deeper analysis, by new developments in mathematics and physics. Recent studies of the principles of mathematics and of logic have thrown fresh light on the theory of knowledge, and led to a new realism which, turning from the general philosophic systems of the past, studies limited philosophic problems as science studies limited scientific ones, and seeks metaphysical reality beneath scientific phenomenalism.

To some modern philosophers the determinism of science seems to be due to its method of abstraction. Its concepts, the modern equivalent of Platonic ideas, are alone concerned in its abstract reasoning and theories; they have logical consequences, which are indeed inevitable and determined by the nature of the concepts. But it is a misplaced concreteness which transfers that determinism to the objects of sense. Again, "vitalism" held that in living matter physical and chemical laws are suspended by some higher agency. This idea too is discredited nowadays, but some physiologists point but that the biological organism shows a co-ordination, an integration, of its physical and chemical functions beyond the reach of a purely mechanical explanation. Nevertheless, others contend, mechanism has to be assumed at each stage of physical or chemical investigation, though it is possible that it may ultimately break down in a final physical principle of uncertainty. Teleology, to be convincing, may have to take account of the whole of existence instead of only individual organisms. The universe may be completely mechanical when viewed from the abstract standpoint of mechanics, and yet completely spiritual from the aspect of mind. A ray of starlight may be traced by physics from its distant source to its effect on an optic nerve, but, when consciousness apprehends its brightness and colour and feels its beauty, the sensation of sight and the knowledge of beauty certainly exist, and yet they are neither mechanical nor physical.

Physical science represents one analytical aspect of reality; it draws a chart which, as experience shows, enables us to predict and sometimes to control the workings of nature. From time to time great syntheses of knowledge are made. Suddenly bits of the puzzle fit together; different and isolated concepts are brought into harmony by some master-mind, and mighty visions flash into sight—Newton's cosmogony, Maxwell's co-ordination of light and electricity, or Einstein's reduction of gravity to a common property of space and time. All the signs point to another such synthesis, in which relativity, quantum theory and wave-mechanics may fall into the all-embracing unity of some one fundamental concept.

At such historic moments physical science seems supreme. But the clear insight into its meaning which is given by modern scientific philosophy shows that by its inherent nature and fundamental definitions it is but an abstraction, and that, with all its great and ever-growing power, it can never represent the whole of existence. Science may transcend its own natural sphere and usefully criticize some other modes of contemporary thought and some of the dogmas in which theologians have expressed their beliefs. But to see life steadily and see it whole we need not only science, but ethics, art and philosophy; we need the apprehension of a sacred mystery, the sense of communion with a Divine Power, that constitute the ultimate basis of religion.

Chapter I

SCIENCE IN THE ANCIENT WORLD

The Beginnings of Civilization—Babylonia—Egypt—India—
Greece and the Greeks—The Origins of Greek Religion and
Philosophy—Religion and Philosophy in Classical Times—The
Ionian Philosophers—The School of Pythagoras—The Problem
of Matter—The Atomists—Greek Medicine—From the Atomists
to Aristotle—Aristotle—Hellenistic Civilization—Deductive
Geometry—Archimedes and the Origins of Mechanics—
Aristarchus and Hipparchus—The School of Alexandria—The
Origins of Alchemy—The Roman Age—The Decline and Fall
of Learning.

AT the dawn of history, civilization first appears out of the *The Beginnings* darkness in the valleys of the great rivers, the Euphrates *of Civilization* and the Tigris, the Indus, and the Nile. Of the people who dwelt in those valleys, we know most about those of Egypt and Babylonia, primarily from references found in the writings of Greek historians. But that meagre source of information has been greatly augmented in recent years by the discovery of the remains of many of their buildings, sculptures and tablets, and by the excavations of Royal Tombs in which domestic objects, decorations and inscriptions have been found. Such knowledge is of course fragmentary, depending as it does upon the double chance of the survival of ancient records and of their discovery and correct interpretation by present-day researchers; but much information has already been obtained, and more is constantly coming to hand.

The surest foundation for the origin of science in its practical *Babylonia* form is to be found in the co-ordination and standardization of the knowledge of common-sense and of industry. An early sign of such co-ordination can be traced in the edicts of the Babylonian rulers as far back as 2500 years before Christ, when the realization of the importance of fixed units of physical measurement led to the issue under royal authority of standards of length, weight and capacity.

The Babylonian unit of length was the finger, equal to 1·65 centimetres, or about $\frac{2}{3}$ inch; the foot contained 20 fingers, and the cubit 30 fingers; the pole was 12 cubits and the surveyor's cord was 120 cubits; the league was a distance equal to 180 cords, that is 6·65 miles. In measures of weight, the

Babylonia   grain was equal to 0·046 gramme; the shekel 8·416 grammes; and the talent 30·5 kilogrammes, or $67\frac{1}{3}$ pounds.[1]

In the earliest recorded times barley seems to have been the medium of exchange. By the third millennium before Christ, ingots of copper and of silver were also used, though barley continued to be current for some payments. The value of gold in terms of an equal weight of silver varied at different times from six to twelve.

The elements of arithmetic also were known to the Babylonians. The multiplication table and tables of squares and cubes have been found among their tablets. A duodecimal system of units, making the calculation of fractions easy, existed together with a decimal system derived from our ten fingers, special importance being assigned to the number sixty, as a combination of the two systems. The parallel use of this double notation was the basis of the whole scheme of weights and measures—the circle with its subdivisions of angular measurement, the fathom, the foot and its square, the talent and the bushel.

The beginnings of geometry, too, illustrate the origin of an abstract science from the needs of everyday life, and are to be found in the rudimentary formulae and figures for land surveying. Plans of fields led to more complicated plans of towns, and even to a map of the world as then known. But actual knowledge was woven in an inextricable manner with magical conceptions, and together the two passed from Babylon westwards. For centuries European thought was dominated by the idea of the virtue of special numbers, their connection with the gods, and the application of geometrical diagrams to the prediction of the future.

In Babylon also the systematic measurement of time began at an early date. The importance of a knowledge of the seasons grows as agriculture develops among a primitive people. Wheat and barley seem to be indigenous in the neighbourhood of the river Euphrates, and we know that they were there cultivated as food plants at an early date, for they are mentioned on the clay tablets, and the plough is depicted in Babylonian art. The cultivation of cereals, which require seasonal treatment and an ample water supply, makes a

[1] L. J. Delaporte, *La Mésopotamie*; Paris, 1923. Eng. trans. London, 1925; p. 224.

calendar almost a necessity, and we may have here one reason why the beginnings of astronomical observation occurred in the basins of the Euphrates and the Nile. The day as a unit of time was imposed on man by nature. When a longer unit was wanted, the month was first taken, each month beginning with the appearance of the new moon. Then attempts were made to determine the number of months in the cycle of the seasons, and about 2000 B.C. the Babylonian year settled down to one of 360 days or twelve months, the necessary adjustments being made from time to time by the interposition of extra months. The day was divided into hours, minutes and seconds, and the sun-dial, in the form of a simple vertical rod or gnomon, was invented to mark the passing hours.

The apparent movement of the Sun and planets among the fixed stars was observed, and the naming of seven days after the Sun, Moon and the five known planets, gave the week as another unit of time. The journey of the Sun across the sky was mapped out into twelve divisions to agree with the months. Each division was named from some mythical deity or animal, and was represented by the appropriate symbol. Thus arose the association of parts of the sky with the Ram, the Crab, the Scorpion and other beasts, which afterwards became connected with the definite groups of stars which we still call by those names.

The Babylonians pictured the Universe as a closed box or chamber, the floor being the Earth. In the centre the floor rose to snowy regions, in the midst of which was the source of the Euphrates. Round the Earth lay a moat of water, and beyond it stood celestial mountains supporting the dome of the sky.[1]

Astronomical observation in Babylon can be traced back for more than twenty centuries before the Christian era, the first accurate records known being those of the rising and setting of the planet Venus. From this early date the priests, aided by the brilliancy of the atmosphere, observed the aspects of the heavens night by night, and noted their observations on clay tablets. Gradually the periodicity of astronomical events became apparent, till, according to a document of the sixth century B.C., the relative positions of the Sun and Moon were calculated in advance, and the prediction of eclipses was made

[1] G. Maspero, *The Dawn of Civilization*, Eng. trans. 5th ed. 1910.

Babylonia possible.[1] This may be regarded as the origin of scientific
astronomy, for which Babylonia, with its three schools of Uruk,
Sippar and Babylon with Borsippa, can claim the credit.

On this basis of definite knowledge, a fantastic scheme of
astrology was built up, and, indeed, was regarded by the
Babylonians as the chief and most worthy object of the underlying science. Starting doubtless from accidental coincidences,
there arose a belief that the stars fixed and foretold the course
of human affairs. By such observations and interpretations of
the heavens, the Babylonian astrologer acquired a very real
power over the minds of men. "Astronomy, as thus understood, was not merely the queen of the sciences, it was the
mistress of the world." Each temple put together a library
of astronomical and astrological literature from which the
methods of divination might be learned. One such library,
consisting of some seventy clay tablets, was of special repute
in the seventh century before Christ, and is considered to have
possessed records dating from 3000 years earlier.

Astrology reached its zenith in Babylon about 540 B.C., after
the country had been conquered by the Chaldaeans, and two
centuries later it spread to Greece and then over the known
world, although by that time it was showing signs in its
original home of passing into more rational astronomy.
Nevertheless, Chaldaean astrologers continued to be famous
and were much in request, while sorcerers and exorcists
acted as physicians, despite their ignorance of the elements
of medicine.

Modern study of primitive peoples shows that magic usually
begins in its "sympathetic" form, whereby men try to
obtain control over nature by mimic copying of the process
they wish to bring about, or by acting a drama in which it is
represented. Thus, to take but one example out of multitudes,
when frogs croak it rains. The savage feels he can do that too;
so he dresses as a frog and croaks to bring the wished-for rain.
Hence arise ritual and mystery cults, prior to the dogma or
mythology afterwards invented to explain them. For, at a
later stage, when rite and ritual have to be accounted for, the
powers of nature are thought to be animate, and long-

---

[1] G. Sarton, *Introduction to the History of Science*, vol. i, Washington and
Baltimore, 1927, p. 71, quoting from L. W. King, *A History of Babylon*, London,
1915.

established magic rites, unchanged or perhaps modified, take *Babylonia* the form of propitiatory ceremonies.

This later type of magic seems to have been reached in Babylon before the earliest times of which records have survived. Although some gods, such as Oannes, the source of all human knowledge, were thought to be beneficent,[1] Babylonian magic suggested to those who practised it that the gods in general were inimical to man. This view may have been reinforced, and indeed the underlying magic determined, by the insecurity of life on the banks of the Tigris and the Euphrates, where sudden storms and floods were always ready to sweep away man and his puny works together in unforeseen ruin.

Again, the idea that man's destiny was controlled by the stars, an idea which arose in early times in Babylon, led to the concept of an inexorable, inhuman Fate. Black magic and deadly nature indicated hostile gods, and, in turn, doubtless the idea of hostile gods intensified the savage element in Babylonian magic and astrology. In a world dominated by such a gloomy outlook, there was little opportunity for science or rational philosophy to develop.

When we turn to consider the other great civilization of *Egypt* early times—that of Egypt—a certain difference in religious attitude is seen. In Egypt the divine powers were for the most part represented in mythology as friendly, as watching over man, ready to protect and to guide him in life, in death and in the afterworld.

It is possible that this difference was due, partly at all events, to physical surroundings. In Egypt the climate is more equable than in Chaldaea, and the Nile, with its regular and unfailing rise and fall, the source of all fertility, was steady, friendly and trustworthy, typical of the supernatural powers that rule the world.

In very early times Egyptian civilization was at a comparatively advanced stage of development and a definite yearly calendar seems to have been established. The best achievements in practical arts seem to have occurred between 2000 and 1500 years before Christ. But the possibility of a long and slow growth in knowledge had not dawned on

[1] C. J. Gadd, *The History and Monuments of Ur*, London, 1929.

Egypt   the minds of men. It seemed clear to them that their ancestors, left to their own human resources, could never have made such discoveries as those of speech and of writing, of building or of calculation, and it was therefore natural to imagine a divine intervention to account for the origin of every craft, art or science. As among the Babylonians, all knowledge was ascribed to the revelation of the gods, especially that of Thot, represented by the Ibis or the Baboon, and of his ally Maît, the goddess of truth. Thot, one of the legendary race of divine sovereigns or legislators, was essentially a moon-god, who measured time, counted days and recorded the years. But he was also lord of speech, master of books and inventor of writing. Moreover, he had established in the temples the services of those "watchers of the night", who, from age to age, recorded astronomical events.

In arithmetic, the knowledge of the Egyptians was about on a level with that of the Chaldaeans. They counted by a decimal notation, expressing numbers up to ten by strokes placed side by side and tens by symbols like inverted U's. There is little doubt that the periodic submersion of the ground beneath the waters of the Nile with the consequent obliteration of boundaries led to the development of the art of land-measurement, though the Egyptians themselves referred its origin directly to the benevolent intervention of Thot.

It seems that, at a very early date, surveyors or "rope-stretchers" measured land with ropes and recorded the results. But documentary evidence of the history of arithmetic and geometry begins with a papyrus forming part of the Rhind collection in the British Museum. It was written some sixteen to eighteen hundred years before Christ by a priest named Ahmôse, who states that it was copied from an older roll of the days of a King who is known to be of the XII Dynasty, i.e. before 2200 B.C. Some account is given of fractions and of the common operations of arithmetic, multiplication being performed by repeated additions. Rules for mensuration are also set forth.[1]

Egyptian astronomy, though it may have rivalled the corresponding Chaldaean science in age, never reached the same

[1] W. W. Rouse Ball, *History of Mathematics*, 3rd ed. London and Cambridge, 1901, p. 3; T. E. Peet, in *Cambridge Ancient History*, 1923–1928, vol. II, pp. 216–220.

advanced stage of development. The importance attached by *Egypt* the Chaldaeans to astrology gave a more powerful motive for astronomical research. The wealth and power at the disposal of a successful astrologer would probably give him the pecuniary resources needed for astronomical work, which may have been his real interest. This is what Kepler found, and in our own time it is a recognized fact that those workers who study branches of knowledge which bear a practical application to the arts of life are more easily able to acquire the means to carry on their researches than are those who deal with subjects of only theoretical interest.

The Egyptians identified the constellations with the deities of their mythology, and so represented them on astronomical ceiling decorations or on the insides of coffin lids. From an early period, the year was taken to begin with the annual flooding of the Nile and, when an exact calendar was invented, on the day when the sun rose with the star Sotkis, the Sirius of the Greeks and ourselves. The stellar year of 360 days consisted of thirty-six weeks of ten days each, and the changes in the appearance of the sky from week to week were recorded on charts.[1]

The Egyptian idea of the Universe was, in essentials, much like that prevalent in Babylon. It was represented as a rectangular box, with its greater length running from north to south. It had a slightly concave bottom, at the centre of which lay Egypt. The sky was a flat or vaulted ceiling supported by four columns or mountain peaks, and the stars were lamps hung from the sky by cables. Round the edge of the box ran a great river, and on this river there travelled a boat bearing the Sun, a disc of fire. The Nile was a branch of this celestial stream.[2]

If Egypt lagged behind Babylon in astronomy, and possessed no astrologers with the reputation of the Chaldaeans, in medicine the relative positions were reversed. Four important Egyptian papyri, giving treatises on medicine, have been discovered and deciphered. The best data have been obtained from the Ebers papyrus, which dates from about 1600 B.C. The first physician, mythical or real, whose name survives is

[1] L. S. Bull, "An Ancient Egyptian Astronomical Ceiling Decoration", *Bulletin Metro. Museum of Art, U.S.A.* vol. xviii, 1923, p. 283; abstract in *Isis*, No. 22, 1925, p. 262.

[2] Maspero, *loc. cit.*

Egypt I-am-hotep or Imhotep, "he who cometh in peace," who lived about 4500 B.C. and was afterwards deified as a god of medicine.[1] Babylon possessed no school of rational medicine: all disease was referred exclusively to the action of malignant powers, and sorcery and exorcism alone were relied upon in the treatment of it. Incantations were used by the Egyptians also, but their medicine was more rational, and became highly specialized. An elementary knowledge of anatomy was almost forced on them from the practice of embalming the dead, though they seem only to have traced the larger organs of the body and held quite erroneous views about their functions.[2] Nevertheless, surgery began and, in carvings referred to about 2500 B.C., we can trace the performance of operations by Egyptian surgeons. There were physicians trained at the priestly schools, bone-setters for the treatment of fractures, and oculists to cure the eye-troubles always prevalent in Egypt. Mental diseases seem to have been left to exorcists, who, by means of amulet and charm, were believed to drive out the evil spirits responsible for these infirmities. The art of dispensing drugs and essences had been brought to a high state of excellence, and many Egyptian remedies became of world-wide repute. Indeed, Egyptian medicine generally had an extensive influence. It spread to Greece, perhaps by way of Crete, and, from Greece and Alexandria, in after ages, it passed into Western Europe.

India Since little is yet known about the claims that have been made for a very early development of science in China, the only other country in the ancient world which we need consider is India. It is difficult to trace much scientific activity there before the time of Alexander.[3] But in ethical philosophy the name of Buddha (560–480 B.C.) is of course pre-eminent, and schools of medicine existed at the same early date. In the time of Buddha himself, according to tradition, Atreya, the physician, taught at Kasi or Benares, and Susruta, the surgeon, at Taksasila, or Taxila.[4] The work of the latter, at all events, seems to be historical, and a Sanscrit text of it is extant, though the date is uncertain to within a

---

[1] C. Singer, *A Short History of Medicine*, Oxford, 1928.
[2] Peet, *loc. cit.*
[3] J. Burnet, *Greek Philosophy*, Pt. I, London, 1914, p. 9.
[4] G. Sarton, *loc. cit.* p. 76 (quoting Hoernlé and others).

century. A number of operations are described, such as those for cataract and hernia; some account is given of anatomy, physiology and pathology, and over 700 medicinal plants are noted. The memory of Atreya was preserved by Caraka of Cashmir, who, about A.D. 150, wrote a compendium of Atreya's system of medicine, as handed down by his pupil Agnivesa.

With the uncertainty about dates, it is difficult to say whether Hindu or Greek medicine is the older, or to trace the relative influence of the one on the other.

Perhaps the paucity of Indian contribution to other sciences may in part be due to the Hindu religion. Buddha founded his system on love and knowledge, and a respect for reason and truth; but these tenets, favourable to science as they might have been, were neutralized by the other components of his philosophy. The transitoriness and vanity of personal existence were emphasized; self-annihilation and loss of individuality were made the condition upon which the attainment of spiritual completion depended. This attitude of mind, by distracting attention from all immediate surroundings, tends to arrest that desire for material improvement, which is often the incentive leading to an advance in practical scientific knowledge. But the gentle art of healing was consistent with the Buddhist religion, and for this reason, perhaps, the works of Atreya and Susruta with their stores of medical and surgical learning have survived.

In one point the Buddhist philosophy of India touched a problem definitely scientific. A primitive atomic theory was formulated, either independently or by derivation from Greek thought, and about the first or second century before Christ the idea of discontinuity was extended to time. "Everything, according to this theory, exists but for a moment, and is in the next moment replaced by a facsimile of itself, very much as in a kinematoscopic view. The thing is nothing but a series of such momentary existences. Here time is as it were resolved into atoms."[1] The theory was apparently invented to explain an assumed perpetual change in things by imagining a process of continual creation.

Indian arithmetic is remarkable, in that there is evidence to show that as early as the third century B.C. a system of

[1] Hastings' *Encyclopaedia of Religion and Ethics*; Art. Atomic Theory, Indian; H. Jacobi.

India   notation was used from which was developed the scheme of numerals we employ to-day.

It is possible that Indian thought influenced the schools of Asia Minor, and through them those of Greece; and it is certain that, at a later time, during the Arab domination in the lands of the Eastern Mediterranean, traces of the mathematics and medicine of India mingled with the learning saved from Greece and Rome, and re-entered the schools of Western Europe by way of Spain and Constantinople. This explains the fact that, when the Indian scheme of notation replaced the clumsy Roman figures, the primary source of the numerals was forgotten and they were misnamed Arabic.

Greece and the Greeks   All the separate streams of knowledge in the ancient world converged on Greece, there to be filtered and purified, and turned into new and more profitable channels by the marvellous genius of the race which was the first in Europe to emerge from obscurity.

To understand the origins of the natural philosophy of the Greeks, a natural philosophy which formulated so many of the problems afterwards attacked by science, and propounded so many solutions, we must consider briefly the Greek people, their religion, and the physical and social conditions of their existence.

The earliest civilization in the lands which lie in and around the Aegean Sea appears to have begun in Crete, where its probable centre has been found by Sir Arthur Evans in the ruins of Knossos. Crete was influenced by Egypt, and later, in its turn, influenced Mycenae. An interval of some centuries elapsed between the destruction of Knossos and Mycenae and the beginning of the new and ruder culture of Homeric times. The evidence points to some social cataclysm.

It is held by archaeologists such as Sir William Ridgeway, and anthropologists like Dr Haddon, that Homer's Achaeans were a tribe of conquerors belonging to a tall, fair-haired race from the north, perhaps from the valley of the Danube.[1] Had lon says: "The earliest historical movement of this stock was that of the Achaeans, who, about 1450 B.C., with their iron weapons mastered the bronze-using inhabitants of Greece".

Nevertheless, in spite of clear indications and the weight of

[1] Sir William Ridgeway, *The Early Age of Greece*, 1901; A. C. Haddon, *The Wanderings of Peoples*, Cambridge, 1911, p. 41.

this authority, some classical scholars point to the fact that no tradition of a northern origin appears in Greek literature,[1] while Herodotus treats the Achaeans as among the indigenous inhabitants of Greece. But such evidence, mostly of a negative character, seems of little value compared with the positive indications of a northern origin.

Homer, writing probably in the ninth century before Christ, gives to the Achaeans epithets like fair or brown; the Mediterranean folk buried their dead, but the heroes of Homer passed to the next world in the flames of a funeral pyre; they used iron instead of the bronze of the earlier Grecian peoples; the Olympian gods of classical mythology first came on to the scene in the writings of Homer and Hesiod.

The Achaeans were overthrown in turn by the Dorians, who invaded the Peloponnese in the twelfth or eleventh century before Christ. Here too there is evidence of a descent from the north, the last incursion before definitely historic times.

Thus the inhabitants of Greece were of mixed race, though, after the Dorians settled down, the people acquired a sense of unity, of national culture in a common Hellas, in spite of the particularism of the individual cities and states. Probably differences in race underlay the distinction found in some states between ruling and servile classes, while other slaves were in origin Eastern or Northern barbarians.

In the Homeric poems, which sing the heroes of a conquering race, we find a joyousness of outlook that shows the lifting of the tyranny of primitive magic, and a state of friendly relationship with fully developed divine powers. These beings were figured simply and naturally as super-men and super-women, always interested in mankind, partisans and politicians of the most pronounced type, who took a share in the life of the nation, its wars, its trials and its successes. We find, too, as in Egypt, that the invention of the arts and sciences was attributed to the gods and demi-gods, who were always ready to appear among men, to build their cities, to beget heroes to be the fathers of the nations, and to outwit the ancient shadowy powers, which loomed distressfully in the background.

As early as the sixth century before Christ, the philosophical poet Xenophanes of Colophon recognized that, whether or no it be true that God made man in His own image, it is certain

---

[1] J. B. Bury, in *Cambridge Ancient History*, vol. II, p. 474.

Greece and the
Greeks

that man makes gods in his. And from the gods of the old
Greek mythology we get an insight into the genius of the
Greeks that nothing else can give. We see the picture of a race,
false, boastful, and licentious perhaps, but with a sense of
beauty, a confident joy in life and a warmth of affection that
bespeak a gallant, vigorous, open-hearted, conquering people:
a people of extraordinarily brilliant intellectual endowment,
placed in a land of glorious beauty, where the wine-dark sea
brought the trade and knowledge of all the world to their
doors, where the climate smiled upon their fortified homesteads,
where abundant slaves made life easy and gave leisure for the
growth of the highest forms of philosophy, literature and art.[1]

The Origins of
Greek Religion
and Philosophy

Till recent years, Greek religion has meant mythology as
seen in literature, and no serious attempt was made to study
Greek ritual. But now that anthropologists have shown the
importance of ritual as more fundamental than belief, the
misleading tendency of this literary outlook has become clear.
"The first preliminary to any scientific understanding of Greek
religion is a minute examination of its ritual...the Olympians
of Homer are no more primitive than his hexameters. Beneath
this splendid surface lies a stratum of religious conceptions,
ideas of evil, of purification, of atonement, ignored or suppressed by Homer, but reappearing in later poets and notably
in Aeschylus."[2]

The Greeks themselves in classical times recognized two
forms of ritual, Olympian and Chthonic, and two forms of
mythology also appear. Beneath the friendly Olympian gods
was an underworld of spirits, whose intention towards men was
doubtful, if not hostile. Below this again were vestiges of
rites and beliefs, remnants of that more primitive system of
magic which springs spontaneously from the confusion between
the life of nature and the life of the tribe, and is more fundamental than any dogmatic mythology. Here, probably, we
have the influence of the religious outlook which still appealed
to the mass of the population, a primitive outlook, with its
traditional rites for the promotion of fertility by purgation,
the placation of ghosts, and propitiation of gods or demons.[3]

[1] See, for instance, G. Lowes Dickinson, *The Greek View of Life*, 1896.
[2] Jane E. Harrison, *Prolegomena to the Study of Greek Religion*, Cambridge,
1903 (3rd ed. 1922).
[3] See for example, *Cambridge Ancient History*, W. R. Halliday, vol. ii,
p. 602, and F. M. Cornford, vol. iv, p. 522.

The scanty records of the sixth century before Christ show the prevalence of two primitive cults, the Eleusinian and Orphic mysteries, and from this dark background the Olympic mythology on the one hand and the earliest philosophy and science on the other stand out.

The Origins of Greek Religion and Philosophy

Apparently the Eleusinian mysteries sought to secure the fertility of the earth and of its inhabitants by magic rites in which were pictured the autumn ploughing and sowing and the new birth and growth of spring. The rites were secret, and their nature can only be inferred from chance references in authors often hostile, or from such sources as the Homeric Hymn to Demeter, which connects the mysteries with a hope in the survival of death.

Orphism was thought by Herodotus to have come from Egypt. In it were incorporated the usual mystic rites to promote fertility by celebrating the annual cycle of life and death. It had a cosmogony, which pictured a primordial night from which a world-egg appeared and divided into Heaven and Earth, representing the Father and Mother of Life. Between them flew a winged spirit of Light, sometimes called Eros, who joined the cosmic parents, from whose marriage sprang the Divine Son, Dionysos or Zeus. In this symbolism the mysticism of the age felt its way towards union with the Unseen. In their higher forms Orphic ideas penetrated Greek idealist philosophy and through it Christianity; in their lower forms, they passed into and reinforced every ignorant superstition for centuries.

Out of this primitive world of ideas came two distinct currents of philosophic thought, separate in origin and tendency—the Ionian rationalist nature-philosophy of Asia Minor and the mystical Pythagoreanism of southern Italy. Their relations with each other and with the mystery religions and the Olympic mythology must now be traced.

The main function of the Greek religion, as of many others, when mythology crystallized out of magic and ritual, was to interpret nature and its processes in terms which could be understood—to make man feel at home in the world. The

Religion and Philosophy in Classical Times[1]

---

[1] For a summary see F. M. Cornford, in *Cambridge Ancient History*, vols. IV and VI; references in Sarton, *loc. cit.* For details see Ed. Zeller, *History of Greek Philosophy*, Eng. trans. 1881, T. Gomperz, *Griechische Denker*, Leipzig, 1896, Eng. trans. London, 1901, and J. Burnet, *loc. cit.*, and *Early Greek Philosophy*, London, 1892 and 1908.

animistic conceptions in which the mythology came to be expressed were of unusual beauty and insight. Each fountain lived in its nymph, each wood in its dryad. The grain-bearing earth was personified as Demeter; the unharnessed sea came to life in Poseidon, the earth-shaker.

From generation to generation the divine figures were multiplied and more clearly delineated, new attributes were assigned to them, and cycles of stories clustered round each name. We see a continual process of evolution. Each poet was free to adapt the myths to his own purpose; to introduce a recovered legend, to weave a new allegory, and to re-interpret at his will. As the ages passed and the intellect mastered the emotions, the desire for a higher creed was felt, until at length Aeschylus, Sophocles and Plato evolved out of the older crude polytheism the idea of a single, supreme and righteous Zeus. All this was wrought quite naturally, with hardly any thought of innovation, by those whose object it was to preserve, purify and expound the old faiths. It occurred simultaneously with a change in philosophic outlook, when men turned from a belief in capricious happenings dependent on the chance will of irresponsible gods, to a vision of the uniformity of nature under divine and universal law.

Together with this process of conservative religious evolution, a sceptical criticism was going on. A religion so frankly anthropomorphic as that of Olympus appealed rather to the imagination than to the intellect, and its weakness on the philosophic side became apparent when growing doubt began to express itself more openly. But the decay of the Olympian mythology led to a recrudescence of older magic rites and the invasion of new cults. That of Dionysos was by this time essentially the worship of enthusiasm, which led through physical intoxication or spiritual ecstasy to union with the divine. To this Orphism added asceticism, and raised the primitive rites of initiation and communion in crude sympathetic magic till they came to have spiritual value.

The very weakness of the Olympian orthodox religion, coupled with the essential freedom of intellectual outlook in the Greek world, led to a natural and metaphysical philosophy, which, even from the earliest times, was almost untrammelled by theological pre-conceptions.

Eighteen hundred years later, after the confusion of the

Dark Ages and the reconstruction of knowledge in the philosophical and theological synthesis of mediaeval Scholasticism, the pioneers of modern science had to work under the hampering conditions of a system of rationalized knowledge which included the current dogmas of theology and the recovered philosophy of Aristotle. This system completely dominated the thoughts of all men, even of those working at other problems, and supplied to physical and biological questions, as well as to those of metaphysics and religion, an interpretation not to be gainsaid. After the Renaissance, philosophy and natural science had a hard struggle for freedom, when their disintegrating effect on Scholasticism was realized.

Religion and Philosophy in Classical Times

But in the growth of Greek natural philosophy the circumstances were different. It is true that outward obstacles were not wanting; the common people took their gods seriously—Anaxagoras was driven from Athens as an atheist, and the same charge was one of the counts in the indictment of Socrates who opposed his views. Aristophanes pointed his inimitable jests at the physical speculations current in his day, speculations which were thought to have an atheistic tendency. Nevertheless, the fluidity of the Greek religion, the variety of its ever-changing myths, its adaptability to the needs of poetic and artistic beauty, as well as its readiness to incorporate and adorn new ideas, led to a freedom and openness of intellectual outlook quite foreign to the mediaeval mind.

When the Greek States developed and outgrew their earlier limits, the geographical position of the country and its economic needs brought its people into contact with older civilizations. The early Greek philosophers drew most of their facts from alien sources—their astronomy from Babylonia, and their medicine and geometry from Egypt, possibly in part by way of Crete. To these facts they added others, and then, for the first time in history, subjected them to a rational philosophic examination.[1] This mingling of ideas moved gradually westwards. The effect first appeared in the Ionian shores of the Aegean Sea, when the Greeks, probably maintaining traditions of past Minoan civilization and also in touch with the lore of Babylon and Egypt, conceived the ideas of deductive geometry and the systematic study of nature. The zenith of its

[1] W. Whewell, *History of the Inductive Sciences*; 3rd ed. London, 1857; vol. I, p. 25, and J. Burnet, *Early Greek Philosophy*, Introduction.

Religion and
Philosophy in
Classical Times

philosophical development, more metaphysical than scientific, was reached under Plato and Aristotle at Athens and in the cities of the mainland about 350 B.C., and its influence spread to the Greek colonies in South Italy and Sicily, where, a century later, the mathematical and practical genius of Archimedes marked its highest achievement in physical science. It then passed eastwards again to the new city of Alexandria.

The Ionian
Philosophers

The first European school of thought to break away definitely from mythological traditions was that of the Ionian nature philosophers of Asia Minor, of whom Thales of Miletus (c. 580 B.C.), merchant, statesman, engineer, mathematician and astronomer, is the earliest known to us. The importance of this Milesian School of philosophy lies in the fact that it possessed a unity of purpose and a definite aim, setting out by means of such reasoning as was then possible, to answer the question, "Of what, and in what way is the world made?" The idea of a cycle of change appears, a cycle from air, earth and water through the bodies of plants and animals to air, earth and water again. Thales observed that the food of plants and animals is moist, and revived the old theory that water or moisture is the essence of all things. This idea of a primary element tended to encourage philosophical scepticism; for if wood and iron are essentially the same as water, then the evidence of the senses must be untrustworthy.

Traditional anecdotes of Thales have been handed down by Aristotle and Plutarch. He is said to have visited Egypt, and, from empirical rules for land surveying, originated the science of deductive geometry on the lines afterwards developed by others and systematized by Euclid. He is also said to have predicted an eclipse, either that of 610 or that of 585 B.C., probably making use of Babylonian tables. He taught that the Earth was a flat disc floating on water, and thus improved upon the Babylonian and Egyptian pictures of the Cosmos.

Anaximander (610–545 B.C.), who followed him, seems to have been the first Greek to make a map of the known world. He was also the first to recognize that the heavens revolve round the pole star, and to draw the conclusion that the visible dome of the sky is half of a complete sphere, at the centre of which is the Earth. Until Thales and Anaximander propounded this new theory, the Earth had been imagined as

a floor with a solid base of limitless depth. It was now represented as a finite flattened cylinder, originally surrounded
by envelopes of water, air and fire, and floating within the
celestial sphere. It was thought that the Sun and stars,
shattered fragments of the original fiery envelope, were attached
to celestial circles, and with them revolved about the Earth,
the centre of all things. The Sun passed underground at night,
and not round the rim of the world, as it was supposed to do
in the older systems.

In Anaximander's cosmogony worlds were supposed to arise
by division of opposites from the primordial stuff of chaos in
a way which suggests the visions of Orphism, but Orphism
freed from myth and anthropomorphic ideas and from confusion of becoming with birth. Anaximander was feeling his
way towards a more rational mechanistic philosophy.

In the realm of practical arts, we hear by tradition of
shadowy figures like that of Anacharsis (c. 592), who is said
to have invented the potter's wheel; Glaucus (c. 550), who first
learnt to solder iron; and Theodorus (c. 530), who devised the
level, the lathe and the set-square.[1] Anaximander is said to
have introduced from Babylon the style or gnomon. This was
a rod placed upright on horizontal ground and used as a sun-
dial; it also served to determine the meridian, and the time of
year when the Sun's altitude at noon was greatest.

In organic nature Anaximander taught that the first
animals arose from sea slime, and men from the bellies of fish.
Primary matter he believed to be eternal, but all created
things, even the heavenly bodies, were doomed to destruction
and to return to the undivided unity of universal being.

Anaximenes (died c. 526) departed further from Orphic
mysticism, and held the primary world stuff or element to be
air, which becomes fire when rarefied, and first water and then
earth when condensed. In the air the Earth and planets
float; the Moon shines by light reflected from the Sun.

As against the rationalizing tendency of the Ionian philosophers, Pythagoras (born at Samos but moved to Southern
Italy about 530 B.C.) and his followers showed a mystical
attitude of mind derived directly from Orphism, accompanied
by a readiness to observe and experiment. "Pythagoras of
Samos", says Heraclitus, "has practised research and enquiry

[1] G. Sarton, *History of Science*, vol. I, Baltimore, 1927, p. 75.

The School of
Pythagoras

more than all other men, and has made up his wisdom out of polymathy and out of bad arts."

Pythagoras and his school gave up the idea of one single element, and held matter to be composed of earth, water, air and fire, which were supposed to be derived by the combination in pairs of four underlying qualities, hot and cold, wet and dry; water, for instance, being cold and wet, while fire was hot and dry. They carried further the deductive science of geometry, and arranged in logical order something like the first two books of Euclid. The forty-seventh proposition of the first book of Euclid is called the Theorem of Pythagoras. The "rule of the cord" for laying out a right angle may have been discovered empirically both in Egypt and in India, but it is likely that Pythagoras gave the first deductive proof that the square on the hypotenuse of a right-angled triangle is equal to the sum of the squares on the other two sides.

The Pythagoreans also were the first to bring into prominence the abstract idea of number. To us the concept of number is familiar; we are accustomed to deal with an abstract three or five, irrespective of fingers, apples or days, and it is difficult for us to realize the great step made both in practical mathematics and in philosophy when the essential *fiveness* of groups of quite different things was first seen. In practical mathematics that discovery made arithmetic possible; in philosophy it led to the belief that number lies at the base of the real world. "The Pythagoreans", says Aristotle, "seem to have looked upon number as the principle and, so to speak, the matter of which existences consist." Such ideas of definite, indivisible units as fundamental entities seemed inconsistent with another great Pythagorean discovery, the existence of incommeasurable quantities (see Chapter x) but they were greatly strengthened when the Pythagoreans experimented with sound, and proved that the lengths of strings which gave a note, its fifth and its octave were in the ratios of $6 : 4 : 3$. The theory of the Universe was sought in this scheme of related numbers, which were held to refer to indivisible units of space. It was also thought that the distance of the planets from the Earth must conform to a musical progression, and ring forth "the music of the spheres". Ten was the perfect number (for $10 = 1 + 2 + 3 + 4$), so the moving luminaries of the heavens must be ten also. But as only nine were visible, it was argued

that there must be an invisible "counter-earth". At a later
date Aristotle very rightly criticized this juggling with facts.

Nevertheless the Pythagoreans made a real advance in
cosmogony, our knowledge of which is chiefly derived from
the works of Philolaus, who wrote about the middle of the
fifth century. They recognized the Earth as a sphere, and
eventually realized that the apparent rotation of the heavens
could be explained, and explained more simply, by supposing
a moving Earth. The Earth was thought to revolve, not on its
own axis, but, balanced by the counter-earth, round a point
fixed in space, as would a stone at the end of a string, and to
present its inhabited outer face successively to each part of
the surrounding sky. At the fixed point was a central fire, the
Altar of the Universe, never seen by man. This idea gave rise
in later years to the mistaken belief that the Pythagoreans
had devised a heliocentric theory of the Universe, and had
thus anticipated Aristarchus and Copernicus.

The mystic view of nature, clearly seen in their doctrine of
numbers, shows also in the Pythagoreans' notion of the
fundamental importance of contrasted principles—love and
hatred, good and evil, light and darkness—a notion which
often recurred in Greek thought, that facts about things can
be deduced from the meaning of words. The mystic view
again appeared in the writings of Alcmaeon the physician,
in the idea that man the microcosm is a miniature of the
Universe the macrocosm; his body reflects the structure of the
world, and his soul is a harmony of number. The Pythagorean
system was a philosophy of form as contrasted with the Ionian
philosophy of matter. Early in the fifth century it divided;
one wing became a religious brotherhood, and the other
developed the doctrine of number on quasi-scientific lines.

The essence of Pythagorean philosophy, including the theory
that ultimate reality is to be found in numbers and their
relations, will be traced in this book through Plato's doctrine
of ideas to the Neo-Platonists and Saint Augustine. Under
his influence it helped to form that Platonic background of
mediaeval thought which survived as an alternative to the
scholastic system derived from Aristotle. Even in Scholasticism,
the Pythagorean idea of numbered order in geometry, arithmetic, music and astronomy made those four subjects the
quadrivium of mediaeval instruction. After the Renaissance,

The School of Pythagoras

the idea of the importance of number was taken up by Copernicus and Kepler, who laid chief stress on the mathematical harmony and simplicity of the heliocentric hypothesis as the best evidence of its truth.[1] In our own day, Aston with his integral atomic weights, Moseley with his atomic numbers, Planck with his quantum theory, and Einstein with his claim that physical facts such as gravitation are exhibitions of local space-time properties, are reviving ideas that, in older, cruder forms, appear in Pythagorean philosophy.[2]

The Problem of Matter

If astronomical phenomena are the more striking, and therefore the first to arrest attention, the problem of the nature of matter cries equally to thoughtful minds for an explanation. The origin of chemistry is to be sought in arts that are as old as mankind, and especially in the discovery and use of fire. Cooking, the fermenting of grape juice, the smelting of metals, the making of stoneware, are prehistoric achievements. The Egyptians were skilled in dyeing, in tempering iron, in making glass and enamel, and in the use of metallic compounds as mordants, pigments and cosmetics, while, as far back as fifteen hundred years before Christ, the people of Tyre produced the famous Tyrian purple dye from shellfish.

As in geometry, so in the problem of matter, the Greeks seem to have been the first to theorize. They ignored the vast amount of knowledge which must have been available in what they regarded as base mechanic arts, and reasoned only on what was obvious to every Greek gentleman. We find the Ionian philosophers tracing the changes of substances from earth and water to the bodies of plants and animals, and back again to earth and water. They began to realize the conception of the indestructibility of matter, and, from Thales onwards, despite the obvious superficial differences in bodies, speculated on the possibility of a single "element", water, air or fire, as a common basis of all things.

At the beginning of the fifth century philosophy passed into controversy, and attacks were made both on the Ionians and the Pythagoreans from two sides. All concerned showed the characteristic Greek love of theorizing from first principles and dogmatizing about phenomena.

[1] E. A. Burtt, *Metaphysical Foundations of Modern Science*, London and New York, 1925, pp. 23, 44. Also see below Chapter III.
[2] A. N. Whitehead, *Science and the Modern World*, Cambridge, 1927, p. 36.

Heraclitus (c. 502), poet and philosopher, expressed contempt for the materialist tendency of Anaximander and Anaximenes. To him the primary element or reality was the aethereal fire, a kind of soul stuff, of which all is made and to which all returns. The perpetual alternation of opposites in this world—sleeping and waking, death and life—cease in the pure and final fire. All things move in order, and all are in a state of flux—πάντα ρεῖ. Truth can only be found within, a reflection of the universal Logos or reason.

Another type of critical philosophy was also reached *a priori* by the philosophers of Elea in Southern Italy, of whom the chief was Parmenides, who flourished about the year 500.

Entranced by the operations of the human mind, Parmenides pushed to an extreme the characteristic Greek assumption that what is inconceivable is impossible, even if the senses tell us that it has, in fact, happened. He argued thus: Creation is impossible because something cannot be conceived to arise from nothing, or being from non-being, indeed non-being cannot be. Conversely, destruction is impossible because something cannot vanish into nothing. Even change is impossible, because a thing cannot arise from another thing which is in essence unlike itself. Thus the appearances of change, of diversity and multiplicity, of time and space, which we see or think we see in nature, are but false impressions of sense, which thought proves to be self-contradictory. Hence, sense cannot lead to truth, which can be found by thought alone. Sense perceptions are unreal, non-being; thought alone is real, true being. Interpreted in other terms, to touch reality we must eliminate all differences in bodies, and thus get left with a single uniform essence. This is the only reality, one, eternal and unchangeable, limited only by itself, evenly extended and therefore spherical. In the apparent world of phenomena, the unreal but still observed Universe is a series of concentric shells of fire and earth; though all this is but "opinion" and not necessarily "truth".

Some of these ideas were carried further by Zeno of Elea, a younger contemporary of Parmenides, who opposed the Pythagorean doctrine that all things are made of integral numbers and thought he had discredited multiplicity by his famous series of paradoxes. A manifold must be divisible to infinity and therefore must itself be infinite, but, in trying to

The Problem build it up again, no number of infinitely small parts can
of Matter make a finite whole. The swift Achilles, pursuing a tortoise,
reaches the spot whence the tortoise started; the tortoise has
now moved on to a further spot; when Achilles arrives there,
the tortoise has once more advanced—and so on to infinity,
but Achilles never catches the tortoise.

Parmenides seems to dispute about the meanings accidentally assigned to words, meanings always arbitrary and often
changing, and Zeno's paradoxes rest on misconceptions about
the nature of infinitesimals and the relations of time and space
cleared up by modern mathematicians. But Zeno certainly
proved that the idea of division without limit into infinitesimal units as then understood was inconsistent with
experience. The discrepancy could only be resolved completely when different kinds of infinity, not equivalent to
each other, were distinguished in the nineteenth century.

Nevertheless, the Eleatic philosophy is important to us in
two ways. In the first place, by discrediting the senses, it
helped the atomists to seek reality in things imperceptible to
the senses, and to explain what afterwards came to be called
the secondary or separable qualities of bodies, such as hotness
or colour, as mere sense perceptions. Secondly, the search for
a single unity, representing the underlying reality in all things,
while it aided the physicists in their search for a single chemical
element, led the philosophers to separate substance ($ο\mathring{υ}σία$)
from qualities or accidents ($πάθη$). Put in final form by
Aristotle, this idea of the nature of matter dominated mediaeval
thought.

Anaxagoras was another Ionian philosopher, born near
Smyrna about 500 B.C., who took the more materialist Ionian
ideas of philosophy with him to Athens forty years later. To
Anaxagoras matter was a crowd of different entities each with
different qualities or accidents as the senses suggest. However
far division is carried, the parts contain things like the whole,
though differences may arise from different proportions in the
ingredients. Motion was originally started by Mind ($νο\mathring{υ}ς$), a
subtle fluid causing rotation which spreads and so makes and
orders the world. The heavenly bodies are matter of the
same nature as the Earth; the Sun is not the God Helios,
but an ignited stone; the Moon has hills and valleys. Besides
these speculations Anaxagoras made some real advance in

exact knowledge. He dissected animals, gained some insight into the anatomy of the brain, and discovered that fishes breathe through their gills.

We see other ideas of matter in the famous hypothesis of four elements, held by the Pythagoreans and worked out in a more definite form by the Sicilian philosopher Empedocles (450 B.C.), who taught that the " roots " or elements were earth, water, air and fire—a solid, a liquid, a gas, and a type of matter still rarer than the gaseous. These four elements were combined throughout the Universe in different proportions under the influence of the two contrasted divine powers, one attractive and one repulsive, which the ordinary eye sees working among men as love and hatred, ideas which recall the conceptions of Pythagoras. By the various combinations of the four elements all the many types of matter are formed, just as a painter makes all shades and tints by combining four pigments.

Parmenides had argued against the existence of empty space, which men thought they perceived in air. Anaxagoras and Empedocles demonstrated the corporeal nature of air, and, by experiments with a water-clock, the latter showed that water can only enter a vessel as air escapes. This discovery proved air to be distinct both from empty space and from vapour.

The idea that all things are made of four elements seems to have been derived from a natural misinterpretation of the action of fire. When burned, it was thought, a substance must be resolved into its elements; combustible matter is complex, while the small quantity of ash left by burning it is simple. For instance, when green wood is burnt, the *fire* is seen by its own light, the smoke vanishes into *air*, from the ends of the wood *water* boils off, and the ashes are clearly of the nature of *earth*.

Other theories based on this conception of fire followed in later times. It was the first great guiding idea of chemistry. Marsh says: " The fire theories are: the Greek theory of the four elements, the alchemical theory of the composition of metals, the iatrochemical theory of the hypostatical principles and the phlogiston theory ",[1] which was developed during the eighteenth century. The rise and fall of these theories will be traced in the later chapters of this book.

Empedocles thought that, by imagining his four elements

[1] J. E. Marsh, *The Origins and Growth of Chemical Science*, London, 1928.

The Atomists united in different proportions, he could explain all the endless kinds of different substances known to man. Leucippus and Democritus carried this simplification further, and developed into a theory of atoms the older and alternative hypothesis of a single element.[1]

The ground on which the atomic theory of the Greeks was founded was very different from the definite experimental facts known to Dalton, Avogadro and Cannizzaro when they formulated the atomic and molecular theories of to-day. The modern chemists had before them exact quantitative measurements of the proportions in which chemical elements combined by weight and by volume. These limited and definite facts led irresistibly to the idea of atoms and molecules, and gave to them at once relative atomic and molecular weights. The theory thus formulated was found to conform with all the rest of the many isolated or interconnected facts and relations which had become the common heritage of science, to be supported by other successive experiences, and to serve as a useful guide in the study and even in the prediction of new phenomena. Although, like every other scientific generalization, it had philosophic meaning, it was not deduced from, or even necessarily bound up with, any complete philosophic theory of the Universe. It was a humbler but more useful affair.

The Greeks had neither definite experimental facts to suggest an exact and limited theory in the first place, nor the power of testing by experience the consequences of the theory when deduced. The Greek theory was founded on and incorporated in a cosmic scheme of philosophy, and it remained a doctrine, like the metaphysical systems in ancient and modern times, dependent on the mental attitude of its originators and their followers, and liable to be upset and replaced from the very foundations by a new system of a rival philosopher. And this indeed is what happened.

The Ionian philosophers reasoned from the general knowledge of their time in the light of the prevalent metaphysical ideas. When matter is divided and subdivided, do its properties remain unchanged? Is earth always earth, and water

[1] See works already mentioned, esp. Burnet; also J. Masson, *The Atomic Theory of Lucretius*, London, 1884; Paul Tannery, "Démocrite et Archytas", *Bull. des Sciences math.* vol. x, 1886, p. 295; F. A. Lange, *Geschichte des Materialismus*, 1866 and 1873, Eng. trans. London and New York, 1925; Cyril Bailey, *The Greek Atomists and Epicurus*, Oxford, 1928.

water, however far the process is carried? In other words, are the properties of bodies ultimate facts of which no further explanation can be given, or can we represent them in terms of simpler conceptions, and thus push the limits of ignorance one step further back?

It is this attempt at a rational explanation, in what seemed simpler terms, that makes the efforts of the Greeks to solve the problem of matter important in the history of scientific thought. According to the ideas that preceded their attempt, and followed the fall of the atomic philosophy, the qualities of substances were thought to be of their essence; the sweetness of sugar, and the colour of leaves, were as much a reality as the sugar and leaves themselves, and not to be explained by reference to other facts, or as varieties of human sensation.

It is of interest to trace the origins of the Greek atomic theory. Thales took water, Anaximenes air, and Heraclitus fire, as primary elements. Anaximenes' element, air, suffered condensation and rarefication with its essence unchanged. Heraclitus' theory of endless flux suggested the idea of invisible moving particles, realized in the evaporation of water and in the diffusion of scent. This led back to the Pythagorean doctrine of integral monads, conforming to the laws of number, as the ultimate reality. The conception of vacant space empty of matter was also held by the Pythagoreans, though they confused it with air. It was attacked by Parmenides, but it was revived by the atomists owing to the difficulty of explaining how particles could move in a fully packed space or plenum. Air was now known to be corporeal, and thus to the atomists empty space became a real vacuum.

Such were the trains of thought which suggested the theory that matter consists of ultimate particles scattered in a void, a theory which explained all the relevant facts then known— evaporation, condensation, motion, and the growth of new material. It is true that the fundamental problem remained, and was emphasized by other Greek philosophers. Were the atoms themselves infinitely divisible? The atomist evaded the logical pitfall, and held that atoms were physically indivisible because there was no void within them.

The earliest atomists whose fame has reached us are Leucippus, a shadowy figure of the fifth century who is said to have founded the school of Abdera in Thrace, and Democritus,

The Atomists who was born at Abdera in 460 B.C. Their views are known to us by references in the works of later writers such as Aristotle, and by the work of Epicurus (341–270), who adopted and taught the theory of atoms at Athens as part of a complete philosophy of ethics, psychology and physics, set forth again two centuries later in the poem of the Roman Lucretius.

Leucippus laid down the basal idea of atomism and also the principle of causation—"Nothing happens without a cause, but everything with a cause and by necessity". He and Democritus carried further the attempt of the Ionian philosophers to explain the properties of matter in terms of simpler elements. They saw that to admit the qualities of bodies as fundamental and inexplicable would stop all further enquiry. In contradistinction to this view, Democritus taught: "According to convention there is a sweet and a bitter, a hot and a cold, and according to convention there is colour. In truth there are atoms and a void". Thus, although he opposed Protagoras, who held the relativist view that "man is the measure of all things", so that, for instance, honey may be sweet to me but bitter to you, Democritus saw that reality could not be reached through the senses alone.

The atoms of Democritus were uncaused, existent from eternity, and never annihilated—"strong in solid singleness". They were many in size and shape, but identical in substance. Thus difference in properties is due to differences in size, shape, position and movement of particles of the same ultimate nature. In stone or iron the atoms can only throb or oscillate, in air or fire they rebound at greater distances.

Moving in all directions through infinite space, the atoms strike against each other, producing lateral movements and vortices, thus bringing similar atoms together to form elements and starting the formation of innumerable worlds, which grow, decay and ultimately perish, only those systems surviving which are fitted to their environment. Here we see a faint forecast of the nebular hypothesis, and of the Darwinian theory of natural selection.

In the original form of the theory there is no idea of an absolute up or down, levity or heaviness. Moreover, motion persists unless opposed. To Aristotle, these sound ideas were incredible, and later on the theory seems to have been modified to meet his criticism. The truth had to be rediscovered by Galileo. In astronomy the atomists were reactionary, picturing the Earth as flat; but in other respects they were in advance of their contemporaries and their successors.

Democritus' teaching, as transmitted to us by Lucretius, effects a wonderful simplification in the mental picture of nature previously held. In fact, the picture is too simple. The atomists passed unconsciously over difficulties which, after the lapse of twenty-four centuries, are still unsolved. Fearlessly they applied the theory to problems of life and consciousness which still defy explanation in mechanical terms. Confidently they believed they had left no mysteries, blind to the great mystery underlying and surrounding all existence, a mystery none the less profound to-day than when the atomic theory was first formulated.

The philosophic question at issue between the atomists and their opponents was the same as that which reappeared in the eighteenth century, when Newton's physics were made the basis of a mechanical philosophy by his French disciples. Is the reality underlying nature something which in its essence resembles nature as it appears to the human mind, or is it a vast machine indifferent to man and his welfare? Is a mountain in reality a mass of rock clad in the green mantle of trees and the white coverlet of everlasting snow, or is it in essence a concourse of minute particles with no human qualities, particles which somehow produce the illusion of form and colour in the human mind? The physicist analyses matter into particles, and finds that their forces and motions can be described in mathematical terms. The materialist pushes this scientific result into philosophy, and says that there is no other reality. The idealist revolts against an inhuman Cosmos, and in Greece the atomic philosophy, which seemed to demand it, was rejected. In the eighteenth century Newtonian science was too firmly established to be upset, and other roads of escape had to be sought in the dualism of Descartes or the idealism of Berkeley.

Whatever be its value in philosophy, in science the Democritean atomic theory is nearer to the views now held than any of the systems which preceded or replaced it, and its virtual suppression under the destructive criticisms of Plato and Aristotle must, from the scientific standpoint, be counted a

The Atomists

misfortune. Platonism in its various forms was left to represent Greek thought to later ages, a fact which was one of the reasons why the scientific spirit vanished from the earth for a thousand years. Plato was a great philosopher, but in the history of experimental science he must be counted a disaster.

Greek Medicine

Greek medicine[1] contained much that was derived directly or indirectly from Egypt. The two most famous Grecian schools were those of Cos and Cnidos. In the former, disease was treated as a derangement of the normal and healthy body and reliance was placed on the *vis medicatrix naturae*; in the latter, each specific disease was studied and a specific remedy was sought.

With regard to the earliest historic times, it is interesting to note that in Homer's *Iliad* the effects of different wounds are accurately described, and the treatment prescribed is simple and straightforward, showing the wholesome tradition of a rational spirit in medicine and surgery among the race of Homeric heroes. But it seems that this tradition was not general. In the *Odyssey* magic appears, and, among the bulk of the people in Greece as in other southern and eastern lands, spells and incantations formed the prevalent type of treatment. Even in later times the two modes of thought were mingled. Towards the end of the classical period, after the height of Greek medical knowledge had been reached, there was still a large element of magic and sorcery in the medical treatment provided by the temples of Aesculapius (the god of healing) at Epidaurus, Athens and elsewhere. But we must not forget that, even to-day, charms are still relied on in some parts of England and Wales.

As medicine was developed, the deductive method so dear to the Greeks was introduced, and preconceived notions about the nature of man or the origin of life were used as the basis of medical treatment, and doubtless cost many patients their lives. When theorizing was kept within bounds, the art of medicine made rapid progress; the status of the physician rose with it, and an excellent code of professional life was adopted, and afterwards formulated in the famous Hippocratic oath.[2]

Most Greek philosophers dealt, incidentally at any rate, with

[1] C. Singer, *A Short History of Medicine*, Oxford, 1923; R. O. Moon, *Hippocrates and his Successors*, London, 1923.
[2] Singer, *loc. cit.* p. 17.

the theory of medicine. To it the Pythagoreans applied their special tenets. Alcmaeon of Croton (c. 500 B.C.), probably the first to practise dissection and the chief pre-Socratic embryologist, discovered the optic nerve, and realized that the brain is the central organ of sensation and of intellectual activity. Anaxagoras made experiments on animals and studied their anatomy by dissection. Empedocles taught that blood flowed to and from the heart, and that health depended on a right equilibrium of his four elements in the body.

Greek medicine culminated in the school of Hippocrates (c. 420 B.C.) with a theory and practice of the art somewhat resembling those which are current to-day, and far in advance of the ideas of any intervening epoch till modern times are approached. Their physiology, unlike that of Aristotle and Galen, was not concerned with final causes; it dealt more with how than why, and was thus modern in spirit. The use of experiment appears: for instance, the Hippocratic writer concerned with embryology advises the observer to open hens' eggs day by day as incubation proceeds. Disease was reckoned as a process subject to natural laws. The insistence on minute observation and careful interpretation of symptoms pointed the way to modern clinical medicine, while many diseases were accurately described and appropriate treatment indicated. Anatomy was practised to some extent, but it was not till later, probably at Alexandria under the sway of the Ptolemies, that systematic human dissection first gave a firm basis of ascertained fact to human anatomy and physiology.

The atomic philosophy marks the culmination of the first great period of Greek science. It was followed by a pause or even a retrogression, an indication of the danger of philosophic *a priori* methods in dealing with nature. Perhaps the rise of Athens as a democratic state turned men's chief energies to rhetoric and politics. Fluent speech became the only road to power, and philosophers tended to study economics and ethics rather than mathematics and natural science.

When an advance in knowledge can again be traced, we meet it first in the writings of the early historians. Herodotus (484–425 B.C.) had travelled far, and in his works are valuable descriptions of peoples and countries. He showed a laudable curiosity, as may be seen in his enquiries into and speculations upon the causes of the regular flooding of the Nile, but a more

From the
Atomists to
Aristotle

accurate and critical spirit is to be observed in Thucydides (460–400 B.C.). The latter criticized the mythical period of Greek history in the spirit of a scientific historian, described the Peloponnesian War as an eye-witness, and gave an account of the plague at Athens, and of the solar eclipse in the year 431.

The influence of atomism is again seen in the scepticism of some of its opponents, who, like the atomists, doubted the power of the senses to give us information about the external world. But an opposite conclusion was drawn. The atomists had assigned reality to matter rather than to mind; the opposing school held that, since sensation certainly exists while its messages about reality are doubtful, sensation is the only reality. A corresponding reaction from a mechanical philosophy to phenomenalism is seen in a later age.

A critical type of the reaction appears in Socrates, who, in the pose of an enquirer, cross-examined sophist, politician or philosopher, exposing ignorance, stupidity and pretentiousness wherever he found them. He upheld the supremacy of the mind, since, by "reminiscence" of many instances, it apprehends the true "forms" or ideals towards which the objects of sense are only tending. Equality is an ideal; but two stones can never do more than approach equality as a limit. Socrates regarded introspection as the only worthy mode of study, and his influence tended to turn men's attention away from the investigation of nature. Indeed, from one point of view, Socrates led a religious reaction against the materialistic attitude of the nature philosophers of Ionia, although popular clamour charged him with atheism. His rejection of a mechanical determinism is explained in the famous scene described by Plato in the *Phaedo*, where Socrates in prison is waiting the time when he must drink the hemlock. He tells his friends that to Anaxagoras the causes of his sitting there may be the nature of his bones and sinews:

And if again he should give other similar reasons for my conversing with you, assigning as causes, voice, air and hearing, and ten thousand other things of the kind, omitting to mention the real causes, that, since it appeared better to the Athenians to condemn me, I therefore thought it better to sit here and more just to remain and submit to the punishment which they have ordered, for, by the dog, I think these sinews and bones would have been long ago in Megara or Boeotia, borne thither by an opinion of that which is best, if I had not thought it more just and honourable to submit to whatever sentence the city might order rather than to flee and run stealthily away.

Socrates here shows a natural reaction from a premature mechanical philosophy, and perhaps a certain misunderstanding of and antagonism to the scientific attitude of mind. Certainly he turned philosophy from a study of the past and present to a consideration of the future—the end for which the world was created. But it should be remembered that Aristotle says there are two things that may fairly be attributed to Socrates, universal definitions and inductive reasoning.

In his disciple Plato (428–384 B.C.), who was the greatest exponent of idealism, sceptic and mystic were combined. Plato's ideas of nature were deduced *a priori* from human needs and predilections. God is good and the sphere is the most perfect of forms, therefore the Universe must be spherical. Primary matter is identical with extended space; the four elements are not letters of Nature's alphabet or even syllables of her words. For the making of time there are heavenly bodies carried in cycles, to which God has given circular motion. Plato clearly shows the influence of the Pythagorean mystical doctrine of form and number, though his application of it to astronomy was less modern than that of the Pythagoreans, who had learnt to regard the stars as floating free in space. But a combination of Plato's cycles could be made to represent the apparent path of the Sun round the Earth, a system of astronomy afterwards developed in detail by Hipparchus and Ptolemy, though, in his old age, Plato is said to have realized that a moving Earth would give a simpler account of the phenomena.

Plato's physics and biology were anthropomorphic, even ethical. His cosmos was a world soul, by which the world became a living organism. In the *Timaeus* he deduces from this theory a view of the nature and structure of the universe, even of human physiology, on the fanciful analogy between the cosmos and man, between the macrocosm and the microcosm.

Based on such ideas, Plato's science is for the most part fantastic. He roundly condemned experiment as either impious or a base mechanical art. Mathematics, a deductive science, on the other hand, he prized highly. Plato himself formulated the idea of negative numbers, and treated the line as "flowing" from a point—the germ of the "method of fluxions" invented by Newton and Leibniz. In mathematics mental concepts, suggested perhaps by observation, but purified by reason, were subjected to logical analysis, and their consequences unfolded. Here indeed was a delight and a task worthy of a philosopher.

Such views naturally led Plato to accept and develope the Socratic or Pythagorean theory of "intelligible forms"—the doctrine that "forms" or ideas alone possess full being and reality. This theory was afterwards applied to the problem of classification. In nature we find numberless groups more or less similar; triangles, let us say, on the one hand, and animal and vegetable species on the other. The Greeks and Mediaevalists never properly distinguished between these two sides of the problem, or realized the difficulties inherent in the classification of natural living objects. They regarded classes as sharply defined, separate as the words used to name them, and proceeded to consider *a priori* the similarities in the individuals composing the classes.

To explain the similarity, the mind imagines a primary type to which, in some way, the individuals conform. Socrates and Plato found that, when the mind begins to frame definitions and to reason about them in general terms applicable to any particular case, the definitions and reasonings are connected with these hypothetical types. All natural objects are in a constant state of change; it is only the types imagined by the mind that remain constant and unchangeable. Hence Plato was led to his characteristic form of idealism, known to later ages as realism, the theory that these ideas of the mind are real and, in fact, the only realities. Individuals, whether dead substances or living beings, are but shadows. There is no reality in them till the mind abstracts their essence, and thus discovers classes or universals. The ideas or universals alone are fit subjects for rational analysis and therefore alone are real.

Plato's school at the Academy in Athens lasted for nine centuries—till closed by the Emperor Justinian in A.D. 529.

Aristotle

Aristotle,[1] who was born in 384 B.C. at Stagira in Chalcide, and died in 322 in Euboea, was a son of the physician to Philip, King of Macedon, and was himself the tutor of Alexander the Great. After many years of study as a disciple of Plato,

[1] An English translation of Aristotle's works is being issued by the Oxford University Press, 1908–. See also W. D. Ross, *Aristotle*, London, 1923.

he founded a new school of philosophy, known as the Peri-   *Aristotle*
patetic, from the custom of master and pupils walking together
in the gardens of the Lyceum at Athens.

Aristotle was the greatest collector and systematizer of
knowledge which the ancient world produced. His supreme
importance in the history of science consists in the fact that,
till the Renaissance of learning in modern Europe, though
appreciable advances in our knowledge of special parts of
nature were made by single individuals, no systematic survey
and no complete grasp of knowledge at all comparable with
his appeared in all the centuries that followed him. One of
the intellectual tasks of the early Middle Ages was to assimilate
as much of his works as could be gleaned from imperfect and
incomplete compendiums; and the later mediaeval writers
devoted their strength to recovering his meaning when the full
text of his books appeared in the West. Aristotle's works are
an encyclopaedia of the learning of the ancient world, and,
save in physics and astronomy, he probably made a real
improvement in all the subjects he touched. Moreover he was
one of the founders of the inductive method, and the first to
conceive the idea of organized research. But it is his own
labours in science and in the classification of knowledge that
give him his great title to fame.

Among his many writings which have survived, the *Physical
Discourse* deals with the philosophy of nature, the principles
of existence, matter and form, motion, time and space, the
ever-moving sphere of the outer heaven, and the Unmoved
Mover who must exist to keep it in motion. Aristotle holds that
a continually acting cause is needed to keep a body moving,
while Plato seems to assume that a cause is only needed to
deflect it from a straight path. Aristotle's book *On the
Heavens* gradually descends from the outer region to the
material and perishable, and thus leads to an account of
Generation and Destruction, in which the opposing principles of
hot and cold, wet and dry, produce by their mutual action the
four elements. Hot and dry produce fire; hot and wet, air; cold
and dry, earth; cold and wet, water. To the terrestrial elements
Aristotle added aether, which naturally moves in circles and
makes up the heavenly bodies, perfect and incorruptible.

The *Meteorologics* treat of the region between heaven and
earth, the realm of the planets, comets and meteors; but in

Aristotle the fourth book, probably written not by Aristotle but by his successor Straton, we have an account of primitive ideas on chemistry. Of two exhalations imprisoned within the earth, the one, steamy or wet, gives rise to the metals, and the other, smoky or dry, to the rocks and minerals that cannot be melted. Ideas are given on solidification and solution, generation and putrefaction, and on the properties of composite bodies. Aristotle's meteorology, which to us seems much less satisfactory than his work on biology, had considerable influence during the later Middle Ages.

Perhaps the greatest of Aristotle's advances in exact knowledge were those he made in biology. He defined life as "the power of self-nourishment and of independent growth and decay". He divided zoology into three parts: (1) Records about Animals, dealing with the general phenomena of animal life, i.e. natural history; (2) On the Parts of Animals, organs and their functions, i.e. anatomy and general physiology; and (3) On the Generation of Animals, reproduction and embryology. He mentions some five hundred different animals, some with an accuracy and detail which show personal observation, and fifty with a knowledge gained by dissection and illustrated by diagrams. For his account of others he relied on fishermen, hunters, herdsmen and travellers.

Naturally such a mass of information is of unequal value, but Aristotle records many facts only rediscovered in recent centuries. He recognized that whales are viviparous; he distinguished cartilaginous from bony fishes; he described the development of the embryo chicken, detected the formation of the heart, and watched it beat while it was yet in the egg.

In general embryology his ideas mark an important advance. Earlier views, possibly derived from Egypt, regarded the father as the only real parent, the mother providing merely a home and nourishment for the embryo. Such beliefs were widespread, and largely underlay patriarchal customs both in the ancient and the modern world. Aristotle recognized the female contribution to generation, and held that she supplied substance for the active male principle to form. He regarded the embryo as an automatic mechanism which only needs to be started.

In classifying animals, Aristotle rejects the older principle of dichotomy, whereby animals were placed in contrasted groups, such as land and water animals, winged and wingless.

He observed that this principle led to the separation of animals nearly related, such as winged and wingless ants. He recognized that it is necessary to use as many distinguishing qualities as possible, and, by the help of this method, he drew up a table of classes which was much nearer modern systems of classification than any previously adopted.

Even in physiology, though his conclusions and theories are often wrong, he seems to have practised vivisection, and in general his methods mark a great step in advance. For instance, after giving a description of the views on respiration held by earlier naturalists, he points out that "the main reason why these writers have not given a good account of the facts is that they had no acquaintance with the internal organs, and that they did not accept the doctrine that there is a final cause for whatever Nature does. If they had asked for what purpose respiration exists in animals, and had considered this with reference to the organs, e.g. the gills and the lungs, they would have discovered the reason more rapidly". Here the insistence on the need for observation of anatomical structure before the framing of views on the functions of organs is sound, though the insistence on an enquiry into final causes is dangerous. In the treatment which follows, Aristotle passes in review the structure of a number of animals, and describes the action of their lungs or gills. In drawing conclusions, he had, of course, little knowledge of chemistry to help him, the idea of gases other than air was unknown, and the only change in air which could be suggested was its heating or cooling. Aristotle's theory that the object of respiration is to cool the blood by contact with air, though to us obviously false, was perhaps the best of which his age was capable. On the other hand, it seems strange that although Alcmaeon and Hippocrates had recognized that the seat of intelligence is in the brain, Aristotle should have returned to the view that it is in the heart, the brain being to him a mere cooling organ. Furthermore, his denial of the sexuality of plants caused a long delay in its rediscovery and final acceptance.

In physics in the modern sense, and in astronomy, Aristotle was less successful than in biology, which till recent years was still chiefly an observational science. The success of his attack on the atomic philosophy shows the insecurity of physical theories which, though sound in themselves, are not founded

Aristotle   on a broad and detailed basis of experimental fact. He rejected the atomic theory altogether because its consequences did not agree with his other ideas of nature, and, in the absence of definite confirmatory evidence, he was able to secure a general acceptance of his views.

As an example of Aristotle's method of criticism, his treatment of the problem of falling bodies is instructive. Democritus had taught that in a vacuum the heavier atoms would fall faster than the lighter ones. Aristotle, on the other hand, held that in a vacuum bodies must fall equally fast, but argued that such a conclusion is inconceivable, and that therefore there can never be a vacuum.

With the possibility of empty space, he rejected all the allied concepts of the atomic theory. He also argued that if all substances were composed of the same ultimate material they would all be heavy by nature, and nothing would be light in itself or tend to rise spontaneously. A large mass of air or fire would then be heavier than a small mass of earth or water, and the earth or water could not sink through air or fire as it is known to do.

Aristotle's error arose from the fact that, in common with other philosophers before Archimedes, he had no idea of the conceptions now known as density or specific gravity; he failed to see that it is the weight per unit volume compared with that of the surrounding medium which determines rise or fall, and, following the teaching of Plato, he attributed the motion to an innate instinct leading everything to seek its own natural resting-place. This doctrine, that bodies are essentially heavy or light in themselves, was accepted with the rest of Aristotle's philosophy by the Schoolmen and theologians of the later Middle Ages. Thus his dead hand held back the advance of knowledge till Galileo, in the years 1589 to 1591, appealing to actual experiments carried out from the leaning tower of Pisa, showed that, save for a difference produced by the resistance of the air, heavy bodies and light ones fall at the same rate, and thus destroyed the Aristotelian conception of heaviness and lightness as essential qualities.

Aristotle, too, though he accepted the spherical form of the Earth, maintained the geocentric theory which regarded the Earth as the centre of the Universe, and his authority did much to prevent the heliocentric theory, when put forward by

Aristarchus, from being accepted by astronomers till the days of Copernicus seventeen hundred years later.

In rejecting the atomic theory, Aristotle fell back on the view originating with the Pythagoreans that the essence of matter was to be found in four primary and fundamental qualities, existing in contrasted and opposite pairs—the hot and the cold, the wet and the dry. These qualities united in binary combination to form the four elements, earth, water, air and fire, which, in varying proportions, build up different kinds of matter. Water was wet and cold, fire hot and dry, and so on. Later writers mixed this theory with the Hippocratic doctrine that the body was composed of four liquids or humours: blood, phlegm, black bile for melancholy and yellow bile for anger. The combination of these was supposed to determine bodily constitution, and excess of one or the other produced sanguine, phlegmatic, melancholic or choleric temperaments. Blood was supposed to be related to fire, phlegm to water, yellow bile to air, and black bile to earth.

All this, to us fanciful nonsense, is necessary for the comprehension of ancient and mediaeval thought, and indeed for an understanding of one of the sources of some of the words still used in our language. The doctrine of the four elements lasted till the seventeenth century, and we still use the terms of the theory of four humours to describe the dispositions of our friends.

Besides his work on different branches of science, Aristotle wrote on many philosophic subjects, and, in them all, influenced profoundly his own and succeeding ages. From Plato, his master in philosophy, he took over many metaphysical ideas, some of which he modified in accordance with his greater knowledge of nature. Plato had no insight into the meaning of experimental science; his interests were philosophical. Hence perhaps arises the fact that Plato's theory of nature as a whole, and even that of his pupil Aristotle, were less in accordance with what we now hold to be the truth, than the conclusions of the older nature-philosophers, though in metaphysics Plato went deeper, and in points of scientific detail Aristotle far surpassed them in knowledge.

With the more metaphysical aspects of Greek thought we are but little concerned. Yet, owing to its importance in mediaeval controversy and in the development of modern

Aristotle   science after the Renaissance, we must touch once more on Plato's doctrine of ideas, and Aristotle's variation of it.

Plato, as we have seen, allowed no full reality to individual things or individual beings—to actual lumps of stone, to single plants or animals. The idea in a living mind of a universal class, whether of stones or of plants, alone is fully real.

To Aristotle, often immersed in the detailed study of definite individual animals or other concrete objects, this thorough-going idealism was not a convenient attitude of mind, and he broke away from it. But the influence of his master remained and indeed increased in his later years, though he never returned to Plato's extreme position. While admitting the reality of the individuals, the concrete objects of sense, Aristotle came to recognize also a secondary reality in the universals or ideas. In later ages Aristotle's divergence from the "realism" of Plato was developed into what was called "nominalism", in accordance with which the individuals are the sole realities, the universals being only names or mental concepts. To this whole question we shall be brought back when dealing with mediaeval thought.

Whatever be the truth of Plato's doctrine of ideas from a metaphysical point of view, the mental attitude which gave it birth is not adapted to further the cause of experimental science. It seems clear that, while philosophy still exerted a predominating influence on science, nominalism, whether conscious or unconscious, was more favourable to the growth of scientific methods. But Plato's search for the "forms of intelligible things" may perhaps be regarded as a guess about the causes of visible phenomena. Science, we have now come to understand, cannot deal with ultimate reality; it can only draw a picture of nature as seen by the human mind. Our ideas are in a sense real in that ideal picture world, but the individual things represented are pictures and not realities. Hence it may prove that a modern form of the realism of ideas may be nearer the truth than is a crude nominalism. Nevertheless, the rough-and-ready suppositions which underlie most experiments assume that individual things are real, and most men of science talk nominalism without knowing it, as Monsieur Jourdain talked prose.

The characteristic weakness of the inductive sciences among the Greeks is explicable when we examine their procedure. Aristotle, while dealing skilfully with the theory of the passage from particular instances to general propositions, in Aristotle practice often failed lamentably. Taking the few available facts, he would rush at once to the widest generalizations. Naturally he failed. Enough facts were not available, and there was no adequate scientific background into which they could be fitted. Moreover, Aristotle regarded this work of induction as merely a necessary preliminary to true science of the deductive type, which, by logical reasoning, deduces consequences from the premises reached by the former process.

Aristotle was the creator of formal logic, with its syllogistic form and show of conclusiveness. It was a great discovery, and by itself would have been enough to make the reputation of a lesser man. Aristotle applied his discovery to the theory of science, choosing as examples the mathematical subjects and especially geometry, which had already passed from its early tentative stage, in which perhaps Thales was trying to rationalize the empirical rules of land-surveying, to a later, more completely deductive form.

But syllogistic logic is useless for experimental science, where discovery, and not formal proof from accepted premises, is the main object sought. To start from the premise that an element cannot be broken up into simpler bodies would have led to a correct list of known elements in 1890, but in 1920 it would have excluded all those that are radio-active. Thus the premise has had to be modified, and the word "element" has changed its meaning. But that fact does not destroy its utility, nor does it invalidate modern physics.

Fortunately modern experimenters have not troubled about the formal rules of logic; but the prestige of Aristotle's work did much to turn Greek and mediaeval science into a search for absolutely certain premises and into the premature use of deductive methods. The results were the assignment of infallibility to many very fallible authorities and much false reasoning in deceptive logical form. As Dr Schiller says:

The whole theory of science was so interpreted, and the whole of logic was so constructed, as to lead up to the ideal of demonstrative science, which in its turn rested on a false analogy which assimilated it to the dialectics of proof. Does not this mistake go far to account for the neglect of experience and the unprogressiveness of science for nearly 2000 years after Aristotle?[1]

[1] *Studies in the History and Method of Science*, ed. C. Singer, Oxford, 1917, p. 240.

Aristotle   Aristotle was followed as head of the Peripatetic School by his pupil Theophrastus, born about 370 B.C., whose chief work was in botany, both systematic and physiological. It is held by some that records collected by the scientific staff which accompanied Alexander on his campaigns were used by Theophrastus, who did much good work in describing and classifying plants, and gained some knowledge of plant organs and their functions. For instance, he distinguished bulbs, tubers and rhizomes from true roots. His botanical work was much used by Andrea Cesalpini, who led the revival of botanical science at the Renaissance, and, like that of Aristotle on animals, it was not surpassed for two thousand years.

Theophrastus was succeeded by Straton, a physicist, who tried to reconcile the views of Aristotle and the Atomists, though he himself held a thoroughgoing mechanical philosophy. From this time the school of the Lyceum became less important, and, by the middle of the third century, its work was done.

Between the times of Plato and Aristotle, about 367 B.C., Eudoxus of Cnidos did good work in astronomy, though his cosmogony was a relapse from the ideas of the Pythagoreans with their moving Earth. Eudoxus held that the Earth was the centre of all things, and that the Sun, Moon and planets revolve round it in concentric crystal spheres. This was the first serious attempt to explain the apparently irregular movement of those bodies. The system of Eudoxus led to the more elaborate schemes of Hipparchus and Ptolemy, whose cycles and epicycles satisfied astronomers till the time of Copernicus. In its day, the now discredited geocentric theory, which gave a quantitative explanation of the phenomena, was an immense advance over the ideas which preceded it. A false hypothesis, if it serve as a guide for further enquiry, may be more useful at the time than a truer one for which verifiable evidence is not yet at hand.

Hellenistic   The literary bent which has characterized modern studies of
Civilization[1]   ancient times has directed attention chiefly to the ages when the poets and sculptors of Athens were putting forth their masterpieces. It would be unfair to say that the classical period of Greece produced no science. There was geometry before Euclid; the medicine of Hippocrates and the zoology of Aristotle were

---

[1] W. W. Tarn, *Hellenistic Civilization*, London, 1927; W. H. S. Jones and Sir T. L. Heath, "Hellenistic Science and Mathematics", in *Cambridge Ancient History*, vol. VII, p. 284.

based on sound observation. Yet the philosophic outlook was *Hellenistic* metaphysical and not scientific; even the atomic theory of *Civilization* Democritus was speculative philosophy and not science.

With the marches of Alexander the Great we reach a new epoch. He carried to the East that Greek culture which was already spreading westwards over the Mediterranean, and in return he brought Babylonia and Egypt into closer touch with Europe, while his staff collected vast stores of facts in geography and natural history. Thus began three centuries of Hellenism, from the death of Alexander in 323 to the establishment of the Roman Empire by Augustus in 31 B.C., centuries during which Greek culture, having passed its zenith in its original home, spread to other lands and dominated the known world. A form of the Greek language, ἡ κοινή, the common speech, was understood "from Marseilles to India, from the Caspian to the Cataracts", and the upper classes from Rome to Asia accepted Greek philosophy and the Greek outlook on life. Commerce became international, and thought was free as it was not to be again till recent days.

The increased knowledge of the world led to more curiosity about natural things, and a more scientific attitude of mind. We are at once conscious of a more familiar atmosphere— indeed there is much resemblance to our own times, though there were then no machines and many slaves. A change in method appears. We pass from general philosophic systems and encyclopaedic surveys of knowledge to more modern specialization. Definite and limited problems are isolated from others and attacked singly, and real progress in natural knowledge is seen. Indeed, the change from the synthetic philo- sophies of Athens to the analytic science of Archimedes and the early Alexandrians is closely parallel to the change from the Scholasticism of late mediaeval writers to the modern science of Galileo and Newton.

In Hellenistic learning the Greek element was predominant, but other influences were not wanting. Babylonian astronomy, making simultaneous advance under Kidinnu (or Kidenas) of Sippar, was becoming available in Greek translations, bringing with it the fantasies of Chaldaean astrology. The most important development in philosophy, Stoicism, was due to Zeno of Citium, who was reckoned a Phoenician.

The Hellenistic period comprised two phases; the first

Hellenistic Civilization

expansive and creative in politics, literature, philosophy and science, the second showing an exhaustion of the creative impulse and a reaction, both material and spiritual, of the East on the West. "The Graeco-Macedonian world is caught between that reaction and Rome, until Rome, having destroyed the Hellenistic state-system, is ultimately compelled to take its place as the standard-bearer of Greek culture." But the more purely Greek period of Hellenism went down in the civil wars of Rome, and the Empire developed a culture which was Graeco-Roman, unable to exclude for long Asiatic influences.

Even in the earlier period, soon after the time of Alexander, eastern ideas began to spread. Star-worship began at a very early date in Babylon; the idea of a correspondence between the heavens above and man beneath suggested that the planets, which move in fixed paths, determine men's actions, for man the microcosm is a counterpart of the macrocosm, and his soul but a spark of the fire which glows in the stars. Hence arose the terrible Babylonian idea of the Fate which rules alike stars and gods and men.

Plato had heard of astrology, but effective knowledge of it was first brought to the Greeks by Berossus about 280 B.C. In the second century, when science began to fail, astrology spread rapidly, and, under the influence of Poseidonius, it began an evil career which did not end even with Copernicus and Newton.

As a means of escape from Fate, men looked first to the heavens themselves, where incalculable bodies like comets suggested room for freedom. But more hopeful seemed the three roads opened by magic, by the mystery religions, and by what in early Christian times was called gnosticism.

The gnostic held that a god had revealed a secret key to the Universe to some chosen soul, and, if man could but rediscover it, his soul would be free, for Knowledge is above Fate.

Magic is almost ubiquitous, but in the second century a fresh flood from Asia followed astrology into Europe, and gave men the hope of controlling nature, the gods and the stars. The papyri of the time are full of recipes for charms and spells.

The mystery religions, based on the prehistoric rites of initiation and communion, for the most part sought salvation by personal union with a saviour-god, known under many names, who had died and risen again. These religions, as we have seen, had long been known in Greece, but, with the breakdown of the local deities of Olympian mythology in the international atmosphere of Hellenistic times, they swept the world. From the second century onward men's religious sense deepened, and, till the rise of Christianity, their needs were mostly met by the mystery religions.

Astrology, magic and religion make their appeal to all men, but philosophy and science only to the few. The most characteristic and most important Hellenistic philosophy was Stoicism. Zeno began teaching in Athens soon after 317 B.C., and his doctrines spread till they became the chief philosophy of Rome. Though Stoicism took physics as theoretically the basis of logic and ethics, it had little direct contact with physical science. Its theology was a form of pantheism, and its real meaning and its real power lay in a high and stern concept of morality.

Of more importance in the history of science is the system of Epicurus, because, although its interests were mainly philosophical and not scientific, it was based on the atomism of Democritus. It thus preserved the atomic theory till Lucretius came to enshrine it for us in his poem.

Epicurus, who was born at Samos in 342 B.C. and died at Athens in 270, led a reaction against the idealist philosophy of Plato and Aristotle, a reaction which involved a belief in a dualism of mind and body. To Epicurus, all that exists is corporeal, though some things such as atoms are too small for the senses to appreciate directly. Man's soul is but a warm breath, and death is the end of all. There are gods, but they, like man, are a product of nature and not its creators; they exist in perfect blessedness and tranquillity and are to be worshipped neither in fear nor in hope. They are

careless of mankind.
For they lie beside their nectar, and the bolts are hurled
Far below them in the valleys, and the clouds are lightly curl'd
Round their golden houses, girdled with the gleaming world.

The only test of reality is sensation; ideas are but fainter images produced by repeated sensation, stored in memory, and recalled by names. The less obvious phenomena of nature are to be explained on analogy with what is familiar. Nature is made of atoms and a void as in the scheme of Democritus. Our world is but one of many produced by chance conjunctions of atoms in infinite space and endless time.

Man is subject neither to the tyranny of capricious gods nor

Hellenistic Civilization

to the blind immutable Fate imagined by the Babylonians and by some Greek philosophers; he is as free as he seems to himself to be. Man, like a god, can withdraw himself from external troubles, and seek grave and solemn pleasure in quiet ease of heart. Prudential wisdom is more than philosophy. Thus Epicurus used the atomic theory and a primitive sensationalism as a basis on which to build a system of cheerful if superficial optimism. His physics are subservient to his ethics.[1]

Deductive Geometry

The higher value assigned by Aristotle to deductive as compared with inductive reasoning, serves to show why the most successful product of the Greek mind was the deductive science of geometry.[2] The details of its history are not within the scheme of this book, but in any account of science it must find some place, even if it be regarded as merely one of the tools which natural science has used most freely.

Geometry, as its name implies, arose from the practical need of land-surveying, and this need was greatest, and was best met, in Egypt, where the inundations of the Nile periodically removed the landmarks. Tradition says that it was Thales of Miletus, earliest of Ionian philosophers, who, after a visit to Egypt, conceived the thought of an ideal science of space and form based on the empirical rules for land-surveying. The next great step seems to have been taken by Pythagoras and his disciples, who not only proved new theorems, but arranged in some sort of logical order those already known.

A history of geometry was written by Eudemus of Rhodes about 320 B.C. Fragments of this work remain, and from them can be gathered some idea of the gradual additions which were made to geometrical propositions. Existing knowledge was collected, developed and systematized by Euclid of Alexandria about 300 B.C. From a few axioms, regarded as self-evident properties of space, a wonderful series of propositions was deduced by logical principles, in a manner which, till quite recent years, remained the only accepted method.

Geometry can now be looked at in two ways. Firstly, it can be taken as the deductive step in one of the observational and experimental sciences. From the empirical facts of Egyptian land-surveying, certain axioms and postulates are laid down.

---

[1] Cyril Bailey, *The Greek Atomists and Epicurus*, Oxford, 1928.
[2] See Whewell and Rouse Ball, *loc. cit.* Also G. J. Allman, *Greek Geometry*, Dublin, 1889.

They seem to be self-evident facts, but really they are hypo-theses as to the nature of space, obtained by a process of imaginative induction from the observed phenomena. From these hypotheses mathematical geometry deduces by logical reasoning an immense number of consequences, such as those given in the books of Euclid and in geometrical astronomy. Till quite recently, all these consequences were found to agree with the observations and experiments made on nature. In particular the mathematical astronomy of Newton and his followers, to the days of Adams and Leverrier, an astronomy which assumed Euclidean space, verified the hypotheses to a high degree of accuracy. On this view, as we have said, geometry is but the deductive part of an experimental science.

Deductive Geometry

But it is possible to look at it in another way. Common observation suggests space of a certain kind. The mind adopts the suggestion, and defines an ideal space, which *is* perfectly what observed space seems to be. At a later stage the mind defines other kinds of space—non-Euclidean, perhaps impossible of physical representation. Having obtained its definitions, the mind is now free to develope their logical consequences, with no reference to what is or is not in accordance with nature. If space is defined as having three dimensions, one set of consequences follows. If we assume that space, or what corresponds to space, has n dimensions, we get other consequences. It is a pretty and intellectual game, but necessarily it has nothing directly to do with nature or with experimental science, though the methods learnt in the game may afterwards prove useful.

Both these two points of view are essentially modern. The Greek mathematicians and philosophers accepted implicitly the simple intuitional idea, in which the axioms of geometry are taken to be facts self-evident to the mind. But whatever view we may now take of its philosophic meaning, deductive geometry was especially suited to the Greek genius, and, unlike some other products of Greek thought, it marked a permanent step in the advance of knowledge, a step which never had to be retraced. Indeed, Greek geometry may well be considered to share with modern experimental science the highest place among the triumphs of the human intellect.

The origins of the sciences of mechanics and hydrostatics are to be sought in the practical arts, rather than in the writings of the early Greek philosophers, but they were placed on a

Archimedes and the Origins of Mechanics

Archimedes and the Origins of Mechanics

sound footing when observation was allied to the deductive methods learnt in geometry. The first known to have done this was Archimedes of Syracuse (287–212 B.C.), whose work, more than that of any other Greek, shows the true modern combination of mathematics with experimental enquiry; a combination in which definite and limited problems are attacked, and hypotheses are set forth only to have their logical consequences deduced and tested by observation or experiment.[1]

The idea of the relative densities of bodies, which, as we have seen, was unknown to Aristotle, was first formulated clearly by Archimedes, who, moreover, discovered the principle known by his name—that, when a body floats in a liquid, its weight is equal to the weight of liquid displaced, and, when it is immersed, its weight is diminished by that amount. It is said that King Hiero, having entrusted some gold to the artificers who were to make his crown, suspected them of alloying it with silver. He asked Archimedes to test this suspicion. While thinking over the problem, Archimedes noticed in his bath that he displaced water equal in volume to his own body, and saw at once that, for equal weights, the lighter alloy would displace more water than the heavier gold. This flash of insight revealed to Archimedes his principle, but he then proceeded to deduce it mathematically from his fundamental conception of a fluid as a substance that yields to any, even the smallest, shearing stress, that is, a force tending to cause one layer to slide over another.

Archimedes also considered the theoretical principle of the lever, the practical use of which must be of immemorial antiquity and is illustrated in the sculptures of Assyria and Egypt two thousand years before the days of Archimedes. Nowadays we treat the law of the lever as a matter for experimental determination, and deduce other, more complicated, results from it. But, with the Greek love of abstract reasoning, Archimedes deduced that law from what he regarded either as self-evident axioms, or as statements which could be verified by simple experiment: (1) that equal weights placed at equal distances from the point of support balance; (2) that equal weights placed at unequal distances do not balance, but that which hangs at the greatest distance descends. Implicitly, however, the principle of the lever, or of the centre of gravity,

[1] Sir T. L. Heath, *Works of Archimedes*, Cambridge, 1897; E. Mach, *Die Mechanik in ihre Entwickelung*; John Cox, *Mechanics*, Cambridge, 1904.

which is equivalent to that of the lever, is contained in these axioms. Nevertheless, the co-ordination of the law of the lever with ideas which then seemed simpler was a step in advance. It is, indeed, the type of most scientific explanation, which, in its essence, generally consists in describing new phenomena in terms of others more familiar to our minds.

Archimedes and the Origins of Mechanics

Archimedes' chief interest lay in pure geometry, and he regarded his discovery of the ratio of the volume of a cylinder to that of a sphere inscribed in it as his greatest achievement. He measured the circle by inscribing and circumscribing polygons, increasing the number of sides till the polygons nearly met on the circle. By this method of exhaustion he showed that the ratio of the circumference to the diameter was greater than $3\frac{10}{71}$ and less than $3\frac{1}{7}$. The mechanical contrivances for which he was famous—compound pulleys, hydraulic screws, burning mirrors—were considered by him as the recreations of a geometer at play.

Archimedes was no mere compiler. Nearly all his writings are accounts of his own discoveries. It is a sign of the modernity of his outlook that the greatest man of the Renaissance, Leonardo da Vinci, sought for copies of the works of Archimedes more eagerly than for those of any other Greek philosopher. And nearly indeed were his writings lost to the world. Apparently at one time the only survival was a manuscript, probably of the ninth or tenth century, which has long ago disappeared. But fortunately three copies were made, and are extant; and from these the printed editions have been taken.

Archimedes, the first and greatest of physicists of the modern type in the ancient world, who helped with his engines of war to keep the Romans at bay for three years, was killed by a soldier after the storming of Syracuse in the year 212. His tomb was discovered and piously restored in 75 B.C. by Cicero, who was then Quaestor in Sicily.

Meanwhile there had been developments in astronomy and cosmogony. In the fourth century before Christ, geographical discovery made considerable progress. Hanno passed the Pillars of Hercules, and sailed down the west coast of Africa; Pytheas voyaged round Britain towards the polar seas, and Alexander marched to India. It was known that the Earth was a sphere, and some idea of its true size began to be formed. This growth in knowledge was not favourable to the

Aristarchus and Hipparchus

Aristarchus and
Hipparchus

ideas of the counter-earth or central fire imagined by Philolaus, and those parts of Pythagorean astronomy were thenceforward discredited. But the knowledge gained of the variations with latitude in the length of day and night led Ecphantus, one of the latest of the Pythagoreans, to the simpler conception of the revolution of the Earth on its own axis at the centre of space. This was also taught about 350 by Heraclides of Pontos, who held that, while the Sun and major planets revolve round the Earth, Venus and Mercury revolve round the Sun as it moves.

A much bolder step was taken by Aristarchus of Samos (c. 310–230 B.C.),[1] an older contemporary of Archimedes, who, in his extant work *On the Sizes and Distances of the Sun and Moon*, applies some very capable geometry to that problem. By considering firstly the phenomena to be observed at an eclipse of the Moon, and secondly those seen when the Moon is half full, he arrived at the conclusion that the ratio of the diameter of the Sun to that of the Earth must be greater than 19 : 3 and less than 43 : 6, i.e. about 7 : 1. This figure is of course much too small, but the principle of his investigation is sound, and the realization that the Sun is larger than the Earth was in itself a remarkable achievement.

According to Archimedes, Aristarchus also put forward the hypothesis "that the fixed stars and the sun remain unmoved, that the earth revolves round the sun on the circumference of a circle, the sun lying at the centre of the orbit". This theory of Aristarchus is mentioned by Plutarch also. To explain the apparent immobility of the fixed stars in face of the movement of the Earth, Aristarchus rightly concluded that their distances are enormous compared with the diameter of the Earth's orbit.

The heliocentric view of the Cosmos was too far in advance of the time to receive general assent. According to Plutarch, the belief was held confidently in the second century B.C. by Seleucus the Babylonian, who strove to find new proofs and defended it vigorously. But the rest of mankind, including even the philosophers, still considered the centre of the Universe to be the Earth, whether they regarded it as a floating ball round which the heavens revolved, or as the fixed, stable, bottomless solid it seemed to the senses.

The pressure of common-sense, reinforced by the balance of

[1] Sir T. L. Heath, *Aristarchus of Samos, the Ancient Copernicus, a History of Greek astronomy to Aristarchus*, Greek text and translation, Oxford, 1913.

authority, was too great for the revolutionary views of *Aristarchus and* Aristarchus. About 370–360 B.C. Eudoxus of Cnidos, as we *Hipparchus* have seen, had explained the apparent motion of the Sun, Moon and planets by imagining them carried round in crystal spheres all concentric with the Earth. This conception proved to be the basis on which it was possible for later astronomers to elaborate the geocentric theory. About 130 B.C., Hipparchus developed it into a form which, expounded by Ptolemy of Alexandria about A.D. 127–151, held the field till the sixteenth century of our era.

Hipparchus was born at Nicaea in Bithynia, and worked in Rhodes and then in Alexandria from 160 to 127 B.C. Only fragments of his writings remain, but his work was fully set forth by Ptolemy. He made use of the older Greek and Babylonian records; he invented many astronomical instruments, and made therewith many accurate observations, being the first of the Greeks to divide the circle of such instruments into 360 degrees in the Babylonian manner.[1] He is usually considered to have discovered the precession of the equinoxes, though a claim to priority for Kidenas the Babylonian has been put forward by Schnabel,[2] and it is certain that Hipparchus knew Kidenas' work. Hipparchus estimated the precession at 36 seconds of arc a year, the real value being about 50 seconds. He calculated the distance of the Moon to be $33\frac{2}{3}$ times the diameter of the Earth, and its diameter to be $\frac{1}{3}$ that of the Earth, the true figures being 30·2 and 0·27. He invented both plane and spherical trigonometry, and made an attempt to determine the position of places on the Earth by measuring their latitude and longitude.

The cosmogony of Hipparchus, though erroneous in its main underlying assumption, and therefore complicated in its details, was successful in representing the facts. Accepting the Earth as centre, Hipparchus showed that the apparent motions of the Sun, Moon and planets could be explained by supposing that each body was carried round in an orbit or epicycle, while this orbit was itself carried as a whole round the Earth in an immensely larger circular orbit or cycle. From direct observation, the positions and dimensions of these cycles and epicycles could be determined. Tables were then drawn up, from

[1] For astronomical instruments, see Whewell, *loc. cit.* vol. I, p. 198.
[2] Tarn, *loc. cit.* p. 241.

Aristarchus and
Hipparchus

which the position of the Sun, Moon and planets at any future time could be predicted, and solar and lunar eclipses could be foretold with a considerable degree of accuracy.

The great difficulty which faced astronomers from the days of Aristotle till Galileo discovered the principle of inertia, was that of explaining the continued motion of the heavenly bodies. According to Aristotle's view, which replaced that of Plato, continued motion needed a continual moving force; Aristotle therefore postulated an Unmoved Mover, and the more mechanically minded found it necessary to suppose the skies filled with crystal spheres, which carried round the heavenly bodies in their cycles and epicycles.

It is easy to disparage this astronomy in the light of modern knowledge, but the fact remains that, complicated as the theory became, it served for many centuries to interpret successfully the phenomena of the heavens, and guided the labours of many competent astronomers from Ptolemy to Tycho Brahe. The credit for its chief development must be assigned to Hipparchus. Unfortunately the geocentric theory, which the weight of his great name upheld, conduced to the follies of astrology. As long as the Earth was the centre, and the Sun and stars in their courses circled round it, such beliefs were inevitable.

There is a legend of a glass on the Pharos which enabled those who watched to see ships beyond the normal range of vision. Cornford suggests that, if this be true, and if some Greek philosopher, overcoming his prejudice against mechanic crafts, had made a telescope, Aristarchus might have been justified, and the course of scientific history changed.

The School of
Alexandria

By the end of the fourth or the beginning of the third century before Christ the intellectual centre of the world had moved from Athens to Alexandria, the city founded in 332 by Alexander the Great. One of Alexander's generals, Ptolemy, founded there a Greek dynasty which became extinct on the death of Cleopatra in the year 30 B.C. Among those who made the schools of Alexandria illustrious in the reign of the first Ptolemy, 323 to 285, were the great geometer Euclid and Herophilus the anatomist and physician.

In the Greek civilization of Alexandria a new and more modern spirit appears, as in other Hellenistic lands. Instead of the complete intellectual systems in which the Athenian philosophers were pre-eminent, the men of Alexandria, following the lead of Aristarchus of Samos and Archimedes of Syracuse, *The School of* *Alexandria* undertook limited and special enquiries, and therefore made more definite scientific progress.

About the middle of the third century, the famous Museum, or place dedicated to the Muses, was founded at Alexandria. The four departments of literature, mathematics, astronomy and medicine were in the nature of research institutes as well as schools, and the needs of them all were served by the largest library of the ancient world, containing some 400,000 volumes. One section of the library was destroyed by the Christian Bishop Theophilus about A.D. 390, and, after the Muslim conquest in the year 640, the Muhammadans, whether accidentally or deliberately is uncertain, destroyed the rest of what remained. But for some centuries the Library of Alexandria was one of the wonders of the world.

We have already considered the work of Euclid under the head of deductive geometry. He systematized the writings of older geometers and added many new theorems of his own. He also studied optics, realized that light travels in straight lines, and discovered the laws of reflection.

The Alexandrian school of medicine was established chiefly by the work of two men, Herophilus and Erasistratus. The former, born at Chalcedon, flourished at Alexandria under Ptolemy I. He was the earliest distinguished human anatomist, and the greatest physician since the days of Hippocrates. His medicine was empirical and almost free from theoretical preconceptions. He gave a good description of the brain, of the nerves and of the eye, of the liver and other internal organs, of the arteries and veins; and he definitely established the fact that the seat of intelligence is the brain, and not the heart as maintained by Aristotle.

Erasistratus, a younger contemporary of Herophilus, practised human dissections and made experiments on animals. He was keenly interested in physiology, and was the first to treat it as a separate subject. He added to the knowledge of the brain, of the nerves and of the circulatory system, holding that there are in the body and the brain special vessels for the blood and for the spirit ($\pi\nu\epsilon\hat{\nu}\mu\alpha$ $\zeta\omega\tau\iota\kappa\acute{o}\nu$) which he identified with air. Taking over from Epicurus the tenets of the atomic theory, Erasistratus was opposed to medical mysticism, though he believed in nature acting as an external

4-2

power, framing the human body for the ends it is to serve. Herophilus, Erasistratus and a third anatomist, Eudemus, made their century remarkable in the history of medicine.

In the latter part of the third century B.C., another group of great men appears, younger contemporaries of Archimedes. Among them we must mention Eratosthenes, who was born at Cyrene about 273 and died at Alexandria about 192. He was Librarian of the Museum, and the first great physical geographer. He calculated the circumference of the Earth by estimating the latitudes and distances apart of Syene and Meroe, two places on nearly the same meridian. His result was 252,000 stades, probably equal to about 24,000 miles, a surprisingly close approximation to the modern estimate of about 24,800 miles. Eratosthenes argued from the similarity of the tides in the Indian and Atlantic Oceans that those oceans must be connected and the inhabited world of Europe-Asia-Africa an island, so that it should be possible to sail from Spain to India round the south of Africa. Moreover, it was probably he who conjectured that the Atlantic might be divided by land running from north to south and thus inspired Seneca's prophecy of the discovery of a new world. Poseidonius later on rejected this idea, and, underestimating the size of the Earth, proclaimed that a man sailing west for 70,000 stades would come to India. This was the foundation of Columbus' confidence.

A striking advance in mathematics was made at Alexandria in the latter half of the second century B.C. by Apollonius of Perga, who collected the knowledge of conic sections due to Euclid and his predecessors, and carried the subject much further by his own work. Apollonius showed that all conics could be considered as sections of one cone; he introduced the names parabola, ellipse and hyperbola; he treated the two branches of the hyperbola as a single curve, and thus made clear the analogies between the three kinds of section. He obtained a solution of the general equation of the second degree by means of conics, and determined the evolute of any conic. His treatment of the whole subject is purely geometrical.

In the second century at Alexandria we meet again with Hipparchus, whose great work in astronomy has already been described. By this time Alexandria was losing its supremacy in Greek learning, which later was shared with Rome and

Pergamos. Of uncertain date, somewhere between the first century B.C. and the third A.D., is Hero (Ἥρων ὁ μηχανικός), mathematician, physicist and inventor. He found algebraic solutions of equations of the first and second degree, and worked out many formulae for the mensuration of areas and volumes. He struck upon an important principle when he pointed out that the line of a reflected ray of light is the shortest possible path.[1] But he is chiefly remembered for his mechanical contrivances, such as siphons, a thermoscope, the forcing air pump, and the earliest steam engine, in which the recoil of steam issuing from a jet is used to make an arm carrying the jet revolve about an axis.

The chief name which distinguishes later Graeco-Roman Alexandrian science is that of the astronomer Claudius Ptolemy,[2] who must not be confused with the kings of Egypt of the same name. He taught and made observations at Alexandria between the years A.D. 127 and 151. His great work, μεγάλη σύνταξις τῆς ἀστρονομίας, later called by its contracted Arabic name of *Almagest*, is an encyclopaedia of astronomy, which was based on and expounded the work of Hipparchus, and remained the standard treatise till the days of Copernicus and Kepler. In spite of greater fulness of treatment, and new observations, such as a second inequality in the Moon's motion, it does not alter materially the theories elaborated by the earlier astronomer, and the only new instrument described seems to be a mural quadrant. Ptolemy, like his master, improved and developed the science of trigonometry, with the view of basing his work "on the incontrovertible ways of arithmetic and geometry". He reasserted the general principle that, in attempting to explain phenomena, it is necessary to adopt the simplest hypothesis that will co-ordinate the facts, a principle which eventually became the chief weapon of those who disproved the geocentric theory which Ptolemy had consummated.

Ptolemy was a geographer as well as an astronomer, and he exercised an influence in this department of knowledge which was only gradually superseded by the maritime discoveries of the fifteenth and sixteenth centuries. It is difficult to assign

[1] G. Sarton, *History of Science*, vol. I, Baltimore, 1927, p. 208; *Isis*, No. 16, 1924, p. 76.

[2] G. J. Allman, Sir E. H. Bunbury and C. R. Beazley, art. "Ptolemy", in *Encyclopœdia Britannica*.

the merit of much of the work to the respective shares of
Ptolemy himself and his immediate forerunner, Marinus of
Tyre, whose writings have not separately survived. Ptolemy
undoubtedly placed geography on a secure footing by insisting
that correct observations of latitude and longitude must
precede any satisfactory attempts at surveying and map-
drawing; but his own materials for carrying out such a design
were very inadequate, for there was then no method by which
longitudes could be determined with any accuracy. Nevertheless, Ptolemy's maps retain their interest. They were put
together from information brought by traders and explorers,
and depicted a world extending from the shores of the Malay
Peninsula and the coastline of China to the Straits of Gibraltar
and the Fortunate Islands, and from Britain, Scandinavia and
the Russian Steppes to a vague land of lakes at the head
waters of the Nile. His general treatment of the subject is
that of an astronomer rather than a geographer, for he makes
no attempt to describe climate, natural productions or even
the aspects which would now be included under physical
geography; nor does he avail himself, to any large extent, of
the descriptions and accounts of lands within the Roman
Empire which must have been accessible in military "itineraries".

A book on Optics is also assigned to Ptolemy. It is only
known in a twelfth-century Latin translation from the Arabic,
and may or may not be his work. It contains a study of
refraction including atmospheric refraction, which is described
by Sarton[1] as "the most remarkable experimental research of
antiquity". The author finds that when light passes from one
medium to another, the angles of incidence and refraction are
proportional, a relation which is approximately true for small
angles.

With all this good work in real science, it is curious to find
that Ptolemy seems to have written a book on astrology. But
about this time the classical gods had been moved from
Olympus to the sky, and Jupiter, Saturn, Mars, Mercury and
Venus continued as planets to rule the destinies of men.
Natural Astrologers (i.e. astronomers) observed the sky and
made astronomical records, and Judicial Astrologers cast
horoscopes and obtained, from a study of the stars, divine
guidance in human affairs. Probably his astrology had much

[1] *History of Science*, vol. I, 1927, p. 274; *Isis*, No. 16, 1924, p. 79.

to do with Ptolemy's long influence in mediaeval Europe, and, indeed, in an unscientific epoch, it was impossible to tell, save by the method of trial, that the stars did not influence the history of mankind.

The School of Alexandria

Among the practical and intellectual activities of Hellenistic Alexandria we can trace the origins of alchemy. The earliest Greek alchemist probably lived in the first century of our era, but the oldest works on alchemy known to us are those of the so-called pseudo-Democritus of uncertain date, and of Zosimos, who flourished in Upper Egypt in the third or fourth century A.D. There are also writings, probably of the third century, assigned to "Hermes Trismegistos", the Greek equivalent of the god Thoth. They are chiefly concerned with Platonic and Stoic philosophy, but they also contain much astrology as well as alchemy, and were afterwards well known in Latin translations.

The Origins of Alchemy

In order to understand the beginnings of alchemy we must realize both the state of the arts and the philosophic atmosphere of Alexandria.[1] In the preceding centuries there had arisen in all Mediterranean countries an industry, derived from early chemical processes, which supplied imitations of things too expensive for the people. Imitation pearls, cheap dyes which matched the costly Tyrian purple, alloys which looked like silver and gold, all became articles of commerce.

Alchemy, from an early date, was linked with other prevailing realms of thought, and particularly with astrology. The Sun, which vivifies all nature, generates gold, his image or antitype, in the body of the Earth. The white Moon represents silver, Venus copper, Mercury quicksilver, Mars iron, Jupiter tin, and Saturn, farthest and therefore coldest of the five planets, the heavy and dull metal lead.

Platonic philosophy, as set forth in the *Timaeus*, gave a complete monist idealism, and emphasized the theory that matter, an essentially unimportant though necessary element in the sentient world, was fundamentally of one kind. Nothing really exists except in so far as it embodies an ideal, and is therefore good; all nature is living, and (a later Gnostic development) is striving towards improvement. Matter itself, the alchemists believed, is unimportant, but its qualities are real. Men's bodies are all of the same stuff, and men are made good or bad by changing not their bodies but their souls. So

[1] A. J. Hopkins, in *Isis*, No. 21, 1925, p. 58.

metals can be changed by changing their qualities, as, they said, artisans know well; indeed, the qualities *are* the metals. Metals are striving for improvement towards the ideal fire-proof spirit of gold, hence it should be easy to help them on the road. It was known that the mordant salts used in dyeing would etch metals, so that, if a small quantity of gold be added to a base metal, the alloy can be etched to leave a golden surface. Thus, they thought, the higher metal, acting as a ferment or yeast, overcomes the baseness of the mass, changing it into the spiritual quality of gold.

The chief property of the noble metals is their colour—the white of silver, the yellow of gold. Copper can be turned yellow by chemical treatment, and thus be transmuted into gold. This they thought was done either by removing the base earth, and with it the tendency to tarnish, or by increasing the better elements, air and fire, through an improvement in their fire quality or colour. When dead matter has received the colour spirit, it becomes alive, as a man receives a soul.

In practical alchemy, four steps were usually indicated. (1) Tin, lead, copper and iron were fused together into a black alloy in which each had lost its individuality and mingled in the "oneness" of Plato's first matter. (2) Mercury, arsenic or antimony was added, to whiten the copper, and thus simulate silver. (3) A "ferment" of a little gold was then given, and the white alloy treated with sulphur water (i.e. calcium sulphide) or mordant salts. Thus the alloy acquired the colour of gold—indeed, to the Alexandrian alchemist, it *became* gold. To him the essence of matter was not, as it is to us, its mass and specific physical properties and chemical reactions, but the Aristotelian qualities such as colour, readily changeable. Thus, if a metal was given yellow colour and sheen, the essential qualities of gold, it became gold. Unlike some of his successors, the Alexandrian alchemist was neither a fool nor a charlatan; he was experimenting, both in science and in art, in conformity with the best philosophy of his age.

Alchemy flourished in Alexandria for about three centuries. Then it ceased, according to one account, by order of the Emperor Diocletian, who in A.D. 292 commanded all books on the subject to be destroyed. When alchemy revived elsewhere, first among the Arabs and then in Europe, the philosophy under which it had arisen had become modified, and later writers understood neither the terminology nor the spirit of the Alexandrians. They tried to make gold by the old recipes, not knowing that the meaning of the words "gold" and "transmutation" had meanwhile changed with the philosophy. For the most part they hid their failure in a flood of mystical verbosity till the true science of chemistry began to emerge from their debased alchemy.

The Origins of Alchemy

Astrology and alchemy have an underlying basis of observation of nature, and rational, though mostly erroneous, thought; hence they played a real and respectable part in the early development of astronomy and chemistry. On the other hand, except among primitive peoples, magic is never respectable, and the only reality in it is its psychological influence on human credulity and desire for immediate and irresponsible power. Though magic had something to do with the origins of science, its spirit is definitely opposed to that of science, which shows always a slow, cautious and humble-minded search for truth. In the Hellenistic age the growth of magical superstitions coincides with a decline in ancient science, and in later times science was reborn, not because of, but in spite of, man's belief in magical arts.[1]

In the ancient world original scientific thought was almost entirely confined to the Greeks. It would naturally seem probable that the composition of the population of Italy must have been similar in character to that of Greece. But the inhabitants of the two countries showed considerable differences in development and achievement, thus suggesting a difference in race. The Romans, with their exaltation of the State, and their exceptional aptitude as soldiers, administrators and framers of law, had little creative intellectual force, though the numerous compilations that came into being seem to indicate a considerable curiosity about natural objects. Their art, their science, even their medicine, were borrowed from the Greeks; and, when Rome became mistress of the world, Greek philosophers and Greek physicians resorted to the banks of the Tiber, though they established no native schools of philosophy worthy to succeed those of Athens. The Romans seem to have cared for science only as a means of accomplishing practical work in medicine, agriculture, architecture or engineering.

The Roman Age

[1] Lynn Thorndike, *A History of Magic and Experimental Science*, 2 vols. New York, 1923. But see a review by G. Sarton, in *Isis*, No. 16, 1924, p. 74.

They used the stream of knowledge without replenishing its source—the fount of learning loved for its own sake—and in a few generations the source, and with it the stream, ran dry.

The opposition felt by conservative Romans to the coming supremacy of Greek thought is shown in the book of Cato the Censor (234–149 B.C.), grandfather of another, more famous Cato. The elder Cato wrote in his old age the first Latin treatise on agriculture, which incidentally gives us information concerning Roman medicine. About the same time Diogenes the Babylonian brought to Rome the philosophy of Stoicism, a system which, reinforced later by elements of Platonism in the teaching of Posidonius, became the characteristic Roman philosophy for three hundred years and is seen in its highest form in the writings of the Emperor Marcus Aurelius. Posidonius is also to be remembered as a traveller, astronomer, geographer and anthropologist. He explained the tides by the joint action of the Sun and Moon, indeed the influence of the heavens on earthly affairs seems to have been the essence of his philosophy. He set Zeus above Fate, and his outlook was religious, but he believed in divination and astrology, and did more to spread such ideas in Europe than perhaps any other man. He wrote a commentary on Plato's *Timaeus,* and his science, like that of Plato, was deduced from, and made subservient to, his philosophy.

Two generations later, by the first century before Christ, the Romans had conquered the world, and Greek learning had conquered the Romans. Much was done to create a philosophical language in Latin and to popularize Greek philosophy by Marcus Tullius Cicero (106–43 B.C.), the Roman lawyer and statesman. He wrote a cosmological work, *de Natura Deorum,* which contains information about the scientific knowledge of the time. He also put forward a teleological theory of the human body, and made many effective attacks on superstitious beliefs and magic rites.

Greek scientific philosophy in the form of atomism was expounded and applauded in the poem *de Rerum Natura* of Titus Lucretius Carus (98–55 B.C.).[1] This poem, like some of Cicero's prose, aims at the overthrow of superstition and the

[1] H. A. J. Munro, *Lucretius, Text, Notes and Translation,* 3 vols. 4th ed. London, 1905–1910. See also references for Democritus, p. 21 above. E. N. da C. Andrade, *The Scientific Significance of Lucretius,* introduction to Munro's *Lucretius,* 4th ed. 1928.

exaltation of reason as shown in the atomic and mechanical
philosophy. In one respect Lucretius is less modern than
Leucippus and Democritus, for his primordial atoms, instead of
moving in all directions, fall together through space. Here we
trace the influence of Aristotle's idea of an absolute up and
down. Probably Lucretius' poem contains no new thought, but
in magnificent language it sets out to show how the principle
of causation holds sway over all things from the invisible
evaporation of water to the majestic phenomena of the heavens
bounded by the shining walls of the Universe—*flammantia
moenia mundi*.

The greatest figure of the century, Gaius Julius Caesar
(100–44 B.C.), is of chief interest to us because of his establishment, with the technical help of Sosigenes, of the reformed
Julian calendar, in which the year is taken as being $365\frac{1}{4}$ days.
This estimate is a little too large, and led slowly to a discrepancy in dates and seasons. But the calendar remained in
general force in Europe till in 1582 its error amounted to
eleven days. It was then superseded by order of Pope
Gregory XIII. Caesar also planned a survey of the Roman
Empire, which was executed later by Agrippa and set forth
in a great map of the world.

About the year A.D. 20 a comprehensive work on geography
was written in Greek by Strabo of Amasia in Pontus, a work
which throws light on other contemporary sciences. The Roman
conquests were, of course, increasing the knowledge of the
Earth's surface, and itineraries describing the roads of the
Empire began to be composed.

A treatise on architecture, containing a full account of allied
physical and technical knowledge, was written by Vitruvius,
who understood that sound was a vibration of the air, and gave
the first known account of architectural acoustics.

Useful observations on hydrodynamics were made by Sextus
Julius Frontinus (A.D. 40–103), a Roman soldier and engineer,
who was Superintendent of the Aqueducts of Rome (*curator
aquarum*).[1] Frontinus wrote on the water supply of the city,
and found from experiment that when water flows from an
orifice the rate of flow depends not only on the size of the
orifice, but also on its depth below the surface of the water.

[1] Art. "Hydromechanics", in *Enc. Brit.* 9th ed.; G. Sarton, *loc. cit.*
p. 255.

The Roman Age   Virgil (c. 30 B.C.) described in the *Georgics* the poetry as well
as the art of agriculture, and another book on farming was
written by Varro, which contains observations on the growth
of plants, and suggests the idea that the contagion of disease
is due to invisible micro-organisms.

The first official school of Greek medicine was founded in
Rome about the year A.D. 14 under Augustus. The best
physician of the age was Celsus, who in the reign of Tiberius
wrote in Latin a great treatise on medicine and surgery, which
is the chief source of our knowledge of the history of the
medicine of Alexandria as well as that of Rome in his own day.
Celsus describes many surprisingly modern surgical operations
and in medicine holds a middle course between the empirical
and methodological schools of antiquity, believing in both
theory and observation. His work was lost throughout the
mediaeval period, but it was recovered in time to influence the
medicine of the Renaissance.

About the middle of the first century of our era Dioscorides,
botanist and military physician, wrote a treatise on botany
and pharmacy, which gives an account of some six hundred
plants and their medical properties, and remained in use for
fifteen centuries.[1]

In the second half of the century a certain revival of learning
appears. In especial one Roman citizen, the elder Pliny
(A.D. 23–79), is to be remembered for having produced in the
thirty-seven books of his *Naturalis Historia* an encyclopaedia
of the whole science of the period, and of the knowledge and
beliefs of a series of forgotten writers of Greece and Rome.[2]
Starting from a general theory of the Universe as consisting
of the sky and the stars in space, which he regarded as a manifestation of the Deity, he passed on to review the earth and
its contents. He dealt successively with geography, with man
and his mental and physical qualities, with animals, birds,
trees, agricultural operations, forestry, fruit-growing, wine-
making, the nature and uses of metals, and the origin and
practice of the fine arts. He discourses with equal satisfaction
on the natural history of the lion, the unicorn and the phoenix,
unable to distinguish between the real and the imaginary, the

[1] G. Sarton, *loc. cit.* p. 258.
[2] Text ed. by L. von Jan and K. Mayhoff, 5 vols. Leipzig, 1906–1909;
Eng. trans. J. Bostock and H. T. Riley, 6 vols. London, 1885–1887; art.
"Pliny", in *Enc. Brit.*

true, the credible and the impossible. He preserves for us the
superstitions of the time, and recounts in all good faith the
practice and utility of various forms of magic. But, to his
credit, it must be remembered that he died a victim to his
curiosity in natural knowledge. He was in command of the
Roman fleet at the time of the great eruption of Vesuvius,
which destroyed Pompeii and Herculaneum. He landed in
order to watch the upheaval, ventured too far, and was
overwhelmed by the storm of falling ashes.

Much of our knowledge of Greek philosophers, and indeed
of Greek philosophy, is derived from the information preserved
in the *Lives of the Philosophers*, written some two hundred years
later by Diogenes Laertius, but information has also been
obtained from the works of Plutarch (c. A.D. 50–125).[1] He
himself wrote on the constitution of the Moon and gave an
account of Roman mythology,[2] in which appears the idea of
a comparative study of religions. Two other contemporary
historians must be mentioned, Josephus (c. 37–120), who
wrote a record of the Jews, and Tacitus (55–120), our great
Latin authority for the political and social history of early
Britain and Germany.

In the next generation, while Ptolemy the astronomer was
working at Alexandria, Greek medicine flourished there and
at Rome, as well as in other schools which by this time had
been established. From the doctors who worked in them we
can trace a line of intellectual descent to Aretaeus of Cappa-
docia, and his more famous contemporary Galen (Galenus), after
Hippocrates the most renowned physician of the ancient world.

Galen was born at Pergamos in Asia Minor in the year 129,
and practised at Rome and elsewhere till about A.D. 200.[3] He
systematized Greek anatomical and medical knowledge, and
united the divided schools of medicine. He dissected animals
and a few human bodies, and discovered many new facts in
anatomy and physiology pathology and therapeutics. He
made experiments on living animals; in this way he examined
the action of the heart and made an investigation of the spinal
cord which Sarton classes as one of the two most notable
experiments of ancient times.[4] In philosophy he held that all

[1] Text with Eng. trans. by B. Perrin, 6 vols. London, 1914–1918.
[2] *The Roman Questions*, Eng. trans. and notes by H. J. Rose, Oxford, 1924.
[3] G. Sarton, *loc. cit.* p. 301; Sir T. C. Allbutt, *Greek Medicine in Rome*,
London, 1921.   [4] *Isis*, No. 16, 1924, p. 79.

The Roman Age   was determined by God, and the structure of the body formed by Him for an intelligible end. Galen's system of medicine, in opposition to the mechanistic views of the atomists and their followers, was founded on the idea of spirits of different kinds pervading all parts of the body. Galen's πνεῦμα ψυχικόν was translated into Latin as *spiritus animalis* and thus became our familiar "animal spirits" the meaning of which is perhaps sometimes misunderstood. It was for dogmas deduced with great dialectic subtlety from these views, and the authority with which he expounded them, rather than for his really great observations and experiments, or his practical skill in his profession, that Galen became famous, and influenced medicine for fifteen hundred years. His theistic attitude of mind appealed both to Christendom and to Islam, and partly explains his great and lasting influence.

His general theory of the bodily functions held its ground till Harvey discovered the circulation of the blood. Galen taught that the blood is formed in the liver from the food and then mixed with "natural spirits" which give it nutritive properties. Some of this blood passes to the body through the veins and back by the same channels to the heart in a tidal ebb and flow. The rest of it goes from the right side of the heart to the left through invisible pores in the septum, and is there mixed with air drawn from the lungs. By the heat of the heart it is laden with "vital spirits"; this higher kind of blood ebbs and flows into the parts of the body through the arteries, and thus enables the various organs to perform their vital functions. In the brain the vital blood generates "animal spirits", which, pure and unmixed with blood, pass along the nerves to bring about movement and the higher functions of the body.[1]

This scheme of physiology, wonderfully ingenious and successful considering Galen's knowledge, is of course very far from the truth. Unfortunately Galen's doctrine became more important in men's eyes than Galen's own free spirit of enquiry, and his authority blocked the road of physiology after the Renaissance till Harvey had the courage to ignore it.

The Romans may have achieved little in theoretical science but in practice they were notable. Sanitation and public health were well organized in Rome. Mighty aqueducts brought

[1] Sir Michael Foster, *History of Physiology*, Cambridge, 1901, p. 12.

fresh water to the city, a public medical service was established, hospitals built, and the armies equipped with medical officers.

The schools of medicine continued, but from the time of Galen, or even earlier, general science and philosophy in the ancient world show clear signs of their final eclipse. With the exception of Diophantus of Alexandria, who lived in the second half of the third century after Christ, and was the greatest Greek writer on algebra, there is no other man of the first rank. Before his day algebraic problems were treated either by geometry or by reasoning in words,[1] but he introduced abbreviations for those quantities and operations which continually recur, and was thus enabled to solve simple equations and a binomial quadratic. He dealt also with indeterminate expressions where the number of unknown quantities is greater than the number of equations.

This work marks the beginning of algebra as a separate subject, but after Diophantus no serious contribution to scientific knowledge was made by the ancient world. Although the first three centuries of the Empire marked the culmination of the great achievement of Roman Law, it is obvious that, even before the decay of Rome as a political power, science had come almost to a standstill, in common with other forms of philosophic thought. No advance in knowledge was being made, and the only activity was that shown in the writing of compendiums and commentaries, chiefly on the Greek philosophers. Among the commentators we must mention Alexander of Aphrodisias, head of the Lyceum about the year A.D. 200, who strove to preserve the pure Peripatetic doctrine. Aristotle was still regarded as the great authority on all questions of scientific theory and even of actual fact, though the prevailing metaphysical philosophy, at any rate in the then predominant school of Alexandria, was derived from Plato, through the more mystical Neo-Platonic school, of which Alexandria was the centre. About the beginning of the fourth century a Latin commentary on Plato's *Timaeus* was written by Chalcidius. This became almost the only source of mediaeval knowledge of Plato, and, during the centuries when the works of Aristotle were forgotten, it gave to the

[1] Sir Thomas L. Heath, *Diophantus of Alexandria, a Study in the History of Greek Algebra*, 2nd ed. Cambridge, 1910; Paul Tannery, papers in his *Memoirs*, 1879–1892; W. W. Rouse Ball, *History of Mathematics*, London, 1901, p. 107.

Middle Ages a philosophy of nature from which many of their fantastic ideas were derived.

As we have seen, the scientific work of the Alexandrian school was carried on, almost entirely, by men of Greek descent. But other elements in the population began gradually to play their part, especially in the more metaphysical branches of philosophy. Among these non-Greek elements one of the most important was supplied by the Jews. At Alexandria a school of thought arose, influenced on the one hand by Hellenistic culture, and on the other by Jewish and Babylonian tradition. It must be remembered that but a small and relatively unimportant number of the Jews returned to Palestine at the end of the Babylonian captivity, while many of the remainder established themselves as traders in the cities of Asia Minor and the Levant, and formed a network of communication, commercial, political and intellectual, throughout the East. Alexandria became the commercial and intellectual, while Jerusalem remained the religious centre of this scattered community, and for this reason Alexandria was the first important meeting-ground between Greek philosophy and Oriental religions, especially Judaism and Christianity. Many of the early Greek Fathers of the Christian Church lived at Alexandria or drew their philosophy therefrom. It was by their means that much Greek philosophy retained its vitality and took its place in that synthesis of Jewish, Greek and Christian thought which went to the composition of Patristic theology. The ideas of Plato, and to a lesser degree those of Aristotle, thus passed into early Christian theology, and became current in mediaeval Europe long before their origin was suspected by the Churchmen, who, when Greek authors were afterwards rediscovered, were amazed to find the prototypes of familiar Christian doctrines embedded in the works of heathen philosophers.

Though the early Fathers lived during the period under consideration, and though their writings form a connecting link between mediaeval religion and the more metaphysical elements in classical philosophy, it will be better to postpone till the next chapter the short but necessary account of their work and its influence on scientific thought, for they have little to do with the mathematical or observational science of the ancient world.

Chapter II

THE MIDDLE AGES

The Middle Ages—The Fathers of the Church—The Dark
Ages—The Reconstruction of Europe—The Arabian School of
Learning—The Revival of Learning in Europe—The Thirteenth
Century—Thomas Aquinas—Roger Bacon—The Decay of
Scholasticism.

UNTIL recent times the term "Middle Ages" was applied to
the whole long interval of a thousand years between the fall of
the ancient civilization and the rise of the Italian Renaissance.
But the revival of interest in the history, art and religion of
the thirteenth and fourteenth centuries has led to a clear
recognition of the fact that by then a new civilization had
arisen, and there is now a growing tendency to restrict the
name "mediaeval" to the four hundred years which preceded
the Renaissance and followed what are generally called the
"Dark Ages".

Nevertheless, to the historian of science there are advantages
in the older classification. The "Dark Ages" of Western
Europe coincided with the beginning of a remarkable growth
of learning in those Asiatic countries which were soon afterwards conquered by the Arabs. The Persian and Arabic school
originally based its teaching on translations from Greek
authors, but at a later time it added appreciable contributions
of its own to natural knowledge. Europe learnt much from
the Arabs, but not till the period of the Renaissance did the
western world recover an adequate and direct knowledge of
ancient science, learn to examine it critically, or endeavour to
find a path of its own in the new experimental method. The
period from the year 1100 onward, like the dark age that
preceded it, is to the historian of science but a time of preparation. The two divisions are part of the same whole, and
may well be treated together, though for the historian of
politics, literature or art they are distinct and separable. To

---

[1] For a general account of mediaeval thought see (1) H. F. Stewart, "Thought
and Ideas", in *Cambridge Mediaeval History*, vol. I, ch. 20; (2) H. O. Taylor,
The Mediaeval Mind, 2 vols., New York and London, 1911 and 1914. For facts
and references down to the year A.D. 1100 see G. Sarton, *Introduction to the
History of Science*, vol. I, Baltimore, 1927.

W

The Middle   us, then, the Middle Ages have their old significance—the
Ages   thousand years that passed between the fall of the ancient
learning and the rise of that of the Renaissance: the dark
valley across which mankind, after descending from the
heights of Greek thought and Roman dominion, had to struggle
towards the upward slopes of modern knowledge. In religion,
and in social and political structure, we are still akin to the
Middle Ages from which we have so recently emerged; but in
science we are nearer to the ancient world. As we look back
across the mist-filled hollow, we see the hills behind more
clearly than the nearer intervening ground, illumined only by
the "dim light of scholasticism and theology".

The Fathers of   In order to appreciate the causes which produced the great
the Church   failure of Europe to increase the stores of natural knowledge
in the Middle Ages, it is necessary to trace the development of
the mediaeval mind. We must first realize the general outlines
of the theology of Christian faith and ethics framed by the
early Fathers in terms of Hebrew Scripture, Greek philosophy,
the mystery religions and the underlying primitive rites. Next,
we must follow the changes in the resultant doctrines as they
were moulded by each succeeding age into instruments of controversy with pagan or heretic. We shall then begin to understand why much Patristic and early mediaeval Christianity was
inimical in spirit to secular learning; why, under its influence,
philosophy became the handmaid of theology, and natural
science vanished from the earth.

The older Greek philosophies were frankly founded on
observation of the visible world. With Socrates and Plato the
enquiry took a deeper turn, and moved from questions of
phenomena to those of underlying reality, from natural to
metaphysical philosophy of an idealistic and mystical tendency. "The Greek mind became entranced with its own
creations." To Plato, external facts, whether of nature or of
human life and history, only became real when apprehended
by the mind. Their true meaning must lie in that aspect of
them which accords with the mind's consistent scheme of
concepts, for thus alone can the facts be thought of, and thus
alone can they be. The inconceivable is in truth the impossible.

Such a philosophy clearly could not foster accurate and un-
prejudiced observation of nature or of history. The structure
of the Universe had to conform to the ideas of Platonic

philosophy; history was in its essence a means of vivifying argument or of pointing illustration.

Aristotle was more interested in the observation of nature than was Plato, though even Aristotle's greatest strength lay in metaphysics and logic rather than in science, and as regards the latter in biology rather than in physics. He created the subject of logic, and in biology, at all events, he showed the true method of detached observation. His physics were not objective like those of Democritus, who sought the ultimate nature of things in atoms and a void. To Aristotle, the concepts by which nature must be interpreted were substance, essence, matter, form, quantity, quality—categories developed in an attempt to express man's direct sense-perception of the world in terms of ideas natural to his mind. At the beginning of the Dark Ages, the works of Aristotle in imperfect form were the most scientific of the Greek sources available, but his influence, great though it was, gradually ceased to be dominant. By the sixth century his writings had passed out of fashion, and for seven hundred years almost all that survived were commentaries on his book on Logic.

The philosophy of the Stoics, best known to some of us in the writings of Marcus Aurelius, was especially suited to the Roman mind, and must not be overlooked in any estimate of the different streams of thought on which the Patristic theologians floated their ark. For the Stoic, the central reality was the human will. Metaphysics and a knowledge of the natural world were only of importance when they subserved the ends of his philosophy as guides of life and conduct. Stoicism was essentially a scheme of ethics, and it diverted physical science from truthful observation in order to secure conformity with the preconceptions of morals.

The modes of thought inaugurated by Plato were wafted into even more super-rational heights by the Neo-Platonists, whose philosophy was the last product of late paganism. From the time of Plotinus the Alexandrian (d. A.D. 270) to Porphyry (d. 300) and Iamblicus (d. c. 330) philosophy became less and less physical and experimental, and more and more concerned with mystical ideas. Plotinus lived in a pure region of "metaphysics warmed with occasional ecstasy", and to him the highest good was the super-rational contemplation of the Absolute. In the writings of Porphyry, and still more in those

5-2

of Iamblicus, these mystical views were brought down to practical life, and their application thereto led to greater credulity in magic and sorcery. The soul needs the aid of god, angel, daemon; the divine is essentially miraculous, and magic is the path to the divine. Thus Neo-Platonism countenanced and absorbed every popular superstition, every development of sorcery and astrology, and every morbid craving for asceticism, of which a decadent age was prodigal. The life of Iamblicus, as told by a Neo-Platonic biographer, is as full of miracle as Athanasius's contemporary life of Saint Anthony.

This mystical philosophic atmosphere contained currents of eastern faiths such as Mithraism and Manichaeism, the latter of which enunciated a dualism of the powers of good and evil, destined to reappear again and again. Mithraism, which disputed with Christianity the possession of the Roman Empire, was a Persian example of the mystery religions, which, as we have said, took the place in Hellenic times of the Olympian mythology when that picturesque faith decayed towards the end of the classical period. Our knowledge of these mystery religions is far from complete.[1] Their ritual involved secret rites of initiation and communion; their beliefs were expressed in sacred legends of the gods peculiar to each cult, legends which were accepted by the people literally, and by the educated as symbolical of the mystery of life and death. Beneath the rites and legends primitive nature-worship appears—sun gods and moon gods and the celebration in divine imagery of the drama of the year: the full life of nature in the summer, its death in winter, and its joyous resurrection in each new spring.

Modern anthropology has thrown much additional light on the origins of primitive ideas such as those which underlie the mystery religions, and of their ritual, which is itself derived from even more primitive rites based on the idea that nature can be coerced by sympathetic magic and witchcraft.[2] Such rites and the more advanced ritual which may develope from them are prior to and much more persistent than any definite system of religious dogma. It is clear that, in the first few centuries of our era, besides the formal religions and philo-

[1] For short accounts see Percy Gardner, in Hastings' *Encyclopaedia of Religion and Ethics* and also in *Modern Churchman*, vol. xvi, 1926, p. 310.

[2] Sir J. G. Frazer, *The Golden Bough*, 3rd ed. See especially Part v, "Spirits of the Corn and Wild", vol. ii, p. 167.

sophies which appear in literature, there existed a deep and *The Fathers of*
pervading undercurrent of these more primitive magic rites *the Church*
and beliefs. In them may be traced ideas of initiation, sacrifice,
and communion with the divine powers, ideas which appear in
more complex form in the mystery religions. The effect on
the origins of Christianity of these primitive rites and more
developed mystery religions has at all times been a subject
of discussion among historians and theologians, a discussion
which has varied in the light of the knowledge available to
each succeeding generation. In trying to understand the
mental atmosphere of early Christian times, we must not
ignore these contemporary practices and beliefs.

Saint Paul saved Christianity from settling down as a Jewish
sect doomed to early extinction, and preached it as a world
religion. When it grew and spread, it inevitably came in touch
with Greek philosophy, and the chief work of the early Fathers
of the Church lay in combining that philosophy with Christian
doctrines.

Foremost in this work was Origen (c. 185–c. 254), who proclaimed the conformity of ancient learning, especially Alexandrian science, with the Christian faith, and did more than
anyone else to win adherents among the educated and intelligent. In his day doctrine was still fluid, and alternative
ideas, over which the succeeding ages quarrelled to the death,
are found peacefully side by side in his writings.

Origen's most fundamental tenet is the unchangeableness of
God. This involves the eternity both of the Logos and of the
world, and the pre-existence of souls. It reduces the importance
of the historical aspect of Christianity, and thus allows a more
critical examination of the Old and New Testaments, and a
more liberal-minded outlook than was afterwards orthodox.
But Origen's theology became less and less acceptable, and was
finally condemned by the Council of Constantinople in 553.

Of the Latin Fathers, it was Saint Augustine (354–430) who
exerted the deepest and most prolonged influence on Christian
thought; the *Confessions* and the *City of God* are among the
greatest of Christian classics. He was successively a Manichaean,
a Neo-Platonist and a Christian, and his combination of
Platonic philosophy with the teaching of the Pauline Epistles
formed the basis of the first great Christian synthesis of knowledge, which persisted in the background as an alternative

mode of thought even through the dominance of Aristotle and
Thomas Aquinas in the later Middle Ages. His controversies,
like those of Saint Athanasius, illustrate the way in which
Catholic doctrine was formulated by dispute, and show why
it is that our Creeds are not only statements of belief, but
"paeans of triumph over defeated heretics and heathen".

Neo-Platonism and early Christian theology grew up together and acted and reacted upon each other—indeed each
accused the other of plagiarism. Christianity, like Neo-
Platonism, is based on the fundamental assumption that the
ultimate reality of the Universe is spirit, and, in the Patristic
Age, it accepted the Neo-Platonic super-rational attitude. In
the writings of the early Fathers the highest super-rationalism,
the love of God and the apprehension of the Risen Christ, passed
down through every step to the lowest form of credulity held
in common with the pagan populace and the Neo-Platonic
philosophers. Plotinus, the early Neo-Platonic pagan, and
Augustine, the Christian theologian, laid little stress on divination and magic, and the Latin Father, Hippolytus, exposed
the folly of pagan magic and astrology. But two generations
later, Porphyry and Iamblicus on the one side, and in the next
centuries, Jerome and Gregory of Tours on the other, revelled
in the daemoniac and the miraculous.

Symbolism, which had shown itself in Neo-Platonism, was
extended and developed by the Fathers in their efforts to co-
ordinate the Old Testament with the New, and both with the
prevalent modes of thought. What in the Scriptures or in the
world of nature conforms to the Christian scheme, as interpreted by each Father, may be received as fact; what does not
so agree is to be accepted only in a symbolic sense.

Finally, to understand the Patristic and through it the
mediaeval mind, it is necessary to appreciate the overwhelming
motive introduced by the Christian conception of sin, the need
of redemption, and the hopes and fears of heaven and hell, the
need of mediation to obtain salvation in the one, and to avoid
damnation in the flames of the other.

The pagan world itself had become less confident. The
decadence of the race had carried mankind far from the bright
Greek spirit of life, and the stern Roman joy in home and
State. The mystery religions had brought Oriental ideas to
Europe. Men were beginning to rely more on authority; they

were seized with unrest and vague fears for their safety in this
world and in the hereafter. The phase recurs at various epochs
of history. Even before the ministry of Christ, in Palestine
and wherever Jewish influence was felt, eyes were looking for
a catastrophic coming of the Kingdom of God, a conception
which made the Christian faith of the Apostolic Age largely
a matter of eschatology, and its rule of life but an *Interims
Ethik*, a short preparation for the triumphant Second Coming.
Perhaps in the Patristic Age the end of the world had receded
a little into the future; but the day of judgment was still very
near, and to each man death was an effective door into the
mystery of the next world and the horror of the Shade.
Darkness was covering the civilization of the ancient lands,
and gross darkness the spirit of mankind, almost obscuring
the one transcendent ray of Christ's message of hope and
reconciliation.

With such an outlook on life and such a prospect in death,
it is no wonder that the Fathers showed small interest in
secular knowledge for its own sake. "To discuss the nature
and position of the earth", says Saint Ambrose, "does not
help us in our hope of the life to come." Christian thought
became antagonistic to secular learning, identifying it with the
heathenism which Christians had set out to conquer. A branch
of the Library of Alexandria was destroyed about the year
390 by Bishop Theophilus, and, in general, ignorance was
exalted as a virtue. When Christianity became the religion of
the people this attitude grew more brutal. We have an illustration of this result in the year 415, when Hypatia, the last
mathematician of Alexandria, daughter of the astronomer
Theon, was murdered with revolting cruelty by a Christian
mob, which, according to the common opinion, was instigated
to the deed by the Patriarch Cyril.

The last great philosopher of Athens was Proclus (411–485),
who made the final synthesis of Neo-Platonism, and gave it
"that form in which it was transferred to Christianity and
Islam in the Middle Ages".[1] The works of Proclus formed one
of the links with Plato and Aristotle, and partly created and
nourished mediaeval mysticism.

Gradually the desire and the power to investigate nature
with an open mind passed away. With the Greeks natural

[1] Zeller, quoted in "Neo-Platonism", *Enc. Brit.* 9th ed.

science became merged in metaphysics; with the Roman Stoics
it faded into the need to support the morality of the human
will. So in the early Christian atmosphere natural knowledge
was valued only as a means of edification, or as an illustration
of the doctrines of the Church or the passages of Scripture.
Critical power soon ceased to exist, and anything was believed
if it accorded with Scripture as interpreted by the Fathers.
The contemporary knowledge of natural history, for instance,
was represented by a second-century compilation called *Physio-
logus*, or the *Bestiary*, in which the subjects and the accounts
of them, originally Christian allegories with imagery taken
from the animal world, were frankly ruled by doctrinal considerations. For example, it is stated seriously that the cubs
of the lioness are born dead, but that on the third day the
lion breathes between their eyes, and they wake to life,
thus typifying the Resurrection of our Lord, the Lion of
Judah.

In their views of history and biography, the pagan historians
were always ready to modify their accounts to serve the
rhetorical fitness of the occasion, and the Church writers
carried this tendency to greater lengths. In their hands history
became a branch of Christian apologetics, and the lives of the
saints, the characteristic form of early mediaeval literature,
became simply a means of edification. Any legend which
accorded with the author's conception of the holiness of his
subject was received unhesitatingly.

The power of Patristic theology was strengthened by the
ecclesiastical organization which grew up to enshrine it. And
when, with the conversion of the Empire to Christianity, that
organization could rely on the still overwhelming though
decaying strength of Roman tradition, it became irresistible.
The Roman Empire died, but its soul lived on in the Catholic
Church, which took over its framework and its universalist
ideals. The Bishop of Rome found it immeasurably easier to
acquire the Primacy of the world, and gradually to tighten the
bands of uniformity, because even barbarians had come to
look to Rome as their metropolis, their Holy City, and to
Caesar as their semi-divine ruler. Philosophically the Catholic
Church was the last creative achievement of Hellenistic civilization; politically and organically it was the offspring and
heir of the autocratic Roman Empire.

Such was the intellectual position in Europe when the last gleams of sunset of the ancient civilization were fading away into the dark night of the sixth and seventh centuries. And such was the nature of the ideals to which the succeeding ages looked back as they emerged into the feeble light of a new morn, looked back as to a brighter day whose glorious noon culminated in God's crowning revelation by His Son, and whose resplendent eve was illuminated by the inspired writings of the Fathers of the Church. It is small wonder that the men of the new time took all that came to them from across the darkness as endowed with supernatural sanction, and that they viewed it with no critical insight.

Almost the only traces of secular learning which in the West survived the seventh century were the works of Boëthius, a Roman of noble birth, who was put to death in 524. It seems now to be agreed, after a long controversy, that Boëthius was a Christian and even a martyr. However that may be, he was certainly the last in direct descent to show the true spirit of ancient philosophy. He wrote compendiums and commentaries on Aristotle and Plato, and treatises, founded on the writings of the Greeks, on the four mathematical subjects which he called the quadrivium: arithmetic, geometry, music and astronomy. These manuals were used as schoolbooks in the Middle Ages, in the earlier part of which the only knowledge of Aristotle was derived almost entirely from Boëthius' commentaries.

Dr H. F. Stewart, the biographer of Boëthius, gives me the following note:

Boëthius was the last of the Romans; but he was also the first of the Schoolmen in virtue of the classification of the sciences for which he supplied material. The uniform distribution of knowledge into natural sciences, mathematics and theology which he recommended was adopted by his successors and finally accepted and defended by Thomas Aquinas. His definition of *persona* as *naturae rationalis individua substantia* held the field till the end of the scholastic period.

After Boëthius and his younger contemporary Cassiodorus, the classical spirit vanished from the earth. The schools of philosophy founded by Plato at Athens, which by this time were teaching a mystical, half-Christian Neo-Platonism, were closed in the year 529 by order of the Emperor Justinian, partly in order to destroy the last vestiges of the teaching of heathen philosophy, and partly to prevent competition with the official Christian schools.

Yet the Byzantine Empire maintained a background of civilization through the worst times of barbarism in the west of Europe. Its armies cleared Italy from the Goths, and its lawyers codified Roman law in the *Institutes* of Justinian. Founded on definite principles, those of the Stoics, Roman law gave an ideal of rational order, which survived the times of chaos, and helped to form both the Canons of the Universalist Church, the heir of the Roman Empire, and later on the intellectual synthesis of Scholasticism. Again, the knowledge which survived in Byzantium from classical times, even in its decay, shone as a torch amid the darkness of Europe, to light the way to a revival of western learning. Before the light failed altogether, that revival had begun.

But meanwhile in the West the break with the past was much more complete than was necessarily involved by the mere fall of Greece as a civilizing influence and of Rome as a world power. Not only were Athens and Rome destroyed as political States and social structures, but both the race of the Greeks, the artists and philosophers, and the race of the Romans, the lawyers and administrators, had ceased to be.

The beginning of the decline of Rome has been assigned to many causes. One important factor, often overlooked, is traced by the historian Alison to the economic disturbance caused by a shortage of currency.[1] The gold and silver mines of Spain and Greece began to fail, and the treasure of the Empire available for money, estimated at the equivalent of £380,000,000 in the time of Augustus, had shrunk to about £80,000,000 in that of Justinian. In spite of occasional debasements of the currency,[2] internal prices within the Empire fell, that is the value of money measured in goods and services rose, and all the evils inevitable in times of deflation followed. Productive industry and agriculture ceased to be remunerative; taxes became oppressive; imports from countries like Egypt and Libya outside the area of monetary disturbance, were stimulated, and Roman land went out of cultivation, as did land in

[1] Sir Archibald Alison, *History of Europe*, vol. i, Edinburgh and London, 1853, p. 31.
[2] A. R. Burns, *Money and Monetary Policy in Early Times*, London, 1927.

England from similar causes from 1873 to 1900 and again from   *The Dark Ages*
1921 to 1928.

With the failure of cultivation, vast tracts of country were
rendered uninhabitable by malaria;[1] swarms of alien immi-
grants corrupted the purity of the race, and the fall in the
birth-rate among the nobler and abler stocks, together with
the constant drain of incessant wars and—among the Romans
—of foreign administration, lowered the average quality of the
nations. The races which in Greece and Rome had effected such
great things in the history of the world gave place to mongrel,
cross-bred populations, composed of incompatible Northern,
Mediterranean, African and Semitic elements, fated to inward
decay by their lack of cohesion, want of common ideals and
disregard of statecraft, and to outward destruction at the hand
of the first strong, pure-bred people that encountered them.
Thus the overthrow of Rome by the Northern invaders was
not essentially a destruction of civilization by barbarians. It
was much more the clearing away of a doomed and crumbling
ruin, in preparation for future rebuilding.

A new civilization had to be evolved from chaos; nations
with definite ideals and well-marked characteristics had to be
formed out of the medley of races comprised in the decadent
universalist Empire; and those nations had to advance far in
the reconstruction of social order and the determination and
specialization of intellectual attributes before they could form
a suitable seed-bed for the germination and growth of a new
science and scientific philosophy.

Here and there in Europe, through the gloom of the Dark
Ages, we see tiny plants of knowledge struggling to the light.
It is probable that in Italy some of the secular schools maintained their continuity in the large towns throughout the times
of turmoil and confusion. But the rise of the monasteries gave
the first chance of a secure and leisured life, and, consequently,
it is in the cloister that the first signs of the new growth of
learning are to be seen.

In view of the character of the Gospel story, it was impossible
for the Fathers of the Church to despise the art of healing as
they despised or ignored other secular knowledge. Hence the
tending of the sick remained a Christian duty, and medicine

[1] W. H. S. Jones, *Malaria, a Neglected Factor in the History of Greece and
Rome*, Cambridge, 1907.

was the earliest science to revive. Monastic medicine was at first a mixture of magic with a faint tincture of ancient science. In the sixth century the Benedictines began to study compendiums on the works of Hippocrates and Galen, and they gradually spread a knowledge of these writings throughout the West. The monks were also practical farmers, who kept alive some knowledge of the art of agriculture.

The first new secular home of learning appears in the schools of Salerno, a city to the south of Naples, on the Bay of Paestum, and from this centre proceeded many compilations founded on the writings of Hippocrates and Galen. In the ninth century Salernian physicians were already famous; in the eleventh they began to read translations from Arabic works; and their schools continued to flourish till the twelfth century, when they were overshadowed by the general spread of Arab medicine in Europe. Since Salerno is known to have been first a Greek colony, and then a Roman health resort, and since the traditions of Greek medicine seem never to have been entirely interrupted in Southern Italy, it is possible that here a direct and unbroken link existed between the learning of the ancient and that of the modern world.

It should be noted, however, that countries at a distance from Rome were among the first to show signs of a new and distinctive spirit. The literary and artistic development of Ireland, Scotland and the north of England, beginning with Irish sagas full of poetic extravagance, was quickened by the absorption of Christian teachings. In the fervour of its missionary zeal, that culture carried some of its secular learning into more southern lands. This northern development culminated in the works of the Anglo-Saxon monk, Bede of Jarrow (673–735), who incorporated into his writings all the knowledge then available in Western Europe. His science was founded chiefly on Pliny's *Natural History*, though he added something on his own account, such, for instance, as a few observations on the tides. He stands between the Latin commentators Boëthius, Cassiodorus, Gregory, and Isidore of Seville, who caught the last direct echoes of the classical or Patristic learning, and the scholars of the abbey schools founded by Charlemagne. Chief among these latter was Alcuin of York, who did much to overcome the prevalent idea that secular learning was opposed to godliness, and carried the

tradition of classical knowledge into definitely mediaeval *The Recon-*
times. Bede wrote in Latin, mainly for monks; but one *struction of*
hundred and fifty years later culture had so broadened that *Europe*
Alfred the Great (849–901) translated or caused to be translated many Latin books into Anglo-Saxon, and the influence
of Latin literature began to pass into native languages.

By this time mediaeval Europe was taking shape. Nations
had crystallized out from the mixture of the Romanized Gauls
with the vigorous Teutonic tribes that overran the Roman
provinces. Northern lands that had never seen the Roman
eagles, or from which the Romans had retreated, were developing a culture and even a literature of their own, on which
Roman ideals and Roman civilization only acted as external
and foreign influences.

While European learning was at its lowest ebb, a con. *The Arabian*
siderable amount of culture of mixed Greek, Roman and Jewish *School[1]*
origin survived in the Byzantine Imperial Court at Constantinople, and in the countries which stretch from Syria to the
Persian Gulf. One of its earliest centres was the Persian school
of Jundishapūr, which gave refuge to Nestorian Christians in
489, and to the Neo-Platonists who left Athens when Plato's
Academy was closed in 529. Here translations, especially of
Plato and Aristotle, brought Greek philosophy into touch with
that of India, Syria and Persia, and led to the growth of a
school of medicine, which survived till the tenth century,
despite its comparative isolation.

Between 620 and 650, under the stimulus of Muhammad,
the Arabs conquered Arabia, Syria, Persia and Egypt.
A hundred and fifty years later, Hārūn-al-Rashid, the most
famous of the Abbāsid Caliphs, encouraged translations from
Greek authors, and thus helped to initiate the great period of
Arab learning. At first the advance was slow, for new terms
and constructions, suitable for the expression of philosophic
and scientific thought, had to be formed and incorporated into
the Syriac and Arabic languages. As in the analogous revival
of learning which took place in Europe in the later Middle
Ages, the first task of the Arabs, and of the races under their
influence, was to recover the hidden and forgotten stores of
Greek knowledge; then to incorporate what they recovered in

[1] See especially G. Sarton, *Introduction to the History of Science*, vol. i,
Baltimore, 1927.

The Arabian School   their own languages and culture; and finally to add to it their own contributions.

For two centuries after the death of Muhammad, there was intense theological activity in Islam. The atomic system of Epicurus, and the problems of time and space raised by the paradoxes of Zeno, stimulated the Muslim mind, which may possibly have been influenced also by the Buddhist atomism of India.[1]

In the Korân, Allah has created and upholds the world, which has only a secondary existence in the absolute existence of Allah. This orthodox view was modified by Greek philosophy, Neo-Platonic and Aristotelian, as well as by another Islamic school of thought. This latter added to the implied unilateral pantheism of Muhammad the Neo-Platonic endless chain of existence, and the Aristotelian idea of the Cosmos. Thus it arrived at the complementary view that conversely the Cosmos is God. A third group, trying to explain nature in orthodox Muhammadan terms, reached a theory of time, similar to, if not derived from, the Buddhist atomic philosophy of India. The world is made of atoms all exactly alike, which Allah creates anew from moment to moment. Space too is atomic, and time is composed of indivisible "nows". The qualities of things are accidents, which belong to the atoms and are created and re-created with them by Allah. If Allah were to cease re-creating from moment to moment, the Universe would vanish like a dream. Matter only exists by Allah's continued will, and man is but a kinematographic automaton. Thus the apparently godless system of Epicurus is converted into an intense monotheism.

By the side of these theological interests there became manifest a curiosity concerning that nature to which the theologians denied permanence or reality. Islamic science grew while that of Christendom was decaying, and by the second half of the eighth century the lead had definitely passed from Europe to the Near East. In the ninth century the Arabic schools of medicine were improved by the study of translations of Galen, and new and striking work was achieved in that primitive chemistry which underlay alchemy.

[1] See chap. i, p. 9 above; also D. B. Macdonald, in *Isis*, No. 30, p. 327; arts. "Atomic Theory (Indian)", by H. Jacobi, and "Muhammadan", by De Boer, in Hastings, *Encyclopaedia of Religion and Ethics*.

The earliest practical chemistry is concerned with the arts of life such as metal-working on the one hand, and with the preparation of drugs on the other. The speculations of the Greeks in classical times about the nature of matter, with their ideas of atoms and primary elements, are too much divorced from observational or experimental facts to be classed as chemistry. The Alexandrian alchemists of the first century may be considered to have been the first who realized and attacked chemical problems. Little was done after their day till, six hundred years later, the Arabs took up their work.

It is true that, misunderstanding the origins of the art in Alexandria, the later alchemists set before themselves two great aims, both of which proved impossible of attainment—the material transmutation of baser metals into gold, and the preparation of an *elixir vitae* that would cure all human ills. Their search was doomed to failure, yet they acquired much sound chemical knowledge and discovered many useful remedies.

The Arabic alchemists obtained their initial knowledge from two sources, the Persian school mentioned above, and the writings of the Greeks of Alexandria, partly through Syriac intermediaries and partly by means of direct translations. The Arabic-speaking people studied alchemy for seven hundred years, the chief centres of their labours being first in Irak and later on in Spain. In the hands of these men, alchemy developed into chemistry, and from them, chiefly through the Spanish Moors, the European chemistry of the later Middle Ages was derived. While some Arabic writers and their European followers thus passed from alchemy to chemistry, others, not understanding the technical knowledge and philosophic outlook of the Alexandrian alchemists, and unable to take the newer, more scientific view, degraded their work into a sordid search for gold, or a background for magic based on chicanery or self-delusion.

The most famous Arabian alchemist and chemist was Abu-Musa-Jābir-ibn-Haiyan, who flourished about 776, and who is thought to have been the original author of many writings which appeared later in Latin, and were assigned to a shadowy "Geber" of uncertain date. The problem of their origin is not yet solved.[1] From an examination of new translations of some

---

[1] *The Arabic Works of Jâbir-ibn-Hayyân*, ed. by E. J. Holmyard, I, Paris, 1928; *The Works of Geber*, R. Russell, 1678, ed. by E. J. Holmyard, London, 1928.

of the Arabic manuscripts, Berthelot[1] concluded in 1893 that the knowledge of Jābir was much less than that of the Latin "Geber". But Holmyard[2] and Sarton[3] state that other Arabic works, still untranslated, show that Jābir was a much better chemist than Berthelot thought. He seems to have prepared (to use the modern nomenclature) lead carbonate, and separated arsenic and antimony from their sulphides; he gave accounts of the refinement of metals, the preparation of steel, the dyeing of cloth and leather, and the distillation of vinegar to yield concentrated acetic acid. He held that the six known metals differed because of the different proportions of sulphur and mercury contained in them. But Jābir's real place in history cannot be assigned till a critical study of all his Arabic works has been made, and a careful comparison effected with those of the Latin "Geber".

In the history of chemistry the idea that the principles of sulphur or fire and mercury or liquidity are primary elements is of great importance. It seems to have arisen from the discovery that mercury and sulphur combine to give a brilliant red sulphide. As silver is white and gold is yellow, red must be made of something even more noble and fundamental than gold. To sulphur and mercury salt was afterwards added to represent earth or solidity. The theory that salt, sulphur and mercury were the primary principles of things lasted as an alternative to the four elements of Empedocles and Aristotle till the days of Robert Boyle's *Sceptical Chymist*, published in 1661.

The increasing importance of scientific chemistry is shown by a controversy, which began in the ninth century, concerning the real value of alchemy. At this time also translations into Arabic were made of Euclid's *Elements* and Ptolemy's great work on astronomy, which from this translation acquired its best known name of *Almagest*. Greek geometry and astronomy were thus brought into the Muslim world. The Hindu numerals were completed by the invention of a sign for zero, and in an early form reached the Arabs. Muslim trade was widespread; through its agency these convenient numerals became known to the world as Arabic, and, after some centuries, displaced the clumsy Roman notation. The earliest Latin

[1] *La Chimie au Moyen Age*, Paris, 1893.
[2] E. J. Holmyard, in *Isis*, No. 19, 1924, p. 479.
[3] *Introduction to the History of Science*, vol. I, p. 532.

example of the use of the new system seems to be found in a
manuscript written in Spain about 976, but the zero sign was
not universally adopted until a somewhat later date.

The renown attaching to the works of the Greeks was used
by some Arabic authors to gain acceptance for their own
writings. For instance, a compilation of folklore and magic,
known as the *Secretum Secretorum,* was popular in mediaeval
Europe as a translated work of Aristotle. The original may
have been drawn from Greek sources, but it now seems probable that it was written in Arabic or Syriac and given out as
a translation from the Greek.

The translation of Ptolemy's book stimulated Muslim astronomers. From his observatory at Antioch Muhammad al-
Batani (c. 850) recalculated the precession of the equinoxes and
drew up a new set of astronomical tables. He was followed by
others of less eminence, and about the year 1000 advances in
trigonometry were made and observations on solar and lunar
eclipses were placed on record at Cairo by Ibn Junis, or Yūnus,
who was perhaps the greatest of all the Muslim astronomers.
He was encouraged in his work by al-Hakim, the ruler of
Egypt, who founded at Cairo an academy of learning.

The classical period of Arabian science may be said to date
from the tenth century, beginning with the medical work of
the Persian Abu Bakr al-Rāzi, known to Europe either as
Bubachar or Rhazes, who practised in Baghdad and compiled
many encyclopaedic textbooks, including a famous treatise on
measles and smallpox. He is held to be the greatest physician
of Islam, indeed of the whole world during the Middle Ages.
He was also a chemist, who applied his chemistry to medicine,
and a physicist who used the hydrostatic balance to measure
specific gravities.

The most eminent Muslim physicist was Ibn-al-Haitham
(965–1020), who also worked in Egypt under al-Hakim. His
chief work was done in optics, and showed a great advance
in experimental method. He used spherical and parabolic
mirrors, and studied spherical aberration, the magnifying
power of lenses, and atmospheric refraction. He improved
knowledge of the eye and of the process of vision, and solved
problems in geometrical optics by capable mathematics. The
Latin translation of his work on optics exerted considerable
influence on the development of western science, especially

w

6

through Roger Bacon and Kepler. About the same time the physician and philosopher Ibn Sīnā, or Avicenna (980–1037), a native of Bokhara, wandered from court to court among the rulers of Central Asia, vainly seeking some place of settlement where he could find an opening for his talents and carry on his literary and scientific labours. He wrote on all the sciences then known. Sarton states that in alchemy he disbelieved in the transmutation of metals, regarding the differences between them as too deep-seated to be overcome by changes of colour. His *Canon*, or compendium of medicine, "a codification of the whole of ancient and Muslim knowledge", represents one of the highest achievements of Arabic culture. It afterwards became the textbook of medical study in the European Universities; until the year 1650 it was used in the schools of Louvain and Montpellier, and is said to be still the chief medical authority in Muhammadan countries.

A contemporary, less well known but not less great in mind, was al-Bīrūni, philosopher, astronomer and geographer, who lived from 973 to 1048. He carried out geodetic measurements, and determined latitudes and longitudes with some accuracy. He measured the specific gravity of precious stones, and explained natural springs and artesian wells on the principle of water finding its own level in communicating channels. He wrote a clear account of parts of India and their people, and also the best mediaeval treatise on Hindu numerals.

At this time Arabic had become the acknowledged classical language of learning, and everything written in Arabic carried the prestige that in earlier (and again in later) ages was accorded to Greek. The first systematic translator of Arabic texts into Latin was Constantine the African, who worked at Monte Cassino from about 1060 till his death in 1087. He visited Salerno, and his work had much influence on the Salernian School, stimulating, both there and elsewhere, the absorption of Arabic knowledge by the Latin nations.

Nevertheless the highest point of Arabic learning had been reached. In the eleventh century appeared the important algebraic work of the Persian poet Omar Khayyam, and the theological writings of al-Ghazzāli, who did for Muhammadanism the philosophic and synthetic work that Thomas Aquinas did for Christianity. But by the close of the century the decline of Arabic and Muslim learning had set in.

Politically also any prospect of a stable Arabian Empire had been put to an end by the internal quarrels of the Muhammadan princes and generals, and by the gradual disintegration and destruction of the gifted, noble and old-established Arab families, which had provided the necessary governors, soldiers and administrators. The distant provinces, one after another, separated themselves from the weak, overgrown and heterogeneous Empire, re-created their native characters, and re-asserted their political independence.

It was in Spain, the farthest province of the Muhammadan conquest, that the best results of the intercourse of Arabian, Jewish and Christian civilizations became apparent. For three centuries, from 418 to 711, a West Gothic kingdom, which had established itself in Spain, maintained law and order from its capital at Toulouse. The Sephardim Jews, originally deported from Palestine to Spain under Titus, had preserved traditions of Alexandrian learning, amassed wealth, and kept open communications with the East. This continued after the Muhammadan conquest of Spain in A.D. 711. The tolerance of thought accorded by the Arabs, as long as their supremacy remained unquestioned, allowed the establishment of schools and colleges which, however, owed their continued existence, not to the general support of the people as a whole, but to the occasional and spasmodic patronage of a liberal-minded or free-thinking ruler.

The course of Spanish-Arabian philosophy developed on much the same lines as that of the Christian schools which followed it a hundred years later. There was the same attempt to harmonize the sacred literature of the nation with the teachings of Greek philosophy, and an analogous contest between those theologians who relied on reason and rational authority, and those who put their trust either uncritically in revelation, or in mystic religious experiences, and in both cases denied the validity of human reason in matters of faith.

Orthodox Muslim Scholasticism with its rational philosophic theology was chiefly founded by the Persian al-Ghazzāli, who flourished at Baghdad. Similar views were prevalent in Spain, but the real fame of the Spanish-Arabian school of thought is due to the work of Averroes, who was born at Cordova in 1126. While showing a profound reverence for the teachings of Aristotle, Averroes nevertheless introduced a new

6-2

conception into the relations between religion and philosophy. According to him, religion is not a branch of knowledge that can be reduced to propositions and systems of dogma, but a personal and inward power, distinct from the generalities of "demonstrative" or experimental science. Theology, the mixture of the two, he regarded as a source of evil to both, fostering on the one hand a false impression of the hostility between religion and philosophy, and, on the other, corrupting religion by a pseudo-science.

It is not surprising that the teaching of Averroes came into fierce conflict with that of the orthodox Christian theologians, but, in spite of opposition, especially from the great Dominican school of thought, his words fell upon willing ears. By the thirteenth century, Averroes had become a recognized authority in the Universities of South Italy, Paris and Oxford, worthy, according to the opinion of Roger Bacon and of Duns Scotus, to be placed by the side of Aristotle as a master of the science of proof.

Another great Cordovan of this period was Maimonides (1135–1204), a Jewish physician, mathematician, astronomer and philosopher, whose chief work was the construction of a Jewish system of Scholasticism, comparable with the Muslim Scholasticism of al-Ghazzāli, and the Christian Scholasticism soon afterwards completed by Thomas Aquinas. Maimonides sought to reconcile Jewish theology with Greek philosophy, especially with that of Aristotle. His work had much influence in the later Middle Ages, when some of his followers pressed his views so far as to regard the whole of Biblical history as symbolic, a theory which naturally aroused acute controversy.

In the Europe which received and slowly absorbed this stream of Arabic knowledge, the apparatus of learning had made appreciable progress. In the Eastern Empire at Constantinople a definite revival of knowledge took place in the ninth and the tenth centuries, when Constantine VII patronized art and learning, and ordered the compilation of a number of encyclopaedic treatises. From Constantinople, Russia was converted to Christianity by the irresistible persuasion of Vladimir the Terrible, Duke of Kiev, and Russian art, directly derived from that of Byzantium, began at the end of the tenth century. To this Byzantine Renaissance we also owe the reproduction and preservation of many Greek manuscripts, which would otherwise have been lost. But in original science the Byzantines were not on a level with the Arabs, or with the nations under Arabic influence or control.

As we have seen, a centre of secular studies, and especially of medicine, had existed since a very early date at Salerno, and, in Northern Europe, the encouragement bestowed on scholars by Charlemagne and Alfred had given an impetus to teaching generally. Gerbert, the learned French educator and mathematician, taught at Rheims, and elsewhere, from 972 till 999, when he was elected Pope, taking the name of Sylvester II. In his writings he dealt with the abacus, a simple form of calculating machine, and with the astrolabe, as well as with the Hindu numerals.

The effect of the increasing demand for teaching was that the monastic and cathedral schools, hitherto in most places the only educational institutions, were found insufficient to meet the growing needs, and new secular schools began to assume their modern form of Universities[1].

A revival of legal studies took place in Bologna about the year 1000, and, in the twelfth century, schools of medicine and philosophy were added to that of law. A Students' Guild, or *Universitas*, was formed for the mutual protection, at first of the foreign students, who were at the mercy of the inhabitants, and later of all students, whether native or foreign. These guilds hired their own teachers, and the University of Bologna, even in later years, continued to be a students' University, in which the governing power was held by the learners.

On the other hand, a school of dialectic at Paris in the first decade of the twelfth century was organized by the teachers, and shortly afterwards a community, or *Universitas*, of teachers in that city set the constitutional model to most of the Universities of Northern Europe including England. Thus it is that at Oxford and Cambridge the governing power has always rested with the teachers instead of with the students as at Bologna and to some extent in Scotland, where the election of the Rector shows a surviving trace of undergraduate control.

As early as the Carolingian period, the academic subjects of study had settled down into an elementary trivium,

[1] H. Rashdall, *The Universities of Europe in the Middle Ages*, Oxford, 1895.

comprising grammar, rhetoric and dialectic, three subjects which dealt with words, and a more advanced quadrivium, music, arithmetic, geometry and astronomy, which four were supposed, at all events, to deal with things. Music contained a half mystical doctrine of numbers, geometry merely a series of Euclid's propositions without the proofs, while arithmetic and astronomy were esteemed chiefly because they taught the means of fixing the date of Easter. All were treated as a preparation for the study of the sacred science of theology. Throughout the Middle Ages, this division of subjects held good for the elements of academic learning, and, as interest grew in philosophy, that study was merely added as a more advanced part of the simpler logical dialectic. Indeed it has been said that the philosophy of the Middle Ages was but a mixture of logic and theology.

The old controversy between Plato and Aristotle on the nature of "intelligible forms" or "universals" found its way into the writings of Porphyry and the commentaries of Boëthius, and so reached the mediaeval mind as the problem of classification. Why is it that we are able to classify? Are individuals the only realities, classes or universals existing merely as mental concepts or names, as the nominalists maintain, or have they a certain independent reality, existing in and with the objects of sense as the essence of those objects, as Aristotle taught? Or, on the other hand, have the ideas or universals a quite separate existence and a reality apart from the phenomena or the isolated beings, as Plato held in his idealist philosophy, which had come to be called realism? For instance are Democritus and Socrates realities, and humanity only a name? Or is man a species with a reality of its own, receiving here and there certain forms which make it Democritus or Socrates, accidents of the real substance, humanity? Are we to say *universalia ante rem* with Plato, *universalia in re* with Aristotle, or *universalia post rem* with the nominalists?

To our scientific minds, more at home with Archimedes than with either Aristotle or Plato, this controversy seems both foolish and tiresome. Yet it is necessary to study it if we are to unearth the buried seeds of modern science which germinated at the Renaissance. In its effect on the theory of knowledge, even to the Greeks it was of great importance, and in it the mediaevalists eventually discovered the whole problem of

Christian dogma, the only difficulty being to determine on which side persecuting orthodoxy was to take its stand.

In the ninth century Erigena, or John Scot, a disciple of Origen, propounded a mystical theory, based on the idea that the divine is the only reality. The theory contained the first great mediaeval, as contrasted with Patristic, synthesis of Christian faith with Greek philosophy, in this case the philosophy of the Neo-Platonic school. To Erigena true philosophy is true religion, and true religion true philosophy. Reason leads to a system which coincides with Scripture properly interpreted. Erigena was a realist, but his realism shows a fusion of Platonic and Aristotelian views, and the discussion between realism and nominalism only became acute later. In the eleventh century critical reasoning was applied to theology and the issues at stake began to be seen. Nominalism made its appearance in the writings of Berengarius of Tours (999–1088), who criticized the doctrine of transubstantiation, holding that a change of substance could not take place in the bread and wine with no corresponding change in the accidents of appearance and taste. Nominalism appeared also in Roscellinus (d. c. 1125), who held that the individual is the sole reality, and thus reached a Tritheistic conception of the Trinity. This at once crystallized the opposing realism, especially in William of Champeaux and Anselm of Canterbury, and established it as the orthodox view for several centuries.

But the inherent difficulties of the theory of realism led to many varieties of it; an interminable discussion raged in the schools and employed the philosophic acumen of the scholastic dialecticians for two hundred years. Abelard, a Breton (1079–1142), attacked his master William of Champeaux, and taught a modified doctrine verging on nominalism, though it was a nominalism not so consistent as that of Roscellinus. In Abelard the doctrine of the Trinity was reduced to the conception of three aspects of the One Divine Being. Abelard showed signs of independence from the dogmatic frame within which the mediaeval mind was accustomed to work. He made the pregnant statements that "doubt is the road to enquiry", that "by enquiry we perceive the truth", and that "it is necessary to understand in order to believe", a saying which may well be compared with the *credo quia impossibile* of the Patristic Tertullian, and the *credo ut intelligam* of Anselm.

Abelard was called to account by Saint Bernard, who held in abhorrence the wisdom of this world, and did much to foster ecclesiastical suspicion which saw heresy everywhere. But for a time the speculative spirit was exhausted, and the middle of the twelfth century marks the beginning of a pause of fifty years in logical and philosophical dialectic, and the return to a passing interest in classical literature, an interest which centred in John of Salisbury and his school at Chartres.

If the philosophic discussions of the mediaevalists are still of living interest to some modern metaphysicians, their general conception of the physical Universe appears to us strange, unreal and confused. For the most part no distinction was drawn between natural events, moral truths and spiritual experiences. Doubtless ultimate reality contains all three, but history shows that natural events, at any rate, need to be viewed in isolation if our knowledge of their interrelations is to be increased.

The mediaeval mind was fascinated by a supposed analogy between the nature of the Godhead, the astronomical constitution of the Cosmos, or macrocosm, and the anatomical, physiological and psychological structure of man, the microcosm. The whole Cosmos is usually imagined as permeated and bound together by a living spirit, the νοῦς or world spirit of Neo-Platonism, which in its turn is pervaded and controlled by the Godhead. Thus primordial matter, the principle of death and dissolution, is held in subjection.

The idea of the macrocosm and microcosm is set forth in Plato's *Timaeus*, and can be traced back to the Pythagoreans, but it was attributed by some mediaeval authors to Hermes, the somewhat doubtful Alexandrian figure to whom so many alchemical writings are referred and who probably represents the Egyptian god Thoth. The theory appears in simple form in the works of Isidore of Seville, and of the alchemist "Geber". It was developed later by Bernard Sylvestris of Tours (c. 1150), and by the Abbess Hildegard of Bingen (c. 1170).[1] It is constantly to be seen represented allegorically in mediaeval art.

In other illustrations, which represent only the physical

[1] *Studies in the History and Method of Science*, ed. by Charles Singer, Oxford, 1917, "St Hildegard", p. 1.

Cosmos, we see some such picture as the following. The Earth
is imagined as a central sphere, in which the four elements,
originally in harmonious order, are in confusion since Adam's
fall. The Earth is surrounded by concentric zones of air, aether
and fire, containing stars, sun and planets, all kept in motion
by the four winds of heaven, which are related to the four
elements of Earth and the four humours of man. Heaven is
the empyrean space beyond the zone of fire, and hell is
within the sphere of Earth under the feet of men.

The conception of the essential similarity of macrocosm and
microcosm held throughout the Middle Ages. It survived the
Renaissance, and persisted in literature into almost modern
days. The idea of the Universe as composed of concentric
spheres or zones was developed and made classical in mediaeval times: perhaps it reached its culmination in the Vision
of Dante. Copernicus destroyed its rational basis, but did not
uproot the popular tradition. Indeed, drawings clearly derived
from these confused imaginings of the ancient world and the
Middle Ages may still be seen decorating the covers of certain
almanacs which circulate among the ignorant of all classes even
now.

Somewhat similar notions are found in the system of Jewish
theosophy known as the Caballa, which, professing to set forth
esoteric truths revealed by God to Adam and carried down
the ages by tradition, afterwards came to exert a considerable
influence on Christianity.

It is impossible here to trace a tithe of the enormous and
intertwined tangle of astrology, alchemy, magic and theosophy
which enmeshed the Middle Ages, and is so difficult for us
to understand or even to read with patience. But it must not
be forgotten that such ideas were essentially characteristic of
the mediaeval mind, which in them felt at home. Scientific
thought, of which in those times we find rare examples, was
quite foreign to the prevailing mental outlook. The scattered
seedlings of science had to grow in a vast and confused jungle
which was always threatening to choke them, and not in the
open healthy prairie of ignorance which seems to be envisaged
by some historians of science. If agricultural land be left un-
cultivated, in a few years the jungle returns, and signs are not
lacking that a similar danger is always lying in wait for the fields
of thought, which, by the labour of three hundred years, have

been cleared and brought into cultivation by men of science. The destruction of a very small percentage of the population would suffice to annihilate scientific knowledge, and lead us back to almost universal belief in magic, witchcraft and astrology.

If the intellectual task of the Dark Ages was to save what it could out of the wreck of ancient learning, that of the first succeeding centuries was to master and absorb what had been recovered. The chief intellectual achievement of the early mediaeval period was the welding together of the remains of ancient classical knowledge, as preserved by the writers of Latin compendiums, with the Christian faith, as interpreted by the early Fathers in the light of Neo-Platonism. From the ninth century onward we may watch this process at work, and there the constructive period of the Middle Ages may be said to begin.

By the twelfth century the dual heritage from the past had been surveyed and mapped out, absorbed and transformed by the mediaeval mind. Then came a pause in the work of philosophic theology, during which we see the culmination of mediaeval appreciation of classical writings as literature. None of the more advanced works of Aristotle were known in a complete form; and thus no scientific book had come to hand to disturb the literary outlook of those scholars who cared for the classics as a bypath of study, or as a means of understanding better the language of Scripture and the writings of the Fathers. In spite of the indirect influence of Aristotle, exerted through commentaries, the predominant theological attitude was still Platonic or Neo-Platonic and Augustinian, idealistic and mystical rather than rational and philosophical.

But in the thirteenth century a great change of outlook took place, coincident and perhaps connected with the humanizing movement associated with the coming of the friars. An increasing desire for secular knowledge was satisfied by the rendering of Greek authors into Latin, firstly by retranslation from the Arabic, and later by direct translation from the Greek. The complete story has not yet been worked out, for our knowledge of Arabic scientific literature, even of that part of it which is extant, is still so fragmentary that it is impossible to specify exactly what additions the Arabs made to Greek science.

The most active work in translation from Arabic to Latin went on in Spain, where a succession of translators, busy with many subjects, can be traced from about 1125 to about 1280. "To them we owe texts of Aristotle, Ptolemy, Euclid and the Greek physicians, Avicenna, Averroes, and the Arabic astronomers and mathematicians, a great mass of astrology, apparently also a certain amount of alchemy."[1]

Next to Spain in importance were Southern Italy and Sicily, whence came translations both from Arabic and from Greek, made possible by the presence of resident Arabs and Greeks, and by diplomatic and commercial relations with Constantinople. From this source were obtained medical works, a geographical treatise and map, and Ptolemy's *Optics*. Of scattered or unknown origin are translations of Aristotle's *On Animals*, *Metaphysics* and *Physics*, and other less important works which appeared in the West from 1200 onwards.

The current language of scientific literature was Arabic, and translations from the Arabic, even of Greek authors, were highly valued. The Arabic-speaking races and the Jews living among them had at this time a real interest in science, and it was by contact with Muhammadan countries that mediaeval Europe passed from its earlier outlook to a more rationalist habit of mind.

The greatest change was produced by the rediscovery of Aristotle. Between 1200 and 1225 his complete works were recovered and rendered into Latin, like those of other authors, first from Arabic versions and then by direct translations from the Greek. In this latter work one of the foremost of scholars was Robert Grosseteste, Chancellor of Oxford, and Bishop of Lincoln, patron of the new uncloistered mendicant Orders. Grosseteste invited Greeks to England and imported Greek books, while his pupil, Roger Bacon, a Franciscan friar, wrote a grammar of the Greek language. Their aim was not literary but theological and philosophical, to unlock the original tongue of Scripture and of Aristotle.

The new knowledge soon produced an effect on the current controversies. Realism survived, but it became less thorough and less Platonic. It was seen that Aristotle's modified realism might be formulated in psychological terms which brought it

[1] C. H. Haskins, in *Isis*, No. 23, 1925, p. 478.

nearer to nominalism. But in wider questions Aristotle opened up a new world of thought to the mediaeval mind. His general outlook, at once more rational and more scientific, was quite different from Neo-Platonism, which had hitherto chiefly represented ancient philosophy. His range of knowledge, both in philosophy and in the science of nature, was far greater than anything else then available. It was a heavy task to absorb and adapt the new material to mediaeval Christian thought, and the work was not effected without misgiving. The Schoolmen were convinced of the intellectual supremacy of the Church as the recipient of all revealed knowledge and of the conformity therewith of the mystical Neo-Platonism which represented secular learning. Hence it needed a real and courageous intellectual effort to accept the newly recovered works of Aristotle, with all the scientific or quasi-scientific knowledge those works contained, and to undertake the task of reconciling that knowledge with Christian dogma, and it is not surprising that the early study of Aristotle aroused alarm. At first the Arabic channels by which his books reached the West mingled his philosophy with Averroist leanings, and mystical heresies were the result. Aristotle's works were condemned by a Provincial Council at Paris in 1209, and this prohibition was repeated later. But the new knowledge was irresistible, and in 1225 the University of Paris formally placed Aristotle's works upon the list of books to be studied.

The chief of the scholars who interpreted Aristotle at this time was the Dominican Albertus Magnus of Cologne (1206–1280), who interwove Aristotelian, Arabian, Jewish and Neo-Platonic elements into a whole which included all contemporary knowledge of astronomy, geography, botany, zoology and medicine.[1]

The prevalent trend of thought may be illustrated by the developments which followed Albertus's teaching of Aristotle's embryology. Aristotle held that in generation the female contributed substance and the male form. The mediaeval mind with its desire for values made the male element the more noble, and later on developed a theological embryology, in which the moment of entry of a soul into the embryo became the problem of supreme importance.

The work of Albertus on one side shows affinity with his

[1] E. Michael, *Geschichte d. deutschen Volkes vom 13 Jahrh.*, 1903, v, iii, p. 445 *et seq.*

younger contemporaries, the Oxford Franciscans Grosseteste
and Bacon, and on another led directly to the more systematic philosophy of his famous pupil Saint Thomas Aquinas.
Though his mind was cast in a less scientific mould than that
of Albertus, the importance of Aquinas in the history of philosophy and of the origins of science is great. By carrying on
Albertus's work of rationalizing the existing stores of knowledge, both sacred and profane, he stimulated intellectual
interests and made the Universe seem intelligible. But, when
his writings had been accepted and become authoritative, they
delayed for many years the liberation of scientific thought
from the trammels of theology, for to Saint Thomas's Aristotelianism was mainly due the predominantly hostile attitude
both of academic secular learning and of the Roman Church
towards the initial development of modern science at the
Renaissance.

Thomas was the son of a Count of Aquinum and was born
about 1225 in Southern Italy. At the age of eighteen he joined
the Dominican Order. He studied at Cologne under Albertus
Magnus, taught at Paris and Rome, and, after a life of incessant activity, died in 1274 at the age of forty-nine.

His greatest works, the *Summa Theologiae* and the *Summa
Philosophica contra Gentiles*, the setting forth of Christian
knowledge for the ignorant, recognize two sources of knowledge: the mysteries of the Christian faith as transmitted
through the channels of Scripture, of the Fathers and of
Christian tradition, and the truths of human reason—not
the fallible individual reason, but the fount of natural truth
of which the chief exponents were Plato and Aristotle. The
two sources cannot be opposed, since they both flow from
God as the one source. Hence philosophy and theology must
be compatible, and a *Summa Theologiae* should contain the
whole of knowledge; even the existence of God can be demonstrated by reason. But here Thomas Aquinas parts company
with those who went before him. Erigena and Anselm, under
the more mystical Neo-Platonism, sought to prove the highest
mysteries of the Trinity and the Incarnation. But Thomas,
under the influence of Aristotle and his Arabic commentators,
held that these mysteries could not be proved by reason,
though they can be examined and apprehended thereby. These
doctrines, accordingly, are henceforth detached from the sphere
of philosophic theology, and transferred to that of faith.

Throughout his work Aquinas's interests are intellectual. Perfect beatitude of any created rational being lies in the action of the intelligence directed to the contemplation of God. Faith and revelation are belief in a proposition and presentment of truth. It is an entire fallacy to suppose that Scholasticism and the later orthodox Roman theology which is derived from it are opposed to, or belittle, human reason. That was the attitude in early days, when, for instance, Anselm feared the use of reason by the nominalists of his time. But the later Scholastics did not decry it. On the contrary, they regarded human reason as formed for the purpose of apprehending and examining both God and nature. They profess to give a rational account of the whole scheme of existence.

With this outlook, Thomas proceeds to deal with all rational knowledge in mingled terms of Scripture, the Fathers and Aristotle. The existence and attributes of God, of angels and of men are successively passed in review. The whole of creation is a procession, a going out of all creatures from God; ideas are prototypal forms existing in the divine mind, and the meaning of individuation is to be sought in the existence of determinate matter. This solution of the old problem of universals involved the obvious difficulty of explaining the individual existence of angels, and of disembodied souls. Averroes had maintained that individuality was extinguished at death, and, to avoid this conclusion, Aquinas assumed that such spirits possessed a principle of individuation in themselves. They are immaterial forms, since they can grasp the universal, and the soul unit is not merely the rational spirit, as Aristotle taught, but possesses sensitive functions which depend on bodily perceptions in life, but are in essence independent of them.

More important for us is the fact that the whole of the scheme of Aquinas was framed in accordance with Aristotle's logic and science. His logic, known already through compendiums, acquired a wider influence when a rational synthesis of knowledge was attempted. Based on the syllogism, it professed to give rigorous proof from perfectly certain premises. It led naturally to the idea of knowledge derived from intuitive axioms on the one side, and authority—that of the Catholic Church—on the other. It was singularly ill adapted to lead men to, or guide them in, the experimental investigation of nature.

Aquinas also took over from Aristotle and from the Christian doctrine of the day the assumption that man is the centre and object of creation, and that the world is to be described in terms of human sensation and human psychology. Aristotle's physics, his weakest scientific subject, made all this possible. A striking anticipation of more modern physical views was contributed by Democritus when he said: "According to convention there is a sweet and a bitter, a hot and a cold, and according to convention there is colour. In truth there are atoms and a void." This theory is that of modern objective physics, which seek to get behind crude sensation and discover the workings of nature irrespective of man. But, as we know, Aristotle rejected it all, and would have none of the atomic concepts. To him a material body was not, as to Democritus, a collection of atoms, or, as to us, something which has to be conceived as possessing mass or inertia, and other definite physical, chemical and perhaps physiological properties. It was a subject or an entity about which can be said things which fall into certain categories. First it is substance, "that which is not asserted of a subject but of which everything else is asserted"; for example, man, bread, stone; though Aristotle was not thinking of a concrete thing but of an essential nature. Then it has qualities, heaviness, hotness, whiteness; and, of less importance, it can be said to have existed in some place and at some time. These are all accidents, less fundamental than substance, but an integral part of the subject at any given moment.

In the nineteenth century all this would have seemed futile and almost meaningless, though we are able to recast it in more modern form nowadays. But points of view held in the nineteenth or twentieth century would have been equally foreign to men of the Middle Ages, and their attitude of mind had important historical consequences. If heaviness is a natural quality opposed to lightness, it is easy to see how Aristotle arrived at his doctrine of natural places, according to which heavy bodies tend downward and light ones upward, so that the heavier a body the faster it falls. On this point the Scholastics quarrelled with Galileo's facts. Furthermore, Aristotle's distinction of the underlying substance from the

appearances, accidents or species made the doctrine of transubstantiation, an article of faith since 1215, seem natural to
the mediaeval mind, even when mystical Neo-Platonism had
been replaced by rational Aristotelian Thomism.

Aquinas accepted the Ptolemaic system of astronomy, but
it is a remarkable fact that he regarded it merely as a working
hypothesis—"*non est demonstratio sed suppositio quaedam*".[1]
But Saint Thomas's caution was overlooked, and the geocentric
theory became part of the Thomist philosophy. As man was
the object of creation, so the Earth was the centre of the
Universe, and round it revolved concentric spheres of air,
aether and fire—"the flaming walls of the world"—which
carried the Sun, stars and planets. Mediaeval pictures
of the Day of Judgment show how naturally this view led to
the vision of heaven localized above the sky, and hell beneath
the ground. Within the premises given by contemporary
Christian dogma and Aristotelian philosophy, the scheme was
worked out with subtlety and skill, and, accepting the premises, it all held together in a consistent and convincing whole.

Aristotle's doctrine of the eternity of the world was rejected
as irreconcilable with an act of creation in time, but in other
respects even the details of Aristotle's science were brought
into line. From the idea that all motion implies a continual
exertion of force, Aquinas deduced results in accordance with
the theology of his age, such as *Movetur igitur corpus celeste
a substantia intellectuali*. The deductions being regarded as
verified, the premises became strengthened, and thus the whole
of natural knowledge was welded with theology into one rigid
structure, the parts of which were believed to be interdependent,
so that an attack on Aristotelian philosophy or science became
an attack on the Christian faith.

In the Thomist philosophy, both body and mind are realities,
but there is none of the sharp antithesis between them first
formulated by Descartes and so familiar in later ages. Aquinas
was not troubled by such modern metaphysical difficulties as
the relation between these two apparently incommensurable
entities, or the allied problem of how natural knowledge comes
to be possible to the mind of man. There was as yet no need
for this analysis; it only became necessary four centuries later,
when Galileo had shown that, from the dynamical point of

[1] *Lib. Physicorum*, i, cap. 2, lect. iii, 7.

view, the Aristotelian concept of substance with its qualities had to be replaced by the idea of matter in motion, and that accidents like colour, sound and taste were not inherent qualities of the substance, but mere sensations in the mind of the recipient. In the thirteenth century these ideas would have been incomprehensible, and the difficulties involved in them would have been meaningless.

In Saint Thomas Aquinas, Scholasticism reached its highest level. Its grip on the human mind was intense and prolonged. Though the surviving Scholastics opposed the new experimental science after the Renaissance, it was the thorough rationalism of their system that formed the intellectual atmosphere in which modern science was born. In one sense, science was a revolt against this rationalism, an appeal to brute facts whether conformable to a preconceived rational scheme or not. But underlying it is the necessary assumption of the regularity and uniformity of nature. As Dr Whitehead has pointed out,[1] the idea of an inevitable fate—the central theme of Greek tragedy—passed down through the Stoic philosophy to Roman Law, which was based on the moral principles of that philosophy. In spite of the anarchy which followed the fall of the Empire, the sense of legal order always survived, and the Roman Church upheld the universalist traditions of imperial rule. The philosophic rationalism of the Schoolmen arose from and fitted into a general ordered scheme of thought, and prepared for science the belief that "every detailed occurrence can be correlated with its antecedents in a perfectly definite manner, exemplifying general principles. Without this belief the incredible labours of scientists would be without hope". "The habit remained after the (scholastic) philosophy had been repudiated, the priceless habit of looking for an exact point and of sticking to it when found. Galileo owes more to Aristotle than appears on the surface...he owes to him his clear head and his analytic mind." And "the pilgrim fathers of the scientific imagination as it exists to-day, are the great tragedians of ancient Athens, Aeschylus, Sophocles, Euripides. Their vision of fate remorseless and indifferent, urging a tragic incident to its inevitable issue, is the vision possessed by science".

[1] A. N. Whitehead, *Science and the Modern World*, Cambridge, 1927, pp. 11–15.

Roger Bacon[1]   The thirteenth century saw the triumphant and applauded
work of Thomas Aquinas, the greatest exponent of the scholastic
philosophy, and it saw also the tragic life of Roger Bacon, the
only man in Europe throughout the Middle Ages, as far as
records have reached us, who approaches in spirit either the
great Arabians who preceded him or the men of science of the
Renaissance who followed. The tragedy of Bacon's life was
as much internal as external, as much due to the necessary
limitations of his modes of thought in the existing intellectual
environment, as to the persecutions of ecclesiastical authority.

Roger Bacon was born about the year 1210, near Ilchester,
in the Somerset fens. His family seem to have been people of
position and considerable wealth. Roger studied at Oxford,
where he came under the influence of two men, both East
Anglians, Adam Marsh, the mathematician, and Robert
Grosseteste, Chancellor of Oxford, and afterwards Bishop of
Lincoln. "But one alone knows the sciences, the Bishop of
Lincoln", said Bacon; and again, "In our days Lord Robert,
lately Bishop of Lincoln, and brother Adam Marsh were perfect
in all knowledge".

Grosseteste seems to have been the first in England, perhaps
in Western Europe, to invite Greeks to come from the East as
instructors in the ancient form of their language, which was
still read at Constantinople. Bacon himself was equally impressed with the importance of the study of the original
language of Aristotle and the New Testament, and put together
a book on Greek grammar. He was never tired of insisting that
the prevailing ignorance of the original tongues was the cause
of the failure in theology and philosophy of which he accused
the doctors of the time. In anticipation of modern textual
criticism, he pointed out how the Fathers adapted their
translations to the prejudices of their age, and how subsequent
corruptions must have crept in through carelessness and
ignorance, or by that tampering with the text which had gone
on, especially among the Dominicans. Bacon himself, be it
observed, was a Franciscan.

But that which marked Bacon out from among the other
philosophers of his time—indeed of the whole of the European

[1] E. Charles, *Roger Bacon, sa Vie, ses Ouvrages, ses Doctrines*, Paris, 1861;
The Opus Majus of Roger Bacon, translated by R. B. Burke, Philadelphia,
1928.

Middle Ages—was his clear understanding that experimental methods alone give certainty in science. This was a revolutionary change in mental attitude, only to be appreciated after a course of study of the other writings of his day. Bacon read all the authors he could reach, Arabic (probably in Latin translations) as well as Greek, but instead of accepting the facts and inferences of natural knowledge from Scripture, the Fathers, the Arabians, or Aristotle, Bacon told the world that the only way to verify their statements was to observe and experiment. Here again was an anticipation, this time of the doctrine of his more famous namesake, Francis Bacon, Lord Chancellor of England, who lived three hundred and fifty years later, and seems to have made use of some of his predecessor's ideas. This comes out especially in his analysis of the causes of human error. These are taken by Roger to be: Undue Regard to Authority; Habit; Prejudice; False Conceit of Knowledge: an analysis to which Francis's four Idola bear too great a likeness to be accidental.

Roger, at any rate, seems to have practised his own precepts, for he says he spent two thousand pounds, an enormous sum in those days, on his researches, though the experimental results he obtained seem to be meagre. After spending some years in Paris, where he was made a doctor, he returned to Oxford. The growing suspicion of his labours, however, soon caused him to be sent back to Paris for more strict supervision by his Order, and he was forbidden to write or to teach his doctrines. But now came the chance of his lifetime.

Guy de Foulques, an open-minded jurist, warrior and statesman, who had become interested in Bacon's work at Paris, was elected Pope, taking the name of Clement IV. Bacon wrote to him, and in reply Clement sent a letter to *Dilecto filio, Fratri Rogerio dicto Bacon, Ordinis Fratrum Minorum*, commanding him, notwithstanding the prohibition of any prelate or the constitution of his Order, to write out the work for which he had formerly asked permission. For some unknown reason, the Pope added an injunction of secrecy, which increased Brother Roger's difficulties. As a friar he was pledged to poverty, but, by borrowing from friends, he got together enough to provide materials, and in 1267, after some fifteen or eighteen months, he despatched three books to

Clement: an *Opus Majus*, containing his views at length; an *Opus Minus*, or epitome; and an *Opus Tertium*, sent after the others for fear of miscarriage. It is from these books that we chiefly know his work.

Clement died soon after, and Bacon, deprived of his protection, suffered without redress a sentence of imprisonment passed in 1277 by Jerome of Ascoli, General of the Franciscans, who became Pope Nicholas IV. It is probable that Bacon was not released until the death of Nicholas in 1292. In that year he wrote a tract called *Compendium Theologiae*, and thereafter we hear no more of the great friar.

Bacon, for all his comparatively advanced outlook, accepted most of the mediaeval attitude of mind. No man can do more than advance a little way in front of the ranks of that contemporary army of thought to which, whether he will or no, he belongs. Naturally Bacon pictured the Universe as bounded by the sphere of the fixed stars with the Earth at the centre. He accepted the absolute authority of Scripture, could the pure text be recovered, and the entire frame of dogmatic theology in which Christianity was presented to that age. A more hampering preconception was his agreement with the scholastic view, which in other ways he assailed vehemently, that the end of all science and philosophy was to elucidate and adorn their queen, theology. Hence came some of the confusion and the inconsistencies which at every turn are seen in his writings, mixed with originality and insight far beyond his time and even in advance of the next three centuries. Struggle as he might, he never cast off the shackles of the mediaeval habit of mind; it mars his work, as the persecution of his Order marred his life.

It is one of the signs of Bacon's greatness that he realized the importance of a study of mathematics both as an educational exercise and as a basis for other sciences. Mathematical treatises translated from the Arabic were becoming available. They often contained astrological applications. Astrology was a form of fatalism or determinism incompatible with the Christian doctrine of free-will, and mathematics and astrology were chiefly studied by Muhammadans and Jews. Hence both got a bad name and were associated with black arts. But Bacon, with the courage of his convictions, proclaimed that mathematics and optics, which he called perspective, must underlie other studies. Both these sciences, *Roger Bacon* he says, are understood by Robert of Lincoln. Mathematical tables and instruments are necessary, though costly and liable to destruction. He pointed out the errors of the calendar, and calculated that it had gained one day in excess for each 130 years. He also gave a long description of the countries of the known world, estimated its size, and supported the theory of its sphericity. In this he influenced Columbus.

He seems to have become specially interested in light, probably through a study of the Latin version of the works of the Arabian physicist Ibn-al-Haitham. Bacon described the laws of reflection and the general phenomena of refraction. He understood mirrors and lenses and described a telescope, though he does not appear to have made one. He gave a theory of the rainbow, using it as an example of the method of inductive reasoning.

He described many mechanical inventions, some actually known to him, and some as possibilities for the future, among the latter mechanically driven ships, carriages and flying machines. He considered magic mirrors, burning glasses, gunpowder, Greek fire, the magnet, artificial gold, the philosopher's stone, all in a confused mixture of fact, prediction and credulity. In the *Mirror of Alchemy* he still held the Alexandrian theory of all things striving towards improvement. "Nature", he wrote, "has always had for an end and tries ceaselessly to reach perfection—that is, gold."

In trying to appraise the value of Bacon's work we must not forget that his fame would have rested on popular tradition of his magic had not Pope Clement commanded him to write his books. Doubtless others besides Bacon were touched by the same interests but have failed to leave direct traces. Indeed, reflections of the work of such men are found in Bacon's own writings, where he says, "There are only two perfect mathematicians, Master John of London, and Master Peter de Maharn-Curia, a Picard". Master Peter recurs when Bacon deals with experiment.

There is one science, he says, more perfect than others, which is needed to verify the others, the science of experiment, surpassing the sciences dependent on argument, since these sciences do not bring certainty, however strong the reasoning, unless experiment be added to test their conclusions.

Roger Bacon Experimental science alone is able to ascertain what can be effected by nature, what by art, what by fraud. It alone teaches how to judge all the follies of the magicians, just as logic can be used to test argument. This method of experiment no one understands save Master Peter alone; he, indeed, is *dominus experimentorum*, but cares neither to publish his work, nor for the honours and riches it would bring.

But whatever be the truth about these phantom figures which flit across Bacon's pages, it is clear that Friar Roger himself was in spirit a man of science and a scientific philosopher, born out of due time and chafing unconsciously against the limitations of his own restricted outlook, no less than against the external obstacles at which he rails so openly and so often; a true harbinger of the ages of experiment, of whom Somerset, Oxford and England may well be proud.

The Decay of Scholasticism Roger Bacon's criticism of the Scholasticism of Aquinas, though sound from the modern point of view, was out of harmony with the prevailing spirit of the time, and consequently produced little effect.

Much more damaging were the philosophic attacks on Scholasticism which began towards the close of the century. Duns Scotus (c. 1265–1308), who taught at Oxford and Paris, enlarged the theological ground which even Aquinas had reserved as beyond the demonstration of reason. He based the leading Christian doctrines on the arbitrary Will of God, and took free-will as the primary attribute of man, placing it high above reason. Here is the beginning of a revolt against the union of philosophy and religion which the Scholastics sought, and his age believed Thomas Aquinas to have finally and conclusively achieved. A revival of dualism appears, essentially unsatisfying and incomplete, yet necessary as a stage of progress in order that philosophy may be set free from its bondage as the "handmaid of theology", free in fertile union with experiment to give birth to science. At the end of the thirteenth century and at the beginning of the fourteenth the Thomists and Scotists divided the philosophical and theological world between them, while, on the literary side, a definite revolt against the shackles of authority appeared in Italy.

The process begun by Duns Scotus went much further in the writings of William of Occam, a native of Surrey (d. 1347), who denied that any theological doctrines were demonstrable by reason, and showed the irrational nature of many of the doctrines of the Church. He attacked the extreme theory of papal supremacy, and headed a revolt of Franciscans against the control of Pope John XXII. His writings in defence of this action led to his trial for heresy and imprisonment at Avignon. He escaped, however, and sought the protection of the Emperor Louis of Bavaria, whom he aided in a long controversy with the Pope.

This principle of the twofold nature of truth, the acceptance by faith of the doctrines of the Church, and the examination by reason of the subjects of philosophy, was bound up with the revival of nominalism, a belief in the sole reality of individual things, and the reference of universal ideas to the rank of mere names or mental concepts. In their efforts to derive the individual from the universal, the realists had been led to one abstraction after another. This complication was criticized in a statement called "Occam's razor," *Entia non sunt multiplicanda praeter necessitatem.* Here is a forecast of the modern objection to unnecessary hypotheses. By Occam's revival of nominalism stress was laid on the objects of immediate sense perception, in a spirit that distrusted abstractions and made eventually for direct observation and experiment, for inductive research.

The new nominalism was opposed and banned by the Church, and Occam's writings condemned by the University of Paris, which tried to impose realism as late as 1473. But irresistibly the doctrine spread, and a few years afterwards the show of resistance was abandoned. Chancellors of the Universities and Cardinals of the Church became nominalists, and Martin Luther based much of his teaching on the writings of Occam. Finally Rome returned to the modified realism of Aristotle, and in 1879 an encyclical message from Pope Leo XIII re-established the wisdom of Saint Thomas Aquinas as the official Roman philosophy.

Nevertheless, the work of Occam marked the end of the mediaeval dominance of Scholasticism. Thenceforward philosophy was more able to press home its enquiries free from the obligation to reach conclusions foreordained by theology, and, on the other side, religion was for a time detached from rationalism, and was given an opportunity for the development of its no less important emotional and mystical aspects. Hence the fourteenth and fifteenth centuries saw the growth of a new mysticism, especially in Germany, and the appearance of many types of religious experience still known and of value.

Another prominent ecclesiastic who helped to overthrow Scholasticism was Cardinal Nicholas of Cusa (1401–1464), who maintained that all human knowledge is mere conjecture, though God can be apprehended by mystical intuition and comprehends all that is. This led Cusa to views which passed into a form of pantheism afterwards adopted by Bruno. In spite of his views about knowledge, Nicholas made notable advances in mathematics and physical science. He proposed a reform of the calendar, made a good attempt to square the circle, and anticipated Copernicus by rejecting the Ptolemaic system and supporting the theory of the rotation of the Earth.

The task of the Middle Ages was accomplished; the ground was prepared for the Renaissance, with humanism, art, practical discovery, and the beginnings of natural science, as its characteristic glories. With the passing of the universal supremacy of Scholasticism we turn a new page in the history of the world.

To the historian of science mediaeval times are the seed-bed of modern growth. The Arabian school kept alive the memory of Greek learning and made considerable original contributions to our knowledge of nature. But Western men of learning had no science of their own till Roger Bacon stood roughly chafing at his limitations, external and internal, shaking the door which shut him from his natural home in later centuries. The interest for us of mediaeval thought in Europe is that of tracing the changing attitude of the human mind as it passes through states where science would have been impossible to a condition in which its rise follows naturally from the philosophic environment.

The exponents of Scholasticism took the attitude of interpreters; original experimental investigation would have been foreign to their ideas. Yet their rational intellectualism kept alive, indeed intensified, the spirit of logical analysis, while their assumption that God and the world are understandable by man implanted in the best minds of Western Europe the invaluable if unconscious belief in the regularity and uniformity of nature, without which scientific research would never be attempted. As soon as they had thrown off the shackles of scholastic authority, the men of the Renaissance used the lessons which scholastic method had taught them. They began observing in the faith that nature was consistent and intelligible, and, when they had framed hypotheses by induction to explain their observations, they deduced by logical reasoning consequences which could be tested by experiment. Scholasticism had trained them to destroy itself.

In a sense we have seen only the worst aspect of the Christian Middle Ages: they are weakest in the special department of thought necessary for scientific enquiry. We have but glanced at their work of forming and consolidating the nations of Europe. We have not touched on their wonderful achievements in literature and art. The *Chanson de Roland* is to us but a sign that culture has become national; the later romances of chivalry are outside our ken. Dante's *Divina Commedia* has for us little significance, save as the enshrinement in poetry of the concepts of Thomas Aquinas. The glories of cathedral architecture are to us but illustrations of the growth of the builder's art. Even mediaeval religion, which on its philosophic side has concerned us nearly, does not in its essence touch our enquiry. Its saving faith in its divine Founder, its spirit of humble reverence and love for all mankind, its message of salvation to suffering humanity, are hid from our eyes. We meet Saint Bernard, the suspicious Inquisitor, but Saint Francis of Assisi, loving, joyous, simplehearted, does not appear in our pages.

Chapter III

THE RENAISSANCE

The Origins of the Renaissance—Leonardo da Vinci—The Reformation—Copernicus—Medicine and Chemistry—Anatomy and Physiology—Botany—Gilbert of Colchester—Francis Bacon—Kepler—Galileo—From Descartes to Boyle—Pascal—Witchcraft—The Origins of Science.

The Origins of the Renaissance

AFTER the thirteenth century there was a pause in the intellectual development of Western Europe. The economic and social confusion caused by the Black Death and the Hundred Years' War gave little hope of a settled life or quiet study, and the mental activity which had carried the scholastic philosophy to its height seemed to be exhausted.

Nevertheless, there was a continual process of change in the intellectual outlook of mankind, and we may trace, throughout this period of transition, the various streams of thought which, when they met in full vigour, formed the great flood of the Renaissance. The loosening of the universal grip of scholastic ideas by the solvent influence of the philosophy of Duns Scotus and William of Occam has already been indicated, and the flight of Occam from a papal prison to the protection of Louis of Bavaria marks a significant revolt against the power of the Church, a setting up of the rights of nationalities against the universalist tradition of ecclesiastical authority.

The spirit of the Renaissance first became apparent in Italy, then slowly recovering from the devastation of earlier times. Perhaps living among the remains of Roman architecture made it easier for men to return to a love of the classics. A vigorous Northern race had colonized North Italy, and formed an upper class, not yet exterminated by those local wars between Italian States, which then and afterwards proved so fatal to the nobility. But other lands had purer Northern blood, and the reason for Italian pre-eminence in the pursuit of learning must be sought elsewhere. One clue is given by Salimbene of Parma, a thirteenth-century Franciscan, who remarks on the difference between Italy and other countries in one significant particular. In the regions north of the Alps, he says, only the townsfolk dwell in the towns, while the "knights and noble ladies" live

on their estates and superintend the management of their
lands in feudal isolation; but in Italy the upper classes possess
houses in the cities and there spend most of their time.

Now, while it is true that the countryside gains by the
habitual presence of its natural leaders, yet, in an age of slow
communication, country life gives little opportunity for that
contact of mind with mind which leads to intellectual culture
and creation. On the other hand, the city life of the leisured
and intelligent classes in Northern Italy gave an ideal environment for the birth of the Renaissance.

The Renaissance was very far from being exclusively
literary. Many other influences conspired to produce an un-
precedented intellectual ferment, though the literary element
was the earliest and one of the most important. Its harbinger
was Petrarch (1304–1374), in whom we see a spirit quite unlike the scholastic mediaevalism which underlay the poetry of
Dante. Petrarch was the first scholar who tried to restore a
taste for good classical Latin, in place of the dog-Latin of the
Schoolmen, and, more important still, to recover the true spirit
of classical thought, with its claim for the absolute liberty of
the reason.

Petrarch sang before his time, but in the early years of the
fifteenth century a growing interest in classical literature
attracted many Greeks from the East, who, from their knowledge of the modern tongue, were able to teach its ancient
prototype. The capture of Constantinople by the Turks in
1453 hastened this process, and led to the arrival of many
competent teachers, who brought manuscripts with them to
their new homes. The search for manuscripts became a
fashionable pursuit; the monastic and cathedral libraries of
Italy and Northern Europe were ransacked, and merchant
princes with agents in the Levant used all their resources to
procure the copies of Greek writings which had remained
hidden in the East or had been scattered when Constantinople
fell. In this way the language of ancient philosophy and
science became familiar to Western scholars after a lapse of
some eight or nine hundred years.

Of even more value than the language was the spirit of free
enquiry it enshrined, and the impulse towards study of all
kinds that "humane letters" gave once more to Europe after
centuries of mediaevalism. Though the modes of thought due

to an authoritative religion made men prone to accept authority in secular literature also, and the stress laid on the teachings of the Greek philosophers had consequent dangers, nevertheless the humanists prepared the way for the coming revival of science, and played the chief part in that widening of the mental horizon which alone made science possible. Without them, men with scientific minds would never have thrown off the intellectual fetters of theological preconception; without them, external obstacles might have proved insurmountable.

Humanism was brought to the north of Europe by students who had worked under teachers of the New Learning in Italy. One of the earliest was Johann Müller (1436–1476), born at Königsberg and hence called Regiomontanus, who was perhaps the first to combine science with humanism. He translated into Latin the works of Ptolemy and other Greek writers, and in 1471 founded an observatory at Nürnberg, where he made several improvements in practical astronomy. His *Ephemerides*, the precursors of nautical almanacs, were used by the Spanish and Portuguese explorers.[1]

But the main current of the German Renaissance led through Scriptural study to the Reformation. Germany gained new intellectual vigour and interests, but did not adopt the Italian ideal of self-culture, nor the Italian refinement of paganism in social life. In France the Italian spirit proved more congenial, and the movement was more humanist and aesthetic than in Teutonic countries.

The great figure of the northern Renaissance was Desiderius Erasmus (1467–1536), born at Rotterdam but well known in many countries. To him humanism was chiefly a means of bringing the civilizing influence of knowledge to combat the chief evils of the day: monastic illiteracy, Church abuses, scholastic pedantry, and low standards of public and private morality. Scholastic theologians made use of isolated texts artificially interpreted, but Erasmus set himself to show all men what the Bible really said and meant, and what the early Fathers taught.

For one bright interval, culminating with Pope Leo X (1513–1521), the Vatican itself was a vitalizing centre of the ancient culture. But the capture of Rome by the Imperial troops in 1527 broke up this new world of intellectual and artistic life,

[1] *Cambridge Modern History*, vol. I, Cambridge, 1902, p. 571.

and soon afterwards the Papacy, by reversing its previous policy of liberal guidance, and opposing blindly when it was no longer able to understand or to control, became an obstacle in the path of modern learning.

So long as the only method of reduplicating books consisted in the laborious process of manual copying on a somewhat costly and troublesome material, parchment, the possession of a library was within the reach of but few individuals and not many institutions. Paper had been invented in China at about the end of the first century of the Christian era, being traditionally credited to one Tsai Lun, and block printing appeared about the eighth century. The introduction of the art of paper-making into Europe followed the later Crusades, and about a century afterwards the invention of movable type transformed the old attempts at printing with fixed moulds into a practical and useful art, which gradually made books more abundant.

Simultaneously, a renewed ardour for geographical discovery became apparent, and, in spite of the primitive state of the art of navigation, the area of the Earth known to Europe was rapidly increased. A measurement of the Sun's maximum altitude by a cross-staff or a circular "astrolabe" gave a rough value of latitude, but no satisfactory determination of longitude was possible. The first sea chart seen in England is said to have arrived in 1489.

The Portuguese were the first to explore and, under the inspiration of Dom Henrique, Prince Henry the Navigator, they discovered the Azores in 1419 and later pushed along the western shores of Africa, first on a mission to convert the heathen, and then in an open search for slaves and gold. Prince Henry established an observatory at Sagres, near Cape St Vincent, to obtain more accurate tables of the declination of the Sun. The success of the Portuguese encouraged others to emulate them. The Greek theory of the sphericity of the Earth, familiar for several centuries to the makers of cosmogonies, now became a generally accepted belief. It led to the obvious idea, which indeed the Greeks themselves, among others Poseidonius, had propounded, that, by sailing westward into the Atlantic Ocean, the eastern shores of Asia might be reached, and the rich trade of India and Cathay brought direct by sea to Europe. After many failures, there came the man and the hour. Christopher Columbus, born at Cogoletto on the Ligurian coast of North Italy, after overcoming many obstacles, sailed from Palos in Andalusia under the patronage of Ferdinand and Isabella, and succeeded in reaching the Bahamas on October 12th, 1492. Twenty-four years later, Magalhaes' vessel returned after a three years' voyage, having demonstrated the spherical nature of the Earth by the convincing proof of circumnavigation. It was unfortunate for the early circumnavigators that they all sailed to the west, and thus had the prevailing winds against them. To circle the globe from west to east would have been a much easier task.

The wider mental outlook produced by these great voyages of discovery was not their only effect on the human mind, though it was the most direct. As trade with the new lands expanded, a great stimulus was given to home industry and commerce, and thus the material resources of Europe and the total wealth of the inhabitants increased. This increase was brought about in two ways. In the first place, there was the well-recognized growth due to new markets and sources of supply, and their direct and indirect economic effects. And secondly, we can see in the light of recent experience that a monetary factor was also involved. Money is but a token and is not itself wealth; but a variation in the total amount of money in circulation causes great economic changes through its influence on prices. An increase in trade and industry is often hindered by the failure of currency and credit to expand with it. This deficiency leads to a fall in the general price level, a fall which, unlike the real cheapening due to an improvement in the methods of production, depresses industry and thus checks the development of civilization and of learning as part of it. But, after the exploitation of the New World, its treasures of gold and silver more than supplied the currency needed by expanding trade. Money became plentiful and cheap, that is, prices rose. In a time of rising prices, both producers and traders make profits. Furthermore, fixed charges on industry—fixed in terms of money—become less onerous: the customary manorial rents, for example, in the sixteenth century, fell to a nominal charge as their real value in goods and services decreased. Hence both production and trade became profitable. Wealth, and the leisure for intellectual pursuits which wealth gives, increased apace and spread into far wider circles than had been reached with the slender resources of mediaeval times.

The Origins of the Renaissance

It is worthy of note in the history of mankind that the three periods in which the most surprising intellectual developments are found, the crowning age of Greece, the Renaissance, and the century which includes our own day, are all of them times of expansion, geographically and economically, and therefore also of increased wealth and opportunities for a leisured life. In Greece that life was founded on a basis of slavery, at the Renaissance it was produced by the wealth of the Indies, and in the nineteenth century by the Industrial Revolution. In Greece the age of intellectual triumph was followed all too soon by political disintegration, in a nation always comparatively small in numbers. In modern times the Renaissance ushered in a period of four hundred years during which the power of the nations of Europe increased enormously, and the steady growth in population continually put more and more able men at the service of learning, till the enquirers immeasurably exceeded in number the philosophers of ancient Greece. It is perhaps well to bear in mind this fact when exalting modern achievements in the realms of science. Moreover it is impossible to tell whether this growth in knowledge will continue, whether indeed an adequate supply of the able men who alone make it possible will be forthcoming in the social and economic conditions which seem rapidly approaching.

It has often been argued that when we have traced what we know of the different tendencies which combined to make up the Renaissance, and have given due weight to them all, we still cannot but feel that the attempt to explain by obvious causes the amazing change of mental attitude produced in so short a time is not wholly successful. As Bishop Creighton said,[1]

"After marshalling all the forces and ideas which were at work to produce" this change, the observer "still feels that there are behind all these an animating spirit which he can but most imperfectly catch, whose power blended all else together and gave a sudden cohesion to the whole. This modern spirit formed itself with surprising rapidity, and we cannot fully explain the process."

In reply to these arguments three points may perhaps fairly be made. Firstly, the stimulating effect on civilization of the

[1] *Cambridge Modern History*, vol. I, Cambridge, 1902, p. 2.

fertilizing stream of gold and the consequent steady and long-continued rise in the general level of prices has not hitherto been fully realized. Secondly, we must remember that we possess records of but a tithe of the intellectual efforts of the time. Few men then put their thoughts on paper, and of the writings of those few not all have reached us. In Italian city life, knowledge and the change of outlook which knowledge brings must have passed from man to man by word of mouth rather than by writings, and the influence of direct personal intercourse must have been immense. Thirdly, when a number of factors are at work, the total effect at the beginning is but the sum of the separate effects. But there comes a time when the effects overlap and intensify each other; cause and effect act and react. And so it is with all the material, moral and intellectual factors involved in the changes of the sixteenth century—somewhat suddenly they passed the critical stage. Growing wealth increased knowledge, and new knowledge in its turn increased wealth. The whole process became cumulative, and advanced with accelerating speed in the irresistible torrent of the Renaissance.

The influence of personality, doubtless especially strong in the full life of Italian cities, is difficult to trace historically. For the most part, we can only catch glimpses here and there of the power of outstanding figures. But the full grandeur of one such man has been revealed now that some of the inchoate manuscript note books of that tremendous universal genius, Leonardo da Vinci, have been published and given to the world.[1] Leonardo may have meant to collect and systematize his notes in the form of books, but if he did, he never lived to carry out the intention, and for this reason his work as a philosopher has been overshadowed till recent years by his fame as an artist.

Leonardo was the natural son of a lawyer of great vigour and some eminence, Ser Piero da Vinci, and a peasant girl named Catarina. He was born at Vinci, between Florence and Pisa, in the year 1452, and was educated by his father. He entered successively the service of the courts of Florence, Milan and Rome, and died in 1519 in France, the servant and friend of Francis I. In early life he showed the remarkable

[1] Edward McCurdy, *Leonardo da Vinci's Note Books arranged and rendered into English*, 1906.

qualities which impressed both contemporaries and men of
later ages as being sufficient to place him in a class apart from
the rest of mankind. Beauty of person and charm of manner
did but adorn and increase the power of mind and force of
character which took all knowledge for its study and all art
for its expression. A painter, sculptor, engineer, architect,
physicist, biologist and philosopher was Leonardo, and in each
rôle he was supreme. Perhaps no man in the history of the
world shows such a record. His performance, extraordinary as
it was, must be reckoned as small compared with the ground
he opened up, the grasp of fundamental principles he displayed,
and the insight with which he seized upon the true methods
of investigation in each branch of enquiry. If Petrarch was
the harbinger of the literary Renaissance, Leonardo led the
way in other departments. He was not a scholastic, neither
was he a blind follower of classical authority, as were many
of the men of the Renaissance. To him observation of nature
and experiment were the only true methods of science.
Knowledge of the ancient writers, useful as a starting-point,
could never be conclusive.

Leonardo approached science from the practical side, and
it is owing to this lucky circumstance that his intellectual
attitude is so modern. To meet the needs of his crafts he began
experimenting, and in his later years his thirst for knowledge
was even greater than his love of art. As a painter he was led
to study the laws of optics and the structure of the eye, the
details of human anatomy and the flight of birds. As an
engineer, both civil and military, he was faced by problems
which could only be solved by an insight into the principles
of mechanics, dynamic as well as static. Aristotle's opinion
was of small help in correcting a picture out of drawing, in
managing water for irrigation, or in taking a fortified city.
For these problems, the behaviour of things as they are was
of more importance than the opinion of the encyclopaedic
Greek as to what they ought to be.

But Leonardo was also a philosopher, and when we compare
his mode of thought with that of the men of the preceding
age, we see a striking contrast in his almost complete emanci-
pation from theological preconceptions. Even Roger Bacon,
with all his love of enquiry, regarded theology as the true
summit and end of all knowledge, and doubted not that all

Leonardo da Vinci learning if rightly apprehended would prove consistent with the chief dogmas of his day. But Leonardo reasoned with a perfectly open mind. When he turned to theology at all, he attacked frankly and lightly the ecclesiastical abuses and absurdities which had become part of the system of the Church. His own philosophical position seems to have been an idealistic pantheism, in the light of which he saw everywhere the living spirit of the Universe. Yet, with the fine balance of a great mind, he saw the good beneath the load of inconsequent evil, and accepted the essential Christian doctrine as an outward and visible form for his inward, spiritual life. "I leave on one side the sacred writings," he says, "because they are the supreme truth." A great gentleman as well as a great man, the fanaticism of the rude iconoclast was far from Leonardo, and he lived in the brief interval when the Papacy itself was liberal and humanist, and all seemed pointing to a new and comprehensive Catholicism, in which freedom of thought could exist side by side with earnest faith in fundamentals. The dream passed, the Church of Rome became reactionary, and freedom was won painfully and slowly by the rough and unattractive path opened by Luther. Fifty years after Leonardo's death, a position such as his would have been untenable.

Great as Leonardo was, he must not be represented as the originator *de novo* of the scientific spirit he displays. Alberti (1404–1472) had studied mathematics and made physical experiments before him. At Florence he met Paolo Toscanelli (d. 1482), an astronomer who had instigated the voyage of Columbus; Amerigo Vespucci gave him a book on geometry; he knew Luca Pacioli, a mathematician, and he was helped in his anatomical researches by Antonio della Torre. It is clear, therefore, that, a century before the days of Galileo, a small circle of kindred spirits lived in Italy, who were more interested in things than in books, in experimental enquiry than in the opinions of Aristotle, and Leonardo's note books have enabled us to trace the contemporary position of science in a way which would otherwise have been impossible. Doubtless it is true that the rational synthesis of Scholasticism helped to prepare men's minds by teaching them that the Universe was understandable. But the solution offered became inadequate as soon as men began to observe and experiment. A new basis for knowledge was needed: induction from nature

had to replace deduction from Aristotle or Saint Thomas
Aquinas, and this new basis is first to be found in Italian
mathematicians, astronomers and anatomists. *Leonardo da Vinci*

But there is a link with Greek thought behind these men
too, a link with Archimedes. Archimedes' books had not yet
been printed, and good manuscripts were rare. Leonardo
noted the names of his friends and patrons who could procure
him copies, and expressed admiration for the genius of the
great Syracusan. Interest in Archimedes grew rapidly; in 1543
the mathematician Tartaglia published a Latin translation of
some of his works, and other editions followed, so that they
were well known by the time of Galileo, who studied them
carefully. In Archimedes, the geometer and experimentalist,
and not in Aristotle, the encyclopaedic philosopher, is to be
sought the veritable Greek prototype of the masters of modern
physical science; for, among the ancient writers of the Classical
Age whose works have survived, Archimedes possessed most
clearly the true scientific spirit.

Leonardo perceived intuitively and used effectively the right
experimental method a century before Francis Bacon philo-
sophized about it inadequately, and Galileo put it into practice.
Leonardo wrote no treatise on method, but incidentally his
ideas can be seen in his note books. He says that mathematics,
arithmetic and geometry give absolute certitude within their
own realm; they are concerned with ideal mental concepts
(*e tuta mentale*) of universal validity. But true science, he held,
began with observation; if mathematical reasoning could then
be applied, greater certitude might be reached, but, "those
sciences are vain and full of errors which are not born from
experiment, the mother of all certainty, and which do not end
with one clear experiment (*che non terminano in nota ex-
perientia*)". Science gives certainty, and science gives power.
Those who rely on practice without science are like sailors
without rudder or compass.

When we turn from Leonardo's method to his actual
results, we are astonished at his insight. He foreshadowed
the principle of inertia, afterwards demonstrated experimentally by Galileo. "Nothing perceptible by the senses",
wrote Leonardo, "is able to move itself;...every body has
a weight in the direction of its movement." He knew that
the speed of a falling body increases with the time, though

8-2

he missed the exact relation which gives the space fallen through.

He clearly understood the experimental impossibility of "perpetual motion" as a source of power, in this anticipating Stevinus of Bruges (1586). The knowledge of this impossibility was used by him to demonstrate the law of the lever by the method of virtual velocities, a principle realized by Aristotle and used later by Ubaldi and Galileo. The shorter arm, of length l, raises the greater weight W slowly with a velocity v, while the longer arm L is pushed down by the smaller weight w quickly with a velocity V; there cannot be a gain or loss of power, and at each end the power is measured by the product of weight and velocity. Thus

$$Wv = wV.$$

The velocities of the ends are in the proportion of the lengths of the arms, so that
$$Wl = wL \text{ or } \frac{W}{w} = \frac{L}{l},$$

and the weights must be inversely as the lengths. Leonardo regarded the lever as the primary machine, and all other machines as modifications and complications of it.

He also recovered Archimedes' conception of the pressure of fluids, and showed that liquids stand at the same level in communicating vessels, while, if different liquids fill the two vessels, their heights will be inversely as their densities. He dealt also with hydrodynamics: the efflux of water through orifices, its flow in channels, and the propagation of waves over its surface. From waves on water he passed to waves in air and the laws of sound, and he recognized that light shows many analogies which suggest that here too a wave theory is applicable. The reflection of an image is like the echo of a sound; the angle of reflection is equal to the angle of incidence as it is when a ball is thrown against a wall.

In the realm of astronomy Leonardo conceived of a celestial machine conforming to definite laws, in itself a remarkable advance on the prevalent Aristotelian ideas that the heavenly bodies are divine, incorruptible, essentially different from our world, which is subject to change and decay. He calls the Earth a star like the others, and proposes in his projected book to show that it would reflect light as does the moon. Though erroneous in detail, Leonardo's astronomy is true in spirit.

He held that as things are older than writings, the Earth *Leonardo* bears traces of its history before the records of books. Fossils *da Vinci* now on high inland mountains were produced in sea water, and could not have reached their present position in the forty days of the Noachian deluge; indeed the whole waters of the world, clouds, rivers and ocean, could not cover the mountains of the earth. There must, he argued, have been changes in the crust of the earth, and mountains have raised themselves in fresh places. But no catastrophic action was needed: "in time the Po will lay dry land in the Adriatic in the same way as it has already deposited a great part of Lombardy". Here we have the essence of the uniformitarian theory three hundred years before it was revived by Hutton.

As a painter and sculptor, Leonardo felt the need of a precise knowledge of anatomy. In the face of ecclesiastical tradition, he procured many bodies and dissected them, making anatomical drawings which, besides being accurate in all details, are true works of art. Many of them still exist in his manuscripts preserved at Windsor. "And you who say that it would be better to look at an anatomical demonstration than to see these drawings," he remarks, "you would be right, if it were possible to observe all the details shown in these drawings in a single figure, in which, with all your ability, you will not see nor acquire a knowledge of more than a few veins, while, in order to obtain an exact and complete knowledge of these, I have dissected more than ten human bodies."

From anatomy the next step is physiology, and here, too, Leonardo is found to be far in advance of his age. He described how the blood makes and remakes continually the whole body of man, bringing material to the parts and carrying off the waste products, as a furnace is fed and the ashes removed. He studied the muscles of the heart and made drawings of the valves which seem to show a knowledge of their functions. He compared the flow of the blood with the circulation of water from the hills to the rivers and the sea; from the sea to the clouds and back to the hills as rain. It seems that Leonardo understood the general principle of the circulation of the blood a hundred years or more before it was rediscovered and Harvey gave the knowledge to the world. His art led him to another scientific problem—the structure and mode of action of the eye. He made a model of the optical parts,

*Leonardo
da Vinci*

and showed how an image was formed on the retina. He ignored the view still held by his contemporaries that the eye throws out rays which touch the object it wishes to examine.

He dismissed scornfully the follies of alchemy, astrology and necromancy; to him nature is orderly, non-magical, subject to immutable necessity.

Enough has now been said to illustrate Leonardo da Vinci's position in the history of scientific thought. Had he published his work, science must at one step have advanced almost to the place it reached a century later. It is idle to speculate on the influence such a change might have had on the intellectual and social evolution of humanity, but it is safe to say that both would have been modified profoundly.

Though Leonardo never carried out his oft-referred-to project of writing books on different branches of his labours, his personal influence was clearly very great. The friend of princes and statesmen, he also knew all the chief men of learning of his time. Doubtless through them some of his ideas were preserved, and thus, years later, helped to promote a new growth of science. If we had to chose one figure to stand for all time as the incarnation of the true spirit of the Renaissance, we should point to the majestic form of Leonardo da Vinci.

*The
Reformation*

In a society stirring with diverse intellectual interests, we have a mental environment very different from that prevailing a hundred years earlier. The theological atmosphere, which saw everything in the light of the one overpowering motive of salvation, had given place to a much more independent outlook, in which many questions were freely discussed from a rational point of view. The world was still orthodox; the many heresies which had appeared from age to age had been forcibly and effectually suppressed, or perhaps it would be truer to say that the doctrines which survived had been accepted as orthodox. But in the early years of the sixteenth century orthodoxy itself had been aroused and for a time had stretched its bounds: the religious humanists, led by Erasmus, might have liberalized and reformed the Roman Church from within had circumstances been favourable.

The development and meaning of the Reformation are subjects too complex to be lightly summarized, yet a history of scientific thought must take into account the effects of such an upheaval. The Reformers had three chief objects. Firstly, the re-establishment of Church discipline, undermined by the abuses of the Roman Curia and the loose or worldly lives of many of the clergy. Secondly, the reform of doctrine on the lines of some of the earlier suppressed movements, and a return to a supposed primitive simplicity. And thirdly, a relaxation in dogmatic control and a measure of freedom for the private judgment based on Scripture.

It was the first of these objects, aimed as it was at the open and admitted corruption of the Roman Church, that carried the people with it. The second was also important, for mediaeval modes of thought were still powerful, and to the Middle Ages the idea of change and development was foreign. Reform of ritual and doctrine could only gain support if it was believed to be an appeal to an older precedent and to an authority greater even than that of the Roman Pontiff—the practice and belief of the primitive Church of Christ. Indeed, in our own days an appeal to the "first four centuries" has more than once been made, sometimes by those whose knowledge of the centuries in question is not conspicuous in their writings.

The third object of the Reformers is the one which chiefly concerns us here, in that it was a consequence of the Renaissance and a real incentive to the humanist element in the movement. But, as is usual in revolutions, intellectual interests were pushed aside. The rough work could only be done by religious enthusiasts or German princes with political motives, and Calvin was as much a persecutor of free thought as any Roman Inquisitor. But fortunately he had not the power of the mediaeval Church behind him, and the disintegration of Christendom which the Reformation produced, sad though it was from many other points of view, did in the end help indirectly to secure liberty of thought.

The first great change in scientific outlook after the Re- naissance was made by Nicolaus Koppernigk (1473–1543), a mathematician and astronomer with a Polish father and a German mother, who Latinized his name as Copernicus. The geocentric theory of Hipparchus and Ptolemy was successful in explaining the facts with that degree of accuracy which the observations of the time demanded. Its only fault from the geometric point of view was the complication of cycles and epicycles it involved. It had behind it not only the com-mon-sense feeling that the Earth was clearly the solid and

Copernicus immovable base of all things, but also the great authority of Aristotle, whose word in science was accepted by Saint Thomas Aquinas and his scholastics, and also by those who, in questions of philosophy, had come to doubt him. Aristotelian realists and the new nominalists all assumed an Earth at rest beneath their feet, though those who had studied the problem imagined it as a sphere floating in the centre of the Cosmos. Indeed, the opposition to Copernicus when it came was scientific as well as ecclesiastical. If the Earth spun round on its axis, would not a body thrown upward lag behind, and fall to the west of its point of projection? Would not loose objects fly away from the ground, and the Earth itself disintegrate? As the Earth moved round the Sun, would not the stars appear to shift among themselves, unless indeed they were so far off that the distances became ridiculous, if not inconceivable?

To resist all these arguments, then perfectly valid, and to advance an opposing theory, needed not only great originality of mind, but, in that age, some philosophic standpoint from which it could be defended. Now, although Aristotelian scholasticism had held the field for a century, and Occam's nominalism was its only powerful rival north of the Alps, Plato's idealistic realism, especially as interpreted by Saint Augustine, had survived in Italy in the background, as a legacy from the early Middle Ages when Christian theology was linked with Neo-Platonic philosophy. In Neo-Platonism there was a strong Pythagorean element, which delighted to conceive the Universe in terms of a mystical harmony of numbers, or geometrical arrangement of units of space.[1] Hence Pythagoreans and Neo-Platonists were always looking for mathematical relations in nature; the simpler the relation the better mathematically, and therefore, on this view, the nearer to nature. Moreover, the Pythagoreans, alone among the ancients whose works were available in the early sixteenth century, believed the Earth to move round a central fire.

In the fifteenth and sixteenth centuries, while men's minds were stirred by currents of thought new and old, there was a revival in Italy of Platonism containing this Pythagorean element. John Pico of Mirandola taught a mathematical interpretation of the world, and Maria de Novara, Professor

[1] See chap. I, pp. 18, 19, 20.

of Mathematics and Astronomy at Bologna, criticized the   *Copernicus*
Ptolemaic system as too cumbrous to satisfy the principle of
mathematical harmony.

Copernicus spent six years in Italy and became the pupil
of Novara. He says that he studied the writings of all the
philosophers whose books he could obtain, and discovered that,

according to Cicero, Nicetas had thought the earth was moved,...
according to Plutarch that certain others had held the same opinion....
When from this, therefore, I had conceived its possibility, I myself also
began to meditate upon the mobility of the earth....I found at length
by much and long observation, that if the motions of the other planets
were added to the rotation of the earth, and calculated as for the
revolution of that planet, not only the phenomena of the others followed
from this, but that it so bound together both the order and magnitudes
of all the planets and the spheres and the heaven itself that in no single
part could one thing be altered without confusion among the other parts
and in all the Universe. Hence for this reason...I have followed this
system.[1]

Copernicus thus describes his theory of the Universe:

First and above all lies the sphere of the fixed stars, containing itself
and all things, for that very reason immovable; in truth the frame of
the Universe, to which the motion and position of all other stars are
referred. Though some men think it to move in some way, we assign
another reason why it appears to do so in our theory of the movement
of the Earth. Of the moving bodies first comes Saturn, who completes
his circuit in xxx years. After him, Jupiter, moving in a twelve year
revolution. Then Mars, who revolves biennially. Fourth in order an
annual cycle takes place, in which we have said is contained the Earth,
with the lunar orbit as an epicycle. In the fifth place Venus is carried
round in nine months. Then Mercury holds the sixth place, circulating
in the space of eighty days. In the middle of all dwells the Sun. Who
indeed in this most beautiful temple would place the torch in any other
or better place than one whence it can illuminate the whole at the same
time? Not ineptly, some call it the lamp of the universe, others its
mind, and others again its ruler—Trismegistus, the visible God, Sophocles'
Electra, the contemplation of all things. And thus rightly in as much
as the Sun, sitting on a royal throne, governs the circumambient family
of stars....We find, therefore, under this orderly arrangement, a
wonderful symmetry in the universe, and a definite relation of harmony
in the motion and magnitude of the orbs, of a kind it is not possible to
obtain in any other way.[2]

[1] Copernicus, *De Revolutionibus Orbium Celestium*, Letter to Pope Paul III,
quoted by E. A. Burtt, in *Metaphysical Foundations of Modern Science*,
p. 37.

[2] *De Revolutionibus Orbium Celestium*, Lib. i, Cap. x; Eng. trans.; W. C. D.
and M. D. Whetham, *Readings in the Literature of Science*, Cambridge, 1924,
p. 13.

Copernicus　　From this it appears that to Copernicus the primary question was what motions should be assigned to the planetary bodies to give the simplest and most harmonious geometry of the heavens which would accord with the facts.

From the opening phrases of the extract given above, it is clear that he still accepted the ancient view that the stars were fixed to a sphere at a constant distance from the Earth.

Fig. 1.

But he realized that he was shifting the frame of reference for all the planetary movements from the Earth to the sphere of the fixed stars. This involves a physical as well as a mathematical revolution in the subject, and is destructive of the whole of Aristotle's physics and astronomy. To Ptolemy's argument that a moving Earth would fly to pieces, Copernicus replied that a moving sky would do so even more, since it is larger in circumference and therefore, if it revolves, must move faster. This is physical reasoning, but Copernicus dwelt more

on the idea of mathematical harmony, and he appealed to   *Copernicus*
mathematicians to accept his views, on the ground that they
are much simpler as an explanation of the phenomena than
the Ptolemaic system of cycles and epicycles in which the
heavenly bodies move round the Earth.

About 1530 he finished a treatise setting forth his scheme
and published a short abstract in popular form in that year.
Pope Clement VII approved, and sent the author a request
for the publication of the work in full. To this Copernicus only
consented in 1540, and the first printed copy of his book
reached him on his death-bed in 1543.

The Copernican system only won its way very slowly.
A few of the mathematicians to whom Copernicus had appealed
accepted it, but it did not become well known even to the
educated world till Galileo turned his newly invented telescope
to the heavens and revealed Jupiter's satellites, a solar system
in miniature. When the new theory was understood, however,
it brought about a veritable revolution in thought.

Copernicus taught men to look on the World in a new light.
Instead of being the centre of the Universe, the Earth sank
to the lowlier place of one among the planets. Such a change
does not necessarily involve the dethronement of man from his
proud position as the summit of creation, but it certainly
suggests doubts of the validity of that belief. Thus, besides
destroying the Ptolemaic system, which had been incorporated
as a necessary part of his scheme by Thomas Aquinas, Copernican astronomy affected the human mind and human beliefs
in other and more important ways.

It is not surprising that misgivings arose. Europe was
quarrelling over religion; but the questions at issue did not
touch the deeper problems. Both parties accepted a religious
philosophy which accorded man a place of dignity, and made
him feel at home in a world which all agreed had been created
for his ultimate benefit, though the immediate ways of
Providence might sometimes seem unnecessarily mysterious.
Moreover, what would be considered the best scientific opinion
of the time was against the new system. Intellectual revolu-
tionaries like Giordano Bruno, heretic both to Rome and
Geneva, might uphold Copernican views, but more cautious
philosophers held aloof.

Bruno went further than Copernicus and abandoned the old

idea that the stars were at a constant and finite distance. He believed the Universe to be infinite, and the stars to be scattered through the immensity of space. But Bruno, enthusiastic pantheist, openly attacked all orthodox beliefs, and was condemned by the Inquisition, not so much for his science, as for his philosophy and his zeal for religious reform, and was burned at the stake in 1600.

Those responsible, according to the customs of the time, for the intellectual and spiritual welfare of Europe quite rightly paused before they accepted an astronomical system which upset their own deepest convictions, and, as they held, might imperil the immortal souls of those committed to their charge. When Galileo went to Rome, full of enthusiasm to convert the papal court, a clash became inevitable. The academic world, chiefly Aristotelian, urged the Churchmen into action. And so it was that, while in 1530 the Papacy had shown a liberal interest in the new theory, in 1616 it silenced Galileo and pronounced by the mouth of Cardinal Bellarmine that the Copernican theory was "false and altogether opposed to Holy Scripture", and Copernicus' book was suspended till corrected, though it was understood that the new theory might be taught as a mere physical hypothesis. In 1620 Cardinal Gaetani revised the book on these lines, making merely trivial changes. The suspensory edict was never ratified by the Pope; it was virtually repealed in 1757, and in 1822 the Sun received the formal sanction of the Papacy to become the centre of the planetary system.

In spite of Whewell's clear and fair account of the incident, some more recent writers have made altogether too much of the persecution of Galileo for his Copernican views. As Whitehead says:

In a generation which saw the Thirty Years' War and remembered Alva in the Netherlands, the worst that happened to men of science was that Galileo suffered an honourable detention and a mild reproof, before dying peacefully in his bed. The way in which the persecution of Galileo has been remembered is a tribute to the quiet commencement of the most intimate change in outlook which the human race had yet encountered.

The influence of the Renaissance on other branches of science, especially on medicine and subjects associated with it, must now be considered. At first it was thought that the revival of

Greek learning would produce the same brilliant awakening in medicine as in literature and philosophy. A school of medical humanists arose, whose object was to turn men's eyes from mediaeval medicine, derived for the most part from commentaries on Greek writers, some of them transmitted through Arabic channels, and to direct their attention to the fountain-heads of this learning, the writings of Hippocrates and Galen themselves. Doubtless this movement led to a vast increase in knowledge, but, when the knowledge had been systematized, physicians once more came to rely too much upon authority.

As this phase passed, and men began again to observe, think and experiment for themselves, medicine became for a time intimately allied with the chemistry which was emerging from alchemy, and there arose a definite school of physicians who studied chemistry, or iatro-chemists as they came to be called.

The chemistry and alchemy of the Arabs reached Europe in the later Middle Ages, and influenced the work of such men as Roger Bacon. The Arabs took up and modified the Pythagorean theory that the primary elements were to be found in principles or qualities and not in substances. They came to believe that the fundamental principles were those of sulphur or fire, mercury or liquidity, and salt or solidity (see p. 80). This theory passed with other Arab learning to Europe. It was prominently advocated by the Dominican monk Basil Valentine in the latter half of the fifteenth century.

In studying this theory, we must understand that, like the Greek idea of four elements, it arose from an attempt to explain the mysterious action of fire. "Sulphur" did not mean the particular substance of definite atomic weight and chemical properties which we call by that name, but that part of any body which caused it to be combustible and disappeared on burning. "Mercury" was any part which distilled over as liquid, and "Salt" the solid residue. To these elements Valentine added an *Archaeus*, the force or energy by which the Ruler of the Universe determined its phenomena, including chemical changes. It was such ideas as these that chemistry introduced into medicine at the Renaissance.

We are here concerned not with the history of the practice of medicine, but only with the underlying sciences. We must therefore pass by the names of many physicians who lived honourable and useful lives, and turn to a less attractive figure, Paracelsus (c. 1490–1541), who was one of the first to break away from the classical and orthodox Galenic school. Paracelsus was a Swiss alchemist and quack doctor, who took a new name from that of Celsus, the great physician of Roman times. In the mines of the Tyrol he studied indiscriminately rocks, minerals, mechanical contrivances, and the conditions, accidents and diseases consequent on the miner's life and surroundings. He expressed his contempt for Galen, indeed for all orthodox men of science, and wandered over a great part of Europe studying the diseases and remedies of different nations before settling down for a while at Basle, where he aroused the probably well-deserved opposition of vested medical interests. His writings resemble those of other alchemists of the time, who, when they described their work at all, used a cloud of verbiage, calculated to enhance their reputation for learning among the vulgar, and at the same time to conceal from possible competitors the methods by which their results had been reached. As a medical man he turned from the authority of Galen and Avicenna with characteristic self-reliance, and applied to medical problems the results of his own observations and experience, interpreted by intuitive imagination, and expressed in mystical language. His followers were distinguished from the orthodox Galenic school by the use which they made of chemical drugs in medical practice. Doubtless they killed many patients, but, in doing so, at any rate, they made experiments. They discovered a number of drugs which proved to be of value, and incidentally they added to chemical knowledge. For example, Paracelsus describes under the generic name of "sulphur", a substance obtained as an "extract of vitriol" which is clearly ether. He says: "it possesses an agreeable taste; even chickens will eat it, whereupon they sleep for a moderately long time, and reawake without having been injured".[1] It is curious that the anaesthetic properties of ether should have been observed without being appreciated. The first clearly to describe the preparation of ether by the action of oil of vitriol (or sulphuric acid) on alcohol was Valerius Cordus (1515–1544), doctor of medicine and botanist, who, unlike Paracelsus, gives a clear and definite account of his procedure, showing that he had passed from alchemy to chemistry.

[1] Translation by C. D. Leake, in *Isis*, No. 21, 1925, p. 22.

The immediate disciples of Paracelsus followed his methods equally unscrupulously. They employed a mixture of astrology, alchemy and chemical medicine, till medical faculties had to prohibit the use of chemical drugs. But at a later date medical chemistry fell into more reputable hands, and contributed many useful facts to medical knowledge.

Medicine and Chemistry

Important work was done by van Helmont, born in Brussels in 1577, a mystic, but free from the egotism and fanaticism of Paracelsus. He recognized different kinds of aeriform substances, and invented the name "gas" to describe them. He reduced the four elements to one, and, like Thales, took it to be water. He planted a willow in a weighed quantity of dry earth, supplied it with water only, and at the end of five years found that it had gained 164 pounds in weight, while the earth had only lost 2 ounces. This was a very ingenious proof that practically all the new substance of the willow was made of water, indeed a quite convincing proof, until Ingenhousz and Priestley, more than a hundred years later, showed that green plants absorb carbon from the carbon dioxide in the air.

The first to apply some of the new physical knowledge to medicine was Sanctorius (1561–1636) who introduced a modification of Galileo's thermometer and used it for measuring the temperature of the body. He also devised an apparatus for comparing the rate of pulse beats. By weighing himself in a balance, he investigated the changes in weight of the human body, and proved that it loses weight by mere exposure, referring the loss to imperceptible perspiration.[1] The accurate balance was perhaps the best legacy which the alchemists bequeathed to the chemists and physicists who succeeded them.

François Dubois (1614–1672), better known by his Latinized name of Franciscus Sylvius, studied the work of van Helmont and, applying chemistry to medicine, founded a definite school of iatro-chemists. He held that health depended on the fluids of the body, acid or alkaline, which, by union with each other, produced a milder and neutral substance, a doctrine which was adopted in chemistry as well as in medicine. It is of great historical importance as the first general theory of chemistry not based on the phenomena of flame, a theory the fundamental ideas of which are still of use in science. It led Lémery and Macquer to distinguish clearly between acids and alkalis

[1] C. Singer, *A Short History of Medicine*, Oxford, 1928, p. 108.

or bases. The recognition of these opposite qualities in different bodies, and their tendency to unite, sometimes with violence, suggested the idea of chemical attraction or affinity. The formation in this manner of neutral compounds led to the conclusion that every salt was formed by the union of an acid and a base. This is a foreshadowing of the classification of chemical compounds in a series of types, a theory which proved very stimulating in the organic chemistry of the nineteenth century.

The prejudice against the dissection of human bodies lasted long in Europe, and it was not till the thirteenth century, when the writings of Galen and his Arabian commentators first became available, that men began again to study anatomy. The first outstanding figure was that of Mondino, who died in 1327, and, almost immediately after his work, the subject assumed a stereotyped form. Although dissection was included in the regular medical course at the Universities, it was carried out in strict accordance with, and as an illustration of, the text of Galen, or Avicenna, or Mondino, and no attempt was made to increase knowledge.[1] Thus, except in the note books of Leonardo, which produced no general effect on his contemporaries, no further advance in anatomy was made till the last decade of the fifteenth century. Then Manfredi wrote a treatise of which a manuscript is now in the Bodleian Library.[2] It shows a comparison of authorities and some observation. Soon afterwards Carpi published a volume which definitely added to the science. But modern anatomy really begins with Andreas Vesalius (1515–1564), a Fleming by birth, who was trained at Louvain and Paris. Under the aegis of the Venetian Republic, he became Professor at Padua, and also taught at Bologna and Pisa. In 1543 Vesalius published *Fabrica Humani Corporis*, a great book on anatomy, based, not on what Galen or Mondino taught, but on what he himself had seen in dissection and was prepared to demonstrate in the lecture room. He made many advances in knowledge, and his work on the bones, the veins, the abdominal organs and the brain was specially notable. While accepting in the main Galen's physiology, Vesalius described some experiments on animals carried out by himself. But in 1544, disgusted at the opposition

---

[1] Sir Michael Foster, *Lectures on the History of Physiology*, Cambridge, 1902.
[2] *Studies in the History and Method of Science*, ed. by C. Singer, Oxford, 1917.

his book aroused, he relinquished research, and accepted the post of Court Physician to the Emperor Charles V.

Before the end of the sixteenth century anatomy, the earliest of the biological sciences, was freed from the trammels of ancient authority. Physiology was slower to escape: the doctrines of Galen blocked the way. Galen, as we have seen, taught that the arterial blood and the venous blood were two separate tides driven by the heart, which, as they ebbed and flowed, carried the one "vital" and the other "natural" spirits to the tissues of the body. As Foster says:[1]

> To-day our view of any action and process of the body has for its fundamental basis the fact that the life of every tissue-unit of the body is dependent on that body being bathed directly or indirectly by blood which comes to it as oxygen-bearing, arterial blood, and leaves it as venous blood carrying away the products of activity. Let us remember that such a view is impossible under the Galenic doctrine which taught that to and from every tissue there was a flow and ebb of two kinds of blood serving two purposes, one kind travelling in the veins, the other in the arteries. Let us further remember that this Galenic doctrine of the uses of veins and arteries was bound up with the Galenic doctrine of the working of the heart...the mysterious transit of blood from the right to the left side of the heart through the invisible pores of the septum....If we do this, we shall at once see that the true teaching of the mechanism of the bodily heart is as it were the intellectual heart of all physiology.

Michael Servetus, an Aragonese physician and theologian, who was condemned by Calvin for his unorthodox opinions, and burned at Geneva, discovered the circulation of the blood through the lungs, but its actual mechanism, and the function of the heart in maintaining the flow, though suggested in some shrewd speculations by Caesalpinus in 1593, were only made clear to men when William Harvey (1578–1657) was led to "give his mind to vivisections".

Harvey was born at Folkestone in 1578, the son of a prosperous Kentish yeoman or small squire. After studying at Gonville and Caius College, Cambridge, he spent five years abroad, chiefly at Padua. Returning to England when he was about twenty-four years of age, he began to practise as a physician, numbering Francis Bacon among his patients. He was in attendance on James I, and it fell to the lot of this the most modern physiologist of the day to superintend the

---

[1] Sir M. Foster, *loc. cit.* p. 21.

medical examination of women accused of witchcraft. Fortunately he found no physical abnormalities, and they were
acquitted. With Charles I Harvey was on terms of intimacy.
The King had placed the resources of the deer parks at
Windsor and Hampton Court at the disposal of his physician
for purposes of experiment, and with him watched the development of the chick in the egg[1] and the pulsation of its living
heart. Harvey followed the King in his first campaign, and
was in charge of the royal princes at the Battle of Edgehill,
where, during the fight, he is said to have sat under a hedge
reading a book. He retired to Oxford with his master, and for
some time he was Warden of Merton. His book on the heart,
Exercitatio Anatomica de Motu Cordis et Sanguinis, was published in 1628. It is a small volume, but it contains the results
of many years' observation on men and living animals, and
produced a great effect. It at once made obsolete the physiology of Galen, and turned all eyes that could see to the future
instead of to the past.

Harvey points out that, if we multiply the volume of blood
driven forward by each beat of the heart by the number of
beats in half-an-hour, we find that the heart deals in this time
with as much blood as is contained in the whole body. He
therefore infers that the blood must somehow find its way
from the arteries to the veins and so back to the heart:

I began to think whether there might not be *a motion, as it were,
in a circle.* Now this I afterwards found to be true; and I finally saw
that the blood, forced by the action of the left ventricle into the arteries,
was distributed to the body at large and its several parts, in the same
manner as it is sent through the lungs impelled by the right ventricle
into the right pulmonary artery, and that it then passed through the
veins and along the *vena cava*, and so round to the left ventricle in the
manner already indicated, which motion we may be allowed to call
circular.

Harvey was led to his great idea, not by speculation or by
a priori reasoning, but by a series of steps each in turn based
on observations made on the heart by anatomical dissection,
as seen in the living animal, or as he himself says, in "repeated
vivisections". As Vesalius founded modern anatomy, so
Harvey set physiology on its true course of observation and
experiment, and made modern medicine and surgery possible.

[1] The first to do this since Aristotle was Fabricius of Aquapendente (1537–
1619). See Foster, *loc. cit.* p. 36.

To appreciate Harvey's work we must compare it with that of his predecessors and contemporaries, who invoked the aid of natural, vital and animal spirits to explain the functions of the body. Harvey barely mentions these ideas, but treats the problem of the circulation as one of physiological mechanics and solves it as such. His second work, *De Generatione Animalium*, appeared in 1651, and represents the most notable advance in embryology recorded since the time of Aristotle.

Harvey died in 1657, and, having no children, he bequeathed his paternal estate to the Royal College of Physicians, directing them to use the proceeds "to search out and study the secrets of nature".

Harvey's work on the circulation of the blood was soon supplemented by the discovery of the lacteal and lymphatic vessels, which carry the proceeds of digestion into the bloodstream. But his work was only completed when the newly invented microscope was used in physiology. Till the minute structure was thus made visible, it was thought that the arteries delivered the blood into the flesh, which was regarded as a structureless "parenchyma", and that the veins collected it therefrom.

Early compound microscopes gave a distorted and coloured image at any high magnification. But about 1650 simple lenses were much improved, and they made very serviceable instruments of research.

In 1661 Malpighi of Bologna examined microscopically the structure of the lung. He found that the divisions of the windpipe end in dilated air vessels, over the surface of which spread arteries and veins. Eventually, in the lung of a frog, he discovered that the arteries and veins are connected by capillary tubes. "Hence", he says, "it was clear to the senses that the blood flowed away along tortuous vessels and was not poured into spaces, but was always contained within tubules, and that its dispersion is due to the multiple winding of the vessels."[1]

Malpighi also examined microscopically the glands and other organs of the body, and made great contributions to our knowledge of their structure and functions. Harvey showed that the blood swept through the tissues; Malpighi discovered what the tissues were and how the blood swept through them.

[1] Foster, *loc. cit.* p. 97.

He also did much to found modern embryology. Aristotle watched the chick forming in the egg. Fabricius and others repeated his observations, as did Harvey in his later years. But it was Malpighi who gave the first comprehensive description of the microscopic changes which convert an opaque white spot in the egg into the complete living bird.

His work was carried further by A. van Leeuwenhoek (1632–1723), who extended knowledge of capillary circulation, and of muscular fibres. He saw blood corpuscles, spermatozoa and bacteria, and drew figures of them.

The mechanics of muscular motion were first adequately studied by Borelli about 1670, and the irritability of muscles about the same time by Glisson. The latter also disproved the universally held view that a muscle when in action was inflated by "animal spirits". He reached this conclusion by the convincing method of measuring the amount of water the muscle displaced, and thus proving that, instead of being inflated, it actually became smaller in volume.

The study of the circulation of the blood led naturally to the problem of breathing. Galen held that in breathing the air regulates and tempers the heat of the blood, by drawing on an innate store of heat in the heart. The air also, according to him, mixes with blood in the left side of the heart to form "vital spirits".

Borelli, applying the physics of Galileo, Torricelli and Pascal, made clear the mechanics of breathing, and proved that animals die in a vacuum. Hooke showed that the motion of the walls of the chest was not necessary to support life if a current of air be continuously blown over the surfaces of the lungs, and in his *Tractatus de Corde*, published in 1669, Lower announced his discovery that the change in colour from dark purple to bright red—the change which marks the conversion of venous into arterial blood—takes place, not as was thought, in the left side of the heart, but in the lungs. Using Hooke's experiments on artificial respiration, he satisfied himself that the change in colour was due simply to the exposure of blood to the air in the lungs, the blood taking up some of the air.

John Mayow (1643–1679) showed that "a candle enclosed in a flask goes out, although there is still contained in the flask ample abundance of air". He infers that the air is not homogeneous, but contains "a vital fiery and in the highest degree fermentative spirit", which exists also in nitre and in *spiritus acidus* (nitric acid) and may be called *spiritus nitro-aereus* or *igneo-aereus*—clearly our modern oxygen. "Gunpowder is very easily burnt by itself by reason of the igneo-aereal particles existing in it....Sulphureous matter on the contrary can be burnt only with the help of igneo-aereal particles brought to it by the air." He also proved that metal burned into a metallic oxide increased in weight, and concludes that the increase is due to combination with igneo-aereal particles. All this sound work was forgotten, only to be rediscovered a hundred years later by Lavoisier.

Mayow then identified burning and breathing. He showed that a small animal placed in a closed vessel died, and died more quickly if a lighted candle was also placed in the vessel. "It clearly appears that animals exhaust the air of certain vital particles,...that some constituent of the air absolutely necessary to life enters the blood in the act of breathing." This he infers is the nitro-aereal spirit, which by union "with the salino-sulphureous particles of the blood gives rise to the heat of the blood".

All this is a very striking advance on the prevalent ideas. Mayow was a great chemist and a great physiologist; in outlook and knowledge a century in advance of his time.

The contemporary development in the physiology of the brain and nervous system must also be traced briefly. Vesalius accepted the current ideas that the food when absorbed is endowed in the liver with *natural spirit*, that in the heart this natural spirit is converted into *vital spirit* which, in the brain, becomes *animal spirit*, "which is by far the brightest and most delicate, and indeed is a quality rather than an actual thing. And while on the one hand it employs this spirit for the operations of the chief soul, on the other hand it is continually distributing it to the instruments of the senses and of movement by means of nerves, as it were by cords". He shows how, by cutting or ligaturing this or that nerve, the action of this or that muscle can be abolished.

"But", he says, "how the brain performs its functions in imagination, in reasoning, in thinking and in memory...I can form no opinion whatever. Nor do I think that anything more will be found out by anatomy or by the methods of those theologians who deny to brute animals all power of reasoning, and indeed all faculties belonging to what we call the chief soul. For, as regards the structure of the brain, the monkey, dog, horse, cat, and all quadrupeds which I have hitherto examined, and indeed all birds and many kinds of fish, resemble man in almost every particular."

Van Helmont, on the other hand, held that there was no soul residing in plants and in brute beasts, which possess only "a certain vital power...the forerunner of a soul". In man, the sensitive soul is the prime agent of all the functions of the body. It works by means of *archaei* its servants, which, in their turn, act directly in the organs of the body by means of ferments allied to that which gives us wine. The soul dwells in the *archaeus* of the stomach, in some such way as light is present in a burning candle. The sensitive soul is mortal, but co-exists in man with the immortal mind. Van Helmont was a good chemist, but his speculative physiology was not likely to lead to an advance in knowledge.

The "sensitive soul" and "immortal mind" imagined by him are outside and distinct from the animal spirits, which correspond to what might now be called the activities of the nervous tissues. This is true also of the "rational soul" described by the philosopher Descartes, and the distinction enabled him, as will be seen more fully later, to accept and make use of the strictest mechanical conceptions of the nervous phenomena themselves.

Meanwhile, Sylvius applied knowledge gained in chemical experiments to physiology. Like van Helmont, he regarded many changes taking place in the living body as of the nature of ferments. But, whereas van Helmont considered the ferments to be due to subtle agencies whose effects were quite unlike ordinary chemical events, Sylvius denied such differences. To him physiological fermentation was the same in kind as the effervescence he saw when he poured vitriol over chalk. Thus, in opposition to the spiritualistic ideas of van Helmont, Sylvius taught a chemical view of physiology. This enabled him and his pupils to make useful advances in the study of the digestive organs, but it did not greatly help at that time to elucidate the phenomena of the nerves.

Indeed, little advance was made in the physiology of the brain and nervous system till the eighteenth century. The best criticism of the earlier speculations was made by Stensen in 1669. After pointing out the great difficulties which attend the dissection of the brain and the lack of all sound anatomical knowledge, he adds:

> There abounds indeed a rich plenty of men to whom everything is clear. Such, dogmatizing with the utmost confidence, make up and publish the story of the brain and the use of its several parts with the same assuredness as if they had mastered with their actual eyes the structure of so admirable a machine and penetrated into the secrets of the great artificer.

Stensen himself did more than the philosophers and physicians whom he satirized. As the result of his dissections he made one pregnant suggestion, which foreshadows some of the discoveries of the last decades of the nineteenth century:

> If indeed the white substance of which I am speaking be, as in most places it seems to be, wholly fibrous in nature, we must necessarily admit that the arrangement of its fibres is made according to some definite pattern, on which doubtless depends the diversity of sensations and movements.

The use of vegetable drugs in the treatment of disease led to an awakening of interest in the study of plants, a branch of science which was originally a province of the traditional lore of monastery and convent garden. Mediaeval symbolism was slow to relax its grip on botany, where it took the form of the doctrine of "signatures", by which the shape of the leaf or the colour of the flower was regarded as an index or sign of the use designed for the plant by its Creator.

After the Renaissance the increased security of life, the growth of wealth and the development in artistic feeling encouraged the laying out of private parks and gardens, and the more general cultivation of trees, vegetables and flowers. Thus, partly owing to the use of herbs as remedies, partly to a natural curiosity and to a more marked love of beauty and colour, the sixteenth century showed a great development in botanical knowledge.

Botanic gardens were established at Padua in 1545, and afterwards at Pisa, Leyden and elsewhere, and there the rare plants brought home by explorers and adventurers were deposited and cared for. Medicine soon acquired its own gathering grounds and distilleries for herbs. Each Society of Apothecaries had its physic garden, one of which, established by the Apothecaries' Society of London about 1676, yet survives at Chelsea.

Botany   The first observer to depart from the descriptions found in the works of the ancients, and to give accurate accounts drawn from nature, was Valerius Cordus (1515–1544), who in doing so made the first real advance in botany since the days of Dioscorides, fifteen hundred years before.

About this time a number of "herbals" containing descriptions of plants and their properties, medical and culinary, began to appear and to find a place in the libraries of private gentlemen. One famous work, illustrated by woodcuts, was published in England by John Gerard in 1597. Gerard himself was a member of the Court of the Company of Barber Surgeons, and became superintendent of Lord Burghley's gardens at his new house by Stamford Town.

Gilbert of Colchester   The method of experiment was employed in a new direction by William Gilbert of Colchester (1540–1603), Fellow of St John's College, Cambridge, and President of the College of Physicians, who founded the sciences of magnetism and electricity. In his book, *De Magnete*, Gilbert collected all that was known about magnetism, and added many fresh observations of his own.

The magnetic needle seems to have been first discovered by the Chinese, and appears in their literature towards the end of the eleventh century.[1] It was possibly first applied to navigation by Muslim sailors soon afterwards, and was in use in Europe by the twelfth century.

Gilbert investigated the attraction between magnets, and showed that a magnetic needle, when freely suspended, not only set roughly north and south as in the mariner's compass, but also dipped, in England, with its north pole downwards, through an angle depending on the latitude. He pointed out the importance of these results in navigation, and inferred, from his experiments on the set of the magnetic needle, that the Earth itself must act as a huge magnet, with its poles nearly, but not quite, coincident with the geographical poles. He states that, for a uniform lodestone, the strength and range of its magnetism is proportional to its quantity or mass. This seems to be the first realization of mass without reference to weight, and may have given the idea of mass as a separate concept to Kepler and Galileo, and through them to Newton.

[1] Sarton, *loc. cit.* p. 756.

Gilbert also examined the forces developed when certain bodies, such as amber, are rubbed, and he coined the name electricity from the Greek word ἤλεκτρον, amber. To measure these forces he used a light metallic needle balanced on a point, and increased the number of bodies known to show the effect. Besides experimenting, he speculated about the cause of magnetism and electricity. He held that the magnet possesses something like a soul, and the soul of the Earth is its magnetic force. Taking the idea of an aethereal, non-material substance from Greek philosophy, he imagined it to be emitted as an effluvium by the magnet or electrified substance, which by its means embraces neighbouring bodies and draws them towards itself. He extended this idea to explain gravity, the force with which stones are pulled to the ground. In a half mystical way, he applied it also to the motions of the Sun and the planets. Each globe, he thought, had a characteristic spirit within and effused around it, and, by the interaction of these spirits, the orbits of the planets and the order of the cosmos were determined. He accepted the view that the Earth revolves on its axis, and this, too, he explained magnetically; but he was not convinced that the Earth moves round the Sun.

Gilbert of Colchester

Gilbert held the post of Court Physician under Elizabeth and James I; indeed he was awarded a special pension by the Queen to give him leisure to carry out his researches, a notable early appreciation of the value of scientific experiment. His work is mentioned by Bacon in the *Novum Organum* as an example of the experimental method advocated therein.

Impressed by the failure of the scholastic philosophy to advance men's knowledge of and power over nature, and seeing the irrelevance of Aristotle's "final causes" in science, Francis Bacon (1561–1626), Lord Chancellor of England, set himself to consider the theory of this new method of experiment. In order "to extend more widely the limits of the power and greatness of man", he mapped out a course by which progress towards a mastery over nature might be made more sure. He held that, by recording all available facts, making all possible observations, performing all feasible experiments, and then by collecting and tabulating the results by rules which he only very imperfectly formulated, the connections between the phenomena would become manifest and general laws describing their relations would emerge almost automatically.

Francis Bacon

Francis Bacon   Criticism of this method is obvious and easy. There are so
many phenomena to be observed and so many possible experi-
ments to be made that advances in science are seldom achieved
by the pure Baconian method. At an early stage insight and
imagination must come into play; a tentative hypothesis must
be framed in accordance with the facts, a mental process
called induction; its practical consequences must next be
deduced mathematically or by other logical reasoning, and
tested by observation or experiment. If discrepancies appear,
a new guess must be made, and a second hypothesis framed,
and so on till one is found that is in accordance with, or as
we say "explains", not only the primary facts but also all those
brought out by the experiments specially made to test it. The
hypothesis may then be advanced to the rank of a theory,
which may serve to co-ordinate and simplify knowledge,
perhaps for many years. But it is seldom, if ever, safe to say
that a theory is the only possible one which fits the facts; it
is merely an affair of probability. Indeed the facts themselves
may increase in number and complexity as new knowledge
comes to hand, and the theory may have to be modified or
superseded by one more suitable to the enlarged vision of a
later time.

Bacon seems to have had little or no influence on those who
were actually carrying on experimental science, except, perhaps,
on Robert Boyle. Nevertheless, he did something to improve
instructed thought about the scientific problems of his day.
The world had listened to many philosophies, and had seen
no corresponding record of facts wherewith to test them.
Rightly, therefore, in Bacon's eyes, authenticated facts were
the urgent need of the age. Bacon himself made no striking
or successful experimental contribution to natural knowledge,
and his theory and method of science were over-ambitious in
range and inadequate in practice. Yet he was the first to
consider the philosophy of inductive science, and he profoundly
influenced the French Encyclopaedists of the eighteenth
century. In terms of conscious power and statesmanlike
eloquence, he expressed ideas far in advance of his time. The
doctrines of the Schoolmen were both outgrown and outworn;
the world of philosophic thought was astir and ripe for a
change, and Bacon pointed out what was roughly the right
road to a wider and sounder knowledge of nature.

The Copernican theory produced a revolution in astronomy, and indeed in scientific thought generally, but Copernicus was primarily a mathematician and did not add many new facts to the world's store of natural knowledge. The first modern astronomer to make and record details of planetary motions with a new degree of accuracy was Tycho Brahe (1546–1601) of Copenhagen. The year before his death he was joined in his labours by John Kepler (1571–1630), to whom he bequeathed his unique collection of data.

It is usual to regard Kepler's work as consisting of the induction and verification of three statements or "laws" of planetary motion, those three which proved to hold good to a high degree of accuracy, and served as the foundation of Newton's astronomy. But to study only the results which were built into Newtonian science is, on the one hand, to give too modern a cast to our portrait of Kepler, and, on the other, to miss the great historic interest of his attitude of mind. Pythagorean and Platonic influences can be detected underlying the work of Copernicus; in Kepler's writings they lie on the surface, plain for all who read to see.

Kepler's official occupation consisted chiefly in editing the astrological almanacs which were then in favour, and despite his ironical remarks on the value to an astronomer of a lucrative profession, he was a believer in astrology. Nevertheless, he was a distinguished and enthusiastic mathematician, and it was the greater mathematical simplicity and harmony of the Copernican system which converted him thereto. "I have attested it as true in my deepest soul", he says, "and I contemplate its beauty with incredible and ravishing delight."[1] Copernicus' eulogy on the Sun was carried much further by Kepler, who regarded the Sun as God the Father, the sphere of the fixed stars as God the Son, and the intervening aether, through which he thought the power of the Sun impels the planets round in their orbits, as God the Holy Ghost.

Kepler was convinced that God created the world in accordance with the principle of perfect numbers, so that the underlying mathematical harmony, the music of the spheres, is the real and discoverable cause of the planetary motions. This was the true inspiring force in Kepler's laborious life. He was not, as usually represented, tediously searching for

[1] Burtt, *loc. cit.* p. 47.

Kepler   empirical rules to be rationalized by a coming Newton. He was searching for ultimate causes, the mathematical harmonies in the mind of the Creator.

Aristotle traced the essence of things ultimately to qualitative irreducible distinctions, so that a tree, which produces the sensation of greenness in the observer, was to him itself really and essentially green. But to Kepler knowledge must be of quantitative characters or relations, and therefore quantity or number must be the fundamental basis of things and prior to and more important than all other categories.

The three summaries which have survived in science as Kepler's Laws are: (1) the planets travel in paths which are ellipses with the Sun in one focus; (2) the area swept out in any orbit by the straight line joining the centres of the Sun and a planet are proportional to the times; (3) the squares of the periodic times which the different planets take to describe their orbits are proportional to the cubes of their mean distances from the Sun. In these short statements an enormous amount of information about planetary motions acquired by astronomers of his own and former times was summarized and systematized.

Of these three laws Kepler was most pleased with the second. Since each planet was driven by a Constant Divine Cause, Aristotle's Unmoved Mover, it should travel with constant speed, and, although this idea had to be given up in the light of the facts, Kepler was able to "save the principle" by transferring uniformity from the paths to the areas. But to him these were only three out of many mathematical relations revealed by Copernicus' theory.

Another discovery which gave him even greater delight was a second relation in the distances. If a cube be inscribed in the sphere containing the orbit of Saturn, the sphere of Jupiter will just fit within the cube. If a tetrahedron be inscribed in Jupiter's sphere, the sphere of Mars will fit within the tetrahedron, and so on for all the five regular solids and all the six planets. The relation is only roughly true, and the discovery of new planets has destroyed its basis, but to Kepler it gave more joy than the laws for which he is remembered. To him it was a new harmony in the music of the spheres, indeed the true cause of planetary distances being what they are, for to him, as to Plato, God ever geometrizes.

It is one of the ironies of history that a return to the mystical doctrine of numbers should have led Copernicus and Kepler to formulate a system which, through Galileo and Newton, takes us in direct descent to the mechanical philosophy of the French Encyclopaedists in the eighteenth century, and of the German materialists in the nineteenth.

Kepler

Some of the great ideas which had been seething in the minds of men since the Renaissance at last brought practical results in the epoch-making work of Galileo Galilei (1564–1642). Leonardo had foreshadowed the coming spirit of modern science in all the innumerable subjects on which he pondered. Copernicus initiated a revolution in the world of thought. Gilbert showed how the experimental method could add to knowledge. But in Galileo the new spirit went further than in any of his predecessors. With a sound grasp of the new principles, he learned the modern need of concentration, and worked out his carefully delimited problems in a more complete and methodical way than the universal genius of Leonardo could stoop to accomplish. Moreover, unlike Leonardo, he collected and published his researches, and thus gave them at once and for ever to the world. He brought Copernican astronomy, based on an *a priori* principle of mathematical simplicity, to the practical test of the telescope. But above all he combined the experimental and inductive methods of Gilbert with mathematical deduction, and thus discovered and established the true method of physical science.

Galileo

Indeed it is not too much to say that Galileo started modern physical science on the course which has extended unbroken to our own day. In a very real sense he is the first of the moderns; as we read his writings, we instinctively feel at home; we know that we have reached the method of experimental science which still is in use to-day. The old assumption of a complete and rationalized scheme of knowledge, the characteristic of mediaeval Neo-Platonism and scholastic philosophy alike, has been given up. Facts are no longer deduced from, and obliged to conform with, an authoritative and rational synthesis, as in Scholasticism, no longer are they even given meaning thereby, as in the mind of Kepler. Each fact acquired by observation or experiment is accepted as it stands, with its immediate and inevitable consequences, irrespective of the human desire to make the whole of nature at once amenable

Galileo to reason. Concordances between the isolated facts appear but slowly, and the little spheres of knowledge surrounding each fact come into touch here and there, and perhaps coalesce into larger spheres. The welding of all knowledge, scientific or philosophical, into a higher and all-embracing unity, if not seen to be for ever impossible, is relegated to the distant future. Mediaeval Scholasticism was rational; modern science is in essence empirical. The former worshipped the human reason acting within the bounds of authority; the latter accepts brute facts whether reasonable or not.[1]

As an astronomer, Galileo's fame rests on his construction and application of the telescope, and the confirmatory evidence he thus gave to the Copernican system. In 1609 he heard a rumour that a Dutchman had invented a new glass which magnified distant objects. Galileo, from his knowledge of refraction, immediately constructed a similar instrument, and soon made one sufficiently good to magnify to thirty diameters. At once discovery followed discovery.[2] The surface of the moon, instead of being perfectly smooth and unblemished, as held by philosophers, was seen to be covered with markings which gave all the indications of rugged mountains and desolate valleys. Innumerable stars, hitherto invisible, flashed into sight, solving the age-long problem of the Milky Way. Jupiter was seen to be accompanied in its orbit by four satellites with measurable times of revolution, a visible and more complex model of the Earth and its moon moving together round the Sun, as taught by Copernicus. The Professor of Philosophy at Padua refused to look through Galileo's telescope, and his colleague at Pisa laboured before the Grand Duke with logical arguments, "as if with magical incantations to charm the new planets out of the sky".

By means of his telescope Galileo confirmed with sensible facts, which anyone, if he liked, might verify, the new theory of astronomy, which hitherto had been based only on its *a priori* grounds of mathematical simplicity. It was the expression of the heliocentric conclusions drawn from these researches that brought Galileo, when his book had been read and understood, within reach of the Inquisition.

[1] See especially A. N. Whitehead, *Science and the Modern World*, Cambridge, 1927.

[2] Galileo Galilei, *The Sidereal Messenger*, Venice, 1610, quoted in *Readings in the Literature of Science*, Cambridge, 1924.

But his chief and most original work was the foundation of *Galileo* the experimental and mathematical science of dynamics, and in this he showed himself to be a true master of method.[1] Though some advance had been made in statics, especially by Stevinus of Bruges (1586) in his work on the inclined plane and the composition of forces, men's ideas upon motion had hitherto been a confused medley of uninstructed observation and Aristotelian theories. Bodies were thought to be intrinsically heavy or light, and to fall or rise with velocity proportional to their heaviness or lightness because they "sought their natural places" with varying power. In 1591, Galileo, repeating an experiment of Stevinus,[2] dropped a ten-pound weight and a one-pound weight together from the top of the Leaning Tower at Pisa, and showed the incredulous onlookers that, heavy or light, they struck the ground simultaneously.

Copernicus and Kepler had shown that the motion of the Earth and other planets could be expressed in mathematical terms. Galileo felt that parts of the Earth in "local motion" might also move mathematically. So he set himself to discover not *why* things fall, but *how*: in accordance with what mathematical relations. This attitude of mind in itself marks a great achievement in the development of scientific method.

A body falling towards the ground moves with constantly increasing speed. What is the law of the increase? Galileo's first hypothesis, quite reasonable in itself, was that the speed was proportional to the distance fallen through. But he soon discovered that this supposition involved a contradiction, and he therefore tried another, namely, that the speed increased with the time of fall. This hypothesis was found to involve no obvious difficulty, and Galileo proceeded to deduce its consequences, and to compare them with the results of experiment.

The speed of a body falling freely proved too great for easy and accurate measurement with the instruments then available, and it was necessary to bring the speed within convenient limits. Galileo first convinced himself that a body falling down an inclined plane acquired the same velocity as though it had fallen through the same vertical height. He then experimented with inclined planes, and found that the results of his

---

[1] G. Galilei, *Discorsi e dimostrazioni matematiche*, Leyden, 1638. See also E. Mach, *Die Mechanik in ihre Entwickelung*, 1883, Eng. trans. T. J. McCormack, London, 1902. [2] Whewell, *loc. cit.* vol. II, p. 46.

Galileo measurements agreed with those calculated from the hypothesis that the speed is proportional to the time of fall, and its mathematical consequence that the space described increases as the square of the time.

Another equally important result, which had already been recognized vaguely by Leonardo, followed from Galileo's experiments with inclined planes. He found that after running down one plane, a ball will run up another to a height equal to that of its starting-point, whatever be the slope, provided that friction be negligible. The second plane may be made as long as we please, but still, if its height be no more than the height of the first plane, the ball will reach its end. The height alone matters; the speed of the ball is acquired by virtue of its descent, and, in the absence of resistance, is not diminished unless the ball rises. If the second plane be horizontal, the ball will run along it steadily with uniform velocity, until checked by friction or some other opposing force.

To appreciate the importance of this result, it is necessary to remember that, except perhaps by the early atomists and Plato in antiquity and a few like Leonardo and Benedetti (1585) in modern times, it was assumed that every motion required a continual force to maintain it. The planets had to be kept in motion by Aristotle's Unmoved Mover, or by Kepler's action of the Sun, exerted through the aether. By Galileo's investigation it became clear that it is not motion, but the creation or destruction of motion, or a change in its direction, which requires the exertion of some external force: what Plato assumed, Galileo proved. When matter is endowed with inertia, and the planetary system is set in motion, it needs no force to keep the planets moving; though some cause is required to explain their continual deviation from a straight path as they swing round the Sun in their orbits. Never before had it been possible even to formulate the problem correctly, but now the way was open to a solution and the man was at hand. In 1642, the year that Galileo died, Isaac Newton was born.

When we examine the philosophic ideas which in Galileo's mind underlay his scientific work, we can trace his affinities with Kepler on one side and with Newton on the other. Like Kepler, he looked for mathematical relations in phenomena, not however in a search for mystical causes, but in order to

understand the immutable laws in conformity with which *Galileo*
nature works, caring nothing "whether her reasons be or be
not understandable by man".[1]

Here we see at once how far Galileo had travelled from the
homocentric philosophy of Scholasticism, in which the whole
of nature is made for man. To Galileo, on the other hand, it
appeared that God thinks into nature this rigorous mathematical necessity, and then through nature so makes "the
human understanding that it, though at the price of great
exertion, might ferret out a few of her secrets".

Euclid and his predecessors had reduced geometry to mathematical order. Hipparchus, Copernicus and Kepler had shown
that astronomy could be reduced to geometry. Galileo set out
to do the same for terrestrial dynamics, to reduce them also
to a branch of mathematics. In creating a new science from
the confused medley of observed phenomena and vague ideas
which form its subject matter, the first step is always to pick
out concepts which can be given exact definition, good at all
events for a time, and if possible in a form which enables us
to submit them to quantitative mathematical treatment. In
order to put his problem of the acceleration of falling bodies
into a shape possible of investigation, Galileo first gave exact
mathematical form to the old concepts of distance and time.
Aristotle and the Schoolmen were chiefly interested in the
ultimate cause of things and treated terrestrial motion, not as
analogous to the celestial motions of astronomy, but as a
branch of metaphysics. Hence motion had been analysed in
terms of substance, with the help of such vague ideas as action,
efficient cause, end, and natural place. Little was said or
thought about the motion itself, save that a few distinctions
were drawn between natural and violent motion, motion in a
straight line and motion in a circle. All this was useless to
Galileo, who wished to study not why but how motion
occurred. The qualitative method made space and time somewhat unimportant categories in Aristotelian thought. Galileo
gave them that primary and fundamental character which
they have held in physical science since his day. He may
have realized further that there was some quantity in
inertia other than weight, but an exact definition of mass
was first given by Newton, and the concept of energy was

[1] Burtt, *loc. cit.* p. 64.

Galileo only formulated and defined in the middle years of the nineteenth century.

Nevertheless the first and most difficult step in mathematical dynamics was taken by Galileo, the step which passed from the vague teleological categories, into which Scholasticism analysed change and movement, to the definite mathematical concepts of time and space. Professor Burtt holds that this step has led to many of our present philosophic difficulties. It may perhaps be replied that it has revealed and clarified difficulties obscured and concealed by Aristotelian physics. However that may be, it is certain that, without the new outlook of Galileo, dynamical science could not have developed as it did. It was not Galileo's fault that some of his followers over-estimated the bearing of that science on the problem of metaphysical reality. Indeed he was content to wait in acknowledged ignorance upon questions that can only be answered by rash speculation or deduced from philosophic systems. He confessed that he knew nothing about the nature of force, the cause of gravity, the origin of the Universe. Rather than express extravagances, he declared it better "to pronounce that wise, ingenious and modest sentence, 'I know it not'".

Perhaps an equally great change was made by Galileo in the philosophy of the other branches of physics. Kepler had accepted the distinction between the primary or inseparable qualities of bodies, and the secondary, which are less real and fundamental. Galileo went further, and realized that secondary qualities are merely subjective effects on the senses, and unlike primary qualities which, he held, cannot be separated in any way from the bodies of which they are qualities. Here he comes into line with the ancient atomists, whose philosophy had recently been revived.

I feel myself impelled by necessity, as soon as I conceive a piece of matter or corporal substance, of conceiving that in its own nature it is bounded and figured by such and such a figure, that in relation to others it is large or small, that it is in this or that place, in this or that time, that it is in motion or remains at rest, that it touches or does not touch another body, that it is single, few or many; in short by no imagination can a body be separated from such conditions. But that it must be white or red, bitter or sweet, sounding or mute, of a pleasant or unpleasant odour, I do not perceive my mind forced to acknowledge it accompanied by such conditions; so if the senses were not the escorts

perhaps the reason or the imagination by itself would never have arrived   *Galileo*
at them. Hence I think that those tastes, odours, colours, etc. on the
side of the object in which they seem to exist, are nothing else but mere
names, but hold their residence solely in the sensitive body; so that
if the animal were removed, every such quality would be abolished and
annihilated.[1]

In this line of thought Galileo rediscovered the principle so
tersely expressed by Democritus in terms of atoms and a void.[2]
Galileo too accepted the atomic theory of matter, and discussed
in some detail how differences in number, weight, shape and
velocity in atoms may cause differences in taste, smell, or
sound.

Here again Galileo turned away from the picture of nature
as it appeared to his contemporaries. The very qualities which
to the plain man are most real, colour, sound, taste, smell,
hotness or coldness, became to Galileo merely sensations in the
observer's mind, produced by the arrangement or movement
of atoms, themselves subject to immutable mathematical
necessity. The atoms, though blind slaves of nature, are, to
him at least, real, the secondary qualities are but phantoms
of the senses. It was left for Bishop Berkeley a century later
to suggest that, in ultimate analysis, the primary qualities also
are but mental concepts based on sense perceptions.

Galileo's treatment of these problems has been blamed for
the dualist and materialist philosophies which most certainly
developed from it. To do so is perhaps to fall into the same
errors that ensnared the French Encyclopaedists: to mistake
the relations both of one of the sciences to the whole, and of
science in general to the problem of metaphysical reality. But
these problems will be dealt with more fully in later chapters
of this book.

René Descartes (1596–1650), a younger contemporary of   *From Descartes*
Galileo, laid the foundations of modern critical philosophy, and   *to Boyle*
invented new mathematical methods useful in physical science.
He was born in Touraine, of a family of the demi-noblesse;
his chief work was accomplished during a twenty years'
sojourn in Holland, and he died at Stockholm in the service of
Queen Christina of Sweden.

Descartes showed how much unverified assumption lay
beneath the generally received philosophic ideas. He turned

---

[1] Burtt, *loc. cit.* p. 75.   [2] See above, p. 26.

from the still powerful mediaeval accumulations of interwoven thought, built up from Greek philosophy and Patristic doctrine, and tried to raise a new philosophy, free from all occult ideas and based only on human consciousness and experience, ranging from the direct mental apprehension of God to observation and experiment in the physical world. He regarded the methods of geometry and arithmetic with its algebraic developments as models for other sciences.

In mathematics he took the great step of applying the processes of algebra to geometry. Hitherto each problem had to be solved by special treatment and a fresh display of ingenuity, but Descartes introduced a general method by which this isolation was broken down. The primary idea of co-ordinate geometry is easily stated. Two straight lines, *OX* and *OY*, are drawn at right angles to each other from a fixed point *O*, or origin. These lines may then be used as axes to specify the position of any point *P* in their plane by stating the distance *OM* or x of the point from one axis, and its distance *PM* or y from the other. The distances x and y are called the co-ordinates of the point, and different relations between x and y correspond to different curves in the plane of the diagram. Thus if y increases proportionately as x increases,

Fig. 2

that is if y is equal to x multiplied by a constant, we pass evenly over the diagram in a straight line. If y is equal to x^2 multiplied by a constant, we have a parabola, and so on. Such equations may be treated algebraically and the results interpreted geometrically. In this way the solution of many physical problems, insoluble or very difficult before, was made possible for those who attacked them. Descartes' treatise on geometry was studied eagerly by Newton, and had much influence on his youthful mind.

Descartes regarded physics as reducible to mechanism, and even considered the human body as being analogous to a machine. He accepted Harvey's discovery of the circulation of the blood through the arteries and veins, but did not believe it was driven round by the contraction of the heart. He thought that the human machine was kept at work by heat generated in the heart by natural processes. Thus to him the soul (*l'âme raisonnable*) is quite distinct from the body (*machine de terre*) which it inhabits and governs. He held the Galenic theory that the blood generates in the brain "a very subtle air or wind called the animal spirits". But to him, as to van Helmont, the "animal spirits" are not the soul, though they fit the brain to receive the impressions of the soul and also of external objects, and then flow from the brain through the nerves to the muscles and give movement to the limbs.

From Descartes to Boyle

Thus Descartes was the first to formulate complete dualism, that sharp distinction between soul and body, mind and matter, which afterwards became so general a belief and so important a philosophy. Before his day, and indeed among many for some time afterwards, the soul was regarded as of the nature of air or fire; mind and matter differed more in degree than in kind.

Descartes made an attempt to apply the known principles of terrestrial mechanics to celestial phenomena, and here, in spite of his main philosophical position, he seems to have based his treatment on the Greek and scholastic ideas of antithesis. He contrasted the world of matter with the world of spirits. Spirits are personal, discontinuous: matter must therefore be impersonal, continuous, and its essence must be extension. The physical universe must be a closely packed plenum, with no empty spaces. In such a world motion can only be impressed on one body by contact with another, and can only occur in closed circuits; there is no vacuum into which a body can find room to pass. Hence Descartes framed his famous theory of vortices in a primary matter or aether, invisible but filling all space. As a straw floating on water is caught in an eddy and whirled to the centre of motion, so a falling stone is drawn to the Earth and a satellite towards its planet, while the Earth and the planet, with their attendant and surrounding vortices, are whirled in a greater vortex round the Sun.

At a later date Newton showed mathematically that the properties of Cartesian vortices were inconsistent with observation. For instance, the periodic times of different parts of a vortex must be in the duplicate ratio of the distances from the centre, and this must hold good if the planets in their vortices are to be carried round in the Sun's vortex. The relation, however, cannot be reconciled with Kepler's third law, which, as explained above, tells us that the squares of the periodic times are in proportion to the cubes of the mean distances. Nevertheless, this theory of vortices obtained great vogue before, and indeed after, the publication of Newton's work. It was a bold attempt to reduce the stupendous problem of the sky to dynamics, and as such made its mark on the history of scientific thought. It reduced the physical Universe to a vast machine, expressible, though as Newton showed, inaccurately, in mathematical terms.

Descartes' vortices, which produced motion by contact, seemed to his contemporaries much more mechanically comprehensible than forces acting at a distance to produce acceleration, as imagined by Galileo, and afterwards rationalized by Newton, for neither Galileo nor Newton explained the cause or mode of operation of the forces.

Descartes' machine was fundamentally different from the still prevalent views of Plato and Aristotle and the Schoolmen, according to whom God had created the world in order that, through man the crown of it all, the whole process might return to God. In Descartes' scheme, God endowed the Universe with motion at the beginning, and afterwards allows it to run spontaneously, though in accordance with His Will. It is pictured as material rather than spiritual, indifferent rather than teleological. God, ceasing to be the Supreme Good, is relegated to the position of a First Cause.

To Descartes, as to Galileo, the primary qualities, chief of which is extension, are mathematical realities, the secondary are mere translations of the primary by the human senses. But thought is as real as matter—*cogito ergo sum*. Hence Descartes arrived at a clear-cut dualism, shown also in his physiology. On one side there is a world of bodies, their essence being extension; on the other there is the inner realm of thought: *res extensa* as opposed to *res cogitans*. To Descartes matter is really dead and possesses no activity except motion derived from God in the beginning. Some who have called themselves materialists are in analysis pantheists, but Descartes, on one side of his dualism, is a real philosophic materialist, with no idea that the particles of matter are in any sense alive.

Cartesian dualism raises the question of the interrelation of these apparently unrelated entities, mind and matter. How can the unextended, immaterial mind know and produce changes in the extended, material world? How can material *From Descartes* things produce immaterial sensations? The answer of Descartes *to Boyle* and his followers was, in effect, that God had made things so; and for those who find themselves in dualism, there is much to be said for that answer.

Descartes' system was criticized by Thomas Hobbes (1588–1679), philosophically an extreme nominalist, who, after visiting Galileo, developed the new dynamical science into a mechanical philosophy. Not understanding the exact method of mathematical dynamics, Hobbes thought it applicable to all existence. He would have none of the Cartesian dualism: the brain was the organ of thought, and the only reality was matter in motion. Either ignoring or not seeing the difficulties, Hobbes took sensation, thought and consciousness as phantasms due to the action of atoms in the brain.

Hobbes was the first great modern exponent of a mechanical philosophy, and he met with much ignorant obloquy and some instructed criticism. The Cambridge Platonists pointed out that a theory which made extension and its modes the only real properties of bodies could not explain life and thought, and tried to reconcile religion and mechanical philosophy by an apotheosis of space. This process was carried further by Malebranche, who identified Infinite Space with God Himself, a substitute for the Aristotelian Pure Form or Absolute Actuality. Spinoza held a doctrine of one infinite substance, of which all finite existences are modes or limitations. God is thus the immanent cause of a pantheistic Universe, and the Cartesian dualism of mind and matter is resolved in a higher unity when viewed *sub specie aeternitatis*. In one shape or another contemporary philosophers escaped from their growing difficulties by the appeal to God. Nevertheless, Hobbes' influence produced its effect on scientific thought.

The new theories were well discussed by Sir Kenelm Digby, who ridiculed the Aristotelian essential qualities, and held with Galileo that all phenomena were to be explained by particles "working by means of locall Motion". Again, the implications of the new mathematical method of physics introduced by Galileo were clearly set forth in the lectures of Isaac Barrow (1630–1677), Newton's teacher and predecessor in the Lucasian Professorship at Cambridge. The object of science is to study the sensible realm so far as it is intelligible, especially so far as it shows quantitative continuity, and mathematics is the art of measurement. Thus physics, so far as it is a science, is wholly mathematical. The best type of mathematics is geometry. Weights, forces and times, quantities which had become important since Galileo, are difficult to relate to the concept of body as being that which is extended. Barrow said that these quantities are in some sense extended because they can be treated as geometrical quantities. Space and time are absolute, infinite and eternal, because God is omnipresent and everlasting. Space extends without limit continuously, and time flows for ever evenly and independently of sensible motions. Here we meet the first clear formulation of the ideas of absolute time and space as held by Newton. It is interesting to see that they arose in connection with a religious exposition. Time and space are represented by Barrow as being independent of human perception and knowledge, existing in their own right, save in their relation to God. As Professor Burtt says: "From being a realm of substances in qualitative and teleological relations, the world of nature had definitely become a realm of bodies moving mechanically in space and time".[1] Nevertheless, Barrow, Newton and their immediate followers did not deduce a mechanical, anti-religious philosophy from their new mechanical science.

A useful reminder that all could not be reduced to simple mathematical terms was given by Robert Boyle (1627–1691), the physicist and chemist. Boyle proved the important fact that air is a material substance having weight, but he is chiefly remembered for his discovery that the volume of a given quantity of air is inversely proportional to the pressure, and for the Irish epitaph in which, it is said, he was described as Father of Chemistry and Uncle of the Earl of Cork. He was also a philosopher of a very moderate, pleasing and English variety.

As a man of science he carried on the experimentalist tradition of Gilbert and Harvey, and he accepted the theory of experimental method set forth by "our great Verulam". He looked for relations between qualities immediately perceived without necessarily seeking for ultimate causes, whether those causes be scholastic or mathematically mechanical. To explain a fact is merely to deduce it from something else better

[1] Burtt, *loc. cit.* p. 154.

known. In particular he wished to deal thus with the chemistry
of common things without reference to the prevailing half-
mystical theories of chemical principles or elements. He perceived the importance of the atomic theory recently revived
by Gassendi, sought to reconcile it with the Cartesian elements
of space, and used it in his chemical speculations and in his
physics to explain the phenomena of heat.

Boyle accepted, as indeed he must, the view that "secondary
qualities" are only phantoms of the sensations, but he justly
pointed out that after all "there are *de facto* in the world certain
sensible and rational beings that we call men". Since, then,
man with his senses is a part of the Universe, the secondary
qualities are as real as the primary. Here Boyle, from an
opposite side, touched a result reached by Berkeley, and,
moreover, used an argument which seems still valid. The
mechanical world and the thinking world are both parts of the
whole world which philosophy has to face. It may be necessary
to treat them as entirely separate from each other in order to
bring the problem within the compass of human understanding;
but the separation is due to our need of simplifying the problem by treating it successively from different aspects. A better
mind than ours might be able to see the world steadily and
see it whole.

Boyle expressed his philosophy in religious terms. Man's
rational soul, which bears the image of its Divine Maker, is
"a nobler and more valuable being than the whole corporeal
world". God not only made the world in the beginning, but
His "general concourse" is continually needed to keep it in
being and at work. This, the physical aspect of the Christian
doctrine of immanence, is a partial return to the old Indian
and Arabic idea of continual creation. The immediate causes
are mechanical, but the ultimate causes are non-mechanical.

As an experimental physicist Boyle improved the air-pump
invented by von Guericke, and used this "Pneumatical
Engine" in his work on the "Spring and Weight of the Air";
he observed the effect of atmospheric pressure on the boiling-
point of water; he collected many new facts about electricity
and magnetism; he improved the thermometer by sealing it
hermetically, and recorded the unvarying high temperature of
the healthy human body; he recognized in heat the results of
a "brisk" molecular agitation. As a chemist he distinguished

a mixture from a compound; he prepared phosphorus, and actually collected hydrogen in a vessel over water, though he described it as "air generated *de novo*"; he obtained acetone and isolated methyl alcohol from the products of the distillation of wood; he studied the form of crystals as a guide to chemical structure.

But Boyle's greatest advance on the general outlook of his day is to be found in his rejection of the survival in Scholasticism of the old idea of the four "elements", and also of the alternative chemical hypothesis that the basis of substances is to be sought in the "principles" or "essences" of salt, sulphur and mercury. In his more modern application of the term, none of these were true elements.

His ideas are set forth in a dialogue in a book first published in 1661 and entitled *The Sceptical Chymist: or Chymico-Physical Doubts and Paradoxes, touching the Experiments whereby Vulgar Spagirists are wont to Endeavour to Evince their Salt, Sulphur and Mercury to be the True Principles of Things.* Boyle's spokesman thus explains his position:

Notwithstanding the subtile reasonings I have met with in the books of the Peripatetiks, and the pretty experiments that have been shew'd me in the Laboratories of Chymists, I am of so diffident or dull a Nature as to think that if neither of them can bring more cogent arguments to evince the truth of their assertion than are wont to be brought; a Man may rationally enough retain some doubts concerning the very number of those materiall Ingredients of mixt bodies, which some would have us call Elements and others Principles.

It is pointed out that fire, which has been assumed to resolve things into their elements, really produces very different effects at different degrees of heat, and often gives rise to new bodies which are clearly also complex. Gold withstands fire and certainly yields neither salt, sulphur nor mercury, but it can be alloyed with other metals, or dissolved in aqua regis, and yet recovered in its original form, suggesting unalterable atoms of gold, which survive different combinations, rather than Aristotelian elements or Spagirist principles. A cautious proposition is offered: "It may likewise be granted, that those distinct Substances, which Concretes generally either afford or are made up of, may without very much Inconvenience be call'd the Elements or Principles of them". Boyle thus broke away from all previous association of ideas, and formulated a modest definition of an element which might still be used,

despite the revolutions which have changed the face of *From Descartes*
chemistry since he wrote. Boyle himself did not exploit his *to Boyle*
own ideas experimentally, but others made unconscious use of
them, and, a century after Boyle's day, they were adopted by
Lavoisier, and became the basis of modern chemistry.

Before leaving the mathematical and physical science of this *Pascal*
period, it is necessary to refer briefly to a French experimentalist, who was somewhat outside the line of thought we
have been tracing. Blaise Pascal (1623–1662), most widely
known as a theologian, was the founder of the mathematical
theory of probability, the study of which, originating in a
discussion concerning games of chance, has proved to be of
great importance in recent science and philosophy, as well as
in the subject of social statistics. Indeed the intellectual basis
of all empirical knowledge may be said to be a matter of
probability, expressible only in terms of a bet.

Pascal also experimented on, and subsequently wrote a
treatise concerning the equilibrium of fluids. Under his
direction a barometer (an instrument newly invented by
Torricelli in 1643) was carried up the Puy de Dôme, and it
was shown that the height of the mercury column diminished
as the instrument was taken up the mountain and the
pressure of the atmosphere became less. Thus the column is
held up by the pressure of the air, and not by nature's "abhorrence of a vacuum", as taught by the Aristotelians. The
invention of the barometer and this verification of its theory
together constituted the chief advance made in the science
of hydrostatics since the days of Archimedes, whose work had
been repeated and extended by Stevinus and Galileo.

No account of the two centuries which followed the Re- *Witchcraft*
naissance would be complete without some reference to the
belief in witchcraft.[1] The practice of magic is of course prehistoric, and in former chapters we have seen the important
place it filled and fills in the life of primitive men. It may
indeed form the matrix of ideas from which both early religions
and natural science crystallized out. But, when the Church
first conquered the world, magical fertility cults and other
forms of witchcraft were regarded by intelligent men as relics

[1] See W. T. Lecky, *History of Rationalism*; Margaret Alice Murray, *The
Witch Cult in Western Europe*, Oxford, 1921; G. L. Kittredge, *Witchcraft in
Old and New England*, Cambridge, Mass., 1929; C. L'Estrange Ewen, *Indict-
ments for Witchcraft*, 1559–1736, London, 1929.

Witchcraft of paganism and not much feared. Saint Boniface (680–755) classed belief in witches among the wiles of the Devil, and the laws of Charlemagne made it murder to put anyone to death on a charge of witchcraft. The Church, too, took a lenient view—to call up Satan knowing it to be wrong was not heresy; it was merely sin.

But in the later Middle Ages, the Devil became more prominent. The magic of fertility cults revived in connection with Manichaean heresies till Satan became a disinherited Lucifer, an object of worship to the oppressed. Saint Thomas Aquinas exercised his subtle ingenuity in explaining away the former attitude of the Church towards witchcraft, and argued that, while it had been declared heresy to believe that the Devil could create *natural* thunderstorms, it was not contrary to the Catholic Faith to hold that, with God's permission, he could make *artificial* ones. Pope Innocent VIII in 1484 gave the formal sanction of the Church to the popular belief in intercourse with Satan or his demons, and in the active evil powers of sorcerers and witches. All such sinners then became heretics, and a new and terrible weapon was forged for orthodoxy: heretics could be declared sorcerers and popular fury roused against them. Some of the victims, honestly holding their Manichaean heresy or primitive cult as a religion, went to the stake as martyrs for practising its rites. Many others were falsely accused.

At the Reformation these ideas were taken over by the Protestants, who could use the Scriptural injunction "Thou shalt not suffer a witch to live" without having to explain away ancient Church canons which threw doubt on the reality of witchcraft. Protestants vied with Romanists in hunting witches. On the Continent, where confessions and accusations against others were legally and regularly obtained by torture, nearly all of those accused confessed. In England, where torture was only legal for the Prerogative Courts and denied to the Common Law, they mostly died protesting their innocence. The total number of victims for the whole of Europe in two hundred years is variously estimated at three-quarters of a million upwards. It was difficult for those who were accused to escape. If they pleaded guilty, they were forthwith burnt alive; if not, they were tortured till they confessed.

In *Malleus Maleficarum*, a fifteenth-century text-book for

Inquisitors, may be seen an account of the methods to be used   *Witchcraft*
in trying witches.[1] The barbarity and perfidy of the legal
processes described are almost beyond belief. Any means of
obtaining a confession are authorized. Both before and after
torture the judge should promise the accused her life, without
telling her that she will be imprisoned. The promise should be
kept for a time, but then she should be burned. In other
cases the judge should promise to be merciful, "with the
mental reservation that he means he will be merciful to himself
or to the State".

Very few ventured to risk a dreadful death by protesting
publicly against the mania. Perhaps the first was the physician
Cornelius Agrippa (1486–1535), and possibly the second was
John Weyer, physician to Duke William of Cleves, on whose
protection he depended. In 1563 Weyer published a book to
prove that so-called witchcraft is usually due to delusions
induced by demons, who take advantage of the weaknesses
of women to bring about superstitious cruelties and the
shedding of innocent blood in which they delight.[2] Reginald
Scot, a Kentish squire, in his *Discoverie of Witchcraft* (1584),
took the modern, common-sense view that the whole thing is
a mixture of ignorance, illusion, roguery and false accusation.
Scot's book was reprinted several times, and for a while did
"make great impressions on the magistracy and clergy".[3]
A Jesuit, Father Spee, accompanied nearly two hundred
victims to the stake at Würzburg in less than two years.[4]
Horrified at the experience, he declared that he was convinced
they were all innocent. They had made the usual confession
because they preferred to die rather than be tortured again.
In 1631 he published anonymously a book in which he said
that "Canons, Doctors, Bishops of the Church could all be
made to confess to sorcery by the tortures used".

But these brave men, whose names deserve to be held in

[1] *Malleus Maleficarum*, translated into English by Montague Summers,
London, 1928; review in the *Nation and Athenæum*, November 24th, 1928.
The translator, according to the reviewer, believes in witchcraft, and defends
the methods of trial on account of the "horrid craft, foul sorceries, and devilish
commerce" of the witches.

[2] E. T. Withington, "Dr John Weyer and the Witch Mania", *Studies in
the History and Method of Science*, Oxford, 1917.

[3] Art. "Scot", in *Dictionary of National Biography*.

[4] Withington, *loc. cit.*

Witchcraft everlasting remembrance, could not stop the madness which had infected all classes. James I wrote a book on witchcraft in which he reprobated Weyer and Scot; even great physicians like Harvey and Sir Thomas Browne assisted at the examination of witches, and the orgy of torture and fire went on all over Europe till the end of the seventeenth century or later. The whole story forms one of the blackest and most disgraceful pages in the history of mankind.

The belief in witchcraft decayed with as little apparent reason as it arose. The civilized world gradually discovered that it had ceased to believe in the existence of witches even before it had given up the practice of burning them. It was not that the world grew more tolerant or more humane, but that it had become more sceptical, and was ceasing to fear the power of a witch. It was indeed preparing itself for the rationalistic philosophy and the cold intellectualism of the eighteenth century, which, here at any rate, have one good deed to their credit. Clearly this change of attitude was due chiefly to the advance of science, which slowly defined the limits of man's mastery over nature, and disclosed the methods by which this mastery is attained. This stage was only reached in later years, and the great period dealt with in this chapter was disfigured throughout by the irrational belief in witchcraft.

The Origins of Science In this chapter we have seen at last the true beginnings of modern science. At the Renaissance natural science was still a branch of philosophy; but during the period just reviewed it succeeded in finding its own method of observation and experiment, illumined where such methods are applicable by mathematical analysis. Copernicus and Kepler, it is true, still sought ultimate causes in mathematical harmony, and this train of thought persisted long after the time of Newton in a tendency to think that when a phenomenon could be expressed quantitatively in mathematical terms it was explained philosophically as well as scientifically. This tendency, however, did not hamper the experimentalists. They cast off the gilded chains of a rational, universal synthesis, whether Aristotelian or Platonic, and thus became free to accept facts humbly, even though the facts could not be incorporated in a general scheme of knowledge. Here and there the facts began to fit together like the pieces of a puzzle, till parts of a pattern emerged. In the next period this movement was carried on in Newton's formulation of the laws of gravity, the first great scientific synthesis, and then perhaps swung too far in the exaggerated mechanical philosophy of the French Encyclopaedists of the eighteenth century.

Chapter IV

THE NEWTONIAN EPOCH

The State of Science in 1660—Scientific Academies—Newton and Gravitation—Mass and Weight—Improvements in Mathematics—Physical Optics and Theories of Light—Newton and Philosophy—Mathematics and Astronomy in the Eighteenth Century—Chemistry—Botany, Zoology and Physiology—Geographical Discovery—From Locke to Kant—Determinism and Materialism.

The State of Science in 1660

WE have now reached the most important time in the early development of modern science, for by Newton's supreme achievement the work of Galileo and of Kepler was incorporated with that of Newton himself in the first great physical synthesis. It may be well to sketch in bare outline the state of science and philosophy to which Europe had been brought by the changes described in the preceding chapters.

The scholastic structure of universal knowledge, useful as it was as a training in rationalism, had long become inadequate. It had been shaken by the revival of nominalism by Duns Scotus and William of Occam, by the Neo-Platonic movement which gave a philosophic basis for the work of Copernicus and Kepler, and finally by the results of the mathematical and experimental methods of Galileo, Gilbert and their followers. Gilbert and Harvey had shown how experiment could be used empirically, and Galileo had proved that mathematical simplicity, which was to Copernicus and Kepler the underlying meaning of celestial phenomena, could be discovered also in terrestrial motion. The scholastic substances and causes, in terms of which motion had been loosely described in attempts to explain *why* things move, were thus replaced by time, space and force, concepts now first clearly defined and used mathematically to discover *how* things move, and to measure the actual velocities and accelerations of moving bodies.

Galileo had also proved experimentally that no continual exertion of force was needed to keep a body in motion. Once started it would travel forward in virtue of an innate quality somehow connected with weight. Here Galileo touched the concept of mass and inertia, and though he did not define it clearly, his observations on falling bodies were enough, if properly understood, to show its exact relation with weight. But the pride of place given by the Scholastics to the Aristotelian substance and qualities had definitely passed to matter and motion. The mystical meaning assigned to mathematical harmonies by Copernicus and Kepler was in process of being transmuted into the idea that when a change could be expressed mathematically in terms of matter and motion it could also be explained mechanically, either by Galileo's forces or by contact in some such way as Descartes imagined in his vortices. Boyle could still in 1661 argue against the scholastic concepts as ideas to be reckoned with in chemistry; in physics they were dead, though not yet buried, and echoes of old controversies are to be heard in the writings of Newton and his contemporaries. The power of the new mathematical method in dynamics became more evident when, in 1673, Huygens published his researches on gravity, the pendulum, centrifugal forces and the centre of oscillation.

The general ideas of the atomic theory were adopted by Galileo, and the form given to it by Epicurus was revised and expounded more fully by Gassendi. This brought the conception of nature as being fundamentally composed of matter in motion, first realized in the large-scale phenomena of dynamics and astronomy, into man's picture of the intimate structure of bodies. The atomic theory was not necessary for Galileo's dynamics, but it fitted in well with the general scientific outlook which followed from his work.

Another Greek concept which was beginning to play its part in seventeenth century thought was that of an inter-planetary aether. Kepler invoked it to explain how the Sun kept the planets moving; Descartes saw it in the guise of a subtle fluid or primary matter, which formed the vortices of his celestial machine, and thus provided for weight and other qualities not derivable from pure extension; Gilbert used it to explain magnetic attraction, and Harvey as a means of conveying heat from the Sun to the heart and blood of living animals.

The idea of aether was still confused with Galen's concept of aethereal or psychic spirits, which was used by the mystic school in an attempt to explain the nature of being.[1] It must

---

[1] A. J. Snow, *Matter and Gravity in Newton's Physical Philosophy*, Oxford, 1926, p. 170.

be remembered that the modern distinction between matter and spirit had not become clear. The "soul", the "animal spirits", and similar concepts were still regarded as "emanations", "vapours", things to us material. The unity of matter and spirit was thus maintained, except by Descartes, who was the first to see plainly an essential distinction between matter extended in space and the thinking mind. For most men of the period, the line seems to have been drawn between solids and liquids, on the one side, and air, fire, aether and spirit on the other. Thus, to explain phenomena in terms of "aether" was to leave room for direct Divine interposition.

The current ideas are well shown by Gilbert, who supposed that magnetic forces are due to effluvia which draw bodies to the magnet, and that gravity is of the same nature as magnetic forces, each body possessing a "soul", which emanates through space and draws all things unto it.

Finally we must remember that all competent men of science and almost all philosophers of the middle of the seventeenth century looked on the world from the Christian standpoint. The idea of an antagonism between religion and science is of a later date. Gassendi in reviving atomism was careful to avoid the connection with atheism given to it by the ancients. Descartes, who was accused by his opponents of having devised so effective a cosmic mechanism that it left no room for Providential control, held that the mathematical laws of nature had been established by God, Who could alternatively be reached through the world of thought. Thomas Hobbes, it is true, confined philosophy to the positive knowledge gained by natural science, attacked theology, and classified religion as accepted superstition. Yet even he agrees that religion based on Holy Scripture should be established and enforced by the State. His attitude, however, was exceptional. Speaking generally, the fundamental theistic assumption was made by all enquirers, not for purposes of apologetic, but because it was regarded as one of the universally accepted data with which any theory of the Cosmos to be true must necessarily conform.

Again, we must not forget that there were still many survivals of mediaeval ways of thought. We have seen that Boyle found it necessary to argue against scholastic ideas of chemistry no less than against those of the "Spagirists".

Astrology was still taken seriously. The Civil War gave opportunity to astrologers to find, in the chances and changes of the
times, almost certain fulfilment of any prophecy they made.[1]
Even Newton, in his early days, seems to have thought astrology
worth investigating. When he matriculated at Cambridge in
1660 and was asked what he wished to study, he is said to
have replied: "Mathematics, because I wish to test judicial
astrology".[2] Here we have a vivid illustration of the change
in mental outlook which took place during Newton's life, a
change chiefly produced by Newton's own work. Although
astrological works, especially in the form of almanacs, continued to be issued long after his time, by the end of the
seventeenth century they appealed only to the ignorant.

There were other influences which helped to mould Newton's
intellectual environment. The new learning, for long blocked
by the Aristotelians, had by this time found its way into some
of the Universities. The number of those concerned with
natural philosophy was increasing rapidly, and one sign of this
increase was the establishment of societies or academies consisting of men who met together to discuss the new subjects
and to further their progress. The earliest of such societies
appeared in Naples in 1560 under the name of *Accademia
Secretorum Naturae*. From 1603 to 1630 the first *Accademia
dei Lincei*, to which Galileo belonged, existed in Rome, and
in 1651 the *Accademia del Cimento* was founded at Florence
by the Medici. In England a society began to meet in 1645
at Gresham College or elsewhere in London under the name
of the Philosophical or Invisible College. In 1648 most of its
members moved to Oxford owing to the Civil War, but in
1660 the meetings in London were revived, and in 1662 the
society was formally incorporated by Charter of Charles II as
the Royal Society of London for Promoting Natural Knowledge. In France the corresponding *Académie des Sciences* was
founded by Louis XIV in 1666, and similar institutions soon
appeared in other countries. Their influence in securing
adequate discussion, in focussing scientific opinion, and in

[1] *Dictionary of National Biography*, "William Lilly", "Henry Colley", and
"John Case".

[2] Reverend H. T. Inman, *Sir Isaac Newton and one of his Prisms*, Oxford
(privately printed), 1927.

[3] Martha Ornstein, *The Rôle of Scientific Societies in the Seventeenth Century*,
Chicago and Cambridge, 1928; R. W. T. Gunther, *Early Science in Oxford*,
1921 *et seq.*

Scientific Academies

making known the researches of their members has had much to do with the rapid growth of science since their foundation, especially as most of them soon began to issue periodical publications. The oldest independent scientific periodical seems to have been the *Journal des Savants*, which was first issued at Paris in 1665. Three months later it was followed by the *Philosophical Transactions of the Royal Society*, at first the private venture of its secretary. Other scientific journals appeared before long, but, to the end of the seventeenth century or later, mathematicians had to rely chiefly on letters to each other as a means of getting their work known—an inefficient system that led to disputes about priority, as, for instance, between Newton and Leibniz.

Newton and Gravitation

We have now sketched in outline the state of scientific knowledge and philosophic opinion in which Newton began his work. Isaac Newton (1642–1727) was the delicate, post-humous and single child of a small landowner, who farmed his 120 acres. He was born at Woolsthorpe in Lincolnshire, and educated at Grantham Grammar School. He entered Trinity College, Cambridge, in 1661, where he attended the mathematical lectures of Isaac Barrow. He was elected a Scholar of the College in 1664 and a Fellow in 1665. In 1665 and 1666, driven to Woolsthorpe by an outbreak of plague at Cambridge, he turned his attention to planetary problems. Galileo's researches had shown the need of a cause to keep the planets and their satellites in their orbits and prevent them from moving off in straight lines through space. Galileo had represented this cause as a force, and it remained to show that such a force existed.

Newton is said to have grasped the clue while idly watching the fall of an apple in the orchard of his home. He was led to speculate about the cause of the fall, and to wonder how far the apparent attraction of the Earth for the apple would extend, whether, indeed, since it was felt in the deepest mines and on the highest hills, it would reach the Moon and explain that body's continual fall towards the Earth away from a straight path. The idea of a force decreasing as the square of the distance increased appears to have been in Newton's mind already, and, in fact, in other men's also. In a memorandum in Newton's handwriting, found among the collection of Newtonian papers which Lord Portsmouth, a descendant of

Newton's half-sister Hannah Barton, presented to the University of Cambridge in 1872, the following account of these early investigations is given:

And the same year I began to think of gravity extending to y⁰ orb of the Moon, and having found out how to estimate the force with wᶜʰ a globe revolving within a sphere presses the surface of the sphere, from Kepler's Rule of the periodic times of the Planets being in a sesquialterate proportion of their distances from the centers of their Orbs I deduced that the forces wᶜʰ keep the Planets in their Orbs must be reciprocally as the squares of their distances from the centers about wᶜʰ they revolve: and thereby compared the force requisite to keep the Moon in her Orb with the force of gravity at the surface of the Earth, and found them answer pretty nearly. All this was in the two plague years of 1665 and 1666, for in those days I was in the prime of my age for invention, and minded Mathematics and Philosophy more than at any time since. What Mr. Hugens has published since about centrifugal forces I suppose he had before me.

It will be seen that there is no mention here of the story related by his friend Pemberton that Newton put away his calculations because, owing to the use of an inaccurate estimate of the size of the Earth, the force needed to keep the Moon in her orbit did not agree with that of gravity. On the contrary, Newton says that he "found them answer pretty nearly". This has been pointed out by Professor Cajori,[1] who also gives evidence to show that several good enough estimates of the Earth's size were available and likely to be known to Newton in 1666. Among them was one by Gunter, which gave one degree of latitude as 66⅔ English statute miles, instead of the 60 miles which Pemberton suggests that he used. Cajori says:

In view of Newton's purchase of "Gunter's book" it is very probable, almost certain, that he knew Gunter's estimate for the size of the earth, $1° = 66⅔$ Eng. St. mi., which is approximately Snell's value. If Newton used 66⅔, he obtained 15·53 feet, instead of the correct 16·1 feet as the fall of a body from rest in a second. This is an error of 3½ %. Perhaps such a result would have elicited his remark that he "found them answer pretty nearly".

A more likely reason for Newton's delay in publishing his calculations was pointed out in 1887 by J. C. Adams and J. W. L. Glaisher. There was one great difficulty in the way of gravitational theory, which Newton at any rate appreciated. The sizes of the Sun and planets are so small compared with the

[1] *Sir Isaac Newton*, History of Science Society, Baltimore, 1928, p. 127.

distances between them that, in considering their mutual relations, the whole of each body may fairly be treated, approximately at all events, as concentrated in one place. But the Moon is relatively less distant from the Earth, and it was doubtful if taking either body as a massive point could be justified. Still more, in calculating the mutual forces of the Earth and the apple, we have to remember that, as compared with the size of the apple or the distance between the two bodies, the Earth is gigantic. The problem of calculating for the first time the combined attraction of all its parts on a small body near its surface was obviously one of great difficulty. This was probably the chief reason why Newton put aside his work in 1666. Cajori states that Newton also realized the variations of gravity with latitude and the effect of centrifugal force due to the rotation of the Earth, and says that he found their elucidation "more difficult than he was aware of". Newton seems to have returned again to the problem about 1671, but once more took no steps towards publication. Possibly the same considerations deterred him, and moreover he was much worried at that time by the controversies into which his optical experiments had led him, and says that "I had for some years past been endeavouring to bend myself from philosophy to other studies".

During the next interval, two announcements of importance were made. Picart described a new measurement of the Earth, and Huygens published the work to which Newton refers in his account of 1665 and 1666.

In 1673 Christiaan Huygens (1629–1695), son of a Dutch diplomatist and poet, published his work on dynamics, *Horologium Oscillatorium*, and made the greatest advance in the subject since the days of Galileo. Assuming the principle of the conservation of *vis viva*—now called kinetic energy—in dynamical systems, Huygens obtained the theory of the centre of oscillation, and opened a new method applicable to many mechanical and physical problems. He also determined the relation between the length of a pendulum and its time of vibration, and invented the theory of evolutes, including the properties of the cycloid.

But for our immediate purpose his most important results are those on circular motion with which the book ends, though, as has been said before, Newton must have reached the same conclusions in 1666. We may put them in simpler and more modern form.[1] If a body of mass m describes with a velocity v a circular path of radius r, as does a stone whirled at the end of a string, then, according to Galileo's principle, a force must act towards the centre. Huygens proved that the acceleration α produced by this force must be equal to v^2/r.

By 1684 the general question of gravitation was in the air. Hooke, Halley, Huygens and Wren seem independently to have shown that, if the planetary orbits, really ellipses, were taken as circles, the inverse square must be the law of force.[2] This follows at once from Huygens' proof that α in a circle with radius r is v^2/r and Kepler's third law —that the squares of the periodic times, and therefore the values of r^2/v^2, vary as r^3. The latter result shows that v^2 varies as $1/r$. Hence v^2/r, that is the acceleration, and therefore the force, varies as $1/r^2$.

Several Fellows of the Royal Society, carrying the matter further, had been discussing in particular whether a planet moving under attraction in accordance with the inverse square relation, as suggested by Kepler's third law, would describe an ellipse in accordance with his first law. Halley, despairing of obtaining a mathematical solution from other sources, went to visit Newton at Trinity College in Cambridge, and found that he had solved the problem two years before, though he had mislaid his notes. However, Newton wrote out another solution and sent it and "much other matter" to Halley

[1] The acceleration α towards the centre of motion, acting for a short time t, will produce a radial velocity αt. Let us suppose that the velocity in the circular path in Fig. 3, and therefore the velocity at any moment along the tangent to the circle, is v. Then, in the small rectangle at the top of the figure, which represents the velocities along the radius and along the tangent, the adjacent sides are in the ratio of $\alpha t/v$, and this ratio is equal to the small angle between the radii drawn to two successive points on the circumference, or vt/r. Therefore

$$\frac{\alpha t}{v} = \frac{vt}{r} \quad \text{and} \quad \alpha = \frac{v^2}{r}.$$

Since force, as defined by Newton, is measured by the product of mass and acceleration, the centripetal force necessary to maintain a body in circular motion is mv^2/r.

Fig. 3.

[2] W. W. Rouse Ball, *History of Mathematics*, London, 1901, p. 842.

in London. Under Halley's stimulus, Newton returned to the subject, and in 1685, overcoming the difficulties of the calculation, he proved that a sphere of gravitating matter attracts bodies outside it as though all its mass were concentrated at the centre. This successful demonstration justified the simplification by which the Sun, the planets, the Earth and the Moon were taken as massive points, and raised the rough approximate calculations to proofs of great accuracy. The importance of the demonstration was brought out by Dr J. W. L. Glaisher, who says:

> No sooner had Newton proved this superb theorem—and we know from his own words that he had no expectation of so beautiful a result till it emerged from his mathematical investigation—than all the mechanism of the universe at once lay spread before him....It was now in his power to apply mathematical analysis with absolute precision to the actual problems of astronomy.[1]

This success cleared the way for Newton's original investigation, by which he sought to connect astronomical forces with the Earth's pull on bodies falling to the ground. Using the new French measurement of the Earth, he returned to his old question of gravity and the Moon. The Earth could now be taken as having a centre of attraction at the centre of its form, and the verification of his surmise was simple. The distance of the Moon is about 60 radii of the Earth, and the earth's radius is about 4000 miles. It follows that the Moon falls towards the Earth away from a straight path by about 0·0044 feet in one second. If the inverse square law were true, the same force would be $(60)^2$, or 3600, times as intense on the surface of the Earth, and should there cause a body to fall $3600 \times 0·0044$, or about 16 feet, in one second. This was in accordance with the facts of contemporary observation, and the proof was complete. Newton had demonstrated that the familiar fall to the ground of an apple or a stone and the majestic sweep of the Moon in her orbit are due to one and the same unknown cause.

His proof that gravity must make a planetary orbit an ellipse meant the rationalization of Kepler's laws, and extended the result he had obtained for the moon to the motions of the planets. The whole intricate movement of the solar

---

[1] J. W. L. Glaisher, *Address on the bi-centenary of the publication of Newton's Principia*, 1887.

system could then be deduced from the one assumption that each particle of matter behaved as though it attracted every other particle with a force proportional to the product of the masses and inversely proportional to the square of the distance between them. The movements so deduced were found to agree accurately with those observed.

The heavenly bodies, to Aristotle divine, incorruptible, and different in kind from our imperfect world, were thus brought into the range of man's enquiry, and were shown to work in one gigantic mathematical harmony, in accordance with the dynamical principles established by the terrestrial experiments and inductions of Galileo and Newton. The publication in 1687 of Newton's *Principia*, the Mathematical Principles of Natural Philosophy, marks perhaps the greatest event in the history of science.

Among the secondary effects of gravitation are the tides. Much confusion existed on this subject before Newton considered it. Kepler thought that the tides were due to the moon, but Kepler was an astrologer, and believed in many other stellar and planetary influences. Probably it was for this reason that Galileo laughs at him for having "given his ear and assent to the Moon's predominancy over the water, and to occult properties and such like trifles".[1]

In the *Principia* a sound basis for tidal theory was laid down for the first time. Newton investigated mathematically the gravitational effect of the Moon and the Sun together on the waters of the Earth, allowing for the inertia of moving water, and the disturbing effects of narrow seas and channels. The conditions are very complex, but the theory has been elaborated in detail since Newton's day by many mathematicians, among whom we may mention Laplace and Sir George Darwin. But the general treatment given in the *Principia* still holds good.

The idea of mass as giving matter the property of inertia and as distinct from weight, first appears implicitly in the work of Galileo and explicitly in the writings of Baliani, a Captain of Archers at Genoa, who distinguished between *moles* and *pondus*.[2] The distinction was made more definite in the

[1] *System of the World*, Galileo Galilei, Fourth Dialogue, quoted by J. Proudman, *Isaac Newton*, ed. W. J. Greenstreet, London, 1927, p. 87.
[2] See "Newton and the Art of Discovery", by J. M. Child, in *Isaac Newton*, p. 127. Mr Child thinks that Newton may have been influenced by Baliani.

Mass and   *Principia.* Newton approached mass from the side of density,
Weight   having in mind the experiments of Boyle on the pressure and
volume of air. Since pressure p and volume v are inversely
proportional to each other for a given amount of air, their
product, pv, is constant, and may be taken as measuring
the quantity of matter in the volume of the air used, or, on
the atomic theory, as giving the number of particles squeezed
into that volume. Newton defined mass as "the quantity of
matter in a body as measured by the product of its density
and bulk", and force as "any action on a body which changes,
or tends to change, its state of rest, or of uniform motion in
a straight line".

He then summarizes the results of observation and definition
in three laws of motion:

Law I. Every body perseveres in its state of rest or of uniform
motion in a straight line, except in so far as it is compelled to change
that state by impressed forces.

Law II. Change of motion (i.e. rate of change of momentum $= ma$)
is proportional to the moving force impressed, and takes place in the
direction of the straight line in which such force is impressed.

.Law III. Reaction is always equal and opposite to action; that is to
say, the actions of two bodies upon each other are always equal and
directly opposite.

Newton's formulation of fundamental dynamical principles
sufficed to support the development of the subject for two
hundred years. No serious criticism of the assumptions that
underlie it was made till 1883, when Ernst Mach published
the first edition of his Mechanics.[1] Mach pointed out that
Newton's definitions of mass and force leave us in a logical
circle, for we only know matter through its effects on our
senses, and we can only define density as mass per unit volume.

In summarizing the history of the origins of dynamics,
Mach shows that the dynamical work of Galileo, Huygens and
Newton really means the discovery of only one fundamental
principle, though, owing to the historical accidents inevitable
in a completely new subject, it was expressed in many seemingly
independent laws or statements.

When two bodies act on each other, as, for instance, by their
mutual gravitation or by a coiled spring which joins them, the
ratio of the opposite accelerations which they produce on each

[1] Dr E. Mach, *Die Mechanik in ihrer Entwickelung historisch-kritisch dargestellt*, 1883.

other is constant and depends only on something in the bodies
which may, if we please, be called mass. This principle being
established experimentally, we can define the relative masses
of the two bodies as measured by the ratio of their opposite
accelerations, and the force between them as the product of
either mass and its own acceleration.

We thus escape the logical circle involved in Newton's
definitions of mass and force, and obtain a simple statement
based on experiment from which may be derived the various
principles enunciated by Galileo, Huygens and Newton—the
laws of falling bodies, the law of inertia, the concept of mass,
the parallelogram of forces, the equivalence of work and
energy.

By experiments on falling bodies, Galileo found that the
velocity increased proportionally with the time. This gives as
the primary relation that the gain of momentum is measured
by the product of the force and the time, or $mv = ft$, the
Newtonian law. But had Galileo happened first upon the fact
that the square of the velocity produced by an acceleration α
increased with the space s traversed, the relation $v^2 = 2\alpha s$,
which is equivalent to Huygens' equation of work and energy,
$fs = \frac{1}{2}mv^2$, would have appeared primary. Thus it was chiefly
an accident of history which caused force and momentum to
seem simpler and more important, and delayed the acceptance
of the ideas of work and energy. But they are connected, and
either can be derived from the other.

To return to Newton's definitions, we can escape from the
logical circle in another way, which, though it may be less
complete than Mach's method, throws light on the problems
involved. Newton recognized that we get the mechanical
notion of force from the sensation of muscular effort, and he
might have found a way out of the circle by this road. Dynamics
may be regarded as the science whereby we rationalize our
sensations about matter in motion, as the science of heat is
concerned with our sensation of warmth. We have primary
ideas derived from experience about space or length and about
time; our muscular sense similarly gives us the idea of force.
Equal forces, as roughly measured by this sense, are found to
produce different accelerations on different pieces of matter,
and the inertia of each piece, its resistance to the force f, may
be called its mass and defined as measured inversely by the

Mass and Weight acceleration α produced by a given force. Thus $m = f/\alpha$. In this way, the idea of mass is derived from a mental state, our muscular sensation of force. The method may perhaps be criticized by some as bringing psychology into physics, but it is of some interest to note that it is possible to avoid the logical circle of physics by doing so.

Having thus acquired a definite concept of mass, we find by experiment that the relative masses of bodies remain roughly constant. We can then make the hypothesis that this approximate constancy is rigorously true, or, at all events, true to a high degree of accuracy, and use mass M as a third fundamental unit to those of length L and time T. All the innumerable deductions from this assumption were found to conform with observation and experiment quite accurately till the days of J. J. Thomson and Einstein. It was therefore abundantly verified, and still holds good save in very exceptional cases.

Mass being measured by inertia, there remained the problem of finding its relation to weight, the force with which matter is drawn towards the Earth. This problem also was cleared up by Newton.

Galileo had shown by experiments from the Leaning Tower of Pisa that two bodies of different weights, W_1 and W_2, fall to the ground at the same rate. The weights are the forces produced by gravity, and Galileo's result proves that the accelerations α_1 and α_2, under the forces produced by gravity, are the same. With the definition of mass given above, the relative masses m_1 and m_2 of the two bodies are defined by the relations

$$m_1 = W_1/\alpha_1 \text{ and } m_2 = W_2/\alpha_2,$$

or

$$\alpha_1 = W_1/m_1 \text{ and } \alpha_2 = W_2/m_2.$$

Now it is impossible by any juggling with formulae,[1] or any metaphysical considerations such as those which the Scholastics took over from Aristotle, to tell what is the relation between the two accelerations of these two different bodies when falling freely. It needed Galileo's experiments from the Leaning Tower to prove that, as a matter of fact, $\alpha_1 = \alpha_2$. But that

[1] Unless the juggler be Einstein and the formulae contain the principle of Relativity, which is itself based on experiment. Mach seems to go wrong here; he states that the proportionality of weight and mass follows from his definition of mass, but implicitly he introduces the result $\alpha_1 = \alpha_2$.

being proved, it follows from the definitions of mass, weight and force, as formulated in the equations, that

$$\frac{W_1}{m_1} = \frac{W_2}{m_2} \quad \text{or} \quad \frac{W_1}{W_2} = \frac{m_1}{m_2},$$

that is, that the weights of the two bodies are proportional to their masses, a truly remarkable result, which requires that gravity, as Newton said, "must proceed from a cause that... operates not according to the quantity of the surfaces of the particles on which it acts (as mechanical causes are used to do), but according to the quantity of the solid matter which they contain".[1] Newton's astronomical results show indeed that the cause of gravity must "penetrate to the very centres of the sun and planets, without suffering the least diminution of its force".

Galileo's experiments did not attain, and indeed were not susceptible of, any great accuracy. Baliani, in repeating them more carefully, let fall a ball of iron and a ball of wax of the same size, simultaneously from the same point. He found that when the iron ball had fallen 50 feet to the ground, the waxen ball had still a foot to fall. He rightly explained the difference as due to the resistance of the air, which is the same for both but is more effective in opposing the lesser weight of the wax.[2] Newton set out to examine the result more closely. He showed mathematically that the time of swing of a pendulum must vary directly as the square root of the mass and inversely as the square root of the weight. He then made careful and accurate experiments on different pendulums, using bobs of the same size so that the resistance of the air was the same on them all. Some of the bobs were solid, of different materials, and some were hollow and filled with different liquids or particles such as grain. In all cases he found that, for pendulums of the same length at the same place, the times of swing were equal within the narrow limits of error of the measurement. Thus Newton confirmed, to much greater accuracy, the result which might have been inferred from Galileo's experiment, that weight is proportional to mass.

One of the immediate results of the application of mathematical mechanics to the problems of astronomy was the need of improvement in the mathematical tools used in the

---

[1] *Principia*, 1713 ed. pp. 483–484.   [2] J. M. Child, *loc. cit.*

researches. For this reason the period which saw the labours of Kepler, Galileo, Huygens and Newton was marked also by a great increase in mathematical knowledge and skill.

Perhaps the most noteworthy of these achievements was the invention of the infinitesimal calculus, developed in different forms by Newton and Leibniz. Algebra and geometry had begun to assume their modern shapes, trigonometry had been extended to imaginary quantities, but the introduction of the idea of varying velocity demanded a method of dealing with the rates of variation of changing quantities. A constant velocity is measured by the space s described in a time t, and the quantity s/t will be the same however great or small s and t may be. But, if the velocity vary, its value at any instant can only be found by taking a time so short that the velocity does not change appreciably, and measuring the space described in that short time. When s and t are reduced without limit and become infinitesimal, their quotient gives the velocity at the instant, and this was written by Leibniz as ds/dt, which is called the differential coefficient of s with regard to t. Newton, in his method of fluxions, wrote the same quantity as $\dot{s}$, a notation which is less convenient and is now superseded by that of Leibniz. We have taken as an example space and time, but any two quantities which depend on each other may be treated in the same way, and the rate of variation of x with y may be written as dx/dy or $\dot{x}$.[1]

The converse process, the summation of differentials, or the estimation of a quantity itself from a knowledge of its rates of change, is called integration, and is usually an operation of greater difficulty. It is needed in such problems as Newton's calculation of the attraction of a whole sphere from the attractions of each of its myriad particles.[2]

An equation which contains differential coefficients is called a differential equation. Most physical problems can be formulated as differential equations, the difficulty usually is to

---

[1] The values of these differential coefficients for different functions can be calculated; for instance, if $y = x^n$, it can be shown that $dy/dx = nx^{n-1}$.

[2] To each differentiation there corresponds an integration; thus, to the example of differentiation given above, there corresponds the integral of x^n. It can be shown that

$$\int x^n \, dx = \frac{x^{n+1}}{n+1} + c,$$

unless n is -1, when the integral is $\log x + c$. In each case c is an unknown constant, which, in many practical problems, can be eliminated.

integrate and thus to solve them.[1] That Newton was acquainted with the principle is shown by the fact that he calculated a table giving the refraction of a ray of light passing through the atmosphere by a method equivalent to forming the differential equation to the path of the ray.[2]

In the *Principia*, Newton converted his results, many of which were probably obtained by the method of fluxions, into the form of Euclidean geometry. The new infinitesimal calculus only slowly became known; but, in the shape given it by Leibniz and Bernouilli, it is the basis of the whole vast structure of modern pure and applied mathematics.

Newton also made advances in many other branches of mathematics. He established the binomial theorem, developed much of the theory of equations, and introduced literal indices. In mathematical physics, besides the work on dynamics and astronomy already described, he founded lunar theory, and calculated tables by which the future position of the moon among the stars could be predicted—work of the utmost value in navigation. He created hydrodynamics, including the theory of the propagation of waves, and made many improvements in hydrostatics.

Newton's work on optics, even if it stood alone, would have placed him in the front rank of men of science.[3] The true law of refraction, that the sines of the angles of incidence and refraction bear a constant ratio, had been discovered in 1621 by Snell. In 1666 Newton "procured a triangular glass prism to try the celebrated phenomena of colours". In 1669, when he succeeded Barrow in the Lucasian Professorship of Mathematics at Cambridge, he chose optics as the first subject of his lectures and researches. His first published scientific paper was on light, and appeared in the *Philosophical Transactions*

---

[1] As a simple example, the equation $y\,dx + x\,dy = 0$ can be rearranged as

$$\frac{dx}{x} + \frac{dy}{y} = 0.$$

The terms can then be integrated singly, and we get

$$\int \frac{dx}{x} + \int \frac{dy}{y} = c \text{ or } \log x + \log y = c.$$

[2] Letter to Flamsteed. See *Catalogue of the Newton MSS*, Cambridge, 1888, p. xiii.

[3] *Opticks, or a Treatise of the Reflections, Refractions, Inflections and Colours of Light*, by Sir Isaac Newton, Knt, London, 1704, 1717, 1721, 1730. See also "Newton's Work in Optics", by E. T. Whittaker, in *Isaac Newton*, ed. W. J. Greenstreet, London, 1927.

of the Royal Society in 1672. De la Pryme states in his diary that in 1692 Newton left a light burning in his room when he went to Chapel. This started a fire which destroyed his papers, and among them twenty years' work on optics. But there is no reference to this loss in Newton's preface to his book, which says: "A Discourse about Light was written at the desire of some Gentlemen of the Royal Society, in the year 1675...and the rest was added about twelve years after".

By long and careful experiments, he showed that the "celebrated phenomena of colours" were due to the decomposition of white light by the prism, lights of different colours having different refrangibility, the most refrangible being violet and the least refrangible being red. A theory of the rainbow was propounded in 1611 by Antonio de Dominis, Archbishop of Spalatro, who suggested that the light reflected from the inner surface of raindrops was coloured by traversing different thicknesses of water. A better account was given by Descartes, who connected the colour with the refrangibility, and calculated successfully the angle of the bow. Newton cleared up the subject. He also traced to similar causes the colours which disturb the vision through telescopes, and, concluding erroneously that the dispersion of white light into colour could not be prevented without at the same time preventing the refraction on which magnification depends, he gave up as hopeless the attempt to improve existing refracting telescopes, and invented a reflecting telescope instead.

In the next place he examined the colours of thin plates, already well known in bubbles and in other films of solid, liquid or air. By pressing a glass prism on to a lens of known curvature, the colours were formed into circles, since called "Newton's rings". Careful measurements were made of these rings and compared with estimates of the thickness of the air film from point to point. The experiments were repeated using light of one colour only, when alternate light and dark rings became visible. Newton concluded that light of each definite colour was subject to fits of easy transmission and easy reflection. If the rings formed by white light were looked at by reflected light, the particular colour which at a given thickness happened to be transmitted was not reflected to the eye, so that the eye saw white light deprived of that one constituent, that is, saw a complex colour. Newton inferred that some, at all events, of the colours of natural objects are due to their minute structure, and calculated the dimensions necessary to give these effects.

He also repeated and extended the experiments by which Grimaldi had shown that very narrow beams of light, ordinarily travelling in straight lines, are bent at the sharp edges of obstacles, so that the shadows are larger than they should be, and fringes of colour are formed. Newton showed that the bending is increased by passing light through a narrow slit between two knife edges, and he made careful observations and measurements of the breadths of the slit and the angles of deflection.

He also examined the unusual refraction effects discovered by Huygens in Iceland spar. In this mineral one incident ray gives rise to two refracted rays, and, when one of these rays is isolated, it will pass through another crystal of spar if the axis be parallel to that of the first crystal, but it will not pass if the axis of the second crystal be at right angles to that of the first. Newton saw that these facts indicated that whatever a ray of light may be, it cannot be symmetrical, but must somehow be different on its different sides. This is the essence of the theory of polarization.

Besides all this evidence, another fact had to be taken into account in considering the nature of light. In 1676 Roemer had observed that, when the earth is between the sun and Jupiter, the eclipses of his satellites happen seven or eight minutes earlier than the normal times, and, when the earth is beyond the sun, seven or eight minutes later. In the latter case the light of the satellites has to travel a distance greater than in the former by the diameter of the earth's orbit, and, from the observed discrepancy, it became clear that light cannot be propagated instantaneously but travels in a finite time.

Newton says that he planned further experiments on light, but that, as it proved impossible for him to do them, he drew no definite conclusions as to its nature, and only proposed some queries for others to follow up and answer. His final opinion seems to be summarized in Query 29:[1]

Are not the Rays of Light very small Bodies emitted from shining Substances? For such Bodies will pass through uniform Mediums in right Lines without bending into the Shadow,[2] which is the nature of

---

[1] *Loc. cit.* p. 347.
[2] That is, ignoring the very small bending due to diffraction.

the Rays of Light....If Refraction be perform'd by Attraction of the Rays, the Sines of Incidence must be to the Sines of Refraction in a given Proportion.

It is easy to show that, on the emission theory, this "given Proportion" must measure the ratio of the velocity of light in the denser to that in the rarer medium. Newton continues:

> Nothing more is requisite for putting the Rays of Light into Fits of easy Reflexion and easy Transmission, than that they be small Bodies which by their attractive Powers, or some other Force, stir up Vibrations in what they act upon, which Vibrations being swifter than the Rays, overtake them successively, and agitate them so as by turns to increase and decrease their Velocities, and thereby put them into those Fits. And lastly, the unusual Refraction of Island Crystal looks very much as if it were perform'd by some kind of attractive virtue lodged in certain Sides both of the Rays, and of the Particles of the Crystal.

The idea that light is made of particles projected into the eye may be traced back to the Pythagoreans, while Empedocles and Plato taught that something was emitted from the eye as well. This quasi-tentacular theory was held also by Epicurus and Lucretius, who had a confused notion that the eye sees a body somewhat as the hand may feel it with a rod. Aristotle opposed this view, and thought that light was an action (ἐνέργεια) in a medium. All these were mere guesses, and as such equally worthless, whether right or wrong.

Fig. 4.

But some definite evidence was adduced by Alhazen in the eleventh century to show that the cause of vision proceeded from the object and not the eye, though the tentacular view recurred at intervals long after his day.

Descartes held that light was a pressure transmitted through his plenum of space. Robert Hooke suggested that it was a rapid vibration in a medium, and this undulatory theory was worked out in some detail by Huygens. By a geometrical construction (Fig. 4), Huygens traced the process of refraction. When a wave-front (*AC*) of light impinges from air on a

surface (*AB*) of water, each point on the surface becomes the
centre of one little circular wavelet reflected back into the air,
and of another spreading out into the water. If the wavelets be
drawn for successive points on the surface, they will intersect
each other in new wave-fronts, one in air and one (*DB*) in water.
Along these wave-fronts, and there alone, the wavelets rein-
force each other and produce sensible effects. The wave-fronts
thus produced conform to the known laws of reflection and refraction. If the speed of light be less in water than in air, an
assumption opposite to that necessary for the emission theory,
the radius of the wavelets in water at a given moment will be
less than those of the wavelets in air, and the refracted rays
will be bent towards the normal as they are in nature.

The chief difficulty in the way of this wave theory was to
explain the existence of sharp shadows, that is, to explain the
rectilinear propagation of light. Ordinary waves bend round
obstacles and show no such properties. A hundred years later
Fresnel surmounted the difficulty by showing that the extreme
smallness of the wave-lengths of light compared with the
dimensions of the obstacles explained the difference. But to
Newton rectilinear rays seemed to demand a corpuscular theory.

Yet in the passage quoted above, he finds it necessary to
imagine vibrations of some kind, swifter than the rays, to
explain their periodicity. In previous queries he clearly contemplated an aether playing other similar secondary parts.
For instance in Query 18:[1]

If in two large tall cylindrical Vessels of Glass inverted, two little
Thermometers be suspended so as not to touch the Vessels, and the
Air be drawn out of one of these Vessels, and these Vessels thus prepared
be carried out of a cold place into a warm one; the Thermometer *in vacuo*
will grow warm as much, and almost as soon as the Thermometer which
is not *in vacuo*. And when the Vessels are carried back into the cold place,
the Thermometer *in vacuo* will grow cold almost as soon as the other
Thermometer. Is not the Heat of the warm Room convey'd through
the Vacuum by the Vibrations of a much subtiler Medium than Air,
which after the Air was drawn out remained in the Vacuum? And is
not this Medium the same with that Medium by which Light is refracted
and reflected, and by whose Vibrations Light communicates Heat to
Bodies, and is put into Fits of easy Reflexion and easy Transmission?
And do not the Vibrations of this Medium in hot Bodies contribute to
the intenseness and duration of their Heat? And do not hot Bodies
communicate their Heat to contiguous cold ones, by the Vibrations of
this Medium propagated from them into the cold ones? And is not this

[1] *Loc. cit.* p. 323.

Medium exceedingly more rare and subtile than the Air, and exceedingly more elastick and active? And doth it not readily pervade all Bodies? And is it not (by its elastick force) expanded through all the Heavens?

Newton goes on to suggest that refraction is due to the different density of this medium in different bodies; that it is less dense in heavy bodies, and much rarer within the Sun and planets than in free space where it grows denser as the distance from matter increases. He thus seeks to explain both gravitation and that higher velocity of light in dense media which is needed in the emission theory. The diffraction at the edges of obstacles is a kind of refraction produced by the effect of matter on aether extending beyond the surface. Thus to Newton aether forms the intermediary between light and ponderable matter. But we must remember that all these suggestions are put forward merely as queries at the end of the main part of the book. In view of the fact that Newton distinctly states that further experiments are needed, and that he puts forward the queries for others to answer, the complaint that Newton's authority delayed the acceptance of the undulatory theory of light seems to be valid only against those who accepted a query as necessarily implying the answer suggested.

It will be seen that a crucial experiment, which would decide between the two theories, is possible if the velocity of light can be measured or compared in air and in water. This was first done by direct observation by Foucault about 1850. The velocity was found to be less in water, as required by the wave theory.

But the recent discovery of the swiftly moving corpuscles or electrons in cathode rays and in radio-active processes shows that particles very like those imagined by Newton can now be observed; indeed, the most striking feature about Newton's theory is its resemblance to quite modern conceptions, for to Newton, as to Planck and J. J. Thomson, "the structure of light is essentially atomic", while Schrödinger and others have had to imagine a complex of particles and waves, which recalls even more vividly Newton's ideas. When we remember that all these and other discoveries were the achievement of a young man, who devoted his later years as Master of the Mint to the practical work of recoinage, and his leisure to writings on speculative theology, we may well be astonished at the mind of him who, like Democritus of old, *genus humanum ingenio superavit.*

The two most important consequences of Newton's labours were the establishment of the validity of terrestrial mechanics in celestial spaces, and the removal of unnecessary philosophic dogma from the structure of natural science. The Greek and mediaeval view, that the heavenly bodies were of special and divine nature, had been partly dissolved by Galileo's telescope, but Newton carried the process much farther. Philosophy, moreover, was still confused with science. Even Descartes, in framing a mechanical theory of astronomy, founded it upon a scholastic antithesis, and upon the metaphysical view that the essence of matter was extension. Hence Newton's detachment from such preconceptions marks a real advance. How far a new metaphysics was implicit in his interpretation of his results will be considered later.

The way in which the meaning of his work was regarded by his immediate disciples can be seen by Roger Cotes' Preface to the second edition of the *Principia*. Here the surviving scholastic philosophy, with its innate and inexplicable qualities, is contrasted with the Cartesians' premature attempt at a mechanical system of nature founded on a plenum filled with vortices, and with Newton's method of accepting only those hypotheses which can be shown to be in accordance with observation. Cotes says:

Those who have treated of natural philosophy may be nearly reduced to three classes. Of these, some have attributed to the several species of things specific and occult qualities, on which, in a manner unknown, they make the operations of the several bodies to depend. The sum of the doctrine of the schools derived from Aristotle and the Peripatetics is herein contained. They affirm that the several effects of bodies arise from the particular natures of those bodies; but whence it is that bodies derive those natures they do not tell us, and therefore they tell us nothing. And being entirely employed in giving names to things, and not in searching into things themselves, we may say, that they have invented a philosophical way of speaking, but not that they have made known to us true philosophy.

Others, therefore, by laying aside that useless heap of words, thought to employ their pains to better purpose. These supposed all matter homogeneous, and that the variety of forms which is seen in bodies arises from some very plain and simple affections of the component particles; and by going on from simple things to those which are more compounded, they certainly proceed right, if they attribute no other

[1] See in particular the Preface and Scholium in the *Principia*, and Queries in the *Opticks*. Also A. J. Snow, *Matter and Gravity in Newton's Physical Philosophy*, Oxford, 1926; E. A. Burtt, *The Metaphysical Foundations of Modern Science*, New York, 1925.

properties to those primary affections of the particles than nature has done. But when they take a liberty of imagining at pleasure unknown figures and magnitudes, and uncertain situations and motions of the parts; and, moreover, of supposing occult fluids, freely pervading the pores of bodies, endued with an all-performing subtilty, and agitated with occult motions; they now run out into dreams and chimeras, and neglect the true constitution of things; which certainly is not to be expected from fallacious conjectures, when we can scarcely reach it by the most certain observations. Those who fetch from hypotheses the foundation on which they build their speculations, may form, indeed, an ingenious romance; but a romance it will still be.

There is left, then, the third class, which profess experimental philosophy. These, indeed, derive the causes of all things from the most simple principles possible; but, then, they assume nothing as a principle that is not proved by phaenomena. They frame no hypotheses, nor receive them into philosophy otherwise than as questions whose truth may be disputed. They proceed, therefore, in a twofold method, synthetical and analytical. From some select phaenomena they deduce by analysis the forces of nature, and the more simple laws of forces; and from thence by synthesis shew the constitution of the rest. This is that incomparably best way of philosophizing which our renowned author most justly embraced before the rest, and thought alone worthy to be cultivated and adorned by his excellent labours. Of this he has given us a most illustrious example by the explication of the System of the World, most happily deduced from the theory of gravity, That the virtue of gravity was found in all bodies, others suspected or imagined before him; but he was the only and first philosopher that could demonstrate it from appearances, and make it a solid foundation to the most noble speculations.

Underlying Newton's dynamics and astronomy are the conceptions of absolute space and time. Newton says that he "does not define Time, Space and Motion, as being well known to all", but he distinguishes between, on the one hand, relative space and time as measured by our senses in terms of natural bodies and motions, and, on the other, absolute space which exists immovably and absolute time which flows equably "without regard to anything external". Galileo's ball moved in a straight line on the Earth. But the Earth revolves on its axis and moves round the Sun, while the Sun and its planets may travel through the heaven of stars. Newton concluded that a body moves in a straight line through absolute space with a constant speed, unless deflected by some force. Mach pointed out in 1883 that it was not legitimate to push this reasoning beyond reference to the fixed stars, and in the light of recent knowledge, we can see even more clearly that the ideas of absolute time and of absolute space are doctrines which do not necessarily follow from the physical phenomena, though perhaps in the seventeenth century those ideas were fair assumptions from the facts of ordinary experience. Indeed, to avoid using the idea of absolute rotation is still a difficulty for the complete Relativist.

Newton's work was assailed by Huygens and Leibniz as unphilosophical, because he offered no explanation of the ultimate cause of gravitational attraction. Newton was the first to see clearly that an attempt at an explanation, if necessary or possible at all, comes at a later stage. He took the known facts, formed a theory which fitted them and could be expressed in mathematical terms, deduced mathematical and logical consequences from the theory, again compared them with the facts by observation and experiment, and saw that the concordance was complete. It was not necessary to know the cause of the attraction; Newton regarded that as a secondary and independent problem, as yet only in the stage suitable for speculation. We might now go farther, and say that it is not even necessary to know, that such an attraction really exists. All the complex planetary motions *happen as though* each particle in the solar system attracts every other in agreement with the law of mass and inverse square, and that is enough for the mathematical astronomer.

Newton's attracting particles are not necessarily atoms, but it is clear that they can well play that rôle. Newton is brought back to particles in his chemical researches, and his views on the nature of matter are given in the oft-quoted words at the end of the *Opticks*:

All these things being consider'd, it seems probable to me, that God in the Beginning form'd Matter in solid, massy, hard, impenetrable, moveable Particles, of such Sizes and Figures, and with such other Properties, and in such Proportion to Space, as most conduced to the End for which he form'd them; and that these primitive Particles being Solids, are incomparably harder than any porous Bodies compounded of them; even so very hard, as never to wear or break in pieces; No ordinary Power being able to divide what God himself made one in the first Creation....It seems to me farther, that these Particles have not only a *Vis inertia*, accompanied with such passive Laws of Motion as naturally result from that Force, but also that they are moved by certain active Principles, such as is that of Gravity, and that which causes Fermentation, and the Cohesion of Bodies. These Principles I consider not as occult Qualities, supposed to result from the specific Forms of Things, but as general Laws of Nature, by which the Things themselves are form'd; their Truth appearing to us by Phaenomena, though their Causes be not yet discover'd. For these are manifest Qualities, and their Causes only are occult. And the *Aristotelians* gave the name of occult Qualities not to manifest Qualities, but to such Qualities only as they supposed to lie hid in Bodies, and to be the unknown Causes of manifest Effects; Such as would be the Causes of Gravity, and of magnetick and electrick Attractions, and of Fermentations, if we should suppose that these Forces or Actions arose from Qualities unknown to us, and uncapable of being discovered and made manifest. Such occult Qualities put a stop to the Improvement of natural Philosophy, and therefore of late years have been rejected. To tell us that every Species of Things is endowed with an occult specifick Quality by which it acts and produces manifest Effects, is to tell us nothing: But to derive two or three general Principles of Motion from Phaenomena, and afterwards to tell us how the Properties and Actions of all corporeal Things follow from those manifest Principles, would be a very great step in Philosophy, though the Causes of those Principles were not yet discover'd: And therefore I scruple not to propose the Principles of Motion above mention'd, they being of very general Extent, and leave their Causes to be found out.

It is a testimony to the wisdom of Newton's true scientific spirit of caution that, since his day, in spite of many attempts, no satisfactory mechanical explanation of gravitational attraction has been given, and that, in the light of Einstein's researches, the problem has now been shifted to the realms of non-Euclidean geometry. In the *Principia* Newton said, "Hitherto I have not been able to discover the cause of those properties of gravity from phaenomena, and I frame no hypotheses". He only published a suggestion in the form of a query in his book on *Opticks*, a suggestion based on the pressures of a hypothetical inter-planetary aether, getting denser the farther away from matter, and thus pressing bodies together. But guesses played no part in his inductive examination of the facts or his mathematical deductions from his theory.

Returning to his more definite opinions, his view of nature is shown in the Preface to the *Principia*:[1]

The difficulty of philosophy seems to consist in this—from the phaenomena of motions to investigate the forces of nature, and then from these forces to demonstrate the other phaenomena; and to this end the general propositions in the first and second books are directed. In the third book we give an example of this in the explication of the System of the World; for by the propositions mathematically demonstrated in the first book, we there derived from the celestial phaenomena the forces of gravity with which bodies tend to the sun and the several planets. Then from these forces, by other propositions which are also mathematical, we deduce the motions of the planets, the comets, the moon,

[1] English translation by A. Motte, ed. 1803, p. x.

and the sea. I wish we could derive the rest of the phaenomena of nature by the same kind of reasoning from mechanical principles; for I am induced by many reasons to suspect that they may all depend upon certain forces by which the particles of bodies, by causes hitherto unknown, are either mutually impelled towards each other, and cohere in regular figures, or are repelled and recede from each other; which forces being unknown, philosophers have hitherto attempted the search of nature in vain; but I hope the principles here laid down will afford some light either to that or some truer method of philosophy.

Here he clearly contemplates the possibility of explaining all natural phenomena in mathematical terms of matter and motion, though whether he means the "phaenomena of nature" to include those of life or mind is not stated. But as far as other things go, he accepts as possible the mechanical view first propounded by Galileo.

He accepts also Galileo's distinction between primary qualities, such as extension and inertia, which can be handled mathematically, and secondary qualities, such as colour, taste, sound, which are but sensations in the brain induced by the primary qualities.[1] Man's soul or mind is localized in the brain or sensorium, to which motions are conveyed from external objects by the nerves and from which motions are transmitted to the muscles.[2]

Professor E. A. Burtt holds that all this shows that, in spite of Newton's empiricism and insistence on the need for experimental verification at every turn, in spite of his rejection of all philosophic systems as a basis for science and of all unverifiable hypotheses in its building, he did of necessity assume implicitly a metaphysical system which had all the greater influence on thought because it was not explicitly stated.[3]

Newton's authority was squarely behind that view of the cosmos which saw in man a puny irrelevant spectator (so far as a being wholly imprisoned in a dark room can be called such) of the vast mathematical system whose regular motions according to mechanical principles constituted the world of nature. The gloriously romantic universe of Dante and Milton, that set no bounds to the imagination of man as it played over space and time, had now been swept away. Space was identified with the realm of geometry, time with the continuity of number. The world that people had thought themselves living in—a world rich with colour and sound, redolent with fragrance, filled with gladness, love and beauty, speaking everywhere of purposive harmony and creative ideals—

---

[1] *Opticks*, 3rd ed. p. 108.   [2] *Ibid.* p. 328.
[3] E. A. Burtt, *The Metaphysical Foundations of Modern Science*, New York, 1925, p. 236.

was crowded now into minute corners in the brains of scattered organic beings. The really important world outside was a world hard, cold, colourless, silent and dead; a world of quantity, a world of mathematically computable motions in mechanical regularity. The world of qualities as immediately perceived by man became just a curious and quite minor effect of that infinite machine beyond. In Newton the Cartesian metaphysics, ambiguously interpreted and stripped of its distinctive claim for serious philosophical consideration, finally overthrew Aristotelianism and became the predominant world-view of modern times.

Doubtless this eloquent passage represents truly the reaction of those who disliked the new scientific outlook. Yet to Newton and his immediate followers it would have seemed quite unfair. To them the wonderful order and harmony which Newton had brought into the picture of the world gave more aesthetic satisfaction than any confused kaleidoscopic view of nature seen by the naïve outlook of common-sense, by the misleading concepts of Aristotelian categories, or by the mythical imagery of poets, and spoke to them more plainly of the beneficent activity of an all-powerful Creator. The world of colour, love and beauty was still there, though, like the Kingdom of Heaven, it was within the soul of man, a soul inspired by the Spirit of God, which sustains all creation in its majestic complexity, knows far more of its beauty than is visible to man, and beholds it as very good.

The true Newtonian attitude was admirably expressed by Joseph Addison in his famous ode:

> The spacious firmament on high,
> With all the blue etherial sky,
> And spangled heav'ns, a shining frame,
> Their great Original proclaim:
>
> .   .   .   .   .
>
> What though, in solemn silence, all
> Move round the dark terrestrial ball?
> What tho' nor real voice nor sound
> Amid their radiant orbs be found?
>
> In reason's ear they all rejoice,
> And utter forth a glorious voice,
> For ever singing as they shine,
> "The hand that made us is divine".

Indeed, with a very slight misunderstanding of Addison's meaning, he may be taken as giving a prophetic answer to Doctor Burtt.

It must be allowed that, at a later date, Newton's science was taken by others as the basis of a mechanical philosophy, but that was not the fault of Newton or his friends. They did their best, in the theological language which was natural to them, to make clear their belief that Newtonian dynamics did not controvert, rather indeed strengthened, a spiritual view of reality. It might have been safer had they taken explicitly with Newton's science Descartes' metaphysical philosophy of dualism, which left a clear, if more limited, place for mind and soul. Nevertheless, to them theism was fundamental and unquestioned, and they had no fear in accepting fully and entirely the new science.

The meaning of the mechanical view of nature in the light of present knowledge will be considered in later chapters of this book. Newton's assumption that, for "the mathematical principles of natural philosophy", the world consists of matter in motion, seems little more than a definition of the aspect from which dynamical science finds it convenient to regard nature. There are many other aspects, physical, psychological, aesthetic, religious, and only when they are studied together can we hope to catch a fleeting vision of reality.

Newton, in spite of his mathematical power, tried to maintain an empirical attitude. He continually repeats that he makes no hypotheses, meaning metaphysical, unverifiable hypotheses, and puts forward nothing that cannot be confirmed by observation or experiment. It was not that he had no philosophic or theological interests: quite the contrary. He was a philosopher and a deeply religious man, but he regarded these subjects as a vision to be seen from the topmost pinnacles of human knowledge, and not as the foundation on which it must be built: the end and not the beginning of science. The *Principia* opens with definitions and laws of motion which summarize the known facts. Two volumes are filled with the mathematical deductions from these statements which established the great sciences of dynamics and astronomy. A "General Scholium" of seven pages at the end of the book, added in the second edition, contains all that Newton thought could fairly be written in such a work on the metaphysical import of his physical discoveries. It is expressed in the natural theological language of the time. Its sense is that of the argument from design. "This most beautiful System of the Sun, Planets and Comets", he wrote, "could only proceed from the counsel and dominion of an intelligent and powerful Being...." God "endures for ever and is everywhere present, and by existing always and everywhere, he constitutes duration and space". Thus to Newton, absolute time and space are constituted by the everlasting and boundless Presence of God.

In the less systematic and less formal queries in the book on *Opticks*, Newton tells us more about his speculative opinions. "The main Business of Natural Philosophy is to argue from Phaenomena without feigning Hypotheses, and to deduce Causes from Effects, till we come to the very first Cause, which certainly is not mechanical.... Does it not appear from Phaenomena that there is a Being incorporeal, living, intelligent, omnipresent, who in infinite Space as in his Sensory, sees the things themselves intimately, and throughly perceives them, and comprehends them wholly by their immediate presence to himself."[1]

Newton does not conceive of God merely as a First Cause Who makes and starts a machine which then runs for ever alone. God is immanent in nature; "He governs all things and knows all things that are or can be done.... Who being in all Places, is more able by his Will to move the Bodies within his boundless uniform Sensorium, and thereby to form and reform the Parts of the Universe, than we are by our Will to move the Parts of our own Bodies".[2] With a shortsightedness unusual in him, Newton also invoked God to correct by direct interposition irregularities which may gradually accumulate in the solar system owing to disturbing causes, such as the action of comets.[3] When Laplace showed that such causes correct themselves, and proved the essential dynamical stability of the solar system, this argument was used against the conclusion which it had been framed to establish.

Newton's metaphysical ideas were expounded and somewhat misinterpreted by Richard Bentley in his sermons and by Samuel Clark.[4] Bentley concludes that "universal gravitation, a thing certainly existent in nature, is above all mechanism

---

[1] *Opticks*, Query 28.   [2] *Opticks*, 3rd ed. p. 379.   [3] *Ibid.* p. 378.
[4] See A. J. Snow, *Matter and Gravity in Newton's Physical Philosophy*, Oxford, 1926, p. 190.

and material cause, and proceeds from a higher principle, or *Newton and* divine energy and impression", though its routine may be *Philosophy* described in mechanical terms. Clark finds it necessary to suppose that

Gravity cannot be explained by mutual impulsive attraction of matter, because every impulse acts in proportion to the mass of a body. Consequently, there must be a principle which can get inside of a solid and hard body, and—*because attraction at a distance is absurd*—therefore we must postulate *a certain immaterial spirit, which governs matter according to well ordered rules.* This immaterial force is universal in bodies, everywhere and always....Gravity or the weight of Bodies is not any accidental Effect of Motion or of any very subtile Matter, but an original and general Law of all Matter impressed upon it by God, and maintained in it by some efficient power, which penetrates the solid Substance of it.

Newton did not regard gravity as a fundamental property of matter, but as a phenomenon to be explained by further research into physical causes. But Bentley and Clark took his belief in a metaphysical ultimate and final cause of nature as the direct and immediate cause of gravity, from which he had carefully separated it. Here we see a misunderstanding of Newton used in a theistic direction, as it came to be used later in the opposite sense. Indeed, Newton seems fated to have been misunderstood. Action at a distance, which he held to be absurd, was reckoned his essential idea, and its establishment his greatest achievement. The "most beautiful System of the Sun, Planets and Comets", which to Newton could only proceed from a beneficent Creator, was used in the eighteenth century as the basis for a mechanical philosophy, and replaced the atomism of the ancients as the starting point of an atheistic materialism.

It is evident that in the age of Newton—the age of the first great synthesis of scientific knowledge—the revolution in the intellectual outlook of mankind involved a revolution in the statement of dogmatic religious belief. On the one hand, it was impossible to continue to hold the naïve conception of the Cosmos which had become embedded in Aristotelian and Thomist philosophy, impossible any longer to gaze into heaven just above the sky and to shudder at the rumblings of hell beneath the ground. Light ceased to be an all-pervading mysterious substance of colourless purity, the very dwelling-place of God, and became a physical manifestation, having laws to be investigated with mirrors and lenses, and colours to be

Newton and Philosophy

analysed by a prism. On the other hand, the type of instinctive inarticulate Platonism which is seen in pietism and mysticism was equally inapplicable to the new mental attitude. Men were left with the more rational Platonism, which, like the first type, held that eternal truth is reached by an innate power or revelation from within, yet regarded mathematical or geometrical harmony as the essence of being. This variety of Platonism led through the ideas of Galileo and Kepler to the mathematical system of Newton. It accepted the inner power or revelation as the basis of reason, and the theory then became a form of intellectualism, which sought to find the truth about the Divine Nature both in the physical order of the Universe, and in the moral law. "In this way a severe rationalism was put forward in opposition to all the romantic forms of religion that went by the name of 'enthusiasm'. The seat of religious belief was thus moved from the heart to the head: mysticism was excommunicated by mathematics...the way was opened for a liberal Christianity which might ultimately supersede traditional beliefs", and for the "religion within the limits of reason" sought by Kant.[1]

Mathematics and Astronomy in the Eighteenth Century[2]

It was unfortunate that the difference in notation used by Newton and Leibniz in their separate discoveries of the infinitesimal calculus was complicated by a dispute about priority. For one or both of these reasons, there arose a divergence between the work of the English and Continental mathematicians. The former used Newton's symbols, but for the most part neglected his new process of analysis to follow the geometrical methods in which he was accustomed to recast his results. Consequently the English school had little share in the development of the new calculus in the first half of the eighteenth century. Nor did they help much in the translation of Newtonian dynamics and astronomy into analytical terms, or in the development effected therein during the second fifty years by more powerful mathematical tools, even though the tools were developed from those forged by Newton.

On the other hand, it took some time for Newton's work to be appreciated in other countries. It was first made known in France by the writings of Voltaire, who spent the years from 1726 to 1729 in England. Ten years later he and his friend

[1] G. S. Brett, *Sir Isaac Newton*, Baltimore, 1928, p. 269.
[2] See W. W. Rouse Ball, *History of Mathematics*, London, 1901.

Madame du Châtelet, a competent mathematician, published a treatise on the Newtonian system, which proved a source of inspiration to many of the scientific writers in the famous French *Encyclopédie*.

Mathematics and Astronomy in the Eighteenth Century

The first edition of that unequal work was published, under great difficulties, between 1751 and 1780 in thirty-five folio volumes, Diderot being general editor and, for the early years, d'Alembert taking charge of the articles on mathematics. The general tone was preponderatingly theistic but heretical, with an increasing tendency to attack the Government, the Roman Church, and finally Christianity itself. As regards scientific thought, the publication of the Encyclopaedia marks a definite epoch, for it collected and focussed work in many different departments of knowledge, and most of the great men of science in France wrote in its pages.

In mathematics and its applications three men should specially be mentioned: Euler, Lagrange and Laplace. Euler (1707–1783) created new departments in analysis, revised and improved many branches of mathematics, and published books on optics and on the general principles of natural philosophy.

Joseph Louis Lagrange (1736–1813), perhaps the greatest mathematician of the century, was chiefly interested in pure theory. He created the calculus of variations, and systematized the subject of differential equations. But his sweeping generalizations could often be used in physical problems. He himself published work on astronomy, in which he advanced the treatment of the difficult problem of calculating the mutual gravitational effect of three bodies. Also, in his great treatise *Mécanique Analytique*, he founded the whole of mechanics on the conservation of energy in the form of the principles of virtual velocities and least action.

The principle of virtual velocities (or virtual work), used by Leonardo da Vinci to deduce the law of the lever, was defined by Stevin as "What is gained in power is lost in speed". Maupertuis gave the name of "action" to the sum of the products of space (or length) and velocity, and, assuming for metaphysical reasons that *something* should be a minimum in such processes as the propagation of light, showed that the facts agreed with the supposition that light chose the path of least action. Lagrange extended the principle to the motion of any bodies, the "action" being defined as the space integral of the momentum or double the time integral of the kinetic energy. We shall meet this quantity action again in Hamilton's equations, and finally in Planck's recent quantum theory.

Lagrange's differential equations gave to the subject a new generality and completeness. They reduced the theory of mechanics to general formulae from which can be derived the particular equations needed for the solution of each separate problem.[1]

But even more was done to develop the Newtonian system by Pierre Simon de Laplace (1749–1827), the son of a cottager in Normandy, who, by his own abilities and skilful successive adaptations to a changing environment, ended as a Marquis of the Restoration.

Laplace improved the treatment of problems of attraction by adapting Lagrange's method of potential,[2] and he completed Newton's work in one most important aspect, for he proved that the planetary motions were stable, the perturbations produced either by mutual influences, or by external bodies such as comets, being only temporary. Thus Newton's fear that the solar system would become deranged with time by its own action was shown to be unwarranted.

In 1796 Laplace published his *Système du Monde*, which contains a history of astronomy, a general account of the Newtonian system, and of the nebular hypothesis, according to which the solar system was evolved from a rotating mass of

---

[1] By Newton's second law of motion, the rate of change of momentum of a particle is equal to the impressed force. Applying this along each of three axes x, y and z at right angles to each other, we have $m\ddot{x} = X$, $m\ddot{y} = Y$ and $m\ddot{z} = Z$, where m is the mass and X, Y and Z are the components of the force acting. From these expressions Lagrange deduced general equations of motion in the form

$$\frac{d}{dt}\frac{dL}{d\dot{q}} - \frac{dL}{dq} = Q,$$

where L, the Lagrangian function, represents the difference between the kinetic and potential energies of the system, t the time and Q the external force acting on the system so as to tend to increase any co-ordinate q.

[2] The physical meaning of potential may be suggested by saying that the rate of decrease of potential in any direction measures the force in that direction on the unit, mass, electric charge or whatever it be. Laplace showed that the potential V always satisfies the differential equation

$$\nabla^2 V = \frac{\partial^2 V}{\partial x^2} + \frac{\partial^2 V}{\partial y^2} + \frac{\partial^2 V}{\partial z^2} = 0.$$

$\nabla^2 V$ may be termed the local concentration of V. The expression $\nabla^2 V = 0$, in a more general form, became $\nabla^2 V = -4\pi\rho$, a relation which appears in all branches of mathematical physics and "may represent analytically some general law of nature which has not been yet reduced to words" (Rouse Ball).

incandescent gas, a suggestion which had been made in 1755 by Kant, who went further than Laplace, and imagined creation *ex nihilo* and the formation of the nebula from primordial chaos. Modern research shows that this hypothesis is not sound for the comparatively small structure of the Sun and planets, but may hold good for the larger aggregates of stars, seen in the process of formation in the spiral nebulae and at a later stage of development in our own stellar system.

Laplace's analytical discussion was given in his larger work, *Mécanique Céleste*, in 1799–1805,[1] in which he translated the substance of Newton's *Principia* into the language of the infinitesimal calculus, and completed it in many details.

Rouse Ball gives the following account of what happened when Laplace went to present his book to Napoleon:

Someone had told Napoleon that the book contained no mention of the name of God; Napoleon, who was fond of putting embarrassing questions, received it with the remark, "M. Laplace, they tell me you have written this large book on the system of the universe, and have never even mentioned its Creator". Laplace, who, though the most supple of politicians, was as stiff as a martyr on every point of his philosophy, drew himself up and answered bluntly, "Je n'avais pas besoin de cette hypothèse-là". Napoleon, greatly amused, told this reply to Lagrange, who exclaimed, "Ah! c'est une belle hypothèse; ça explique beaucoup de choses".

Laplace's work in physics included an explanation of the phenomena of capillarity by the assumption of forces of attraction insensible at all save minute distances. He also explained the fact that too small a figure was given for the velocity of sound in air by Newton's formula of the square root of the elasticity divided by the density. Laplace traced the discrepancy to heat which, developed in the wave by the sudden compression and absorbed by the sudden expansion alternately, increases the elasticity of the air, and therefore the velocity of the sound.

Further work on gravitational astronomy did little more than complete the work of Newton and Laplace. What seemed a final test of the validity of Newton's hypothesis of attraction was given in 1846 by the prediction of the existence of an unknown planet, a reversal of the method of Newton and Laplace. The perturbations from its orbit of the planet Uranus were not fully to be accounted for by the action of the other

---

[1] A final historical volume was issued in 1825.

known bodies, and, to explain these irregularities, the influence
of a new planet was assumed, and its necessary position
calculated independently by John Couch Adams of Cambridge
and the French mathematician Leverrier. Turning his telescope
to the position indicated by Leverrier, the astronomer Galle
of Berlin detected a planet to which the name of Neptune
was given.

The accuracy of Newton's theory proved to be amazing.
For two centuries every fancied discrepancy was resolved, and,
by help of the theory, generations of astronomers were able
to explain and predict astronomical phenomena. Even now the
experimental resources of civilization must be exhausted in
order to show that Newton's law of gravity involves certain
minute discrepancies with our present knowledge of astronomy.
Lagrange described the *Principia* as the greatest production
of the human mind, and Newton, not only as the greatest
genius that had ever existed, but also as the most fortunate:
"for there is but one universe, and it can happen to but one
man in the world's history to be the interpreter of its laws".
The verdict would be expressed otherwise now, in the light of
the stupendous complexity of nature since revealed to us. But
it serves well to show the effect in the next century of Newton's
work on one of the minds best able to appreciate it.

The union of chemistry and medicine described in the
previous chapter continued to dominate both subjects till the
end of the seventeenth century. The iatro-chemists gradually
cleared chemistry from what had become its disreputable
dependence on alchemy, and brought it within the range of
professional study. The number of known substances and
reactions was largely increased, and a foundation was laid
for an improvement in chemical theory.

We have seen how Robert Boyle in his *Sceptical Chymist*
controverted the survivals of "fire theories"—the Aristotelian
four elements on the one hand and the prevalent chemical
doctrine of the three principles of salt, sulphur and mercury
on the other. His book marks a turning point on the road to
modern views of chemistry.

Newton fitted up a laboratory in the garden behind his
rooms between the Great Gate and the Chapel in Trinity
College. Doubtless it was here that he carried on his experiments in optics and other physical subjects, but he studied

chemistry too. His relative and assistant, Humphrey Newton, *Chemistry*
states:[1]

> He very rarely went to bed before two or three of the clock, sometimes
> not till five or six...especially at spring and fall of the leaf, at which
> time he used to employ about six weeks in his elaboratory, the fire scarce
> going out night or day, he sitting up one night and I another, till he had
> finished his chemical experiments.

Newton's chemical interests seem to have been chiefly concerned with metals, with the causes of chemical affinity, and
with the structure of matter. In the 31st Query in his *Opticks*
we read:

> Have not the small Particles of Bodies certain Powers, Virtues or
> Forces, by which they act at a distance, not only upon the Rays of Light
> for reflecting, refracting and inflecting them, but also upon one another
> for producing a great part of the Phaenomena of Nature? For it's well
> known that Bodies act one upon another by the Attractions of Gravity,
> Magnetism and Electricity; and these Instances shew the Tenor and
> Course of Nature, and make it not improbable but that there may be
> more attractive Powers than these. For Nature is very constant and
> conformable to herself. How these Attractions may be perform'd, I do
> not here consider. What I call Attraction may be perform'd by impulse,
> or by some other means unknown to me. I use that Word here to
> signify only in general any Force by which Bodies tend towards one
> another, whatsoever be the Cause. For we must learn from the Phaeno-
> mena of Nature what Bodies attract one another, and what are the Laws
> and Properties of the Attraction, before we enquire the Cause by which
> the Attraction is perform'd. The Attractions of Gravity, Magnetism and
> Electricity, reach to very sensible distances, and so have been observed
> by vulgar Eyes, and there may be others which reach to so small
> distances as hitherto to escape Observation; and perhaps electrical
> Attraction may reach to such small distances, even without being
> excited by Friction.
> For when Salt of Tartar runs *per deliquium* is not this done by an
> Attraction between the Particles of the Water which float in the Air in
> the form of Vapours? And why does not common Salt, or Salt-petre,
> or Vitriol, run *per deliquium*, but for want of such an Attraction?...And
> is it not from the like attractive Power between the Particles of Oil of
> Vitriol and the Particles of Water, that Oil of Vitriol draws to it a good
> quantity of Water out of the Air, and after it is satiated draws no more,
> and in Distillation lets go the Water very difficultly? And when Water
> and Oil of Vitriol poured successively into the same Vessel grow very
> hot in the mixing, does not this Heat argue a great Motion in the parts
> of the Liquors? And does not this Motion argue that the Parts of the
> two Liquors in mixing coalesce with Violence, and by consequence rush
> towards one another with an accelerated Motion?

[1] *Sir Isaac Newton*, History of Science Society, Baltimore, 1928, p. 214.

13-2

It is probable that Newton spent more time over alchemy and chemistry than over those physical researches which have made him famous. He wrote no book on his work, and beyond the chemical queries in the *Opticks* the only record is to be found in his manuscript notes in the Portsmouth collection. These papers show a special interest in alloys; for instance, Newton states that the most fusible alloy of lead, tin and bismuth contains those metals in the proportions of 5 : 7 : 12. The notes include many extracts copied from alchemical writings, and accounts of a multitude of chemical experiments on flame, on distillation, on the extraction of metals from their ores and on many other substances and their reactions. The manuscripts were examined and a calendar prepared and published in 1888[1], but the extracts given are short, and a new study of the collection seems desirable. It is clear that while Newton made no such striking discoveries in chemistry as he did in physics, yet he showed insight much beyond that of other chemists of his time, as for instance into the meaning of flame, which he concluded only differed from vapour as do bodies red-hot and not red-hot.[2] This is a far more modern view than that of the Aristotelians who held that fire was one of the four elements, or of those contemporary chemists who sought to explain things in terms of the principles of salt, mercury and sulphur.

Newton's views on the constitution of matter have been given above. His acceptance of the atomic theory established it as orthodox, though it could not yet be put in the exact and quantitative form afterwards set forth by Dalton. Voltaire writes in the *Dictionnaire Philosophe*:[3]

The Plenum is to-day considered a chimera...the void is recognized; bodies most hard are looked upon as full of holes like sieves, and in fact this is what they are. Atoms are accepted, indivisible and unchangeable, principles to which is due the permanence of the different elements and of the different kinds of beings.

In the early years of the eighteenth century, experimental chemistry was carried further by many skilful observers. Wilhelm Homberg studied the combination of alkalies with

[1] *A Catalogue of the Portsmouth Collection of Books and Papers written by or belonging to Sir Isaac Newton*, Cambridge, 1888.
[2] *Ibid.* p. 21.
[3] Translated by Ida Freund, *The Study of Chemical Composition*, Cambridge, 1904, p. 283.

acids in different proportions, and thus supplied evidence in favour of the theory that a salt is formed by the union of an acid and a base. This theory, which arose from the work of Sylvius, was the starting point of many of the modern ideas of chemical structure, and fills an important place in history.

The next generation was marked by the work of Hermann Boerhaave of Leyden, who published in 1732 "the most complete and luminous chemical treatise of his time",[1] and Stephen Hales, who investigated gases such as hydrogen, the two oxides of carbon, sulphur dioxide, marsh gas and others, regarding them all as air modified or "tinctured" in different ways by the presence of other bodies.

The chief difficulty of the early chemists was to understand the phenomena of flame and combustion. When bodies are burnt, it seems that something escapes. This something, for long identified with sulphur, was called "phlogiston", the principle of fire, by G. E. Stahl (1660–1734), physician to the King of Prussia. His theory, developed from the ideas of Beccher, was widely accepted after his death and dominated the chemical thought of the later years of the eighteenth century. Both Mayow and Boyle had shown that when metals were burnt the solid increased in weight; therefore phlogiston must possess a negative weight, and Aristotle's conception of a body essentially light was born again out of due time. Chemical science learnt to express its facts in terms of this hypothesis. Owing to its influence, as well as to that of older theories, isolated investigations which pointed to more modern views failed to impress the minds of chemists; the facts had to be rediscovered and then reinterpreted.

As described in the previous chapter, the existence of oxygen in the air and its significance in respiration and combustion had been demonstrated in 1669 by John Mayow, a century before its final discovery. Oxygen was prepared from saltpetre by Borch in 1678, and once more in 1729 by Hales, who collected it over water. Carbon dioxide was obtained and given the name "gas silvestre" by van Helmont about 1640, and the isolation of hydrogen may even be traced back to Paracelsus, who described the action of iron filings on vinegar. Yet all these observations were forgotten and their significance lost; air was still believed to be the only gaseous element.

[1] Sir Ed. Thorpe, *History of Chemistry*, vol. I, London, 1921, p. 67.

The beginning of a change appears in the work of Joseph Black of Edinburgh, who, about 1755, discovered that a new ponderable gas, distinct from atmospheric air, was combined in the alkalies. He named this gas "fixed air". It was what we now call carbon dioxide or carbonic acid. Nevertheless the older ideas still survived. Joseph Priestley (1733–1804) prepared oxygen by heating mercuric oxide, and discovered its unique power of supporting combustion. He also showed that it was essential to the respiration of animals. But he described it as dephlogisticated air, and failed to perceive that his discovery had turned a new page in the history of science. Henry Cavendish (1731–1810) demonstrated the compound nature of water in 1781, thus finally dethroning it from its old proud position as one of the elements. But he still described its constituent gases as phlogiston and dephlogisticated air.

It was reserved for Antoine Laurent Lavoisier (1743–1794), who was sent to the guillotine with other farmers of the taxes, since "the Republic had no need of savants", to materialize modern chemistry out of this cloud of mental nebulosity.

Lavoisier repeated the experiments of Priestley and Cavendish, accurately weighing his reagents and products. For instance, in one experiment he heated to just below its boiling point 4 ounces of mercury in contact with 50 cubic inches of air. Red calx of mercury was formed and increased till the twelfth day. The weight of the calx was 45 grains, and the volume of the residual air was 42 to 43 cubic inches, $\frac{5}{6}$ of the original volume, so that 7 to 8 cubic inches had been used up. The residual air would not support combustion, and small animals died in it in a few minutes.

The 45 grains of red calx were then heated strongly in a small retort. $41\frac{1}{2}$ grains of metallic mercury and a gas were formed. The latter was collected over water, measured, and found to fill 7 to 8 cubic inches and to weigh $3\frac{1}{2}$ to 4 grains. But $41\frac{1}{2} + 3\frac{1}{2} = 45$ grains, so that all the substance was accounted for—the total mass had remained constant. The gas maintained both flame and life more vigorously than ordinary air.

Lavoisier says:

Reflection on the conditions of this experiment shows that the mercury on calcining absorbs the salubrious and respirable portion of the atmosphere, and that the portion of the air which remains behind is a noxious kind of gas incapable of supporting combustion and respiration. Hence atmospheric air is composed of two elastic fluids of different and so to speak opposite nature.[1]

Lavoisier grasped the all-important fact that to explain this and many similar experiments, as well as those of Priestley and Cavendish, the theory of phlogiston was not needed, that it was unnecessary to invent a body with properties fundamentally different from those of other material substances. Newton had based his mechanics on the assumption that mass was constant, an assumption justified by his success. He proved also that, while mass and weight were different conceptions, they were accurately proportioned to each other when compared experimentally. Lavoisier, by the unanswerable evidence of the balance, showed that, although matter may alter its state in a series of chemical actions, it does not change in amount, the quantity of matter is the same at the end as at the beginning of every operation, and can be traced throughout by its weight. The constituents of water were seen to be gases with the ordinary properties of matter, possessing mass and weight, and Lavoisier named them, hydrogen (the water-forming element) and oxygen (the acid-forming element). Burning and respiration were shown to be alike in kind; one a quick, and the other a slow, process of oxidation, each leading to an increase in weight equal to the weight of oxygen combined. The conception of phlogiston with negative weight became unnecessary and vanished from science. The principles established by Galileo and Newton in mechanics were carried over into chemistry, and the road was opened for the tremendous developments of the next hundred years.

The notable effect produced on the study of the structure of the tissues and organs of animals by the invention of the compound microscope has been described in the last chapter. During the period with which we are now concerned, similar methods were extended to botany, and correct ideas began to be formed about the various organs of plants.

From Theophrastus to Cesalpinus no attention seems to have been given to the reproductive organs. The first definitely to describe the function of the stamens and pistils was probably Nehemiah Grew, who in 1676 read a paper to the Royal Society on the Anatomy of Plants. He speaks of the stamens

[1] Quoted by Ida Freund, *loc. cit.* p. 53.

as the male organs, and describes their action, but refers the credit for the theory to Sir Thomas Millington, Savilian Professor at Oxford. Confirmatory evidence and additional details were given by Camerarius of Tübingen, by Morland, and by Geoffroy, in a memoir presented to the Academy in Paris. By these botanists it was made clear that, in the absence of pollen from the anthers of the stamens, no fertilization of the ovum or formation of seed is possible.

The earlier classifications of both animals and plants were based chiefly on utilitarian ideas, or on such obvious external characteristics as led to the division of plants into herbs, trees and shrubs. But in 1660 John Ray (1627–1705)[1] published the first of a series of works on systematic botany, which led to a great improvement in classification and also to advances in morphology, such as the recognition of the true nature of buds. Ray was the first to see the importance of the distinction between monocotyledons and dicotyledons in the embryos of plants, and, by using also the fruit, flower, leaf, and other characters, he initiated a natural system of classification, and indicated many of the plant orders still used by botanists. He then turned his attention to animals, and made great use of comparative anatomy. Here again his work marked an advance towards a natural classification, in quadrupeds, birds and insects.

Ray seems to have obtained some of his terminology from the work of Jung, and through Ray it passed to Linnaeus (Carl von Linné, 1707–1778), the son of a Swedish clergyman, who founded his famous system of classification on the sex organs of plants. This classification held its own till replaced by the modern system which, returning by the light of evolution to the ideas of Ray, and considering all the characters of the organism, tries to place the plants in groups which express their natural relationships.

Linnaeus turned his attention also to the varieties of the human species, having been struck by the obvious differences of race brought to his notice during his wanderings among the Laplanders in his search for arctic plants. In his *System of Nature* he placed man with apes, lemurs and bats in the order of " Primates ", and subdivided man into four groups according to skin colour and other characteristics.

[1] Article "Ray", *Dictionary of National Biography.*

A corresponding development in the knowledge of animals was stimulated by the information acquired by travellers, and by the arrival of specimens of rare and strange beasts to grace the various royal menageries. The close of the first stage in modern zoological science was marked by the publication by Buffon (1707–1788) of an encyclopaedic *Natural History of Animals*. Here again the microscope when applied gave an insight first into intimate structure and then into the functions of the different organs, and moreover showed the existence of vast numbers of minute living bodies, both animal and vegetable, hitherto unsuspected. Though regarding Linnaeus' classification as " une vérité humiliante pour l'homme ", Buffon could not close his eyes to the evidence pointing towards animal relationships, and he ventured the remark, which he afterwards withdrew, that, had it not been for the express statements of the Bible, one might be tempted to seek a common origin for the horse and the ass, the man and the monkey.

Botany, Zoology and Physiology

In ancient and mediaeval times men believed that living things might arise spontaneously from dead matter. Frogs, for instance, might be generated from mud by sunshine, and, when the new world was discovered, it was suggested that perhaps the aboriginal Americans, whose descent from Adam was difficult to trace, might have had the same kind of origin. The first serious doubt about spontaneous generation seems to have been raised by Francesco Redi (1626–1679), who showed that, if the flesh of a dead animal were protected from insects, no grubs or maggots appeared in it. Redi's experiments were considered to be incompatible with the teaching of the Scriptures, and were attacked on that ground; an interesting fact in the light of the controversy which arose in the nineteenth century over the work of Schwann and Pasteur. Here the protagonists had changed sides. Vogt, Haeckel and other materialists upheld the belief in spontaneous generation as a naturalistic explanation of the origin of life, while orthodox theologians welcomed negative results as showing that life had only arisen by a direct act of God. Even in our own day attempts to prove spontaneous generation were reprobated as being based on the assumption that life might arise without direct creation. It seems difficult for some minds to accept facts without reference to their fancied implications. But, to return to the eighteenth century, we find that Redi's work was repeated by the Abbé Spallanzani (1729–1799), who confirmed the experiments, and proved that not even minute forms of life would develope in decoctions which had been boiled vigorously and then protected from the air. Here we see anticipations of Pasteur and of modern bacteriology.

In the last chapter we left animal physiology when Sylvius had thrown aside van Helmont's spiritualistic ideas of ferments governed by *archaei* under the rule of the sensitive soul, and was trying to explain digestion, respiration and other functions of the body by means of an effervescence like that which occurs when vitriol is poured on iron filings or on ashes long exposed to the air.

The pendulum now swung back again.[1] Stahl carried over into physiology the mental outlook from which he had studied chemistry. He maintained the view that all the changes of the living body, though they might superficially resemble ordinary chemical actions, were yet fundamentally different, because they were directly governed by a sensitive soul, *anima sensitiva*, which pervaded all parts.

Stahl's "sensitive soul", unlike that described by van Helmont, had no need of intermediaries—*archaei* or ferments. It controlled directly the chemical and other processes of the body. It differed entirely from the "rational soul" of Descartes' philosophy. To Descartes with his sharp dualism, the human body apart from the soul was a machine, governed by ordinary mechanical laws. To Stahl it was not governed by ordinary physical and chemical laws; but, as long as it was alive, it was controlled in all details by the sensitive soul on a plane far above physics and chemistry. The living body was fitted for special purposes—to be the true and continued temple of the soul, which built up the body and used it for vital ends. The link between soul and body, according to Stahl, was to be found in motion; the preservation and repair of structures, sensation and its concomitants, are modes of motion directed by the sensitive soul. Thus Stahl was the founder of modern vitalism, though his "sensitive soul" passed later into a vaguer "vital principle".

Meanwhile those who did not follow Stahl were divided into a mechanical school and a school that laid more stress on

[1] Sir M. Foster, *History of Physiology*, Cambridge, 1901.

chemical fermentation. Boerhaave combined these views in his *Institutiones Medicae* (1708), though he held that digestion was more of the nature of solution than of fermentation. Dr Singer says that, considering the wide range of his powers, Boerhaave must be regarded as the greatest physician of modern times.[1]

Later in the century, by experiments on kites, dogs and other animals, new insight into digestion was gained, especially by de Réaumur and Spallanzani. Blood pressure was first measured experimentally in horses by Stephen Hales.

Sir Michael Foster considered that the year 1757 marks "the dividing line between modern physiology and all that went before", because in that year was published the first volume of the *Elementa Physiologiae* of Albrecht von Haller (1708–1777).[2] In this work, of which the eighth and last volume left the press in 1765, Haller gives a systematic and candid account of the then state of physiological knowledge about all parts of the body. He himself made important advances in the study of the mechanics of respiration, of the development of the embryo, and of muscular irritability.

He recognized a force inherent in muscle, which for some little time survives the death of the body. But usually the muscles are called into action by another force carried to the muscles from the brain by the nerves. Experiments show, he says, that nerves alone feel; they are therefore the only instruments of sensation as, by their action on muscles, they are the only instruments of movement. All the nerves are gathered into the *medulla cerebri* in the central parts of the brain, whence it may be inferred that "this central part of the brain feels and that in it are presented to the mind the impressions which the nerves, distributed at their extreme ends, have carried to the brain". This is confirmed by the phenomena of disease and by experiments on living animals. Passing on to "conjectures" he suggests that the nervous fluid is "an element of its own kind", that the nerves are hollow tubes to contain it, and that, since both sensation and movement have their source in the medulla of the brain, the medulla is the seat of the soul.

[1] C. Singer, *A Short History of Medicine*, Oxford, 1928, p. 140.
[2] Foster, *loc. cit.* pp. 204, 205.

While astronomy and mathematics were throwing light on the motion of the distant heavenly bodies, and physiology was groping amid the mysteries of the human frame, geographical discovery was widening the knowledge of the surface of the Earth. The art of navigation had been much improved. Stevin invented decimal arithmetic at the end of the sixteenth century and Napier introduced logarithms in 1614. The measurement of longitude became possible when the position of the Moon among the stars could be predicted by Newton's lunar theory, and thus the apparent time of the same celestial phenomenon obtained at two places. The measurement only became easy and accurate when John Harrison perfected the chronometer in 1761–1762 by compensating the effect of changes in temperature by the unequal expansion of two metals. When that was done, Greenwich time could be taken on each ship, and compared with astronomical events so as to give the longitude.

In the seventeenth and eighteenth centuries systematic exploration of the globe began to be undertaken. If the explorers of this period cannot claim for their voyages the full romance associated with the pioneers of discovery in the fifteenth and sixteenth centuries, pioneers who first revealed the Earth as we now know it and mapped the main configuration of continents and oceans, the work of these later navigators is remarkable for the growth of the spirit of scientific investigation which it displays, and it had much to do with the general change in intellectual outlook registered in the French Encyclopaedia.

Among the explorers, I must mention, as in private duty bound, William Dampier (1651–1715), who was one of the first to show the new attitude of mind. His keen eye noted every new tree or plant, and his facile pen described its form and hue with careful accuracy. His *Discourse on Winds* became a classic of meteorology, and he also made notable advances in knowledge both in hydrography and in terrestrial magnetism.[1]

Dampier began his adventures as a buccaneer, and had to make his own way in the world till his books made him famous. Seventy years later, however, scientific interest in exploration had much increased, and with it the status of the explorer. Captain James Cook (1728–1779), who had published work on a solar eclipse, was sent out at the instance of the Royal Society to observe a transit of Venus from the South Pacific

[1] See *Journal Royal Geographical Society*, Nov. 1929, 74, p. 478.

Ocean. His later voyages of discovery were conducted with
keen appreciation of their opportunities for the advancement
of scientific knowledge, and he was one of the earliest recipients
of the Copley Gold Medal, the highest honour the Royal
Society has to bestow.

Geographical Discovery

The voyages and discoveries of the seventeenth and early
eighteenth centuries had much to do with the general intellectual development of France in the years before the
Revolution.[1] The real voyages of Cabot, Baudier, Chardin,
Bernier and others were reinforced by romances, for which
Defoe had set the fashion in *Robinson Crusoe*. Several of those
who wished to criticize the world as it was under the French
Monarchy wrote books to show how much better it would be
in a far island Utopia. By the real observations and false
conclusions of actual explorers and the imaginations of the
romancers, cults arose of fancied "Républiques d'Outre Mer",
of "Le Bon Sauvage" and "Le Sage Chinois". The virtues of
other religions, Buddhist, Confucian or Pagan, were extolled,
and used by Deists and other anti-Christians to attack the
Roman Church.

This literature probably had more effect among the people
at large than had the writings of philosophers and men of
science, and may explain why the eighteenth century accepted
readily the views of Rousseau and Voltaire, views so different
from those expressed a hundred years before by Pascal and
Bossuet. The rosy pictures of primitive life helped such
fallacies as the theory of the social contract, the inevitability
of progress, and the perfectibility of mankind, as well as such
follies as the Revolutionary Reign of Reason. Mistakes like
these are best corrected by history and anthropology. Man,
we find, when he advances at all, does so not by *a priori*
reasoning based on false premises, but by a rough, stumbling
process of trial and error.

The idea of the "noble savage" in romantic literature[2] is the
equivalent of the "golden age" of the ancients, and appears
in Tacitus' descriptions of the Germans. Columbus revived it
in modern times, and in Montaigne it is fully developed. The
first to use the actual words "noble savage" in English was

[1] See Geoffroy Atkinson, *Les Relations des Voyages du XVIII Siècle et
l'Évolution des Idées*, Paris, 1925.

[2] H. N. Fairchild, *The Noble Savage*, Columbia Univ. Press and London,
1928.

Geographical Discovery

perhaps Dryden, but during the romanticism which began in England about 1730 and reached its height about 1790 the idea was frequently employed. Doubtless the Biblical Garden of Eden had much to do with the view that civilization was corrupt compared with primitive life.

From Locke to Kant

In attempting a summary of the scientific thought of the Newtonian epoch, not only must we consider the work of the great physicists, chemists and physiologists, but also the effect produced by writers who were philosophers without being men of science.

The philosopher John Locke (1632–1704), it is true, practised as a physician, and in 1669 found it necessary to argue against scholastic disputations in medicine and in favour of an appeal to experience as exemplified in the methods of his friend Dr Sydenham. He even performed an operation on one Lord Shaftesbury and brought another into the world. But nevertheless his chief work must be taken to be the philosophical *Essay Concerning Human Understanding*.

Both in political and philosophic thought Locke represents a moderate and rational liberalism, in contrast with the political absolutism and philosophic radicalism of Hobbes. Locke had a wholesome British respect for facts and aversion to abstract *a priori* reasoning. He examined the limits of possible human knowledge, and protested against anything being held to be independent of rational criticism. Ideas are not innate, though some knowledge may be self-evident to the educated reason. Other knowledge must be acquired by rational demonstration. All human thoughts are due to experience, either of external things (sensations) or of perception of the operations of our minds (reflections).

From a study of the minds of children and simple folk, Locke infers that the senses first suggest to us primary ideas, such as extension, motion, sound or colour. Then comes an association of what is alike in them, leading to abstract ideas. Thus to sensation comes the internal sense of reflection. We know nothing of substances except their attributes, and those only from sense-impressions such as touch, sight or sound. Only from the attributes showing themselves frequently in a constant connection do we gain the complex idea of a substance underlying the changing phenomena. Even feelings and emotions arise from the combination and repetition of sensations.

When we begin to fix by means of words the abstract ideas thus formed, there is danger of error. Words should not be treated as adequate pictures of things; they are mere arbitrary signs for certain ideas—signs chosen by historical accident, and liable to change. Here Locke's criticism of the understanding passes into a criticism of language—a new idea of great value.

Locke originated modern introspective psychology. Others had looked inward, but, one and all, they had dogmatized after only a hasty glance. Locke quietly and steadily watched the operations of his own mind, just as he watched the symptoms of his patients. He came to the conclusion that knowledge is the discernment of agreement or disagreement, either of our thoughts among themselves or between our thoughts and the external phenomena independent of them. A man is sure that he himself exists, and as he had a beginning there must, to account for it, be a First Cause, which is God the Supreme Reason. But relations between our thoughts and external things can only be established by induction from particular instances. Thus knowledge of nature can be only an affair of probability, liable to be upset by the discovery of new facts.

Thomas Aquinas deduced a synthesis of knowledge from mediaeval theology and the philosophy of Aristotle. Locke, with characteristic British practical sense, and a wide outlook on life and thought acquired at a critical period of history, wrote on the "Reasonableness of Christianity", and essayed to found a rational religion as well as a rational science on the sure ground of experience. Both attempted a synthesis. But while Aquinas' scheme had the rigidity and absoluteness of its chief constituents, Locke's contained the possibility of continual adaptation to the varying needs of intellectual development, and an insistence on the toleration of various religious opinions, which, in an age when each party believed themselves to be the sole depository of absolute truth, was perhaps Locke's greatest proof of originality.

To a certain extent his philosophy supplied a complement to Newton's science, and the two together produced a notable reaction in the mind of George Berkeley (1684–1753), afterwards Bishop of Cloyne in Ireland.

Realizing the danger of the mechanical and materialistic philosophy in a science of matter in motion, a danger which lay hid, even from Newton himself, Berkeley took the bold course. Accepting the new knowledge and its picture of the world as true, he asked in effect, "What is the world of which it is true?" and pointed out that the only answer is that it is the world revealed by the senses, and it is only the senses which make it real. Since the so-called primary qualities, extension, figure and motion are themselves only ideas existing in the mind, they, like the secondary qualities, cannot exist in an unperceiving substance.[1] In his Preface to the 1901 edition of Berkeley's *Works*, Campbell Fraser thus puts it:

> The whole material world, as far as it can have any practical concern with the knowings and doings of men, is real only by being realized in like manner in the percipient experience of some living mind....Try to conceive an eternally dead universe, empty for ever of God and all finite spirits, and you find you cannot....This does not mean denial of the existence of the world that is daily presented to our senses...the only material world of which we have experience consists of the appearances which are continually rising as real objects in a passive procession of interpretable signs, through which each finite person realizes his own individual personality; also the existence of other finite persons; and the sense-symbolism that is more or less interpreted in the natural sciences, all significant of God...God must exist because the material world to be a real world, needs to be continually realized and regulated by living Providence.

All this to the plain man seems to be a denial of the existence of matter. It has led to endless criticism, both well-informed and ill, from the days of Samuel Johnson, who thought he had refuted Berkeley by kicking a stone, to those of a recent writer of Limericks. But it seems true that *the world we know* is only made real by the senses; we cannot know (though we may make inferences about) the world of hypothetical reality which may or may not lie hid within it. But perhaps that is not Berkeley's interpretation of his philosophy.

Berkeley does not, as is sometimes said, deny the evidence of the senses. On the contrary, he confines himself to the evidence of the senses. Locke thought that a belief in the existence of a real world of matter behind phenomena is a reasonable inference from our knowledge of its qualities, though we cannot know its ultimate nature. Berkeley denied the reality of that unknown world, and held that reality exists in the world of thought alone.

[1] Berkeley's *Complete Works*, vol. i, p. 262.

An attitude still more sceptical as regards the possibilities of knowledge was taken by David Hume (1711–1776), who, using Berkeley's arguments, denied reality to mind as well as to matter. Berkeley banished the occult substratum which the men of science had conceived to explain the phenomena of matter; Hume banished also the occult substratum which the philosophers had invented to explain the phenomena of mind. All that is real is a succession of "impressions and ideas".

Hume revived the interminable controversy about the meaning of causation. To him, our idea that one event is the cause of another is due to an association of the ideas of the two events, produced by a long list of instances in which the one has preceded the other. It is merely an affair of experience; in nature events are conjoined, but we cannot infer that they are connected causally. To those empiricists who profess to establish general principles by induction from the facts of experience, Hume points out that, in appealing exclusively to sense-experience, they have made it impossible to pass beyond custom-bred expectation to the inductive inference of universal laws. Thus Hume argues that the principle of causality is merely an instinctive belief: "Nature has determined us to judge, as well as to breathe and to feel".

Hume's contention that causality is neither self-evident nor capable of logical demonstration was fully accepted by Immanuel Kant (1724–1804)[1], who realized also that the same was true of all the other principles fundamental to science and philosophy. The inductive proof of general laws from the data of experience is only possible upon the prior acceptance of rational principles independently established, so that we may not look to experience for their proof. Either Hume's sceptical conclusions must be accepted, or we must find some criterion free from the defects of the rationalist and empirical methods of proof. "How are synthetic *a priori* judgments possible?"

Leibniz, like Hume, had denied the possibility of proving general principles empirically, but, accepting the existence of general principles, he had drawn the opposite conclusion—that pure reason is greater than sense-perception, is, indeed, the revealer of external unchanging truth, not only the actual and real constitution of the material world, but also the wider

---

[1] N. Kemp Smith, *A Commentary to Kant's "Critique of Pure Reason"*, London, 1918.

realm of all possible entities. The real is only one of the many possibilities in the universe of truth.

To Hume, "thought is merely a practical instrument for the convenient interpretation of our human experience; it has no objective or metaphysical validity of any kind". To Leibniz, "thought legislates universally; it reveals the wider universe of the eternally possible; and, prior to all experience, can determine the fundamental conditions to which that experience must conform.... There is no problem, scientific, moral or religious which is not vitally affected by the decision as to which of these alternatives we are to adopt, or what reconciliation of their conflicting claims we hope to achieve".[1] Our modern belief in biological evolution favours the first view: thought may be a mere instrument developed by natural selection for self-preservation. But recent mathematics favour the second: thought has transcended Euclidean space, defining new kinds of space such as no experience reveals.

Kant's task was to discuss these opposing views, and save as much of Leibniz's pure reason as Hume had left undamaged. He starts from the ground common to both—that universality and necessity cannot be reached by any empirical method. He takes the validity of *a priori* thought from Leibniz, but he accepts from Hume the belief that the rational elements in it are of a synthetic nature. The principles which lie at the base of knowledge have therefore no intrinsic necessity or absolute authority. They are prescribed to human reason, and are verifiable in fact; they are conditions of sense-experience, of our knowledge of appearance; but not applicable to the discovery of ultimate reality; they are valid within the realm of experience, but useless for the construction of a metaphysical theory of things in themselves. Kant's rationalism accepts the *a priori* which cannot be shown to be more than relative to human experience.

To Kant, the limits of scientific investigation are laid down by the Newtonian methods of mathematical physics; thus alone, he holds, can scientific knowledge be obtained. And such knowledge, he points out, is of appearance and not of reality. Kant's restriction of scientific knowledge to that won by the methods of mathematical physics is too narrow and would exclude much modern biology. But his distinction between appearance and

[1] N. Kemp Smith, *loc. cit.* p. xxxii.

reality is still of philosophic value. The world of science is the world revealed by the senses, the world of phenomena, of appearance; it is not necessarily the world of ultimate reality.

To Newton, space and time are, by the Will of God, existent in and by themselves, independent alike of the mind which apprehends them and of the objects with which they are occupied. To Leibniz, on the other hand, space and time are empirical concepts, abstracted from our confused sense-perceptions of the relations of real things. Kant points out that, while we cannot tell whether time (or space) is metaphysically real, the *consciousness* of time, in our apprehension of change, is certainly real, and a similar distinction seems to hold for extension or space. Thus he hovers between Newton and Leibniz. He will not finally classify space and time either with the data of the bodily senses or with the concepts of the understanding. They combine predicates seemingly contradictory, and have led to unresolved "antinomies of reason" from the days of Zeno onwards. The world of physics is a manifold of events; the mind distributes them in space and time, but in doing so produces relations between phenomena which prove ultimately to be self-contradictory. We cannot say whether the mechanical picture of events, certainly true in detail, has an ultimate teleological explanation and meaning —some part in working towards an End. We can frame such deep questions, but must be content to leave them unsolved. Now some people hold that, of all the older philosophies, Kant's metaphysic best represents the position to which physical and biological science point in this year 1929. Relativity and the quantum theory; biophysics, biochemistry and the idea of purposeful adaptation; all these latest developments of science, these people say, have brought scientific philosophy back to Kant.[1] On the other hand it is fair to give the opposite opinion of Mr Bertrand Russell who says: "Kant deluged the philosophic world with muddle and mystery, from which it is only now beginning to emerge. Kant has the reputation of being the greatest of modern philosophers, but to my mind he was a mere misfortune".[2] This is another instance of the want of a consensus of opinion which still appears in metaphysical questions.

[1] See J. B. S. Haldane, *Possible Worlds*, London, 1927, p. 124.
[2] *An Outline of Philosophy*, London, 1927, p. 83.

The concordance which some people see between Kant's philosophy and the indications of modern science may be due, partly at any rate, to the fact that Kant himself was a competent physicist. He anticipated Laplace in formulating a nebular hypothesis to explain the origin of the solar system. He was the first to point out that tidal friction must have a slow retarding effect on the Earth's rotation, and that by its reaction it has forced the Moon to present always the same face to the Earth. He showed that the different linear velocities of successive zones on the Earth as it rotates explain the "trade" winds, and other similar steady currents of air. He wrote also on the Causes of Earthquakes, on the Different Races of Men, on Volcanoes in the Moon, and on Physical Geography. Thus it is obvious that Kant had a wide knowledge of the science of his time. He had also the scientific restraint which accepts the suspension of judgment when a decision between alternative possibilities (or impossibilities) cannot logically be made. This attitude is evident also in his treatment of the problem of reality.

Locke and Hume regarded metaphysical reality as beyond investigation by human reason. To Hume especially ultimate problems seemed insoluble by what he regarded as the only method of acquiring knowledge. He considered it dangerous to defend Christianity by logical arguments, saying (possibly ironically) that "our holy religion is founded on faith not on reason". Here we have a modern equivalent of the late mediaeval revolt against the rational synthesis of Scholasticism. Speculative philosophy was still moving in a periodic orbit, while science had started on its steady advance.

Descartes and his successors assume in their dualism that consciousness is ultimate and cannot be analysed. Kant tries to go further and to dissect consciousness into factors. It involves active judgment, an awareness of meaning; it does not reveal itself, but only its objects. So far as our mental states are known at all, they are known objectively, as we know outside bodies. Thus our subjective states, sensations, feelings, desires, are objective in the sense that they are objects of consciousness; they are part of the order of nature which our consciousness reveals. Hence the moral sense is as real as the starry heaven, indeed more real, because it is explicable only on the assumption that it is part of the autonomous activity of a Being which is real and not apparent only. The moral law is the one form in which reality discloses itself to the human mind. Reason prescribes as the end of our actions, as the *summum bonum*, happiness in accordance with moral worth. To our limited minds this seems possible only in a future life, and under the rule of an omnipotent Deity, but Kant holds that we must not conclude that this necessity represents the actual fact merely because it seems to us the only explanation.

Newton and his immediate disciples used the new dynamical science to demonstrate the wisdom and goodness of an all-powerful Creator. In Locke's philosophy this tendency was less vigorous, and it was ruled out altogether in Hume's separation of reason and faith.

In the second half of the eighteenth century the change of outlook became more general. The ablest men in all departments of life, in France at any rate, were for the most part sceptical in matters of religion. Voltaire's attacks on the clergy and their teaching were but the most witty examples of a widespread tendency of thought. Locke and the English Deists had their continental counterparts, Voltaire and others, who undermined orthodoxy, in much the same way as the existence of the Whig Monarchy in England tended to loosen the authority of legitimism in other countries.

Towards this general wave of heretical thought the mechanical philosophy brought perhaps the most important contribution. The astonishing success of the Newtonian theory in explaining the mechanism of the heavens led to an overestimate of the power of mechanical conceptions to give an ultimate account of the whole Universe. As Mach says,[1] "The French Encyclopaedists of the eighteenth century imagined they were not far from a final explanation of the world by physical and mechanical principles; Laplace even conceived a mind competent to foretell the progress of nature for all eternity, if but the masses and their velocities were given". Few would venture to make such a sweeping statement nowadays, and definite indications have quite recently appeared to suggest that such determinism is impossible. But, when first formulated, it was a natural exaggeration of the power of the new

[1] E. Mach, *Die Mechanik in ihrer Entwickelung*, 1888, Eng. trans. T. J. McCormack, London, 1902, p. 463.

knowledge which had impressed the minds of men with its range and scope, before they realized its necessary limits. In fact we have a repetition in changed circumstances of the story of the Greek Atomists, who extended their successful speculative views of physics to the world of life and thought, unconscious of the logical chasms which lay between, chasms not bridged, but only revealed and partially explored, by the work of two thousand years.

Newton thought that his music of the spheres sang of an all-wise and all-powerful God, and, in his modesty, likened himself to a child finding pretty pebbles on the shore while the ocean of truth lay unknown before him. But others were less cautious. In England, where the Church was comprehensive and, for the most part, liberal-minded, where, moreover, each man was free to invent a new religion to suit himself, and a considerable number availed themselves of their freedom, the mechanical outlook never became so prevalent as in the more logical France, where Roman absolutism was the only effective religion. Newton's countrymen in general retained not only Newton's science, but Newton's philosophy and the essence of Newton's faith. This English tendency to hold simultaneously beliefs which, in the knowledge of the time, seem incompatible, is a constant surprise to continental minds. It probably arises from an instinctive apprehension among a political people that there is usually much to be said for both sides of a question, and that further knowledge may reconcile the seeming incompatibles. In abler minds it discloses a truly scientific power of following two lines of useful thought, while suspending judgment on their deeper implications and correlations for the examination of which there is not yet evidence available.

On the other hand, Newton's French disciples taught that the Newtonian system indicated reality as a great machine, in all essentials already known, so that man, body and soul, became part of an invincible and mechanical necessity. Voltaire, for instance, in his *Ignorant Philosopher*, remarks that, "it would be very singular that all nature, all the planets, should obey eternal laws, and that there should be a little animal, five feet high, who, in contempt of these laws, could act as he pleased, solely according to his caprice". Voltaire ignores the problems of the meaning of natural laws, of the significance of life, of the nature of the human mind, of the essence of free-will. Nevertheless, he expresses vividly the current French assumptions as to the philosophic and religious import of the Newtonian cosmogony.

While the philosophers were interpreting Newton's system of dynamics as giving information about appearance only, and not about ultimate reality, and the Deists were using it to attack Roman orthodoxy, a more popular current of thought was setting strongly in the direction of materialism, a word first used in the eighteenth century. Whether or no the hard impenetrable atoms were formed in the beginning by God, as Newton held, they had very little to do with Him when they got into the heads of some of Newton's continental interpreters, and were used to revive the philosophy of the ancient Atomists.

The name materialism is often employed in a loose sense as synonymous with atheism, or indeed as a term of abuse for any philosophy which does not square with the prevailing orthodoxy. But to us it has its stricter meaning—a belief that dead matter, in the hard unyielding lumps pictured by common sense, or the solid impenetrable Newtonian particles, is the sole ultimate reality of the Universe; that thought and consciousness are but by-products of matter; and that there is nothing real underlying it or existing beyond it.

The ancient Atomists attributed sensation not to the substance of the atoms but to their arrangement and movement. This view was accepted on the revival of materialism by de la Mettrie (1748) and Maupertuis (1751), but Robinet (1761) assigned sensation to matter itself.[1]

The allied ideas of mechanical determinism were also emphasized by the French materialists, especially by de la Mettrie in his work *L'Homme Machine*. By attacking Christian morality as well as theism, de la Mettrie incurred widespread reprobation, and for long his name was used as a warning example of the dire effects of unorthodox beliefs. Another famous book, *La Système de la Nature*, seems to have been written chiefly by Holbach, who, in opposition to the dualism of Descartes, argued that since man, a material being, thinks, therefore matter is capable of thought. This is the antithesis of the doctrine of Leibniz, who, in his monads, spiritualized matter instead of materializing the soul.

[1] F. A. Lange, *Geschichte des Materialismus*, Eng. trans. E. C. Thomas, vol. II, 3rd ed. London, 1925, p. 29.

Materialism takes the phenomenal world as real, naïvely and dogmatically. Its attempt to explain consciousness, like those made by other philosophies, is an obvious failure, for how can the motion of senseless particles produce consciousness, or, in the alternative, what is the endowment of matter itself with sensation but an assumption of the very thing to be explained, a restatement of the problem at issue? Materialism cannot even refute Berkeley's idealism, at the opposite pole of thought. It cannot survive the destructive analysis of any critical philosophy. Yet, since it can be "understanded of the people", while philosophic criticism cannot, it supplied for a time the best uninstructed alternative to uninstructed orthodoxy. Moreover, it is the simplest and least mentally fatiguing way of making that intelligible picture of the world which science needs for its advance, or, at all events, needed during the eighteenth and nineteenth centuries. For rough, everyday use, it has its advantages, indeed it is necessary for each *detail* of science, but there is always the danger that it should be taken as the necessary philosophy of science as a whole, and, as a philosophy, gain the prestige which the success of science inevitably gives. This happened for a while in the nineteenth century.

But, as soon as we think a little deeper, we see that matter, like all the other concepts of science, is only known to us through its effects on the senses—we are brought again to the problem of knowledge. The world of science is the world of appearance, revealed and conditioned by our senses and our minds, it is not necessarily the world of reality. In a later chapter we shall see how the hard, massy, ultimate particles of Lucretius and Newton have been resolved into complex systems of protons and whirling electrons, non-material, perhaps only to be represented by wave-equations. We shall see too how, in the light of relativity, matter has ceased to be something which persists in time and moves in space, and has become a mere system of interrelated events. In the eighteenth century such possibilities were still hidden in the future; but Locke and Berkeley and Hume had already shown that nature could only be apprehended through the senses. Even with the knowledge then available, materialism, in ultimate analysis, should have failed to satisfy.

Chapter V

NINETEENTH-CENTURY PHYSICS

The Scientific Age—Mathematics—Imponderable Fluids—
Units—The Atomic Theory—The Electric Current—Chemical
Effects—Other Properties of Currents—The Wave Theory of
Light—Electromagnetic Induction—The Electromagnetic Field
of Force—Electromagnetic Units—Heat and the Conservation
of Energy—The Kinetic Theory of Gases—Thermodynamics—
Spectrum Analysis—Electric Waves—Chemical Action—Theory
of Solution.

I F the nineteenth century has a just claim to be regarded as
the beginning of the scientific age, the reason is to be sought
not merely, or even chiefly, in the rapid growth of our knowledge of nature for which that century was remarkable. The
study of nature is as old as mankind: in the primitive arts of
life we have the application of fragmentary knowledge of the
properties of matter, and in early myth and fable we have
theories of the origin of the world and of man, founded on
the evidence then available. But, during the last hundred or
hundred and fifty years, the whole conception of the natural
Universe has been changed by the recognition that man, subject
to the same physical laws and processes as the world around
him, cannot be considered separately from the world, and that
scientific methods of observation, induction, deduction and
experiment are applicable, not only to the original subject-
matter of pure science, but to nearly all the many and varied
fields of human thought and activity.

In the great inventions of former ages we see the needs of
practical life stimulating the craftsman to further achievement: the need precedes and calls forth the invention, unless
the invention be the result of accidental discovery. But during
the nineteenth century we see scientific investigation, undertaken in a search for pure knowledge, beginning to precede
and to suggest practical applications and inventions. The
invention when produced opens a new field both for scientific
research and industrial development. For example, Faraday's
electromagnetic experiments led to the invention of the
dynamo and other electromagnetic machines, which, in their
turn, have put new problems and new powers of solving them

The Scientific Age

into the hands of men of science. Maxwell's investigation of the properties of electromagnetic waves led in fifty years to wireless telegraphy and telephony, arts which set new problems to the physicists. The discovery by Pasteur, that fermentation, putrefaction and many diseases are due to the action of microscopic living organisms, has produced immensely important results in industry, medicine and surgery. Mendel's experiments in the cloister of Brünn on the heredity of peas have already led to systematized plant-breeding, to improved types of wheat and other grain, and to a knowledge of the principles governing the inheritance of some of the specific qualities of plants and animals, a knowledge which in the future may have incalculable effects on the welfare of the human race. When, from toiling obscurely in the rear of empirical arts, science passed on and held up the torch in front, the scientific age may be said to have begun.

Many of the lines of thought characteristic of the nineteenth century had already come into being when the century opened, and it is impossible to make a sharp chronological division. Moreover, in the applications of technical science, the great industrial revolution which is still in progress had already begun. One of its chief instruments, the steam engine, had reached a serviceable form when James Watt patented the principle of the condenser in 1769. This was a practical invention, to which, at a later stage, scientific principles were applied to carry out developments and improvements. But the electric telegraph, the other great agent in revolutionizing the social conditions of the world, was a consequence of research in pure science, a research the origins of which can be traced back to Galvani's work in 1786. In return, the mirror galvanometer, invented to facilitate submarine telegraphy, proved of the utmost benefit to pure science.

To some men the practical applications of science stand for its main achievement. But the effect of such activities on human thought, though great, is indirect, slow and cumulative. The gradual and apparently inevitable extension of man's power over the material resources of nature gives applied science, by means of which the advance is chiefly secured, an importance in the eyes of uninstructed people far beyond that with which they endow pure knowledge. Indeed, to them, as one triumph after another is won, the effect to all appearance is that of an invincible if slow advance. It seems that no limits can be assigned to the extension of man's mastery over nature; and it is assumed, without warrant, that the mechanical principles by the application of which that expansion is made are competent to account for the whole Universe.

The broad tendency of the period now to be brought under review is the gradual extension of the experimental and mathematical methods of dynamics to the other subjects of physics, and, as far as applicable, to chemistry and biology also. The study of science was, for a time at any rate, divorced from the pursuit of philosophy. Throughout the nineteenth century, most men of science, consciously or unconsciously, held the common-sense view that matter, its primary properties and their relations, as revealed by science, are ultimate realities, and that human bodies are mechanisms perhaps occasionally controlled or influenced by minds. When they thought about ultimate scientific concepts, many physicists realized that these opinions, convenient as working assumptions, would not stand critical examination; but, in the laboratory as in practical life, there was no time for philosophic doubt.

On the foundations laid down by Newton and Lavoisier, physics and chemistry raised an ever-growing and concordant structure. In the light of this success, it came to be assumed that the general lines had been drawn once for all, that no strikingly new discoveries were likely, that the only work which remained to be done was to carry scientific measurement to greater accuracy, and to fill a few obvious gaps in knowledge. This, indeed, was the belief till the very eve of the revolutionary developments at the end of the nineteenth century.

During the nineteenth century many new departments of mathematics came into being. Among them must be mentioned the theory of numbers, theories of forms and groups, the development of trigonometry into theories of functions of multiple periodicity, and the general theory of functions. Synthetic and analytic methods created a new geometry, while the application of many of these methods to physical problems was perhaps the greatest among those stimuli which led later to the tremendous advances in physical science.

The details of the history of mathematics are outside the scope of this book, which is concerned only with the main

Mathematics   outlines of those branches which are of special importance in the more fundamental parts of physics.

In the first place, in his *Théorie analytique de la chaleur*, published in 1822, Fourier showed that any function of a variable, whether continuous or discontinuous, can be expanded in a series of sines of multiples of the variable; a result ever since constantly used in analysis by methods in which Poisson led the way. Gauss developed the work of Lagrange and Laplace, and applied his results to electricity. He also established the theory of errors of measurement.

The great advance made in dynamics by Lagrange when he formulated his differential equations of motion was carried further by Sir William Rowan Hamilton (1805–1865). Hamilton expressed the kinetic energy in terms of the momenta and the co-ordinates of a system, and discovered how to transform the Lagrangian equations into a set of differential equations of the first order for the determination of the motion.[1] Hamilton also invented quaternions.

The assumptions which underlie Euclidean geometry were discussed by Saccheri in 1733, by Lobatschewsky in 1826 and 1840, by Gauss in 1831 and 1846, and by Bolyai in 1832. General attention was directed to non-Euclidean geometry by Riemann in 1854, and further work was done by Cayley, Beltrami, Helmholtz, Klein and Whitehead. These writers showed that it is possible to discuss mathematically the properties of non-Euclidean space, irrespective of the answer to the question whether such space is known to the senses. Their researches became of physical importance when Einstein formulated the modern theory of relativity.

---

[1] If $p_1, p_2, \ldots$ be the momenta, and $q_1, q_2, \ldots$ be the co-ordinates, the Lagrangian equations become $\dot{p}_1 = -\,\partial H/\partial q_1, \ldots$ and $\dot{q}_1 = -\,\partial H/\partial p_1, \ldots$, where H is the total energy.

The potential ψ in a field of force is defined so that the resultant force in any direction is measured by the rate of decrease of potential in that direction,

$$F = -\left(i\,\frac{d\psi}{dx} + j\,\frac{d\psi}{dy} + k\,\frac{d\psi}{dz} \right).$$

Hamilton's operator

$$\left(i\,\frac{d}{dx} + j\,\frac{d}{dy} + k\,\frac{d}{dz} \right)$$

is written as ∇, and the first equation becomes

$$F = -\,\nabla\psi.$$

The symbol of operation ∇ directs us to measure the rate of increase of ψ in each of three rectangular directions and then to compound the vector quantities thus found into one.

At the beginning of the nineteenth century some of the older physical ideas still survived. The conception of a weightless fluid had many years of useful life before it, in spite of the disappearance of phlogiston, and the extension of the principle of the conservation of mass from physics to chemistry. Although the most acute of the natural philosophers, men such as Newton, Boyle and Cavendish, inclined to the opinion that heat was due to a vibratory agitation of the particles of bodies, their opinion could not be developed into a useful working hypothesis in the absence of definite conceptions corresponding to our notions of energy. The advances which were waiting to be made needed the idea of heat as a measurable quantity, unchanged in amount as it passed by contact from one body to another. To undertake experiment, using this conception as a guide, men wanted a definite and suitable representation of the nature of heat. This was at hand in the theory that heat was a subtle, invisible, weightless fluid, passing between the particles of bodies with perfect freedom.

Imponderable Fluids

In the light of this theory, Joseph Black (1728–1799) discovered and investigated the phenomena of the change of state from ice to water, and from water to steam. He found that during these changes large quantities of heat were absorbed with no change in temperature, were, as he said, rendered latent. He explained the facts by supposing that the thermal fluid or caloric united with ice to form water as a quasi-chemical compound, and again with water to form steam. His measurements indicated that, to melt a given mass of ice, it needed as much heat as would raise the temperature of an equal mass of water through 140° Fahrenheit, the true figure being 143°. He underestimated the latent heat of evaporation, finding 810° F. instead of 967°. But accuracy in this determination is difficult. Black also originated the theory of specific heat to explain the different amounts of heat needed to produce the same change of temperature in different substances, leaving the detailed measurements to his pupil Irvine to work out. He thus established the method of calorimetry, or the measurement of a quantity of heat. The caloric or fluid theory of heat sufficed to guide the course of the science till Helmholtz and Joule, between 1840 and 1850, demonstrated the equivalence between heat and work, and established the idea of heat as a mode of motion.

A similar fluid theory, or rather two rival fluid theories, served to guide those who were investigating the phenomena of electricity. The attractions and repulsions between bodies electrified by friction may be described on the supposition that there is a substance, electricity, which, like heat, is a quantity subject to the laws of addition and subtraction. In an early stage of its history, however, the existence of two distinct and opposite varieties of electricity were clearly recognized. An electric charge developed by rubbing glass with silk will neutralize a charge produced by rubbing ebonite with fur. These results were explained by the supposition of two fluids with opposite properties, or of one fluid, of which an excess or defect from the normal quantity gives rise to the electrified state. The terms of speech appropriate to the one-fluid theory, with its positive and negative electricities, are still with us, though, as we shall see later, electricity is now known to be not a continuous fluid but corpuscular or atomic, and to consist of two kinds of corpuscles. Experiments on electrostatics were facilitated when larger quantities of electricity became available, produced by the construction of electrical machines working by friction, and stored in condensers, such as the Leyden jar—a glass bottle coated inside and outside with tinfoil.

As soon as the spark and noise of an electric discharge were noticed, their resemblance to lightning and thunder was recognized, and the identity in nature of the two phenomena suspected. The problem of the establishment of this identity, the bringing of the thunderbolts of Jove into conformity with the laws of physics, seems to have possessed a fascination for the mind of Benjamin Franklin (1706–1790), and many of his later letters are filled with the description of experiments repeating on a small scale with the charges of Leyden jars the effects of lightning in fusing metals, rending materials, etc.

The action of sharp points in discharging electrified bodies suggested the idea of the lightning conductor to d'Alibard and others in France. In order "to determine the question whether the clouds that contain lightning are electrified or not" an iron rod forty feet high was erected at Marli in 1752. When thunder clouds passed, sparks were drawn from the lower end of the rod. This experiment was repeated in other countries, with complete success—a success too complete, indeed, in the

case of Professor Riehmann of St Petersburg, who was killed
by a shock from an iron rod erected on his house. Meanwhile
Franklin himself had safely carried out a similar experiment
by means of a kite.

To the top of the upright stick of the kite is to be fixed a very sharp
pointed wire, rising a foot or more above the wood. To the end of the
twine, next the hand, is to be tied a silk ribbon, and where the silk and
twine join a key may be fastened. This kite is to be raised when a
thunder-gust appears to be coming on, and the person who holds the
string must stand within a door or window, or under some cover, so
that the silk ribbon may not be wet; and care must be taken that the
twine does not touch the frame of the door or window. As soon as any
of the thunder-clouds come over the kite the pointed wire will draw the
electric fire from them, and the kite, with all the twine, will be electrified,
and the loose filaments of the twine will stand out every way and be
attracted by an approaching finger. And when the rain has wet the kite
and twine, so that it can conduct the electric fire freely, you will find it
stream out plentifully from the key on the approach of your knuckle.
At this key the phial may be charged; and from electric fire thus obtained
spirits may be kindled, and all the other electric experiments be performed, which are usually done by the help of a rubbed globe or tube,
and thereby the sameness of the electric matter with that of lightning
completely demonstrated.

During the eighteenth century, many experiments were
made on the electrification produced by heating certain
minerals and crystals, such as tourmaline; and attention was
drawn once more to the benumbing power of shocks given by
torpedo and other electric fish. Their electrical organs were
examined, and the shocks they inflict were ascribed definitely
to electrical manifestations.

The fluid theories of electricity and magnetism were assumed
also in the investigations made at the end of the eighteenth
century on electric and magnetic forces. The torsion balance,
a light horizontal bar hung at its middle by a long fine wire
inside a glass case, was invented in 1784 by Coulomb, a French
military engineer. He placed an electrified ball at the end of
the bar, and deflected it by another ball brought near. He
also replaced the bar by a steel magnet, and deflected one of
its poles by that of another magnet. In this way he found that
both the electric and magnetic forces diminished as the square
of the distance increased, thus proving for these forces the
same relation as Newton had demonstrated for gravitation.
Moreover, the electric force was found to be proportional to
the amount of electric charge, and could therefore be used to

measure it. About ten years earlier, the same law of electric force had been discovered by Henry Cavendish in another way. He proved experimentally that there is no electric force inside a closed charged conductor of any form, and therefore none inside a sphere. Newton had shown mathematically that, if the inverse square law holds good, a uniform shell of gravitating matter exerts no force on a body inside it, and no other law of force will give this result. A similar investigation applies to electric forces, and again no other law than that of the inverse square will explain the experimental fact that there is no internal electric force.

The law of force being established, mathematicians took over the subject of electrostatics, and deduced an elaborate system of relations which proved concordant with observation wherever it was possible to make a comparison. The distribution of electric charge on the surface of conductors, the electric forces and potentials in their neighbourhood, the electrostatic capacity of different arrangements of conductors and insulators, proved amenable to mathematical treatment in the skilful hands of Gauss, Poisson, Green and others.

The theory of a weightless, incompressible electric fluid is consistent with the idea of electricity as a definite quantity, and, though not necessary for these researches, did, as a matter of fact, give a convenient picture by which the phenomena could be represented and examined.

Of more historical importance was the attention directed to the electric force. Like gravitation, it appeared to act at a distance across intervening space. For mathematicians no further explanation was needed; but physicists soon began to speculate about the nature of this space, which somehow could transmit two, apparently distinct; forces. This led, as we shall see, to modern theories of what are now called "field physics".

The multiplicity of weights and measures, which afflicted, and indeed still afflicts, the world, was first replaced by a logical and convenient decimal system by the French. A Report was presented to the National Assembly in 1791; the necessary measurements were finished and adopted in 1799; the system was made permissive in 1812, and compulsory in 1820.

The fundamental unit of length, the metre, was meant to be one ten millionth part of a quadrant of the Earth through Paris. Once adopted, however, the practical unit is the distance at 0° Centigrade between two marks on a certain metallic bar, and this has not been altered though an increased accuracy of geodetic measurement has shown that the length is not the exact fraction of an earth quadrant that it was meant to be. The unit of volume, the litre, should be a cube with a side of one decimetre (one-tenth of a metre) in length, but, as this is difficult to measure, the litre was defined in 1901 as the volume of one kilogram of pure water at the pressure of one atmosphere and 4°C., its temperature of maximum density.

The unit of mass, the kilogram, was meant to be the mass of a cubic decimetre of water, at 4°C., though it is now a mass equal to that of a platinum-iridium standard made in 1799 by Lefèbre-Ginneau and Fabbroni. The accuracy of their work is shown by Guillaume's latest (1927) value of the litre, viz. 1000.028 cubic cms.

The unit of time, the second, is defined as the 1/86400 part of the mean solar day, the time, averaged over the year, between successive transits of the centre of the Sun's disc across the meridian.[1]

In 1822 Fourier, in his *Théorie de Chaleur*, pointed out that secondary or derived quantities had certain dimensions when expressed in terms of fundamental quantities. Thus if we denote length by L, mass by M and time by T, the dimensions of a velocity (v), that is the length described in a unit of time, are L/T or LT^{-1}. Acceleration, the velocity added in unit time, has dimensions v/T, that is L/T^2 or LT^{-2}. Force (f) is mass × acceleration, or MLT^{-2}; work is ML^2T^{-2}. The derivation by Gauss of electric and magnetic units from these dynamical units will be described later.

About 1870, an agreement was reached to adopt for scientific measurements a system based on the centimetre (the hundredth part of a metre), the gram (the thousandth part of a kilogram) and the second as the three fundamental units. This is usually referred to as the c.g.s. system.

In preceding chapters the atomic philosophy has been traced from the days of Democritus onwards. Discredited by Aristotle, it was in abeyance during the Middle Ages, and was only effectively revived after the Renaissance. Galileo regarded it favourably; Gassendi restated it in terms of Epicurus and Lucretius; Boyle and Newton used it in their

The Atomic Theory

[1] For definitions of units, see *Report of the National Physical Laboratory for 1928.*

chemical and physical speculations. It then fell into the background, though it still permeated scientific thought.

At the beginning of the nineteenth century, it came at last into its own. It was put forward anew as the inevitable explanation of physical properties such as the existence of solid, liquid and gaseous states of matter and of the definite quantitative facts of chemical combination.

The overthrow of the theory of phlogiston had the effect of bringing clearly to light the three states or phases of matter, solid, liquid and gaseous, as we know them now. A substance is usually best known in one of the phases, as water is best known in the form of liquid, but in suitable conditions it can generally be converted into either of the three, as water can be frozen into ice, or evaporated into steam. This advance in knowledge was followed by the study of the laws of chemical combination. Gases, in which the laws can be traced most simply, had ceased to be mysterious, half-spiritual entities, and had now been brought into relation with other bodies.

As the result of careful analysis, it had been found, especially by Lavoisier, Proust and Richter, against the weighty opinion of Berthollet, that a chemical compound is always made up of precisely the same amount of the constituent parts, and this fixity of composition played an essential part in the scheme of the new chemistry. Water, however obtained, always consists of hydrogen and oxygen combined in the ratio of one to eight. Thus the conception of combining weight was reached, the combining weight of oxygen being eight, if that of hydrogen be taken as unity. When two elements combine in more than one way to form more than one compound, the proportion of the constituents in one compound was found to be simply related to the proportion in the other: fourteen parts of nitrogen combine with eight of oxygen in one compound and with sixteen parts, exactly double, in another.

John Dalton (1766–1844), the son of a Westmorland handloom weaver, in his scanty leisure as a school teacher acquired a knowledge of mathematical and physical science. He obtained a teaching post in Manchester, where he began to experiment on gases. The properties of gases, he saw, are best explained by a theory of atoms,[1] and at a later date he applied

[1] *The Absorption of Gases by Water*, Manchester Memoirs, 2nd Series, vol. I, 1803, p. 271.

the same ideas to chemistry, pointing out that chemical com- *The Atomic*
bination can be represented as the combination of discrete *Theory*
particles with definite weights characteristic of each element.
Writing in 1808 he says:[1]

There are three distinctions in the kinds of bodies, or three states,
which have more specially claimed the attention of philosophical
chemists; namely, those which are marked by the terms elastic fluids,
liquids, and solids. A very famous instance is exhibited to us in water,
of a body, which, in certain circumstances, is capable of assuming all
three states. In steam we recognize a perfectly elastic fluid, in water a
perfect liquid, and in ice a complete solid. These observations have
tacitly led to the conclusion which seems universally adopted, that all
bodies of sensible magnitude, whether liquid or solid, are constituted
of a vast number of extremely small particles, or atoms of matter bound
together by a force of attraction, which is more or less powerful according
to circumstances....

Chemical analysis and synthesis go no farther than to the separation
of particles one from another, and to their reunion. No new creation
or destruction of matter is within the reach of chemical agency. We
might as well attempt to introduce a new planet into the solar system,
or to annihilate one already in existence, as to create or destroy a
particle of hydrogen. All the changes we can produce consist in separating
particles that are in a state of cohesion or combination, and joining those
that were previously at a distance.

In all chemical investigations, it has justly been considered an important object to ascertain the relative *weights* of the simples which
constitute a compound. But unfortunately the enquiry has terminated
here; whereas from the relative weights in the mass, the relative weights
of the ultimate particles or atoms of the bodies might have been inferred,
from which their number and weight in various other compounds would
appear, in order to assist and to guide future investigations and to
correct their results. Now it is one great object of this work, to shew
the importance and advantage of ascertaining *the relative weights of the
ultimate particles, both of simple and compound bodies, the number of
simple elementary particles which constitute one compound particle, and the
number of less compound particles which enter into the formation of one
more compound particle.*

If there are two bodies, *A* and *B*, which are disposed to combine, the
following is the order in which the combinations may take place,
beginning with the most simple: namely,

1 atom of *A* + 1 atom of *B* = 1 atom of *C*, binary.
1 atom of *A* + 2 atoms of *B* = 1 atom of *D*, ternary.
2 atoms of *A* + 1 atom of *B* = 1 atom of *E*, ternary.
1 atom of *A* + 3 atoms of *B* = 1 atom of *F*, quaternary.
3 atoms of *A* + 1 atom of *B* = 1 atom of *G*, quaternary.

[1] John Dalton, *New Systems of Chemical Philosophy*, Manchester, 1808 and
1810. Reprinted in the *Cambridge Readings in Science*, p. 93.

The following general rules may be adopted as guides in all our investigations respecting chemical synthesis.

1st. When only one combination of two bodies can be obtained, it must be presumed to be a binary one, unless some cause appear to the contrary.

2d. When two combinations are observed, they must be presumed to be a binary and a ternary.

3d. When three combinations are obtained, we may expect one to be a binary, and the other two ternary...etc.

From the application of these rules, to the chemical facts already well ascertained, we deduce the following conclusions: 1st. That water is a binary compound of hydrogen and oxygen, and the relative weights of the two elementary atoms are as 1 : 7, nearly; 2d. That ammonia is a binary compound of hydrogen and azote, and the relative weights of the two atoms are as 1 : 5, nearly; 3d. That nitrous gas is a binary compound of azote and oxygen, the atoms of which weigh 5 and 7 respectively:...4th. That carbonic oxide is a binary compound, consisting of one atom of charcoal, and one of oxygen, together weighing nearly 12; that carbonic acid is a ternary compound, (but sometimes binary) consisting of one atom of charcoal, and two of oxygen, weighing 19; etc., etc. In all these cases the weights are expressed in atoms of hydrogen, each of which is denoted by unity....

Dalton's account naturally contains the errors inevitable at the time: he regards heat as a subtle fluid; his combining weights are not accurate, oxygen, for instance, being given as 7 instead of 8 when hydrogen is unity. His assumption that, if only one compound of two elements is known, it should be taken to be a union of atom to atom, is by no means universally true, and led to errors in his ideas of the constitution of water and of ammonia. Nevertheless, in his realization that the combining weights of chemical elements give the relative weights of the atoms, Dalton made one of the great advances in the history of science, and converted a vague hypothesis into a definite scientific theory.

Dalton represented the elementary atoms symbolically by dots, crosses or stars drawn within little circles. This method was improved by the Swedish chemist Jöns Jakob Berzelius (1779–1848) who introduced our present system, whereby letter-symbols are used to denote the relative mass of an element corresponding to its atomic weight. Thus H denotes not vaguely hydrogen, but a mass of hydrogen equal to 1— one gram, one pound, or what we please—and O represents a mass of oxygen equal to 16 in the same units.

The chief experimental work of Berzelius was the determination of atomic weights, or rather equivalent combining weights, with the greatest accuracy then possible. He also discovered several new elements, investigated many compounds, and opened a new chapter in the study of mineralogy. He shared with Davy the work of establishing the fundamental laws of electro-chemistry, and was thereby led to see an intimate connection between electric polarity and chemical affinity. Indeed, he carried this conception too far for the time, holding that all atoms contain either positive or negative electricity, by whose relative forces they combine. Every compound was regarded as being made up of two parts electrically opposite, and if compounds combined with each other, it was imagined to be due to an excess of opposite electric charges. This dualistic theory was not adequate to deal with advancing knowledge, and it gave way to a theory of types when organic chemistry became prominent. But it is now certain that chemical and electric phenomena are intimately related, though not in the simple way imagined by Berzelius.

The insufficiency of Dalton's atomic conceptions as they stood became apparent when the phenomena of gaseous combination were studied more extensively. Gay-Lussac (1778–1850) showed that gases always combine in volumes that bear simple ratios to each other, and Amerigo Avogadro, Conte di Quaregna (1776–1856), pointed out in 1813 that, on Dalton's theory, it followed from Gay-Lussac's observation that equal volumes of all gases must contain numbers of atoms bearing simple ratios to each other. A similar conclusion was drawn independently by Ampère in 1814, but it was forgotten or ignored till the subject was cleared up by Cannizzaro in 1858. It was then seen, both from the facts of gaseous combination and from physical considerations, that a distinction is necessary between the chemical atom, the smallest part of matter which can enter into combination, and the physical molecule, the smallest particle which can exist in a free state. The simplest method of expression of Avogadro's hypothesis is to suppose that equal volumes of gases contain the same number of molecules. We shall see below that this result can also be deduced mathematically from a physical theory which supposes that the pressure exerted by a gas is due to the impact of molecules in a state of perpetual movement and collision.

But, to return to the case of water, two volumes (and therefore two molecules) of hydrogen combine with one of oxygen to form two volumes (or molecules) of steam. It will be seen that the simplest theory which will explain these relations is one that supposes that the physical molecules of hydrogen and oxygen each contain two chemical atoms, and that the molecule of water vapour has the chemical composition represented by H_2O, the combination being represented by the equation

$$2H_2 + O_2 = 2H_2O$$
(2 vols.) (1 vol.) (2 vols.)

Thus, since the combining weight of oxygen is 8 and one atom of oxygen combines with two of hydrogen, if the atomic weight of hydrogen be taken as unity, that of oxygen is not 8 but 16. Dalton's combining weights, therefore, need to be brought into line with the facts revealed by later experiments before we can assign to the elements their true atomic weights. This was first done systematically, in the light of all the evidence, by Cannizzaro.

The atom of oxygen, combining with two atoms of hydrogen, is said to possess a valency of two. This concept of valency underlay much of the chemical speculation of the succeeding years.

The number of known elements has grown from the twenty recognized by Dalton till now some ninety different kinds of matter have been recorded. The work of discovery has proceeded fitfully. When any new method of research has been applied to chemical problems, a new group of elements has frequently come to light. The separating power of the galvanic current enabled Sir Humphry Davy (1778–1829) to isolate the alkaline metals potassium and sodium in 1807. At a later date spectrum analysis showed the existence of such substances as rubidium, caesium, thallium and gallium: while, in recent years, the still more delicate methods of radio-activity have disclosed bodies like radium and its family of allied elements.

A connection between the atomic weights of the elements and their physical properties was sought by Prout in 1815, and later by Newlands and de Chaucourtois. This connection was successfully demonstrated in 1869 by Lothar Meyer and by the Russian chemist Mendeléeff (1834–1907). On arranging the names of the elements in a list in order of ascending atomic weights, Mendeléeff found that they displayed a certain periodicity—that, as Newlands had shown earlier, each eighth element had somewhat similar properties, while all the elements could be fitted into a complete table in which these similar elements could be placed under each other in columns. The Periodic Table thus constructed gave a means of assigning correct atomic weights to elements of doubtful valency, and blanks in the table were filled hypothetically by Mendeléeff, who thus predicted the existence and properties of unknown elements, some of which were afterwards discovered.

Mendeléeff regarded his Periodic Law as a purely empirical statement of fact. But such relations inevitably bring to mind the old idea of a common basis of matter. Many men, thinking that this common basis might be hydrogen, sought to demonstrate that, if the atomic weight of hydrogen be taken as unity, the weights of the other elements were all whole numbers. But, though many approached whole numbers, several elements, such as chlorine = 35·45, obstinately refused to conform to this scheme, nor did increasing accuracy in the determination of atomic weights by Stas and others reduce the discrepancies. The proof of a common basis of matter and the reduction of atomic weights to whole numbers had to wait for another half century; they were beyond the experimental and theoretical resources of that time.

The different forms of apparatus for the production of electricity, as hitherto described, are all intended primarily to enable us to give a static charge to some insulated body. It is true that, if a conducting circuit be formed, joining an electric machine with the earth, a more or less continuous flow of electricity must proceed along the circuit. Even in the most elaborate form of frictional machine, however, the amount of electricity passing in a second is so small that it is difficult to detect the current in the conducting wires; though, if an air gap be interposed, the high differences of electric potential produced by the machine result in visible sparks.

At the beginning of the nineteenth century a new field of research was opened up by the discovery of the galvanic or voltaic cell. This arrangement gave rise to a series of phenomena, grouped originally under the name of galvanism, which, by the efforts of many observers, were gradually brought into relation with those already grouped under the name of electricity. It finally became clear that a galvanic current is nothing more or less than a flow of electricity, enormous in quantity compared with that given by an electric machine, but driven along by potential differences which are only a minute fraction of those involved in the older type of apparatus. Since no accumulation of electricity can be detected at any point in the circuit, it follows that the current may be represented figuratively by the flow of an incomprehensible fluid along rigid and inextensible pipes.

The discovery of the voltaic cell was due to a chance observation, which seemed at first to lead in a different direction. About the year 1786, an Italian named Galvani noticed that the leg of a frog contracted under the influence of a discharge from an electric machine. Following up this discovery, he observed the same contraction when a nerve and a muscle were connected with two dissimilar metals, placed in contact with each other. Galvani attributed these effects to a so-called animal electricity, and it was left for another Italian, Volta, of Pavia, to show that the essential phenomena did not depend on the presence of an animal substance. In 1800 Volta invented the pile known by his name, which, in the opening years of the following century, provided a means of investigation yielding results of intense interest in his hands and in those of his contemporaries in other countries. The scientific journals of the time[1] are full of the marvels of the new discoveries, the study of which was taken up with an ardour little short of that shown a century later in the elucidation of the phenomena of electric discharge through gases and radio-activity.

Volta's pile consisted of a series of little discs of zinc, copper, and paper moistened with water or brine, placed one on top of the other in the order—zinc, copper, paper, zinc, etc.... finishing with copper. Such a combination is really a primitive primary battery, each little pair of discs separated by moistened paper acting as a cell, and giving a certain difference of electric potential, the differences due to each little cell being added together and producing a considerable difference of potential (or electromotive force as it is inaptly called) between the zinc and copper terminals of the pile. Another arrangement was

[1] See especially *Nicholson's Journal* for those years.

the crown of cups, consisting of a series of vessels filled with
brine or dilute acid, each of which contained a plate of zinc
and a plate of copper. The zinc of one cell was fastened to
the copper of the next, and so on, an isolated zinc and copper
plate, in the first and last cell respectively, forming the
terminals of the battery. Volta thought that the origin of the
effects was to be sought at the junctions of the two metals;
hence the order of the discs in the pile and the terminal metal
plates in the crown of cups. These plates and the corresponding
discs in the pile, were soon found to be useless, though they
figure extensively in early pictures of the apparatus.

If a current be taken from Volta's pile or crown of cups,
that current rapidly diminishes in intensity, owing chiefly to
a film of hydrogen which forms on the surface of the copper
plates. This electrolytic polarization may be prevented by
surrounding the copper plates with a solution of copper
sulphate, so that copper is liberated instead of hydrogen, or
by replacing the copper plates with carbon placed in an
oxidizing mixture, such as nitric acid or a solution of potassium
bichromate which converts the hydrogen to water.

The fundamental observation, from which arose the science
of electro-chemistry, was made in the year 1800, immediately
on the news of Volta's discovery reaching England. Using a
copy of Volta's original pile, Nicholson and Carlisle found that
when two brass wires leading from its terminals were immersed
near each other in water, there was an evolution of hydrogen
gas from one, while the other became oxidized. If platinum
or gold wires were used, no oxidation occurred, but oxygen was
evolved as gas. They noticed that the volume of hydrogen was
about double that of oxygen, and, since this is the proportion
in which these elements are contained in water, they explained
the phenomenon as a decomposition of water. They also
noticed that a similar kind of chemical reaction went on in the
pile itself, or in the cups when that arrangement was used.

Soon afterwards Cruickshank decomposed the chlorides of
magnesia, soda and ammonia, and precipitated silver and
copper from their solutions—a result which afterwards led to
the process of electroplating. He also found that the liquid
round the pole connected with the positive terminal of the
pile became alkaline and the liquid round the other pole
became acid.

In 1806 Sir Humphry Davy (1778–1829) proved that the formation of the acid and alkali was due to impurities in the water. He had previously shown that decomposition of water could be effected although the two poles were placed in separate vessels connected together by vegetable or animal substances, and had established an intimate connection between the galvanic effects and the chemical changes going on in the battery.

The identity of "galvanism" and electricity, which had been maintained by Volta, and had formed the subject of many investigations, was established in 1801 by Wollaston, who showed that the same effects were produced by both, while in 1802 Erman measured with an electroscope the potential differences furnished by a voltaic pile. It became clear that the older phenomena gave "electricity in tension", and the newer, "electricity in motion".

By a convention universally adopted, we agree to suppose that an electric current flows in the direction of the so-called positive electricity, that is, from the zinc to the copper·(or carbon) plate within the battery, and from the copper to the zinc along the wire outside. In accordance with this convention, the copper plate is called the positive and the zinc plate the negative terminal of the battery.

In 1804 Hisinger and Berzelius stated that neutral salt solutions could be decomposed by electricity, the acid appearing at one pole and the metal at the other, and drew the conclusion that nascent hydrogen was not, as had been supposed, the cause of the separation of the metals from their solutions. Many of the metals then known were thus prepared, and in 1807 Davy decomposed potash and soda, which had been considered to be elements, by passing the current from a powerful battery through them when in a moistened condition, and in this way he isolated the surprising metals potassium and sodium. Davy was an able, brilliant and eloquent Cornishman, who, appointed Lecturer on Chemistry at the newly founded Royal Institution, drew large and fashionable audiences by the interest of his discourses.

The decomposition of chemical compounds by electrical means indicated a connection between chemical and electrical forces. Davy "advanced the hypothesis that chemical and electrical attractions were produced by the same cause, acting in the one case on particles, in the other on masses ". This idea was developed by Berzelius, who, as we have already seen, regarded every compound as formed by the union of two oppositely electrified parts—atoms or groups of atoms.

The remarkable fact that the products of decomposition appear only at the poles was perceived by the early experimenters on the subject, who suggested various explanations. Grotthus in 1806 supposed that it was due to successive decompositions and recombinations in the substance of the liquid, the opposite parts of contiguous molecules being exchanged along lines stretching from one pole to the other, the opposite atoms at the two ends of the chain being set free.

After the primary discoveries in electro-chemistry, there was a pause till the subject was taken up by the great experimenter Michael Faraday (1791–1867) who had been Davy's assistant in the Laboratory of the Royal Institution.

A new terminology, which is still in use, was introduced by Faraday in 1833. Instead of the word *pole*, which implied the old idea of attraction and repulsion, he used the word *electrode* (ὁδός = a way, path) and called the plate by which the current is usually said to enter the liquid, the *anode*, and that by which it leaves the liquid the *cathode*. The parts of the compound which travel in opposite directions through the solution he called *ions* (ἴω = I go)—*cations* if they go towards the cathode, and *anions* if they go towards the anode. He also introduced the word *electrolysis* (λύω = I loose, dissolve) to denote the whole process.

By a series of masterly experiments, Faraday reduced the complexity of the phenomena to two simple statements known as Faraday's laws. Whatever be the nature of the electrolyte or of the electrodes, the mass of substance liberated is proportional to the strength of the current and to the time it flows, that is to the total amount of electricity which has passed through the liquid. Secondly, the mass of a substance liberated by a given quantity of electricity is proportional to the chemical equivalent weight of the substance—not to the atomic weight, but to the combining weight, that is, the atomic weight divided by the valency, so that, while 1 gram of hydrogen is liberated, $16 \div 2$, or 8 grams of oxygen appear. The mass of a substance liberated by the passage of unit quantity of electricity is known as its electro-chemical equivalent. For instance, when a current of 1 ampere, one-tenth

Chemical
Effects

of a c.g.s. unit, flows for 1 second through an acid solution, 1.044×10^{-5} gram of hydrogen is liberated, while from the solution of a silver salt 0.001118 gram of silver is deposited. This latter weight can be measured so easily and accurately that it has been adopted for a definition of the ampere as a practical unit of current.

In every case of electrolysis, Faraday's laws seem to apply; the same definite amount of electricity is associated with the liberation of unit equivalent mass of substance. Electrolysis must be regarded as the carriage by the moving ions of opposite electric charges in opposite directions through the liquid. Each ion carries with it a definite charge of electricity, positive or negative, which is given up to the electrode by the liberation of the ion if the electromotive force is enough to overcome the opposing force of polarization. As von Helmholtz said at a later date, Faraday's work shows that "if we accept the hypothesis that the elementary substances are composed of atoms, we cannot avoid concluding that electricity also is divided into definite elementary portions which behave like atoms of electricity". Thus, not only do Faraday's experiments underlie the later development in theoretical and applied electro-chemistry, but the ideas which he formulated are the basis on which has been built the whole great structure of modern atomic and electronic science.

Other
Properties of
Currents

While the early experimenters chiefly directed their attention to the chemical effects of galvanic currents, other phenomena were not overlooked. It was soon found that, when passing through a conductor of any kind, the current evolved heat, the amount of which depended on the nature of the conductor. This thermal effect is now of great practical use in electric lighting, heating, etc. Of even wider interest was another discovery—the power a current has of deflecting a magnetic needle. This property was discovered in 1820 by Oersted of Copenhagen, who found that the effect "passes to the needle through glass, metals" and other non-magnetic substances. He also recognized that what he, or his translator, called "the electric conflict" "performs circles", or, as we should say, that there are circular lines of magnetic force round a long straight current.

The importance of Oersted's observations was recognized at once, especially by André Marie Ampère (1775–1836),

who showed that not only were magnets acted on by
forces in the neighbourhood of currents, but that currents
exerted forces on each other. By experiments with moveable
coils, he investigated the laws of these forces, and showed
mathematically that all the observed phenomena were consistent with the supposition that each short element of current
of length dl produced at a point outside it a magnetic force
$cdl \sin \theta / r^2$, where c is the strength of the current, r the distance
from the element to the point, and θ the angle between r and
the direction of the current. The forces due to electric currents,
thus reduced to a law of inverse squares, were thereby brought
into line with gravitation and with the forces between magnetic
poles and between electric charges. This was another step
towards "field physics".

The current elements, of course, cannot be obtained experimentally in isolation, but nevertheless Ampère's formula
enables us, by summing up the effects of all the elements, to
calculate the magnetic fields in the neighbourhood of electric
currents.[1]

From Ampère's formula we can also deduce the mechanical
forces on currents placed in magnetic fields. The magnetic
force in air due to a pole of strength m is m/r^2; thus m is equivalent to $cdl \sin \theta$. The mechanical force on m in a field H is
Hm, and therefore the force in air on Ampère's current-
element is $Hcdl \sin \theta$. To calculate the mechanical force on an
actual circuit from this formula is then only a question of
mathematics.

Telegraphy began with visual signalling. The many "Telegraph Hills" about the country mark the sites of long dis-
mantled semaphores which were to wave quickly to London
the news of Napoleon's landing. Each fresh discovery in
electricity led to suggestions for electric telegraphs, but
nothing came of them till Ampère applied his electromagnetic
results. After his work, the invention and adoption of a
practical instrument was a mere exercise in mechanical
ingenuity and financial confidence.

---

[1] For instance, at the centre of a circular current, the distance from each
element of the current is the same, and, θ being everywhere a right angle,
$\sin \theta$ is unity. Thus the magnetic force H is given by the relation

$$H = \Sigma \frac{cdl \sin \theta}{r^2} = \frac{c \cdot \Sigma dl}{r^2} = \frac{c \times 2\pi r}{r^2} = \frac{2\pi c}{r}.$$

Other
Properties
of Currents

Much was done about 1827 by Georg Simon Ohm (1781–1854) to pick out from the phenomena quantities suitable for exact definition. He replaced the prevalent vague ideas of "quantity" and "tension" by the conceptions of current strength and electromotive force. The latter quantity corresponds with potential, already used in electrostatics. When the tension or pressure is high, it needs more work to carry electricity from one point to another, and hence difference of potential or electromotive force may be defined as the work done against the electric forces in carrying unit quantity of electricity from one point to another.

Ohm's work on electricity was based on the researches of Fourier on the conduction of heat (1800–1814). Fourier worked out mathematically the laws of the conduction of heat on the assumption that the flux of heat was proportional to the gradient of temperature. Ohm substituted potential for temperature, and electricity for heat, and proved the usefulness of these conceptions by experiment. He found that, if a current from a battery of voltaic cells is flowing through a wire, the rate of fall of potential is constant. Ohm's law is usually put in the form that the current c is proportional to the electromotive force E or

$$c = kE = \frac{E}{R},$$

where k is a constant which may be called the conductivity, and its reciprocal, $1/k$ or R, is known as the resistance. R depends only on the nature, temperature and dimensions of the conductor, being proportional directly to its length, and inversely to its area of cross section. The latter fact indicates that a current flows uniformly through the whole substance of the conductor. This will be found to need some qualification in the case of very rapidly alternating currents.

After the labours of Ampère and of Ohm, the subject of current electricity had reached that important stage in a new physical science when satisfactory fundamental quantities have been selected and defined, and a firm basis found for mathematical development.

The Wave-
Theory of Light

Another old idea resuscitated and established early in the nineteenth century was the wave-theory of light. Held vaguely by Hooke and others in the seventeenth century, it was, as has already been said,[1] put in a more definite form by Huygens. Newton rejected it on two grounds. Firstly, it did not then explain shadows, since waves of light he thought would naturally bend round obstacles as did those of sound. Secondly, the phenomena of double-refraction in Iceland spar indicated that rays of light were different on different sides, and waves with vibrations in the direction of propagation could not have such differences. These two difficulties were overcome by Thomas Young (1773–1829) and Augustin Jean Fresnel (1788–1827), who put the theory in its modern form. Nevertheless it is worth remembering that Newton held that the colours of thin plates indicated that the corpuscles in a ray of light produced accompanying waves in an aether—a theory amazingly like that now invoked to explain the properties of electrons.

Young passed a very narrow beam of white light through two pin holes in a screen, and placed another screen beyond the first. Where the rays from the two pin holes overlapped on the second screen, he saw a series of brilliantly coloured bands. The bands are due to the interference of the similar waves from the two pin-hole sources. If one wave has half a wave-length further to travel than the other to reach the screen, the crest of the one wave will coincide with the trough of the next, and darkness will result. If the distances traversed by the two waves be the same, the crests will be superposed and the light will be doubled. The light actually seen is that composite light left when light of one wave-length is removed from the white light. If instead of composite white light, simple coloured light is used, the bands are alternately bright and dark instead of coloured.

From the dimensions of the apparatus and the breadth of the bands, it is clear that the wave-lengths of the different coloured lights can be calculated. They prove to be exceedingly short—of the order of one fifty thousandth part of an inch, or the one two thousandth part of a millimetre, agreeing with the lengths of Newton's fits of easy reflexion and easy transmission. From this it follows that the dimensions of ordinary obstacles in the path of a beam of light are very large compared with the wave-lengths, and a mathematical investigation proves that, if an advancing wave-front be supposed resolved into a number

[1] Chapter IV, p. 178.

of concentric rings round the point of the wave-front nearest to the eye, the effects of all the rings except those near the point interfere and cancel each other, so that the eye only sees light coming to it along one direct path. That is, light travels almost solely in straight lines, and the bending round obstacles is confined to the minute effect known as diffraction.

Newton's other difficulty was overcome by Fresnel. Hooke had somewhat casually suggested that the vibrations which constitute light might be transverse to the direction of the rays, and Fresnel pointed out that this suggestion gave the possibility of unlikeness in the different sides of a ray. If we look at an advancing wave-front of light, linear vibrations may be either up and down, or right and left. Such linear vibrations would give what may be called plane-polarized light. If a crystal in one position lets one vibration through but not the other, a second similar crystal, turned round its axis through a right angle, will stop the light emerging from the first crystal. These are just the phenomena seen with Iceland spar.

Fresnel developed the wave-theory of light mathematically to a high degree of perfection. Certain difficulties remained, but, speaking broadly, a remarkable concordance was obtained between his complete theory and the observed phenomena. He and those who followed, Green, MacCullagh, Cauchy, Stokes, and others, established the classical wave-theory for a century.

If the waves of light be transverse to the direction of propagation, the medium must be so constituted as to transmit such waves. Neither gases nor liquids can do so; and it follows that, if light is a mechanical wave-motion, the luminiferous aether must have properties analogous to those of a solid—it must possess rigidity. This was the beginning of a long series of elastic solid theories of the aether. The reconciliation of the necessary light-carrying properties with an absence of appreciable resistance to the motion of the planets, taxed heavily the ingenuity of the physicists of the first seventy years of the nineteenth century. At a later date, attempts were made to explain the necessary rigidity by imagining gyrostatic aethers in rotational motion.

As Einstein has pointed out,[1] the success of the wave-theory of light made the first breach in Newtonian physics, though the fact was not understood at the time. Newton's theory of

[1] *The Times*, 4 February, 1929.

corpuscles of light travelling through empty space fitted well
with the rest of his philosophy, though it is not easy to see
why the corpuscles should move with only one constant
velocity. But, when light came to be regarded as wave-motion,
it ceased to be possible to believe that everything real was made
up of particles moving in absolute space. The aether was
invented to preserve the mechanical outlook, and, as long as
light could be thought of as mechanical waves in a quasi-rigid
medium, the aether fulfilled this function, though, as it was
supposed to penetrate everywhere, it was, in a sense, identical
with space itself. But Faraday showed that space had electric
and magnetic properties, and when Clerk Maxwell proved that
light was an electromagnetic wave, the aether ceased to be
mechanical.

The wave-theory of light opened the first chapter in what is
now called field physics. The second, written in the work of
Faraday and Maxwell, connected light with electromagnetism,
and, in the third, Einstein has explained gravitation in terms of
geometry, and hopes to have brought it into connection with
light and electromagnetism in a still wider synthesis.

The induction of statical charges of electricity by other
charges, and the similar action exerted by magnets on soft
iron, suggested to the early experimenters that like effects
might be obtained with the steady currents given by voltaic
cells. Faraday, for instance, wound two helices of insulated
wire on the same wooden cylinder, but could observe no
deflection of a galvanometer inserted in one coil when a steady
current was maintained through the other by a powerful
voltaic battery.

His first successful experiment, which opened a new era in
the history of electrical science, was thus described to the
Royal Society on November 24th, 1831.

Two hundred and three feet of copper wire in one length were wound
round a large block of wood; other two hundred and three feet of similar
wire were interposed as a spiral between the turns of the first coil, and
metallic contact everywhere prevented by twine. One of these helices
was connected with a galvanometer, and the other with a battery of
one hundred pairs of plates four inches square, with double coppers,
and well charged. When the contact was made, there was a sudden
and very slight effect at the galvanometer, and there was also a similar
slight effect when the contact with the battery was broken. But whilst
the voltaic current was continuing to pass through the one helix, no

w   16 galvanometrical appearance nor any effect like induction upon the other helix could be perceived, although the active power of the battery was proved to be great by its heating the whole of its helix, and by the brilliancy of the discharge when made through charcoal.

Repetition of the experiment with a battery of one hundred and twenty pairs of plates produced no other effect; but it was ascertained, both at this and the former time, that the slight deflection of the needle occurring at the moment of completing the connection, was always in one direction, and that the equally slight deflection produced when the contact was broken, was in the other direction.

The results which I had by this time obtained with magnets led me to believe that the battery current through one wire did, in reality, induce a similar current through the other wire, but that it continued for an instant only, and partook more of the nature of an electrical wave passed through from the shock of a common Leyden jar than of the current from a voltaic battery, and therefore might magnetize a steel needle, though it scarcely affected the galvanometer.

This expectation was confirmed; for on substituting a small hollow helix, formed round a glass tube, for the galvanometer, introducing a steel needle, making contact as before between the battery and the inducing wire, and then removing the needle before the battery contact was broken, it was found magnetized.

When the battery contact was first made, then an unmagnetized needle introduced into a small indicating helix, and lastly the contact broken, the needle was found magnetized to an equal degree apparently as before; but the poles were of a contrary kind.

With the much more delicate galvanometers we now possess, it is easy to repeat Faraday's experiments with the primary current derived from a single voltaic cell, and to show that similar transient currents are produced by moving the primary and secondary circuits relatively to each other, or by moving a permanent magnet relatively to a coil connected with a galvanometer. Faraday's discovery of electromagnetic induction has proved to be the foundation of a vast industrial development: almost all electric machinery of practical importance depends on the principles of the induction of currents.

Ampère was content to discover the laws of electromagnetic force in mathematical form, without enquiring by what mechanism the force was propagated. But Faraday, who followed him, was not a mathematician and was keenly interested in picturing the physical properties and state of the intervening space or electromagnetic field of force. If a card be laid on a bar-magnet, and iron filings be scattered over the card, they cling together in chains, showing the lines in which the magnetic force acts. Faraday imagined that such lines or

tubes of force, connecting magnetic poles or electric charges, *The Electro-*
have a real existence in a magnetic or an electric field, perhaps *magnetic Field*
as a chain of polarized particles. If they were in a state of *of Force*
strain like rubber cords, stretched longitudinally and compressed transversely, they would spread themselves throughout
the medium and would draw magnetic poles or electric charges
together, thus explaining the phenomena of attraction. Whether
real or not, Faraday's lines of force give a ready and convenient
way of representing the stresses and strains in the insulating
medium or electric field.

Faraday examined this dielectric medium in another way.
He found that the electrostatic capacity of a conductor, that
is, the quantity of electricity it holds at a given potential or
pressure, increased when the air surrounding it was replaced
by another insulator like shellac or sulphur, increased in a
ratio which he called the specific inductive capacity of the
insulator.

Faraday's ideas were in advance of his time and were expressed in unfamiliar language. But when, thirty years later,
Clerk Maxwell translated those ideas into mathematical form
and developed them into a theory of electromagnetic waves,
their full importance was realized. Thus Faraday laid well
and truly the foundations of three great branches of practical
electric science—electro-chemistry, electromagnetic induction,
and electromagnetic waves. Moreover, his insistence on the importance of the electromagnetic field of force is the historical
starting point of the electrical side of modern theories of field
physics.

To the two German mathematical physicists, C. F. Gauss *Electromagnetic*
(1777–1855) and W. E. Weber (1804–1891), we owe the *Units*
invention of a scientific system of magnetic and electric units,
not defined arbitrarily in terms of quantities of the same kind
as themselves, but based on the fundamental units of length,
mass and time.

In 1839 Gauss published his "general theory of forces
attracting according to the inverse square of the distance".
Electric charges and magnetic poles as well as gravitating
matter conform to this relation, and a charge or pole of unit
strength may be defined as one which, separated by unit
distance (one centimetre) in air from an equal similar charge or
pole, repels it with unit force (one dyne). If another medium

Electromagnetic Units

replaces air, the force will be less in a certain ratio, k for electric forces and μ for magnetic forces. k is Faraday's specific inductive capacity, which here appears as a dielectric constant, and μ is a quantity which was afterwards named the magnetic permeability of the medium. On this foundation, Gauss raised an imposing structure of mathematical deduction[1].

Ampère and Weber showed experimentally that coils of wire carrying electric currents acted in the same manner as magnets of the same size and shape, a circular current being equivalent to a circular disc magnetized at right angles to its plane, so that one face is a north-seeking pole and the other face a south-seeking pole. Thus unit current may be defined as that current which is equivalent to a magnetic disc of unit magnetic strength, a definition which may be shown mathematically to

---

[1] As an example we may take what is known as Gauss' theorem. Let a quantity of electricity be imagined to be surrounded by a closed surface, and let that surface be supposed dissected into a number of small areas, any one of which may be called a, with an electric force N acting at right angles to it. Then Gauss proved that the sum of all the quantities aN is equal to 4π times the total amount of electricity e within the surface, however that electricity be distributed. That is,

$$\Sigma aN = 4\pi e,$$

a relation which can easily be obtained from the law of force by simple mathematics. If we take into account the dielectric constant of the insulating medium inside the surface, this expression becomes

$$\Sigma aN = \frac{4\pi e}{K} \text{ or } \Sigma aNK = 4\pi e.$$

The quantity ΣaNK is called the total normal induction over the surface.

Similar equations hold for gravitational or magnetic forces, and can be used to deduce results only otherwise to be obtained by difficult mathematics. For instance, suppose we have a sphere of gravitating matter of mass m. Let us imagine that we surround it by a concentric spherical surface of radius r. Over this surface Gauss' theorem holds. Hence,

$$\Sigma \hat{a} NK = 4\pi m.$$

But everything is here symmetrical, N is constant, and equal to the total force F. Therefore,

$$4\pi m = N \times \Sigma a = F \times 4\pi r^2,$$

and
$$F = \frac{m}{r^2}.$$

This is the same gravitational force that would be exerted by a heavy particle of mass m placed at the centre of the gravitating sphere. Thus, with the simplest mathematics, we have proved Newton's famous result that a uniform sphere attracts as though its mass were concentrated at the centre, and incidentally we have illustrated the power of Gauss' method. Much of the theory of electrostatics and magnetism may be built up on Gauss' theorem by the use of mathematics, somewhat more complicated perhaps, but no more difficult.

lead to the result that the magnetic field, that is, the force on a unit magnetic pole, at the centre of a circular current is $2\pi c/r$, where c is the strength of the current and r the radius of the circle, an expression which of course agrees with that deduced from Ampère's formula. Therefore, by suspending a small magnetic needle at the centre of a large circular coil of wire (an arrangement known as a tangent galvanometer), and observing the deflection produced by passing a current through the coil, we can measure the current in absolute or centimetre-gram-second (c.g.s.) units. The common unit of current or ampère is designed to be the tenth part of the unit as thus defined, though, for practical purposes and convenience of measurement, the definition has for many years been based on the amount of silver deposited electrolytically as explained above. There is now however (1929) a proposal to revert to the theoretical definition.

Electromagnetic Units

As we have seen, the caloric theory, according to which heat is an imponderable fluid, played a useful part in suggesting and interpreting experiments on the measurement of quantities of heat. But, as a physical explanation, the theory of molecular agitation had always appealed to the more acute natural philosophers, such as Boyle and Newton. In 1738 Daniel Bernouilli had shown that, if a gas be imagined to consist of molecules in motion in all directions, the impact of the molecules on the walls of the containing vessel would explain the pressure, and the pressure would increase proportionately as the gas was compressed or the temperature raised, as experiment required.

Heat and the Conservation of Energy

The development of heat by friction was explained by the calorists on the supposition that the filings or abrasions, or the main substance in its final state after friction, possessed a smaller specific heat than the substance at first, so that heat was squeezed out and thus made manifest. But in 1798 Count Rumford showed by experiments on the boring of cannon that the heat evolved was roughly proportional to the total work done, and had no relation to the amount of shavings. In 1799 Sir Humphry Davy melted two lumps of ice by rubbing them together. The water thus formed was well known to possess a higher specific heat than the ice, so that the caloric explanation failed. Nevertheless, the fluid theory survived for another half century.

Heat and the
Conservation
of Energy

But by 1840 it had become apparent that some at all events of the different powers of nature were mutually convertible. In 1842 J. R. Mayer upheld the possibility of the conversion of work or *vis viva* into heat and heat into work. Assuming that when air is compressed all the work appears as heat, Mayer calculated a numerical value for its mechanical equivalent.[1] In the same year Sir W. R. Grove, English judge and man of science, who was already known by his invention of a new voltaic cell, explained in a lecture the idea of the interrelation of natural powers. This idea he elaborated in a book published in 1846 under the title of *The Correlation of Physical Forces*.[2] This and the independent study in 1847 by H. L. F. von Helmholtz (1821–1894), *Ueber die Erhaltung der Kraft*,[3] contained the earliest general account of the principle now known as the "conservation of energy".

During the years from 1840 to 1850 James Prescott Joule (1818–1889) measured experimentally the amount of heat liberated by the expenditure of electrical and mechanical work.[4] He first proved that heat generated by the passage of an electric current in a conductor is proportional to the resistance of the conductor and to the square of the strength of the current. He then forced water through narrow tubes, compressed a mass of air, and heated liquids by the rotation of paddle wheels. He found that, however work was done, the expenditure of the same amount of work resulted in the development of the same quantity of heat, and from this principle of equivalence he concluded that heat was a form of energy. Even then "it was many years...before any of the scientific chiefs began to give their adhesion", though Stokes told William Thomson that "he was inclined to be a Joulite". In 1853 Helmholtz, during a visit to England, observed much scientific interest in the subject, and in France found that Regnault had adopted the new views. Joule's final results showed that to warm one pound of water through 1° Fahrenheit, at any temperature between 55° and 60°, needed the expenditure of about 772 foot pounds of work. Later experiments indicate 778 as a figure more nearly accurate.

---

[1] *Liebig's Annalen*, May, 1842.
[2] W. R. Grove, *The Correlation of Physical Forces*, London, 1846
[3] Helmholtz, *Abhandlung von der Erhaltung der Kraft*, 1847.
[4] J. P. Joule, *Collected Papers*.

Joule's definite experimental result that work and heat were equivalent gave power and point to the idea called by Grove the "correlation of forces", and by Helmholtz "the persistence of force". That idea was thus developed into the definite physical principle which came to be known as the "conservation of energy". Energy, as an exact physical quantity, was new to science. The concept which underlay it had previously been expressed by an inaccurate and confusing duplication of meaning of the word "force", a confusion which had been pointed out by Young. Energy may be defined as the power of doing work, and, if the conversion be complete, may be measured by the work done. The use of the word "energy" in this specialized sense is due to Rankine and William Thomson, the latter of whom adopted Young's distinction.

Joule's experiments showed that, in the cases he investigated, the total amount of energy in a system is constant, the quantity lost as work reappearing as heat. General evidence led to the extension of this result to other changes, where, for instance, mechanical energy is converted into electrical energy, or chemical energy into animal heat. Till recent years, all known facts were consistent with the statement that the total energy of an isolated system is constant in amount.

The principle of the conservation of energy, thus established, is comparable with the older principle of the conservation of mass. Newtonian dynamics are founded on the recognition that there is a quantity, for convenience called the mass of a body, which remains constant throughout all motion. In the hands of the chemists, the balance showed that this principle holds good also when chemical changes occur. The matter in a body burning in air is not annihilated. When the resultant substances are collected, their total weight is the joint weight of the original body and the air which has been consumed.

And so with energy: another quantity besides mass emerges in our consciousness, chiefly because it remains unchanged throughout a series of transformations. We find it convenient to recognize the existence of that quantity, to use it as a scientific concept, and to give it a name. We call it energy, measure its changes by the amount of work done or by the amount of heat developed, and, somewhat laboriously and after much doubt, rediscover its constancy.[1]

[1] See Chapter x.

Heat and the Conservation of Energy

Heat and the
Conservation
of Energy

By none of the processes known to nineteenth-century physics could matter or energy be created or destroyed. In the twentieth, there have appeared indications that matter itself is a form of energy, and that transformations from one form to the other are not impossible, but, until recent years, matter and energy were rigidly distinguished.

The establishment of the principle of the conservation of energy was of immense importance in the history of physical science and scientific philosophy. It gave a new method of investigation, a new point of view from which physical problems could be regarded. Since the final energy of a closed system must be the same as its initial energy, it became possible in some cases to predict the final state of the system without reference to intermediate steps, to pass at once to the solution of a physical problem without tracing the process by which the goal is attained, as Huygens did in the more limited problems of mechanics. Because of this practical use, and for its own intrinsic interest, the principle of the conservation of energy may be regarded as one of the great achievements of the human mind.

But it had its philosophic dangers. Since the principles of the conservation of matter and energy were found to hold good in all circumstances which could then be investigated, it was natural to stretch the principles into the form of general laws. Matter became eternal and indestructible; the amount of energy in the Universe became constant and immutable, in all conditions and for all ages. The principles passed from safe guides for empirical advance in knowledge into philosophic dogmas of doubtful validity.

The Kinetic
Theory of
Gases

In 1845 J. J. Waterston, in a manuscript memoir, for long lying forgotten in the archives of the Royal Society, developed further the kinetic theory of gases, made more important by the identification of heat and energy. In 1848 Joule also was at work upon the same subject. These two investigators carried the theory beyond the point reached by Bernouilli, and calculated independently the average velocity of movement of the molecules.[1] In 1857 the first adequate kinetic theory of matter was published by Clausius.[2]

[1] *Life of Lord Rayleigh*, p. 45; Joule's *Collected Papers*. Also art. "Joule", in *D.N.B.* by Sir Richard Glazebrook.
[2] O. E. Meyer, *Kinetic Theory of Gases*, Eng. trans. R. E. Baynes, London, 1899.

Owing to the chances of molecular collision, which are assumed to occur with perfect elasticity, at any instant there will be molecules moving with all velocities and in all directions. The total energy of translation of all the molecules measures the total heat content of the gas, and the average energy of each molecule measures the temperature. From these premises it can be deduced mathematically that the pressure p is equal to $\frac{1}{3}nmV^2$, where n is the number of molecules in unit volume, m the mass of each, and V^2 the average value of the square of the velocity.[1]

But nm, the total mass of gas in unit volume, measures its density, so that, if temperature and therefore V^2 be constant, the pressure of a gas is proportional to its density or inversely proportional to its volume—a law which was discovered experimentally by Boyle. If the temperature vary, since p is proportional to V^2, the pressure must increase with the temperature—the law of Charles. If we have two gases at the same pressure and temperature, it follows from the equation that the number of molecules in unit volume is equal for the two gases—the law obtained by Avogadro from chemical facts. Finally, for the two gases, the molecular velocity V must be inversely proportional to the square root of nm, the density, a relation that explains the rates at which gases diffuse through porous partitions, the law of which had been discovered by Thomas Graham about 1830.

From these deductions we see that the elementary kinetic theory, as given by Bernouilli, Joule and Clausius, is in accordance with the simpler experimental properties of gases. Moreover, as Waterston and Joule showed, the theory enables us to calculate approximately the molecular velocities. For

---

[1] If one molecule be moving with velocity V, that velocity can be resolved into three components, u, v, and w, at right angles to each other, and, since the component energies must equal the total energy,

$$V^2 = u^2 + v^2 + w^2.$$

On the whole the molecules will be moving equally in all directions, so that,

$$V^2 = 3u^2.$$

If the gas be contained in a centimetre cube, one molecule, moving to and fro between opposite faces with the resolved velocity u, will strike one face $\frac{1}{2}u$ times a second. If m be its mass, the change of momentum when it strikes the face and rebounds is $2mu$, and the change of momentum per second is $2mu \times \frac{1}{2}u$ or mu^2. If there are n molecules in the cubic centimetre, the total rate of change of momentum on one unit face, which measures the pressure p, is

$$p = nmu^2 = \frac{1}{3}nmV^2.$$

instance, with hydrogen the volume of unit mass is 11·16 litres, or 11,160 cubic centimetres, at 0° C. and at the standard atmospheric pressure of 760 millimetres of mercury or $1·013 \times 10^6$ dynes per square centimetre. Hence the equation $p = \frac{1}{3}nmV^2$ leads to the result that V is 1844 metres, or more than a mile a second. For oxygen the corresponding number is 461 metres per second. These figures give the square root of the average value of V^2; the average value of V itself, the molecular velocity, is a little smaller.

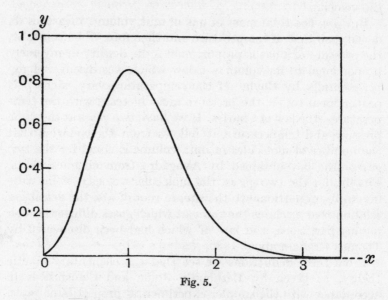

Fig. 5.

The kinetic theory was again developed at a later date by Clerk Maxwell, Boltzmann and others, who made use of more rigorous mathematical methods. Maxwell and Boltzmann applied to the problem of the distribution of velocities Gauss' law of error, derived from the theory of probability, now of importance in many branches of enquiry. The theory shows that molecules subject to chance collisions may be divided into groups, each group moving within a certain range of velocity in a manner illustrated in the diagram. The horizontal ordinate measures the velocity, and the vertical ordinate the number of molecules which move with it. The most probable velocity is taken as unity. It will be seen that the number of molecules moving with a velocity only three times the most probable velocity is almost negligible. Similar curves may be drawn to illustrate the distribution of shots on a target, of the errors in a physical measurement, of men arranged in groups according to height or weight, length of life, or ability as measured by examination. Both in physical and in biological science and in sociology, the theory of probability and the curves of error are now of great importance. It is impossible to predict the length of life of an individual man, or the velocity of a particular molecule at any future instant; but, with a sufficient number of molecules or men, we can deal with them statistically, and predict within narrow limits how many will be moving within a certain range of velocity, or how many will die in a given year—philosophically we may say that we reach a form of statistical determinism, though, at this stage, individual uncertainty remains.

The Kinetic Theory of Gases

The tendency of molecules, originally moving with other velocities, to reach the Maxwell-Boltzmann distribution, which is the most probable arrangement, was investigated by Boltzmann and Watson. It proved to be equivalent to the tendency of a thermodynamic quantity, known as entropy, to reach a maximum. The process of reaching this most probable condition, in which the entropy is a maximum and the velocities distributed according to the law of error, is analogous to the shuffling of a pack of cards. It happens spontaneously in nature as time goes on. It has now (1929) become of great scientific, indeed of philosophic importance.

Maxwell also showed that the viscosity of a gas must depend on the mean free path, that is, the average distance a molecule moves between two collisions. For hydrogen the mean free path is about 17×10^{-6} cms. and for oxygen $8 \cdot 7 \times 10^{-6}$ cms. The frequency of collision is of the order of 10^9 per second, and this very high number shows why, in spite of the great velocity of their molecules, gases diffuse so slowly. The viscosity of a gas does not diminish with the density, as one might expect, but, till very low densities are reached, remains constant as the gas is exhausted. The verification by experiment of this theoretical result gave early confidence in the more advanced parts of the theory.

Temperature is measured on the kinetic theory by the average energy of translation of the molecules, but they may possess also energy of rotation, vibration, etc. Maxwell and

Boltzmann showed that the total energy should be proportional to the "number of degrees of freedom" of a molecule, that is, to the number of co-ordinates needed to specify its position completely. The position of a point in space is fixed by three co-ordinates, and thus the motion of the molecules as wholes, by which temperature is determined, involves three degrees of freedom. If the total number of degrees be n, when a gas is heated a fraction of the heat energy $3/n$ goes into energy of translation to raise the temperature, and the rest, $(n-3)/n$, is used by the molecule in other ways. When a gas is heated at constant volume, all the heat is used to increase molecular energy, but, at constant pressure, the volume will increase, and therefore work is also done against the pressure of the atmosphere. From this it can be shown to follow that the ratio γ of the two specific heats, at constant pressure and at constant volume, is given by $1 + 2/n$, so that, if $n = 3$, $\gamma = 1 + \frac{2}{3} = 1 \cdot 67$. At the time when Maxwell made his calculation, he knew of no gas which gave this ratio, but it was afterwards found to hold good for gases with monatomic molecules, such as mercury vapour, argon and helium, which therefore behave as single points as far as the absorption of heat energy is concerned. Ordinary gases, such as hydrogen and oxygen, have diatomic molecules. They are found to give a value for γ of $1 \cdot 4$, indicating molecules with five degrees of freedom.

Boyle's Law, in the form $pv = $ constant, can be expanded into $pv = RT$, when changes of temperature are brought into account, R being a constant. The effect of molecular attraction, which must depend on the square of the density, or a/v^2, where a is a constant, is to increase p to $p + a/v^2$. The effect of the volume b, occupied by the substance of the molecules themselves, and therefore not subject to compression, is to decrease v to $v - b$. Thus Van der Waals in 1873 obtained the equation

$$\left(p + \frac{a}{v^2}\right)(v - b) = RT,$$

which was found to express fairly well the variations from Boyle's Law observed in some imperfect gases.

Such gases were examined experimentally by several physicists, especially about 1869 by Andrews,[1] who investigated

[1] Royal Society, *Phil. Trans.* 1869, ii, p. 575.

the continuity of the gaseous and the liquid states, and showed that, above a definite critical temperature which was characteristic of each gas, no pressure, however great, would produce liquefaction. The liquefaction of a gas, therefore, was seen to be essentially a problem of reducing the temperature below the critical point. *The Kinetic Theory of Gases*

Direct evidence of the action of molecules was obtained by the irregular movements of very small particles observed under a microscope by the botanist Robert Brown in 1827, and explained in 1879 by William Ramsay as being due to the bombardment of the particles by the molecules of the liquid in which they are suspended. Light vanes, blackened on one side and pivoted in very high vacua, were observed by Crookes to rotate in the direction of the polished faces when placed in sunlight. Maxwell explained this rotation as an effect of the additional heat absorbed by the blackened sides. This heat causes the molecules to rebound with greater velocity when they strike the vane and thus push back the blackened face.

In 1824 Sadi Carnot, the son of the "Organizer of Victory", pointed out that every heat engine needs a hot body or source of heat, and a cold body or condenser, and that, when the engine works, heat passes from the hotter body to the colder one. Regarding heat as a fluid, Carnot thought that it passes through the engine unchanged in amount, doing work by falling from a higher to a lower temperature, as water, falling from a height, does work on a water-wheel. *Thermo-dynamics*

Carnot saw that to investigate the laws of heat engines, it is necessary to imagine firstly the simplest case—that of a perfectly frictionless engine in which there is no loss of heat by conduction. Furthermore he realized that, in the examination of the working of an engine, the engine must be supposed to be carried through a complete cycle of observations, so that the working substance, steam, compressed air, or whatever it may be, is brought back to its initial state. If this is not done, the engine may be drawing work or heat from the internal energy of its working substance, and the external heat which passes through the engine may not be doing all the work.

Carnot left in manuscript the idea of the conservation of energy, but his theory of cycles was put into modern form by Clausius and William Thomson, afterwards Lord Kelvin. When work is transformed into heat or heat into work, the relation between them is given by Joule's results. But, although it is always possible to transform the whole of a given quantity of work into heat, it is not generally possible to perform completely the reverse change. In steam engines and other heat engines it is found that only a fraction of the heat supplied is transformed into mechanical energy; the remainder, which passes from hotter to colder parts of the system, does not become available for the performance of useful work. Experience shows that every heat engine operates by taking a quantity of heat H from the source and giving up part of that heat, let us say h, to the condenser. The difference $(H - h)$ between these two quantities of heat is the maximum amount available for conversion into work W, and the ratio W/H of the actual work done to the heat absorbed may be taken as the efficiency E of the engine.

A theoretically perfect engine can be imagined which will lose no heat by conduction and no work by friction, so that

$$W = H - h,$$

and
$$E = \frac{W}{H} = \frac{H - h}{H}.$$

All such perfect engines must have the same efficiency, or it would be possible by coupling two engines together to obtain work from the heat energy of the condenser, or, by a self-acting mechanism, to pump heat continually from a cold body to a hot one, either of which is contrary to experience. Hence the efficiency, and therefore the ratio of the heat absorbed from the hot body to that given out by the cold one, is independent of the form of the engine or the nature of the working substance. These quantities must consequently depend only on the temperature of the source T, and that of the condenser t; and the ratio of the heat absorbed to that rejected may be used as a means of defining the ratio of the two temperatures by writing $T/t = H/h$, from which it follows that

$$E = \frac{H - h}{H} = \frac{T - t}{T}.$$

Thus William Thomson devised a thermodynamic scale of temperature which is absolute because it does not depend on the form of the apparatus or the nature of the substance in it. If the condenser of a perfect engine were at the zero of temperature, that is, if $t = 0$ or $E = 1$, no heat would be given to the condenser, all the heat absorbed would be converted into work, and the efficiency be unity. No engine can give out more work than the mechanical equivalent of the heat it absorbs, or have an efficiency greater than unity. Hence this zero of temperature is a true absolute zero—no temperature can be colder.

The thermodynamic scale of temperature as thus defined is only a theoretical one. It is not possible practically to compare two temperatures by measuring the ratio of the quantities of heat absorbed and rejected by a perfect engine—if only for the reason that a perfect engine cannot be made. Hence it is necessary to translate the thermodynamic scale into more practical terms.

In one of his investigations, Joule, like Mayer before him, used the compression of air as a means of converting work into heat. But Joule justified its use by repeating a forgotten experiment of Gay-Lussac, and showing that, when air was allowed to expand without doing work, no appreciable change of temperature occurred. Thus it follows that there is no alteration in the molecular state of the gas on expansion or contraction, and all the work done in compressing it appears as heat. Thomson and Joule devised a more delicate method of experiment, and proved that, when gases were forced through a porous plug and allowed to expand freely beyond it, the changes of temperature were very small, air being slightly cooled and hydrogen being even more slightly heated.

From a mathematical consideration of this experiment, it follows that an air or hydrogen thermometer gives indications very nearly those of the absolute or thermodynamic scale, the small differences being calculable from the heat effects on free expansion.

The consequences of thermodynamical reasoning have not only enabled the engineer to place on a firm footing the theory of the heat engine, but have aided materially the progress of modern physics and chemistry in many other directions. Faraday liquefied chlorine by pressure alone in a very simple apparatus. But the theory of an absolute scale of temperature and the porous plug experiments of Thomson and Joule pointed the way to that modern series of researches which eventually liquefied all known gases and thus completed the proof of the continuity of all types of matter in its three states. The porous plug effect, minute at ordinary temperatures, becomes large when gases are previously cooled, and, when a cold gas is forced continuously through a pipe ending in a nozzle, it is cooled further and can be used to cool still more the on-coming stream of gas. The process is thus made cumulative, and the gas is finally cooled below its critical point and liquefied.

To obtain useful work from a supply of heat, a temperature inequality is necessary. But, in nature, temperature inequalities are constantly being diminished by conduction of heat and in other ways. Hence, in an isolated system with irreversible changes going on, the heat energy tends steadily to become less and less available for the performance of useful work, or conversely the mathematical function called by Clausius the entropy, constant in a reversible system, tends to increase. When the availability of the energy becomes a minimum or the entropy a maximum, no further work can be done, and thus the necessary conditions of equilibrium of the system can be determined. In a similar way, equilibrium in an isothermal system (i.e. one at constant temperature) is reached when the thermodynamic potential, another mathematical function, is a minimum. By these considerations, the theory of chemical and physical equilibrium has been built up by Clausius, Kelvin, Helmholtz and Willard Gibbs. A great part of modern physical chemistry, with many industrially important technical applications, is merely a series of experimental illustrations of Willard Gibbs' thermodynamic equations.

Similar ideas, extended to the whole stellar Universe, were taken to indicate that cosmical energy is continually wasting into heat by friction, and heat energy is continually becoming less available by the reduction of inequalities of temperature. Thus physicists were led to contemplate a distant future in which all the stores of energy available in the Universe will have been converted into heat uniformly distributed through matter in mechanical equilibrium, and all further change will become for ever impossible. But this conclusion rested on several unproved assumptions. It supposed that generalizations made from limited observations were true in wider conditions which were as yet largely undetermined; it supposed that the stellar Universe may be treated as an isolated system into which no energy is entering; it supposed that individual molecules, the velocity of which is subject to continual alteration owing to collisions, cannot be followed and separated into fast-moving and slow-moving groups.

Maxwell imagined a minute being or daemon, with faculties fine enough to follow the individual molecules, placed in charge of a frictionless sliding door in a wall separating two compartments of a vessel filled with gas. When a fast-moving molecule moves from left to right the daemon opens the door, when a slow-moving molecule approaches, he (or she) closes the door. The fast-moving molecules accumulate in the right-hand compartment, and slow ones in the left. The gas in the first compartment grows hot and that in the second cold. Thus the power of controlling individual molecules would enable diffused energy to be reconcentrated.

In the conditions of nature known in the nineteenth century, the principle of the dissipation of energy held good as long as molecules could only be treated statistically; the energy by which we live and move seemed to be growing continually less available, and the process of thermodynamic decay threatened slowly to drain away the life of the Universe. How far this conclusion has been modified or confirmed in new terms by recent knowledge will be seen in a later chapter. Here it should be noted that the thermodynamic condition of maximum entropy or greatest dissipation of energy is reached when molecules have their velocities distributed in accordance with the Maxwell-Boltzmann law, the probability of which is a maximum. Thus thermodynamics are linked to the known laws of probability and to the kinetic theory of matter.

The classical distinction between the celestial and terrestrial spheres, which lasted during the whole of the Middle Ages, was broken down by Galileo and Newton, when the mechanical laws of falling bodies, established by experiment, were shown mathematically and by observation to hold throughout the solar system.

But, to complete the proof of identity, it was necessary to demonstrate similarity in structure and composition as well as in motion, to prove that the familiar chemical elements, of which all earthly things are made, exist also in the substance of Sun, planets and stars. It may well have seemed a hopeless problem. Yet, in the middle of the nineteenth century, a solution was found.

Newton had shown that the band of colours produced by passing the Sun's rays through a glass prism was due to the decomposition of white light into physically simpler components. In 1802 Wollaston discovered that this luminous spectrum of sunlight was crossed by a number of dark lines, and, in 1814, Joseph Fraunhofer rediscovered these lines and, increasing the dispersion by using more than one prism, mapped them carefully. On the other hand, light from flames tinged with metals or salts was found to give spectra showing characteristic bright coloured lines on a dark ground, and in 1823 Sir John Herschel suggested that these lines might be used as a test for the presence of the metals. This led to a series of observations in which the position of spectral lines was mapped and recorded.

In 1849 Foucault examined the spectrum of the light from a voltaic arc between carbon poles, and noticed that a bright double line, between the yellow and the orange, coincides exactly with the dark double line called D by Fraunhofer. Foucault found that, when the sun's light is passed through the arc, the line D appears darker than usual, and, when the light from one of the carbons, which of itself gives a continuous bright spectrum with no black lines, is passed through the arc, the black D lines appear. "Thus", says Foucault, "the arc presents us with a medium which emits the rays D on its own account, and which at the same time absorbs them when they come from another quarter."

The theory of Fraunhofer's lines seems first to have been made plain by Sir George Gabriel Stokes (1819–1903) in his lectures at Cambridge, though with characteristic modesty he gave his ideas no wider publicity. Any mechanical system will absorb energy which falls on it in rhythmic unison with its own natural vibrations, just as a child's swing is set in motion by giving it a series of small impulses which coincide with its natural period of oscillation. The molecules of the vapours in the outer envelope of the Sun will absorb the energy of those particular rays coming from the hotter interior, of which the oscillatory period coincides with their own. The light which passes on will be deprived of light of that particular frequency of vibration (i.e. colour), and a black line in the solar spectrum is the result.

During the years 1855 to 1863 von Bunsen, in conjunction *Spectrum* with Roscoe, carried out a series of experiments on the *Analysis* chemical action of light, and in 1859, working with Kirchhoff, he devised the first exact methods of spectrum analysis, whereby chemical elements could be detected by their spectra even if present only in minute quantities. Two new elements, caesium and rubidium, of the same family as sodium and potassium, were thus discovered.

In ignorance of Foucault's experiments, Bunsen and Kirchhoff passed the light from incandescent lime, which gives a continuous spectrum, through an alcohol flame into which common salt was put, and saw the *D* Fraunhofer lines. They repeated the experiment with lithium in the flame of a Bunsen gas burner, and obtained a dark line invisible in their solar spectrum. They concluded that sodium is present in the atmosphere of the Sun, and that lithium is absent, or present in quantities too small to be observed.

Spectroscopic astronomy, thus initiated, was greatly developed by the labours of Huggins, Janssen and Lockyer. In 1878, the last named physicist, observing a dark line in the green of the spectrum of the Sun's chromosphere not coincident with any known line in terrestrial spectra, predicted, jointly with Frankland, the existence of an element in the Sun to account for it, and called that element Helium. In 1895 the element was found by Ramsay in the mineral cleveite.[1]

Doppler pointed out in 1842 that, when a source of waves and an observer are in relative motion, the frequency of the waves as observed is altered. When the source is approaching, more waves reach the observer per second, and the pitch of the sound or the light is raised, while if the source is receding the pitch is lowered. This change is well shown in the flattening of the note of the whistle of an engine as an express train dashes through a station. If a star be approaching the Earth, its spectral lines will be displaced towards the violet, and if it be receding, then towards the red. The Doppler effect though small is measurable, and, in the hands of Huggins and later of many others, it has yielded an immense amount of knowledge of stellar motion, and recently of other problems.

Meanwhile the identity in the physical nature of light and of radiant heat had been fully demonstrated. In 1800, Sir

[1] *Chemical Society Trans.* 1895, p. 1107.

Spectrum
Analysis

William Herschel had shown that a thermometer, placed in the solar spectrum, indicated heat effects which extended beyond the lowest visible red light. Soon afterwards Ritter found rays beyond the visible violet which would blacken nitrate of silver. Between 1830 and 1840 Melloni demonstrated that invisible heat showed properties similar to those of light as regards reflection, refraction, polarization and interference. The equivalence between emissive and absorptive powers, which gives the basis for spectroscopic astronomy, was extended to radiant heat by many observers, especially Kirchhoff and Balfour Stewart. A black body, which absorbs all radiation, was found also to emit when hot complete radiation of all wave-lengths.

Maxwell showed theoretically that radiation should exert a pressure on a surface on which it falls, and the pressure, though exceedingly small, has been demonstrated experimentally in more recent years. In 1875 Bartoli pointed out that the existence of this pressure enables us to imagine that a space filled with radiation might act as the cylinder of a theoretical thermodynamic engine, and in 1884 Boltzmann showed that it must follow that the full radiation of a black body increases as the fourth power of the absolute temperature, or $R = aT^4$, a law which had been discovered empirically by Stefan in 1879. This result is useful, not only in the theory of radiation, but also as a means of measuring the temperatures of furnaces, and even of the surfaces of the Sun and stars, by observation of the heat energy they give forth. As the temperature rises, not only does the total radiation increase in this manner, but the maximum energy emitted is displaced towards the shorter wave-lengths. Advance towards a theory of this displacement also was made, especially by Wien, on a basis of thermodynamics.

Finally, definite relations between the frequencies of the different spectral lines of one element, relations which have become so important in the physics of the twentieth century, began to be noticed in the nineteenth. In particular, Balmer in 1885 showed that the four lines in the visible spectrum of hydrogen could be represented by an empirical formula. This formula was afterwards found by Huggins to express the frequencies of lines in the ultra violet, and also of lines in the spectra of nebulae and of the solar corona at a total eclipse, so that they are all probably due to hydrogen. Thus its presence was inferred in the nebulae and in the sun's corona.

As explained above, much of Faraday's experimental work on electricity was inspired by his instinctive grasp of the importance of the dielectric or insulating medium. When a current deflects a magnetic needle across space, or induces another current in an apparently unconnected circuit, we have either to imagine an unexplained "action at a distance", or to conceive the intervening space to be bridged with something through which the effect is transmitted. Faraday took the second point of view; he imagined lines of force or chains of particles in "dielectric polarization", and even pictured them, having left their source, travelling freely through space. *Electric Waves*

Faraday's ideas were put into mathematical form by James Clerk Maxwell (1831–1879), who pointed out that a change in Faraday's dielectric polarization was equivalent to an electric current. Since an electric current produces a magnetic field, the magnetic force being at right angles to the current, and a change in a magnetic field produces an electromotive force, it is clear that magnetic and electric forces are reciprocally related. As a change in dielectric polarization spreads through the insulating medium, therefore, it travels as an electro-magnetic wave, the direction of the electric and magnetic forces being at right angles to each other in the plane of the advancing wave-front.

Maxwell's mathematical investigation led to a series of differential equations which showed that the velocity of such waves depended, as is natural, only on the electric and magnetic properties of the medium, and was given by the expression
$$v = 1/\sqrt{\mu k},$$
where μ is the magnetic permeability and k the dielectric constant, or the specific inductive capacity, of the medium.[1]

---

[1] Using mathematical methods developed from those of Lagrange and Hamilton, Maxwell obtained for a non-conducting medium the equations

$$k\mu \frac{d^2F}{dt^2} + \nabla^2 F = 0,$$

$$k\mu \frac{d^2G}{dt^2} + \nabla^2 G = 0,$$

$$k\mu \frac{d^2H}{dt^2} + \nabla^2 H = 0,$$

which determine the propagation of a disturbance moving with a velocity $v = 1/\sqrt{\mu k}$.

Electric Waves   Since the electric force between two charges is inversely proportional to k, and the magnetic force between two poles is inversely proportional to μ, the electric and magnetic units which are defined in terms of those forces must involve k and μ. It can easily be shown that the ratio of the electrostatic to the electromagnetic value of any one unit, such for instance as the unit of quantity of electricity, involves the product of μ and k. Hence, by comparing experimentally two such units, the value of v, the velocity of an electromagnetic wave, can be determined.

Maxwell and several other physicists found that v, as thus measured, was about 3×10^{10} cms. per second, as nearly as may be the same as the velocity of light. Maxwell therefore concluded that light is an electromagnetic phenomenon, and that there is no need to invent more than one aether—the same aether will carry both light and electromagnetic waves, which are indeed identical in kind though differing in wavelength.

But what about the elastic solid aether, in the theory of which so much good work had been expended? Are we to regard electromagnetic waves as mechanical waves in a quasi-rigid solid, or are we to express light in terms of electricity and magnetism, the meaning of which is unknown? Maxwell's discovery placed that dilemma before the world for the first time. Nevertheless he strengthened the general belief in the existence of a luminiferous aether. It was clear that it would perform electrical functions as well as carry light.

Maxwell's work, at once accepted in England, attracted less attention than it deserved on the Continent till, in 1887, Heinrich Hertz, using the oscillatory current given by the spark of an induction coil, produced and detected electric waves in space, showing experimentally that they possessed many of the properties of light. The aether, if there be an aether, is now crowded with "wireless waves", a development due primarily to the work of Maxwell and Hertz.

Maxwell focussed the attention of physicists on the insulating medium as the most important part of an electrified system. It became clear that the energy of an electric current passes through the medium, while the current itself is but the line of dissipation of that energy into heat, a line of which the chief function is to guide the flow of energy along the path where dissipation is possible. With very rapidly alternating currents, such as those in the spark of an induction coil or a flash of lightning, the energy can only sink a little way into the conductor before the flow is reversed. Thus only the outer skin of a conducting wire or lightning rod is effective in carrying these currents, and the electric resistance is much higher than it is for steady currents.

Electric Waves

The chief difficulty in accepting Maxwell's theory was its failure to give a clear account of electric charges, or at all events of those discrete, atomic electric charges indicated by Faraday's experiments on electrolysis. The conception of atomic charges became a problem of great importance soon after Maxwell's death, and to its consideration we must now turn. But a digression is first necessary.

The cause and mechanism of chemical action have been the subjects of speculation from early times, and occupied much of Newton's attention. Definite measurements were made in 1777 by C. F. Wenzel, who sought to estimate the chemical affinity of acids for metals by observing the velocity with which chemical change went on. He found that the rates of reaction were proportional to the concentration of his acids, that is, to the active mass of the reagent, a result reached independently by Berthollet.

Chemical Action

In 1850 Wilhelmy examined the "inversion" of cane-sugar in presence of an acid, the process being the decomposition of the sucrose molecules into the simpler ones of dextrose and laevulose. He found that, as the concentration of the cane-sugar grew less while the reaction proceeded, the rate of change diminished proportionally in a geometrical progression with the time. This means that the number of molecules dissociating is proportional to the number present at any instant —a natural result, if we assume that the molecules of sugar dissociate independently of each other. Whenever this relation holds good for a chemical change we may infer that the molecules act singly, that the change is what is called a monomolecular reaction.

On the other hand, if two molecules react with each other—a di-molecular process—the rate of change will obviously depend on the frequency with which collisions occur, a frequency proportional to the product of the concentration or active masses of the two reacting molecules. If the molecular concentrations are equivalent, this product will be equal to the square of the concentration.

If the reaction be reversible, so that while two compounds AB and CD are reacting to form AD and CB, the two latter are also reacting to re-form AB and CD, equilibrium must be reached when the opposite changes are going on at equal rates, that is, when

$$AB + CD \rightleftarrows AD + CB.$$

This conception of a dynamical equilibrium was first clearly formulated in 1850 by A. W. Williamson. A full statement of the mass-law of chemical action was given by Guldberg and Waage in 1864; it was rediscovered by Jellet in 1873 and again by Van't Hoff in 1877. It can be deduced not only as above from kinetic theory, but also by thermodynamic principles from the energy relations of a dilute system. It has been confirmed experimentally in many chemical reactions.

As stated above, the inversion of cane-sugar goes on quickly in presence of an acid, and very much more slowly in its absence. The acid is unchanged, and seems merely to facilitate the action without taking part in it. This phenomenon was first discovered in 1812 by Kirchhoff, who found that starch could be converted into glucose in presence of dilute sulphuric acid. Humphry Davy observed that platinum induced the oxidation of alcohol vapour in air. Finely divided platinum was found by Döbereiner to bring about the combination of hydrogen and oxygen. In 1838 Cagniard de Latour, and independently Schwann, showed that the fermentation of sugar into alcohol and carbonic acid was due to the presence of a living organism, and Berzelius pointed out the analogy between fermentation and such inorganic reactions as those produced by platinum. Berzelius called such actions "catalysis" and to the agents producing them he assigned a "catalytic power". He suggests that the enormous number of chemical compounds formed in living bodies from common raw material, plant juice or blood, may be produced by organic bodies analogous to these catalysts. In 1878 such organic catalysts were called by Kühne "enzymes".

In 1862 Berthelot and Péan de St Gilles found that, when ethyl acetate and water are mixed in molecular proportions, after some weeks the ester ethyl acetate is partly hydrolysed, with the formation of ethyl alcohol and acetic acid at a steadily decreasing rate. Beginning with alcohol and acid, the reverse change went on, and the final proportions of equilibrium were the same. These reactions are very slow, but, in the presence of a mineral acid, the same point of equilibrium is reached in a few hours. Thus the acid acts as a catalyst; the function of a catalyst is seen to be to hasten a reaction, and to hasten it in either direction. In a sense it plays the same part as a lubricant does in mechanical machinery. In 1887 the catalytic action of acids was coordinated by Arrhenius with their electrical conductivity.

Chemical Action

Similar phenomena occur in gas reactions. Dixon found that the explosion of oxygen and hydrogen to form water-vapour will not occur if the gases are quite dry, and in 1902 Brereton Baker showed that, when slow combination goes on and water is formed, no explosion follows. Armstrong suggests that the water produced by the reaction itself is too pure to act as a catalyst. Other cases are known where pure chemical substances are ineffective, and the presence of complex mixtures seems necessary. The importance of organic catalysts or enzymes in biochemistry will be described in the next chapter.

The dissolution of substances in water and other liquids is a familiar phenomenon. Some liquids, e.g. alcohol and water, mix with each other in all proportions, while others, like water and oil, will never mix. Solids like sugar dissolve freely, while metals are insoluble. Air and similar gases are only slightly soluble in water, while ammonia and hydrogen chloride are very soluble.

Theory of Solution[1]

Physical changes may accompany solution. The volume may become less than the sum of the volumes of the solute and the solvent, and heat may be absorbed or evolved. Most neutral salts give a cooling effect when dissolved in water, though a few, such as aluminium chloride, give out heat. Acids and alkalies also usually evolve heat.

These reactions had been studied by many chemists, who recognized that they were of complex nature, involving both mixture and chemical combination, though the continuous variation in composition, unlike the definite proportions of other chemical compounds, showed that special relations were involved. But till the nineteenth century the phenomena of solution were not regarded as a separate problem.

[1] W. C. Dampier Whetham, *A Treatise on the Theory of Solution*, Cambridge, 1902.

Theory of
Solution

The first systematic work on the diffusion of dissolved substances was done by Thomas Graham (1805–1869), whose experiments on the diffusion of gases have already been mentioned. Graham found that crystalline bodies, such as most salts, when dissolved in water pass freely through membranes and diffuse comparatively quickly from one part of the liquid to another. But substances like glue or gelatine, which form no crystals, diffuse very slowly when dissolved. Graham called the first class of bodies crystalloids, and the second colloids. It was thought at first that colloids were always organic substances, but many inorganic bodies, such as sulphide of arsenic, and even some metals like gold, can, by special treatment, be obtained in the colloidal state.

The invention of Volta's cell and the immediately resulting study of the electrical properties of solutions have already been described. In 1833 Faraday showed that the passage of a definite quantity of electricity through an electrolyte was always accompanied by an equally definite separation of ions at the electrodes. If we regard the current as carried by the movement of ions, this means that every ion of the same chemical valency carries the same charge, so that the charge on a univalent ion is a natural unit or atom of electricity.

In 1859 Hittorf made another advance in the subject. A solution between insoluble electrodes is diluted unequally in the regions near the two electrodes by the passage of a current. Hittorf saw that this fact gave a means of comparing experimentally the velocities with which the opposite ions move, since that electrode from which the faster ion comes will lose more electrolyte. Thus the ratio of the opposite ionic velocities could be measured.

In 1879 Kohlrausch invented a satisfactory way of measuring the electric resistance of electrolytes. Owing to polarization, direct currents are inapplicable, but Kohlrausch overcame the difficulty by using alternating currents and spongy electrodes of large area, so as to reduce the surface density of any deposit. Instead of a galvanometer, he used as indicator a telephone, which is responsive to alternating currents. When polarization was thus eliminated, he found that electrolytes conformed to Ohm's Law, i.e. that the current was proportional to the electromotive force. Hence the smallest force produces a corresponding current in the body of the electrolyte; there is no reverse force of polarization except at the electrodes. The ions must therefore have freedom of interchange, as already suggested by Clausius.

Kohlrausch thus measured the conductivity of electrolytes, and pointed out that, as the current is carried by opposite streams of ions, the conductivity must give a measure of the sum of the opposite ionic velocities. Combined with Hittorf's determination of their ratio, this gave a means of calculating the velocities of the individual ions. Hydrogen moves through water with a velocity of about 0·003 cm. per second under a potential gradient of 1 volt per centimetre, while the ions of neutral salts range round about 0·0006 cm. per second. The first of these numbers was confirmed experimentally by Sir Oliver Lodge, who traced the hydrogen ion as it moved through a jelly which was coloured by an indicator sensitive to hydrogen. The values for neutral ions were verified by the present writer, who watched their motion in coloured salts or by the formation of precipitates. These methods have since been improved by other investigators.

Another view of solutions was disclosed by the Dutch physicist Van't Hoff. It had long been known that pressures might be set up by the passage of water into vegetable cells through their containing membranes, and the botanist Pfeffer had measured this osmotic pressure, using artificial membranes deposited chemically in the walls of porous pots. Van't Hoff pointed out that Pfeffer's measurements showed that osmotic pressure resembles gas pressure in its relations: it is inversely proportional to the volume, and increases with the absolute temperature. The reversible passage of water or other solvent through membranes impermeable to the solution, made it possible to imagine an osmotic cell to be the cylinder of a theoretically perfect engine, and thus Van't Hoff was able to apply thermodynamic reasoning to solutions, opening a quite new field of research. He thus connected the osmotic pressure of a solution with its other physical properties, such as its freezing-point and vapour pressure, so that, from a measurement of freezing-point, a comparatively easy operation, the osmotic pressure can be calculated. He proved theoretically that the absolute value of the osmotic pressure of a dilute solution must be the same as the pressure of a gas at the same concentration, and showed that experiment confirmed this

result. It does not follow, as some assumed, that the causes
of the pressures are the same, or that the dissolved substance
is in a gaseous state. Thermodynamic reasoning has nothing to
say about mechanism; it discloses relations between connected
quantities but nothing about the nature of the connection.
Osmotic pressure may be due to impact like gas pressure; it
may be due to chemical affinity or chemical combination
between the solvent and solute. Whatever its nature, if it
exist at all, it must conform to thermodynamic principles, and
therefore, as Van't Hoff proved, in dilute solution it must obey
the gas laws. Its cause however remains undetermined, at all
events by thermodynamics.

In 1887 Arrhenius, a Swede, showed that osmotic pressure
was connected with the electrical properties of solutions. The
pressures of electrolytes were known to be abnormally great,
a solution of potassium chloride or any similar binary salt, for
example, having twice the osmotic pressure of a solution of
sugar of the same molecular concentration. Arrhenius found
that this excess pressure was connected not only with electrolytic conductivity but also with chemical activity, such as the
catalytic power of acids in facilitating the alcoholic fermentation of sugar. He concluded that it indicated a dissociation
of the ions from each other, so that, for example, in a solution
of potassium chloride, while there exist some electrically
neutral KCl molecules, there are also potassium ions and
chlorine ions carrying positive and negative electric charges
respectively, and it is these ions which give the solution
electrolytic conductivity and chemical activity. The more the
solution is diluted, the more salt is dissociated, till, at great
dilution, the liquid contains only K^+ ions and Cl^- ions, which,
separated from each other, are now known to be combined
with the solvent.

The work of Kohlrausch, Van't Hoff and Arrhenius has
proved the starting point of a vast superstructure of physical
chemistry, in which thermodynamics and electrical science
have been combined in an ever-growing extension of theoretical
knowledge and of practical industrial applications. Furthermore, it must not be overlooked that the theory of solutions
gave the idea of an electrical ion to those great physicists who,
investigating the conduction of electricity through gases, have
built up the most characteristic part of modern science.

Chapter VI

NINETEENTH-CENTURY BIOLOGY

The Significance of Biology—Organic Chemistry—Physiology
—Microbes and Bacteriology—The Carbon and Nitrogen
Cycles—Physical Geography and Scientific Exploration—
Geology—Natural History—Evolution before Darwin—Dar-
win—The Fight for Evolution—Anthropology.

IN the epoch of science which began with the Renaissance *The*
the greatest revolution in thought was that produced by the *Significance*
progress made in astronomy and physics. It so happened that *of Biology*
when Copernicus dethroned the Earth from its proud position
as the centre of the Universe, and Newton brought the
phenomena of the heavens under the sway of the mechanical
laws familiar in everyday life, many of the tacit assumptions
on which a whole theory of Divine revelation had been built
up were also undermined. A complete change of outlook was
thus brought about, although many years passed before the
full effects were realized. The current conceptions of the
Earth as the centre of the Cosmos and man as the unique
object and meaning of creation held their place in popular
beliefs long after the astronomical ideas with which it was
thought they were connected had been abandoned by the
instructed.

In the great advance which marked the nineteenth century,
it was not the vast development of physical knowledge, and
still less the enormous superstructure of industry raised on
that knowledge, which most effectually widened man's mental
horizon and led to one more revolution in his ways of thought.
The point of real interest shifted from astronomy to geology,
and from physics to biology and the phenomena of life. The
hypothesis of natural selection, which first gave an acceptable
basis for the old idea of evolution, carried the human mind
over the next long stage of its endless journey, with Darwin
as the Newton of biology—the central figure of nineteenth-
century thought. Natural selection may be unable alone to
explain all the many facts which have since come to light, but
the theory of evolution itself rests on a broad foundation which
time has only strengthened.

To trace the history and appreciate the significance of evolutionary philosophy, it will be necessary to follow the outlines of the progress of biological knowledge from the point where the threads of its story were dropped in Chapter v.

Among the sciences underlying biology, physics and physical chemistry have already been passed in review, but organic chemistry, which first emerged as a definite separate science in the nineteenth century, remains to be considered.

The chemistry of the complicated substances which are found in the bodies of plants and animals is chiefly the chemistry of that remarkable element carbon. The atoms of carbon possess the unique property of combining with each other, as well as with atoms of other elements, to form very complex molecules. We have seen how the old theory of a distinct vital principle survived in opposition to the equally old theory that in living bodies, as in the outside material world, mechanism would ultimately explain all happenings. It had long been thought that the specially complicated substances which are characteristic of animal and vegetable tissues could only be formed under the influence of vital processes, and the belief in a spiritual interpretation of life was thought to stand or fall with the truth of this view. But in 1828 the artificial preparation of urea by Friedrich Wöhler showed that one substance hitherto only found in living matter could be made in the laboratory. Other artificial preparations of natural products followed, till in 1887 Emil Fischer succeeded in building up fructose (fruit-sugar) and glucose (grape-sugar) from their elements. The distinction between organic and inorganic was thus broken down, but the so-called "organic compounds" are so many and so complex that it is still convenient to separate organic chemistry from inorganic chemistry and from physical chemistry.

The fundamental problem of organic chemistry is the determination of the elements present in a compound and the estimation of its percentage composition. This is done by burning the compound in the oxygen given off from oxide of copper and measuring the amounts of the products of combustion. The methods of analysis were invented chiefly by Lavoisier, Berzelius, Gay-Lussac and Thénard, and they were so far perfected by Justus Liebig that in 1830 the empirical

[1] See for example Sir Edward Thorpe, *History of Chemistry*, London, 1921.

composition of carbon compounds could be determined with
fair accuracy. A surprising result was the discovery of
isomerism—that certain compounds, quite different in chemical
and physical properties, had the same percentage composition;
e.g. silver cyanate and silver fulminate, urea and ammonium
cyanate, tartaric and racemic acids. Berzelius explained this
phenomenon as being due to a different arrangement and
connection between the atoms in the molecules of the two
isomeric compounds. A similar phenomenon was also found
among the elements—Lavoisier proved the chemical identity
of charcoal and the diamond.

*Organic
Chemistry*

Berzelius' idea was developed further when the conception of
chemical valency was brought forward by Frankland (1852), by
Couper and by Kekulé (1858). Empirical formulae, e.g. C_2H_6O
for common alcohol, grew into constitutional formulae, such as

$$
\begin{array}{ccc}
\text{H} & \text{H} \\
| & | \\
\text{H---C---C---OH} \\
| & | \\
\text{H} & \text{H}
\end{array}
$$

for the same body, in which the tetravalency of carbon, emphasized by Kekulé, is indicated by its linkages to other atoms
such as hydrogen, or to groups of atoms such as hydroxyl, OH.

In 1865, in a paper on the aromatic compounds, Kekulé
extended these ideas to explain the constitution of benzene
C_6H_6, the simplest of such compounds. Instead of an open
chain like the one given for ethyl alcohol, Kekulé pointed out
that the chemical properties and reactions of benzene could
only be explained by joining the ends of the chain to form a
closed ring as represented by the diagram

$$
\begin{array}{c}
\text{H} \\
| \\
\text{C} \\
\text{H}-\text{C} \quad \text{C}-\text{H} \\
| \qquad | \\
\text{H}-\text{C} \quad \text{C}-\text{H} \\
\text{C} \\
| \\
\text{H}
\end{array}
$$

By imagining one or more of the hydrogens replaced by other
atoms or by groups, the constitution of the more complex
aromatic compounds can be expressed.

Organic
Chemistry

In this way organic chemistry has been rationalized. The existence of new compounds, indicated by the theoretical possibilities of these structural formulae, has been predicted, while many of the compounds so predicted have been prepared and isolated. Thus, as far as organic compounds are concerned, the theory of structural formulae has enabled us to apply deductive methods to chemistry.

In 1844 Mitscherlich, who had previously pointed out the relation between atomic constitution and crystalline form, drew attention to the fact that isomers of tartaric acid, though possessing the same chemical reactions, the same percentage composition and the same constitutional formulae, had different optical properties. In 1848, Louis Pasteur (1822–1895), on recrystallizing racemates, noticed that two kinds of crystals were formed, related to each other as a right hand to a left hand or an object to its image in a mirror. When the two kinds of crystals were picked out, separated from each other and redissolved, one solution was found to rotate the plane of polarization of polarized light to the right and the other to the left. The first solution proved to contain a compound of ordinary tartaric acid, and the second a new salt, which, mixed with the first, gave a salt of racemic acid.

In 1863 Wislicenus concluded from similar phenomena in the case of lactic acid that the two modifications must be due to different arrangements of the atoms in space. In 1874 this idea was taken up independently by Le Bel and Van't Hoff. They inferred that all optically active carbon compounds contained an unsymmetrical atomic structure. Van't Hoff pictured the carbon atom C as occupying the centre of a tetrahedron, at the angles of which four other atoms or groups of atoms were placed. If the four are all different, we get an asymmetrical structure, and two varieties are possible, related to each other as are the object and image in a mirror. Similar phenomena have been discovered with the compounds of elements other than carbon, especially nitrogen, by Le Bel, H. O. Jones, Pope, Kipping and others.

Fig. 6.

It will be seen how the surprising success which attended

these explanations of the complex phenomena of organic chemistry supports the accuracy of the fundamental atomic and molecular conceptions on which the explanations are based.   *Organic Chemistry*

In 1832 Liebig and Wöhler pointed out that in many cases a complex group of atoms—a radicle, as it came to be called—held together as it passed by chemical reaction through a series of compounds, behaving in this respect like the atom of an element. For instance the group OH, hydroxyl, is found not only in water, but in all caustic alkalies and again in alcohols, while countless more complex radicles can be traced in, and are necessary to the processes of, organic chemistry and bio-chemistry.

The idea of radicles led naturally to the theory of types, worked out chiefly by A. W. Williamson from 1850 to 1852. By this theory, chemical compounds were classified according to their types, oxides, for example, being supposed to be built up on the type of water, the hydrogen atoms being replaced, wholly or in part, by other chemically equivalent atoms or groups of atoms. These conceptions of radicles and types replaced Berzelius' electrical dualism as the fundamental idea of chemical constitution.

Some of the enormous number of organic substances which make up living matter were gradually isolated and classed as members or derivatives of one or other of three classes of compounds:

(1) Proteins, containing the elements carbon, hydrogen, nitrogen, oxygen, with (in some cases) sulphur and phosphorus.

(2) Fats, containing carbon, hydrogen and oxygen.

(3) Carbohydrates, containing carbon, hydrogen and oxygen, the hydrogen and oxygen being present in the proportions in which they form water.

Of the three classes, the proteins have the most complex chemical structure, based principally on nitrogen. They are easily broken down into a number of proximate constituents known as amino-acids, containing hydrogen and nitrogen in the group NH_2. Many of these acids were isolated and chemically examined during the nineteenth century. They are of varied structure, but all contain one or more acidic carboxyl (COOH) radicles and one or more basic amino radicles, so that they possess the properties of both acids and bases. The

w   18

Organic
Chemistry

different proteins found in various kinds of living tissue are made up of amino-acids combined in different proportions.

In 1883 Curtius built up artificially a substance which gave a chemical reaction characteristic of protein products. At later dates Fischer investigated its structure and that of similar compounds. He devised several methods for combining amino-acids into complex bodies resembling the peptones which are produced by the action of digestive ferments on proteins. Thus, before the end of the century, some progress was made towards determining the nature, and even towards the synthesis, of the most complex and characteristic constituents of living organisms.

Physiology

One of the earliest conceptions in nineteenth-century physiology was due to Bichat (1771–1802)—the idea that the life of the body is the outcome of the combined lives of the constituent tissues, the specific characters of which Bichat himself did much to determine. He held that there is in life a conflict between vital forces and those of physics and chemistry, which after death resume their undivided sway and destroy the body.

The localization of the functions of the brain had already been suggested by isolated observations, such as that made in 1558 by Massa of Venice, who noted that injury to the parts behind the left eye interfered with the function of speech. Haller[1] had traced the nerves to a common junction in the *medulla cerebri*, but, as late as 1796, competent anatomists were still identifying the fluid in the ventricles of the brain with Galen's "animal spirits" and the Aristotelian *sensorium commune*, or the "organ of the soul". This theory was finally disproved by the dissections of F. J. Gall (1758–1828), a physician who worked first at Vienna and then at Paris.[2] Following up Massa's observation, Gall demonstrated the real structure of the brain, and taught "that the grey matter was the active and essential instrument of the nervous system and the white matter the connecting links". Gall was accused of materialism, and blamed for his insistence on the importance of heredity—an idea then repugnant to ecclesiastical views of moral responsibility. A greater trouble was his habit of mixing undoubted facts with much erroneous theory. This enabled his dismissed assistant Spurzheim to degrade Gall's work on

[1] See above, p. 203.
[2] Article by G. Elliot Smith, *The Times*, August 22nd, 1928.

localization by building on it the follies of "phrenology", and produced an opinion that Gall too was but a sorry charlatan. Yet on the solid parts of Gall's labours modern neurology is founded.

The form of vitalism held by Bichat was modified by Majendie, another French physiologist, who considered that some phenomena of living bodies were due to an inexplicable vital principle. From 1870 onwards, Majendie worked hard and successfully at other phenomena which he thought fit subjects for experimental investigation. In reaction from the dominant theoretical views, he worshipped experiment, even blind experiment; indeed he seems to have been one of the very few experimentalists who adopted the Baconian method. He proved that, as divined by Sir Charles Bell, the anterior and posterior roots of spinal nerves have different functions—a fundamental discovery in the physiology of the nervous system.

Descartes and his disciples held that a stimulus transmitted through nerve-fibres to the central system is converted automatically into an outgoing nervous impulse which excites the appropriate organ or muscle, so that the body of man is a machine. This view was taken by the iatro-medical school, and evidence on the problem at issue was drawn from the work of Bell, of Majendie, and of Marshall Hall (1790–1857) who established the difference between volitional and unconscious reflex action. Many of the common acts of life, coughing, sneezing, walking, breathing, may be taken as reflexes, and other processes formerly thought to involve complex mental operations were referred in the later years of the nineteenth century to reflex action, especially by J. M. Charcot (1825–1893) and his pupils. In the twentieth century further evidence on these problems has accumulated.

In Germany the most prominent physiologist in the early years of the nineteenth century was Johannes Müller, who collected all available knowledge in his famous *Outlines of Physiology*, and did much work himself on nervous action. He made the fruitful discovery that the kind of sensation we experience does not depend on the mode of stimulation of the nerves, but on the nature of the sense-organ; for instance, light, pressure or mechanical irritation, acting on the optic nerve and the retina, all produce luminous sensations. This discovery gave a physiological basis for the philosophical

18-2

Physiology belief, as old as the days of Galileo, that man's unaided senses give him no real knowledge of the external world: from different events we may receive the same sensation, and one event may cause different sensations according to the organ on which it acts.

Notwithstanding the success of this work, even those who were advancing physiology by means of physical and chemical experiments showed a tendency to think that much remained beyond the reach of these methods. And others, whose chief interests were in morphology, took a more thoroughly vitalist outlook. This was especially the case in France, where, in spite of Majendie's experiments, the scientific atmosphere was more that of natural history than physiology, and the influence of the great naturalist Cuvier was exerted in favour of vitalism.

Majendie's most famous disciple was Claude Bernard (1813–1878),[1] who, equally skilful with his master in experiment, recognized also the need for thought and imagination in planning work to be done afterwards in the laboratory. Bernard's work was mainly concerned with the action of the nervous system on nutrition and secretion; it was carried out on the one hand by experimental investigation on nerves, and on the other by direct chemical research. It foreshadowed many of the results of the modern subject of biochemistry.

In Müller's book the chemical changes undergone by food in the stomach were treated as though they constituted the whole process of digestion. Bernard showed that pancreatic juice disintegrates the fats discharged by the stomach into the duodenum, and decomposes them into fatty acids and glycerine; that it converts starch into sugar; and that it dissolves nitrogenous matter or proteins.

Dumas and Boussingault taught that there was a complete contrast in function between plants and animals. Plants absorb inorganic bodies and build them up into organic substances. Animals, essentially parasitic, live by breaking down these substances into inorganic, or at all events simpler, residues; they take organic food as it is given them, sometimes modify it, but, it was thought, can never build up fat, carbohydrate or protein. Bernard showed by experiments on dogs that the liver produced the sugar dextrose from the blood by a process of internal secretion under the control of the nerves. By later

[1] Michael Foster, *Claude Bernard*, London, 1899.

experiments he proved in 1857 that the liver when alive formed a substance named by him glycogen, which, by a process of fermentation independent of life, gave rise to dextrose. Thus he threw light on the cause and possible treatment of diabetes, and showed that animals in certain cases could themselves build up new organic substances.

Bernard's third great discovery was the function of what are called vaso-motor nerves, which are put into motion involuntarily by sensory impulses and control the blood vessels. To this discovery he was led by an investigation of the "animal heat" developed by the section of a nerve—heat which finally proved to be due to dilation of the blood vessels. "There is hardly a physiological discussion of any width", says Foster, "in which we do not sooner or later come upon vaso-motor questions" which arose from one simple experiment of Bernard on a living animal, "an experiment which Bernard, had he lived in this country and in our day, might have been prevented from doing; his work...strangled at its very birth". Indeed it is clear from history that essential parts of our knowledge of all the important organs and functions of the body, circulation, respiration, digestion, what you will—knowledge upon which the whole of modern physiology, of modern medicine and of modern surgery rest—were obtained by experiments on animals. Those who try to prevent all further advance in knowledge by this method take on themselves a terrible moral responsibility, which is in no wise lightened by ignorance of the facts or of the momentous issues involved.

Investigation of the nervous system was carried further by E. H. and E. F. Weber, who discovered inhibiting actions such as the stoppage of the heart's beat by the stimulation of the vagus nerve.

Further knowledge of respiration was acquired in 1838 by Magnus, who showed that arterial and venous blood contain both oxygen and carbon dioxide, though in different proportions. He thought the gases were dissolved in blood, but in 1857 L. Meyer proved that some kind of loose chemical compound is formed. Bernard explained the poisonous action of carbon monoxide by showing that it irreversibly displaces oxygen from the haemoglobin in the red blood corpuscles, whereupon the haemoglobin becomes inert and can no longer carry oxygen to the tissues of the body.

Physiology   Harvey had put the science of observational embryology on a correct basis in his *De Generatione Animalium* in 1651, but the true originator of the modern development was Caspar Frederick Wolff (1733–1794), who was born in Berlin, and died at St Petersburg, to which place he had been summoned by the Empress Catherine. Wolff's work was discredited and neglected during his lifetime, but in truth he foreshadowed all the modern theories of structure. He made a study of cells by means of the microscope, and showed the progressive formation and differentiation of the various organs in a germ originally homogeneous in character.

This multiplication and differentiation of cells was shown by von Baer (1792–1876) to be a process common to all embryonic development, and it was then recognized that organic growth proceeds on identical lines throughout the whole animal creation. In 1827 von Baer also discovered the ovum of mammals, overthrowing the old theory that every egg contains the complete animal in miniature. He may be said to have created modern embryology.[1] He criticized the theory of Meckel (1781–1833) that the history of the individual recapitulates the history of the species, and indeed the premature acceptance of this hypothesis made embryology towards the end of the century the favourite method of studying evolution. Men thought that it disclosed, in the history of each individual, facts which were only otherwise to be discovered with infinite difficulty by an extensive comparative survey of the animal kingdom.

In the year 1838 Schleiden formulated the cell theory. His later work showed that the embryo of a plant arises from a single cell containing a nucleus, and that the development of all vegetable tissues must be referred to the successive division of such cells. This work was extended to animals chiefly by Theodore Schwann (1810–1882), Professor of Anatomy in the University of Louvain, who founded modern histology by tracing animal tissues of different kinds to their origins in nucleated cells. Schwann was the first of Müller's pupils to break away from vitalist principles and to work towards a physico-chemical theory of life.

Hugo von Mohl of Tübingen investigated the contents of

[1] E. Nordenskiöld, *The History of Biology*, Eng. trans. London, 1929, p. 363.

cells, and called the plastic substance within the cell wall by the name of protoplasm. Karl von Nägeli found that this substance was nitrogenous. Max Schultz described the cell as a "mass of nucleated protoplasm", and held that protoplasm was the physical basis of life.

Rudolf Virchow (1821–1892) of Berlin, carried the cell theory into the study of diseased tissues, and thus opened a new chapter in medicine. He discovered that the white corpuscles in the blood have the power of engulfing poisonous bacteria and of thus making them harmless. Cancer depends on the pathological growth of cells, and, if a cure is ever found, it must be based on the control of cell activity.

Simultaneously with the extension of chemistry to cover many vital changes, much advance was made in applying physical principles to the problems of physiology. Harvey explained the motion of the blood as that of a fluid pumped through the tubes of arteries and veins by the mechanical action of the heart, a theory which gave a naturalistic turn to physiological enquiry. But, in the second half of the eighteenth century, the difficulty of the problem led to the almost universal adoption of the hypothesis of vitalism, the *force hyperméchanique* of the French school, which retained its influence till the middle of the nineteenth century. Then the change of opinion, begun by the synthesis of urea and by the physiological work we have described, was reinforced on the physical side by the use of physical apparatus in physiology by Karl Ludwig, and by the work of Mayer and von Helmholtz, who suggested that the principle of the conservation of energy must apply to the living organism.

This was accepted by many as so probable as to need no demonstration, but it was only accurately proved experimentally many years later. Liebig, it is true, had taught that animal heat is not innate, but is the result of combustion. Quantitative proof, however, was only obtained when the heat-value of different kinds of food was measured by burning them in a calorimeter. In 1885 Rubner gave 4·1 calories[1] per gram as the heat-value for proteins and carbohydrates, and 9·2 for fats. In 1899 Atwater and Bryant published the results of more extensive experiments in America. Allowing for the part

[1] This is the so-called "great calorie", the heat which would raise one kilogram of water one degree Centigrade. It is 1000 times the calorie used in physics.

Physiology of the different foods not made available by digestion, they corrected Rubner's figures to 4·0 for proteins and carbohydrates, and 8·9 for fats. The food needed each day for a man in heavy work had a fuel-value of 5500 calories, while a man doing no muscular work needed food to the value of only 2450 calories. More recent work by T. B. Wood and others on farm animals has separated the maintenance ration, the food needed to keep the animal in a stationary state, from the additional food required for growth, milk-production, etc.

To examine the question of the conservation of energy, it is necessary to measure the intake of energy in food and the output in muscular work, heat and excrement. Estimates of income and expenditure in dogs were given by Rubner in 1894, and the two quantities agreed within 0·47 per cent. Experiments on men were published by Atwater, Rosa and Benedict in 1901, and showed agreement within two parts in a thousand. If, as is probable, intellectual work or other uncounted activities use up energy, the amount must be small.

This general accordance with the principle of the conservation of energy showed that the physical activities of the body could be traced ultimately to the chemical and thermal energy of the food taken in. It was natural, if not strictly logical, to conclude that, as the total output of energy was in accordance with physical laws, the intermediate processes could also be described completely by those laws.

The naturalistic standpoint was further strengthened not only by the establishment of the cellular theory by the work of Schleiden and of Schwann, but by other investigations into cell structure and cell function. The knowledge of physical phenomena associated with the solution of jelly-like substances or colloids, was rapidly applied to physiological problems, while the phenomena of nervous action were found to be accompanied by electrical changes.

The variety of idiocy known as cretinism was proved to be due to the failure of the thyroid gland, and in 1884 Schiff discovered that the effects of the removal of the thyroid gland from animals could be obviated if the animal were fed with an extract from the gland. This result was soon applied to mankind, and many children who would formerly have remained hopeless idiots for life have been converted into happy and intelligent beings.

This elucidation by scientific methods of many bodily processes led in the middle of the century to an increase in mechanistic philosophy. The belief arose that physiology was but a special case of "the physics of colloids and the chemistry of the proteids". Whatever be the truth about the whole physiological problem, and the underlying psychological and metaphysical questions, it became clear that, for the progress of science, which deals with single parts or aspects of nature in isolation, it is necessary to assume that physiological processes in detail are comprehensible. If knowledge is to advance, those natural principles must be applied which have already been established, and, from the limited point of view of science, natural principles find their best ultimate statement in the fundamental concepts and laws of physics and chemistry. Whether these analytic methods and concepts are adequate to solve the synthetic problem of the animal organism as a whole, is another and much more profound question. And, to take the extreme case, in man the mind, according to one theory, may use the body as a musician plays on his instrument, even though the instrument is but a physical mechanism.

In the third quarter of the nineteenth century, the study of catalytic actions, analogous to those found in inorganic chemistry, was extended to large numbers of processes going on in living organisms. Organic catalysts or ferments had become of great importance in biochemistry by 1878, and, in that year, the special name of enzymes (ἐν ζύμη, in yeast) was given them by Kühne, who did much to elucidate their action. The essential quality of a catalyst or enzyme is that it facilitates a reaction, and so changes the rate at which it goes on, without itself entering as a constituent into the final substances in equilibrium. Enzymes appear to be colloids, and carry electrical charges which may play a part in their action. Organic processes usually need specific enzymes, and many have been discovered. Some are present in such small quantities that they can only be detected by their appropriate reaction; others can be isolated and examined. Among the more important enzymes may be mentioned: amylase, which decomposes starch; pepsin, which decomposes proteins in an acid medium; trypsin, which decomposes proteins in an alkaline medium; lipase, which decomposes esters; and so on. Although in the living body the most obvious use of enzymes is to facilitate the

Physiology　breaking down of complex bodies into those more simple, their action is reversible. They increase the speed of a reaction in whichever direction it naturally goes. Like other catalysts mentioned above, their function seems to be analogous to the lubrication of machinery. They help and hasten chemical action, but do not determine its direction.

Microbes and Bacteriology　One of the most striking developments of nineteenth-century biology was the growth in knowledge of the origins and causes of microbic diseases in plants, in animals and in man. This knowledge, by increasing our direct control over our environment, has had, like other practical applications of science, a marked influence on our ideas of the relative positions of man and "nature". About 1838 Cagniard de Latour and also Schwann discovered that the yeast present in fermentation consists of minute living vegetable cells, and that the chemical changes which take place in the fermenting liquor are due in some way to the action of the life of these cells. Schwann also perceived that putrefaction was a similar process, and showed that neither fermentation nor putrefaction would occur if precautions were taken to destroy by heat all existing living cells in contact with the substance examined, and to preserve it thereafter from contact with all air save that which had passed through red-hot tubes. Thus both fermentation and putrefaction were proved to be due to the action of living micro-organisms.

These results were confirmed and extended about 1855 by Pasteur, who disproved every known case of supposed spontaneous generation by showing that the presence of bacteria could always be traced to the entrance of germs from outside, or to the growth of those already present. Pasteur demonstrated that certain diseases, such as anthrax, chicken-cholera and the silk-worm disease, were caused by specific microbes. At a later date the germs characteristic of other diseases, many of them prevalent among mankind, have been discovered and their life-history traced. Though chronologically the full results of Pasteur's discoveries have only been reached in more recent years, it is well to follow out the whole story at this point.

The micro-organism which causes tuberculosis was discovered by Koch in 1882, and it was Koch who so developed the technique of bacteriology that it became an art as well as a science, essential in the problems of public health and preventive medicine. The specific micro-organism when isolated is allowed to reproduce itself in a pure culture in gelatine or other suitable medium. Its real pathogenic effects can then be determined by experiment on animals.

Microbes and Bacteriology

It has been found that, in some cases at all events, it is the presence of a definite enzyme in the microbic cells, or its production by their activity, that causes the changes associated with their life. In 1897 Buchner expressed from yeast cells their characteristic enzyme, and showed that it could cause the same fermentation that living yeast cells produce. As usual in such actions, the enzyme itself remains unchanged at the end of the operation; its mere presence is sufficient to start and hasten the chemical action.

At the end of the eighteenth century, Jenner had introduced the process of vaccination, by which inoculation with the virus of small-pox, after its attenuation into cow-pox by transmission through a calf, causes partial or complete freedom from the severer form of the malady. From this discovery began the growth in our knowledge of immunity, so important in the modern study of physiology, especially in its relation to health and disease. Pathogenic organisms produce poisonous substances or toxins, the first of which was discovered in putrefying matter in 1876. By 1888 toxins had been obtained from bacteria by filtering them off from their fluid cultures. In the case of diphtheria, toxin so obtained from cultures of the bacteria is injected in gradually increasing doses into a horse, whose tissues manufacture an anti-toxin. Serum from such an immunized horse will protect human beings who have been exposed to infection, and assist in the recovery of those already suffering from diphtheria. In other cases, by sterilizing cultures of bacteria, vaccines have been prepared which confer partial or complete immunity from the disease produced by the bacteria when alive.

Jenner's principle of attenuation was extended to other diseases by Pasteur, and, in the case of rabies or hydrophobia, it was shown that inoculation was generally effectual even after infection. The mortality from this horrible and previously incurable disease was thus reduced to about one per cent. of the cases treated. No bacteria can here be seen in a microscope. If the disease, as seems probable, is caused by such organisms, they must be much smaller than ordinary bacteria.

The life-history of pathogenic micro-organisms is often very complicated, and some of them pass certain stages of their career in different hosts. Only by most careful experiments carried out by the inoculation of living animals, can their properties be investigated. The hosts themselves sometimes remain unaffected by the invading microbe, and this immunity makes it exceedingly difficult to forecast the direction in which the source of infection must be sought. The final conquest of malaria or ague is an excellent example of the difficulties and dangers which surround research in microbic disease. The malaria germ was discovered by Laveran, a French army surgeon, about 1880. Five years later Italian observers had shown that infection reached man from the bites of mosquitoes, and in the years 1894–1897, Manson and Ross proved that one special kind of mosquito (*Anopheles*) was infested by parasites that proved to be the germs of malaria in an early stage of development. Thus the correct method of attacking the ravages of malarial fever is to destroy the larvae of these insects by draining marshy land, and by covering with a thin coating of oil or other deterrent all pools of standing water which provide suitable breeding-places.

Similarly Maltese or Mediterranean fever has been traced to the action of a microbe which passes part of its life in goats, and is communicated to man by means of the goats' milk, though the animals themselves appear to be perfectly healthy. The discovery of the connection between bubonic plague, rats, and the fleas or other parasites which help to bring the infection from the rats to human beings, provides another instance of the indirect methods by which disease can be fought with greatest success. By taking precautions founded on such new investigations, vast tracts of the earth's surface which were formerly uninhabitable, or only habitable at great cost of life and health, were made fit for occupation. This knowledge of microbic diseases, knowledge won by laborious and in some cases dangerous experiments, led to great improvements in sanitation and preventive medicine.

Lord Lister's application to surgery of Pasteur's results in 1867, and the previous discovery of anaesthetics by Sir Humphrey Davy, by W. T. G. Morton in Massachusetts and by Sir J. Y. Simpson in Edinburgh, made possible surgical operations hitherto quite impossible. The practical outcome of these discoveries in hygiene, medicine and surgery is perhaps most clearly shown in the reduction of the annual death-rate of cities like London from about 80 per thousand two centuries ago to the present figure of some 12 per thousand.

The first thorough study of an ultra-microscopic virus was made by Löffler and Frosch in 1893. They showed that the lymph from an animal suffering from foot-and-mouth disease, when passed through a filter which would stop ordinary bacteria, would still infect a number of other animals in series. They inferred that they had to deal with a reproducing micro-organism and not with an inanimate poison. It is still uncertain whether these ultra-microscopic, filterable viruses, which cause many diseases in animals and plants, are particulate bacteria. If so, they must be so small that they approach molecular dimensions. It has been suggested that they may represent a new type of non-cellular living matter.

We are now ready to trace the cycles of change through which carbon and nitrogen pass in plants and animals and their ultimate return to the ground and the air.

In 1774 Priestley discovered that air "spoilt" by mice was made once more capable of supporting life if green plants were left in it for some time. In 1780 Ingenhousz proved that this action of plants only goes on in sunlight. In 1783 Senebier showed that the chemical change involved is the conversion of "fixed air" into "dephlogisticated air", that is of carbon dioxide into oxygen. In 1804 de Saussure investigated this process quantitatively. These results led to Liebig's researches, and to his formulation of the general theory of the cyclical processes of change which carbon and nitrogen undergo as the bodies of plants and animals alternately grow and disintegrate.

The active substance in the building up of plants is the pigment chlorophyll. Its chemical constitution and its chemical reactions in sunlight are complex, and even yet not fully understood. But it has the power, essential for the existence of life as we know it on the Earth, of using the energy of sunlight to decompose the carbon dioxide of the air, liberate the oxygen and combine the carbon in the complex organic molecules of plant tissues. In the absorption spectrum of chlorophyll, the maximum absorption is seen to coincide with the maximum energy in the solar spectrum—a remarkable adaptation, however it may be produced, of means to ends.

Some animals live on plants, some on each other, so that
all are dependent on the energy of the Sun made available by
chlorophyll. Animals in breathing oxidize carbon compounds
into useful derivatives and others which are excreted, while
the rest of the energy liberated by oxidation maintains bodily
heat. Even plants slowly emit carbon dioxide, though in
sunlight this change is masked by the reverse process. Both
plants and animals give back to the air the carbon dioxide
that plants have removed, while waste organic compounds are
deposited in the ground. Here they are attacked by teeming
multitudes of bacteria living in the soil, by which they are
broken down into innocuous inorganic bodies, while more
carbon dioxide is poured into the air. Thus the carbon cycle
is completed.

The corresponding cycle for nitrogen is of more recent discovery. Although Vergil in his *Georgics* recommended the
farmer to take a crop of beans, vetch or lupins before wheat,
the reason for the recognized beneficial effect was only worked
out in 1888 by Hellriegel and Wilfarth.[1] Nodules on the roots
of these leguminous plants contain bacteria which are able to
fix nitrogen from the atmosphere, convert it by unknown
chemical reactions into protein, and pass it on to the plant.
Another process was traced in 1895 by Vinogradsky, who in
the soil found bacteria which obtain nitrogen directly from
the air, the necessary energy being probably obtained from
the decomposing cellulose of dead plants.

In both these ways plants obtain protein. Waste products
containing nitrogen are converted in the soil, again chiefly by
the help of appropriate bacteria, into ammonium salts, which
first pass into ammonium carbonate, and then, once more by
bacterial action, into salts called nitrites and finally into
nitrates, salts which contain more oxygen and are the best
source of nitrogen for plants to build up into proteins.

The importance of mineral salts in agriculture was demonstrated by Liebig, but he overlooked the supreme need for
nitrogen. This was first investigated scientifically by Gilbert
and Lawes at Rothamsted in the middle of the century, and
their work was the chief foundation of the modern use of
artificial manures. Of the elements necessary for plant life,
those usually present in the smallest amounts are nitrogen,

[1] Sir E. J. Russell, *Soil Conditions and Plant Growth*, 4th ed. London, 1921.

phosphorus and potassium. If one of these is present in insufficient quantities, it gives the limiting factor for the crop, which will only grow freely if more of the absent element is added in an available form.

The Carbon and Nitrogen Cycles

The scientific study of manuring gave farmers much greater freedom in methods of cultivation. The different courses of rotation of crops and fallows, shown by local experience in old days to be necessary to maintain the fertility of different types of soil, could be modified considerably when fertility could be maintained by restoring the elements abstracted from the land in the growth of crops.

During the second half of the eighteenth century the work of systematic exploration of the world proceeded apace, and much of it was undertaken in a true scientific spirit. Trigonometrical surveys were begun in England in 1784, when the Ordnance Department measured a base-line on Hounslow Heath. Accurate maps, initiated by the French cartographer d'Anville, were thus made possible.

Physical Geography and Scientific Exploration

In an account of the progress of knowledge during the period under review, it is not easy to classify the work of Baron von Humboldt (1769–1859), the distinguished Prussian naturalist and traveller, who, for a great part of his life, found his most congenial home in Paris. He spent five years exploring the continent of South America and the seas and islands of the Mexican Gulf, and it was on observations collected during this expedition that he based the claims of physical geography and meteorology to be considered as accurate sciences. Von Humboldt was the first to map the Earth's surface in lines of average equal temperature—isothermal lines—by which he obtained a method of comparing the climates of different countries. He ascended Mount Chimborazo and other peaks of the Andes in order to study the rate of decrease of temperature with increase in height above sea-level. He considered the origin of tropical storms and atmospheric disturbances; he noticed the position of zones of volcanic activity, and suggested that they corresponded to cracks in the Earth's crust; he investigated the distribution of plants and animals as affected by physical conditions; he studied the variations of intensity of the Earth's magnetic force from the poles to the equator, and invented the term "magnetic storm" to describe a phenomenon which he was the first to record.

*Physical
Geography
and Scientific
Exploration*

When he settled in Paris in 1808 and began to put into shape and to publish the results of his explorations, he probably shared with Napoleon Bonaparte the distinction of being thought the foremost man in Europe. His *Kosmos*, containing the entire fruits of his life's work, was not produced till near the end of his career. The first two volumes appeared in 1845 and 1847, but the third and fourth were not published till 1850–1858. In this work von Humboldt endeavoured to give at once an accurate description and an imaginative conception of the world as known to our senses. Though it was impossible to attain complete success in an undertaking of such magnitude, yet doubtless his work will have an abiding value in that it places on record the aspirations and conclusions of a great man at an important stage in the history of knowledge.

The interest excited by von Humboldt's labours and personality gave an impetus to scientific exploration among the nations of Europe. In 1831 the *Beagle* was despatched by Great Britain on her memorable expedition "to complete the survey of Patagonia and Tierra del Fuego; to survey the shores of Chili, Peru and some islands in the Pacific; and to carry a chain of chronological measurements round the world". The expedition was declared to be "entirely for scientific purposes", and Charles Darwin sailed on board as official "Naturalist".

A few years later (1839) Joseph Hooker (1817–1911), son of the well-known botanist Sir W. J. Hooker, joined Sir James Ross in his Antarctic expedition, and spent three years studying plant life. Later on he proceeded to the northern frontiers of India, on an expedition which also was partly financed by the Government. In 1846 T. H. Huxley left England as surgeon in the *Rattlesnake*, and spent several years surveying and charting in Australian waters; though his eager mind and keen powers of observation chafed at the lack of opportunity given for accurate scientific research of general interest. Thus three of the men who played a great part in revolutionizing the thought of the nineteenth century each served an apprenticeship on one of the scientifically planned voyages of exploration. The culminating point of organized discovery and research was reached in the expedition of the *Challenger*, which was despatched in 1872, to cruise for several years in the waters of the Atlantic and Pacific, in order to take a series of records dealing with every branch of oceanography, meteorology and natural history.

By his attempt to give a rational theory of the origin of the solar system, Laplace had directed men's attention to the existence of the problem, and had quickened interest in the study of the Earth itself as a part of the solar system. It was unfortunate that the countries in which freedom of thought had most prevailed against the claims of papal authority should also be those in which the tyranny of the theory of the verbal inspiration of the Bible was most firmly established. A new contest had therefore to be waged before any view of the Earth's origin, other than that to be found in a literal interpretation of the Book of Genesis, could win a general approval. Even in the middle years of the nineteenth century it was seriously contended that fossils, suggesting as they did another story, had been hidden in the ground by God (or perhaps the Devil) in order to test the faith of man.

At a very early date some knowledge of rocks, metals and minerals had been acquired in the processes of mining. Leonardo da Vinci and Bernard Palissy had recognized in fossils the remains of animals and plants, as indeed had some of the Greek philosophers, but, in general, fossils were regarded as *lusus naturae*, the products of a mysterious *vis plastica*, or tendency in nature to produce certain favourite forms in various ways. The possibility of using them to help to trace the history of the Earth was only recognized by a few scattered observers like Niels Stensen (1669), whose ideas gained no general acceptance. The large collection of fossils put together by John Woodward (1665–1728), and bequeathed by him to the University of Cambridge, did much to establish the view that fossils were really of animal and vegetable origin. In 1674 Perrault proved that the rainfall on the surface of the earth was more than enough to explain the origin of springs and rivers.[1] Nevertheless, attempts made to explain how the Earth reached its present state were still forced into conformity with Biblical cosmogonies involving cataclysmic origins by water or fire.

The first to contend systematically against these views was James Hutton (1726–1797), who published his *Theory of the Earth* in 1785. Once more a practical acquaintance with natural processes paved the way for scientific advance. Hutton,

---

[1] F. D. Adams, *Science*, LXVII, p. 500, 1928, quoted in *Isis*, XIII, p. 180, 1929.

Geology in order to improve the husbandry on his small paternal estate in Berwickshire, studied home farming in Norfolk, and foreign methods of agriculture in Holland, Belgium and Northern France. For fourteen years he pondered over the familiar ditches, pits and river beds, and then, returning to Edinburgh, laid the foundations of the modern science of geology. Hutton recognized that the stratification of rocks and the embedding of fossils were processes which were still going on in sea, river and lake. "No powers", said Hutton, "are to be employed that are not natural to the globe, no action to be admitted except those of which we know the principle"—a true precept of science, which seeks to avoid all unnecessary hypotheses.

Hutton's "uniformitarian theory" was not generally accepted till William Smith had assigned relative ages to rocks by noting their fossilized contents; till Georges Cuvier had reconstructed extinct mammalia from fossils and bones found in the neighbourhood of Paris; till Jean Baptiste de Lamarck had made a classification and comparison of recent and fossil shells; and finally till Sir Charles Lyell had collected in his *Principles of Geology*, first published in 1830–1833, all available evidence bearing on the manner and extent to which the Earth is still being moulded into new forms by water, volcanoes and earthquakes, as well as all known facts about fossils. The cumulative effect of long-continued processes was then fully grasped for the first time; and men realized the possibility of tracing the history of the Earth, at any rate throughout its habitable ages, by means of the record of the rocks through inferences based on observation of natural operations that were still taking place.

The problem of the age of man is one of special interest to the human race. The discovery of flint implements, such as are in use among primitive peoples, and of carved pieces of bone and ivory, lying in conjunction with the remains of animals now unknown, or extinct in Europe, enabled Lyell in 1863 to place man in position in the long series of organic types, and to show that his existence on the Earth must have extended over periods vastly greater than any contemplated by the accepted Biblical chronology. It now seems probable that our ancestors emerged from a more primitive state, and in a very real sense became men, at a time somewhere between a hundred thousand and a million years ago, while civilization is only an affair of some five or six thousand years.

After Buffon had produced his great *Natural History of* *Animals*, another Frenchman took up the subject of classification and placed it on a sound and definite basis. Georges Cuvier (1769–1832) was the son of a Protestant officer who had migrated from the Jura district into the region of the Würtemberg protectorate. He spent the period of the early Revolution and the Reign of Terror studying peacefully in Normandy, and then returned to Paris, where he soon won a prominent position in the Collège de France. His great claim to distinction lies in the fact that he was the first among naturalists to compare systematically the structure of existing animals with the remains of extinct fossils, and thus to demonstrate that the past, no less than the present, must be taken into account in any study of the development of living creatures. Cuvier stands on the threshold of the new age of scientific discovery, and his great book, *Le Règne Animal, distribué d'après son Organisation,* forms a connecting link between the work of men who studied the world and its phenomena as a stationary problem and of those who were impelled to look upon it as a series of shifting scenes in the great drama of evolution.

It was a misfortune that no close connection existed between men of science and the practical gardeners and farmers, who, by hybridization and selection, were producing new varieties of plants and animals or developing breeds already established. At the end of the eighteenth century, Bakewell improved the old longhorn type of cattle, and established a new and useful variety of the Leicester sheep. The brothers Colling applied Bakewell's methods to the shorthorns which existed in the valley of the Tees and thus founded the most important breed of English stock.

The spontaneous appearance of large variations was well known to horticulturists:

An inferior variety of pear, for instance, may suddenly produce a shoot bearing fruit of superior quality; a beech tree, without obvious cause, a shoot with finely divided foliage; or a camellia an unwontedly fine flower. When removed from the plant and treated as cuttings or grafts, such sports may be perpetuated. Many garden varieties of flowers and fruits have thus originated.[1]

But most of the gardener's new varieties were obtained by crossing individuals of different varieties or even species. In

---

[1] Art. "Horticulture", in *Ency. Brit.* 9th ed. 1881.

the latter case it was known that the hybrids are usually
less fertile than pure-bred species, and are sometimes quite
sterile.

The idea of an evolutionary process in nature is at least as
old as the days of the Greek philosophers. Heracleitus believed
that all things were in a state of flux. Empedocles taught that
the development of life is a gradual process, and that imperfect
forms are slowly replaced by forms more perfect. By the time
of Aristotle, speculation seems to have gone farther, and to
have conceived the idea that the more perfect type might
have not only followed in time but also have been developed
out of the less perfect. The atomists, who are often claimed
as evolutionists, seem to have contemplated the emergence of
each species *de novo*. But, in their belief that only those types
survived which were fitted to their environment, they touched
in spirit the essence of the theory of natural selection, though
their basis of fact was insufficient. It has been truly observed
that in science "being right is no excuse whatever for holding
an opinion which has not been based on an adequate consideration of the facts involved in it". As in so many other
branches of knowledge, the Greek philosophers could do no
more than formulate the problem and make speculative
guesses at its solution.

Indeed, it required two thousand years of time, and the
labours of many quiet and unphilosophic physiologists and
naturalists, to collect enough observational and experimental
evidence to make the idea of evolution worth the consideration
of men of science. It is a good illustration of the true scientific
attitude of suspension of judgment in the face of inconclusive
data that naturalists, for the most part, left evolution to the
philosophers, and that, till Darwin and Wallace published
their simultaneous work, the balance of scientific opinion,
when expressed at all, was against the theory. On the other
hand, the philosophers also played their true part in maintaining speculation about a theory not yet ripe for scientific
treatment. They kept open a question of paramount importance, and formulated solutions which, in due time, might
serve as working hypotheses for the men of science with whom
lay the ultimate decision. Hence it is in the nature of the
case that when, in the revival of learning, the idea of evolution
once more appears, it is to be found chiefly in the writings of

philosophers—Bacon, Descartes, Leibniz and Kant. The *Evolution before Darwin* scientists, meanwhile, were slowly working at facts which would eventually lead them in the same direction through Harvey's embryology and Ray's system of classification. Some philosophers even reached quite modern ideas in their conceptions of the present mutability of species and the possibility of its experimental examination, but it must not be overlooked that others, who are claimed as evolutionists— forerunners of Darwin—took evolution in an ideal, not in a real, sense. Some of Goethe's views seem to have been of this nature, as were those of Schelling and Hegel. To them, the connection between species lay in the inner ideas which represented them in the conceptual sphere. "The metamorphosis", says Hegel, "can be ascribed only to the notion as such, because it alone is evolution...it is a clumsy idea...to regard the transformation from one natural form and sphere to a higher as an outward and actual production."

This ideal point of view does not, however, destroy the usefulness of the philosophic contribution to evolutionary theory. It is most interesting and remarkable that the division of labour and the difference of outlook between philosophers and naturalists was continued up to the last possible moment. Herbert Spencer, though a competent biologist, was primarily a philosopher. He was preaching a full-grown, concrete evolutionist doctrine in the years that immediately preceded the publication of Darwin's *Origin of Species*, while as yet most of the naturalists would have none of it. Even the botanist Godron, who collected much evidence about variation, rejected the idea of evolution as lately as 1859, the year of the publication of Darwin's work. Philosophers were right and naturalists were right; they were each following their true road. The philosophers were dealing with a philosophic problem, one not ripe for scientific examination. The naturalists were exercising true scientific restraint in not taking, even as a working hypothesis, a speculation for which there was as yet available no convincing evidence, and no satisfying suggestion of a mode of operation.

Nevertheless, even in the eighteenth century, and increasingly in the first half of the nineteenth, one naturalist after another ran counter to the prevailing consensus of scientific opinion, and upheld some form of evolutionary theory. Buffon, who oscillated between the orthodoxy of the Sorbonne and a belief in "l'enchaînement des êtres", put forward a theory of the direct modification of animals by external conditions. Erasmus Darwin, poet, naturalist and philosopher, caught a glimpse of the revelation which was to be given in its fullness to his grandson, and taught that from "the metamorphoses of animals, as from the tadpole to the frog...the changes produced by artificial cultivation, as in the breeds of horses, dogs and sheep,...the changes produced by conditions of climate and season,...the essential unity of plan in all warm-blooded animals,...we are led to conclude that they have been alike produced from a similar living filament".

The first connected and logical theory is that of Lamarck (1744–1829), who sought to determine the cause of evolution by a consideration of the cumulative inheritance of modification induced by the action of environment. While, *pace* Buffon, the effect of change in environment on the structure of the individual is often small, Lamarck held that, if the necessary changes in habits became constant and lasting, they would modify old organs, or, by the need for new organs, call them into being. Thus the ancestors of the giraffe acquired longer and longer necks by continually stretching for leaves on branches just beyond their reach, and the change of structure thus acquired was developed and intensified by inheritance. Though no direct evidence of such inheritance could be adduced, it gave a reasonable and consistent working hypothesis for other naturalists, such as Meckel, to use and elaborate.

The attention drawn to the effect of environment on the individual, and the extent of the changes which may rightly be attributed to external circumstances, have probably had an enormous influence on thought and action. It is difficult to believe that, where the individual can sometimes be modified so profoundly, the species will remain unchanged. Hence, many of the social and philanthropic efforts of the nineteenth century were built up on a tacit assumption of the theory of modification through environment. Nevertheless, as years passed, it became clear that the inheritance of acquired characters, if it occurred at all, was very difficult indeed to detect. Discussion on this subject is not closed yet, even in the year 1929.

Two more nineteenth-century evolutionists who maintained

the direct action of environment on the individual were
Etienne Geoffroy Saint-Hilaire and Robert Chambers, whose
anonymous book, *Vestiges of Creation*, had a great vogue, and
helped to prepare men's minds for Darwin.

But the man to whom Darwin was solely indebted for the
central idea of his work, the man who, by a curious chance,
gave the same clue to Wallace also, was the Reverend Thomas
Robert Malthus (1766–1834), at one time curate of Albury in
Surrey. Malthus, an able economist, lived at a time when the
number of the English people was increasing rapidly. In 1798
he published the first edition of his *Essay on Population*. In
it he proclaimed that the human race always tends to outrun
its means of subsistence, and can only be kept within bounds
by famine, pestilence or war, whereby the redundant individuals are eliminated. In later editions of the book, he
admitted the importance of the prudential check, which then
acted chiefly in the postponement of marriage, and thus, so
far as its application to mankind is concerned, weakened his
main argument in its striking simplicity.

Darwin has himself recorded the effect of this work on his
mind. "In October 1838", he says, "I happened to read for
amusement Malthus on Population, and being well prepared
to appreciate the struggle for existence which everywhere goes
on from long continued observation of the habits of animals
and plants, it at once struck me that under these circumstances
favourable variations would tend to be preserved, and un-
favourable ones to be destroyed. The result of this would be
the formation of new species. Here then I had a theory by
which to work."

The man to whom this flash of insight came was well fitted,
both by heredity and environment, to make full use of it.
Charles Robert Darwin (1809–1882) was the son of a remarkably
able country doctor of ample means, Robert Waring Darwin
of Shrewsbury. His grandfathers were Erasmus Darwin, who
has already been mentioned, and Josiah Wedgwood, the potter
of Etruria, who also was a man of scientific power and
ingenuity. The Wedgwoods were Staffordshire people, an old
family of small landowners; the Darwins, of the same landed
class, came from Lincolnshire. Charles Darwin was educated
first at Edinburgh with a view to a medical career, and then
at Christ's College, Cambridge, with the intention of taking

Darwin   Holy Orders. He got his best training as a naturalist during the five years' voyage of the *Beagle* in South American waters. In tropical and sub-tropical lands, teeming with life, Darwin received the impression of the interdependence of all living things, and within a year of his return he began to compile the first of many note-books on the facts bearing on the transmutation of species. Fifteen months later he read Malthus' book, and found the clue which enabled him to frame a theory of the means whereby new species might develop.

The individuals of a race differ from each other in innate qualities. Darwin offered no opinion about the cause of these variations, but accepted the fact of their existence. If the pressure of numbers or the competition for mates be great, any quality which is of use in the struggle for life or mate has "survival value", and gives its possessor an advantage which carries with it an improved chance of prolonging life, or of securing a mate and of rearing successfully a preponderating number of offspring to inherit the favourable variation. That particular quality therefore tends to spread throughout the race by the progressive elimination of those individuals who do not possess it. The race is modified, and a different and permanent variety may slowly be established. This was the new conception; and its importance in the history of thought was well put by Thomas Huxley, who, by his power of exposition, skill in dialectic and courage in controversy, did more than any other man to compel general acceptance for the views of Darwin and Wallace. Huxley says: "The suggestion that new species may result from the selective action of external conditions upon the variations from the specific type which individuals present—and which we call 'spontaneous' because we are ignorant of their causation—is as wholly unknown to the historian of scientific ideas as it was to biological specialists before 1858. But that suggestion is the central idea of the *Origin of Species* and contains the quintessence of Darwinism".

With this idea as a working hypothesis, Darwin spent twenty years collecting facts and making experiments. He read books of travel and treatises on sport, natural history, horticulture, and the breeding of domesticated animals. He carried out experiments on the crossing of tame pigeons; he studied the transport of seeds, and the geological and geographical distribution of plants and animals. In the assimilation of facts, *Darwin* in appreciating their bearing on all the complicated questions which arose, and in marshalling them at the last, Darwin showed a supreme ability. His transparent honesty, love of truth, and calm, even balance of mind, form a model of the ideal naturalist. Fertile in hypotheses as a guide to work, he never let a pre-conceived view blind him to facts. "I have steadily endea-voured", he wrote, "to keep my mind free so as to give up any hypothesis, however much beloved (and I cannot resist forming one on every subject), as soon as facts are shown to be opposed to it."

By 1844 Darwin had convinced himself that species are not immutable and that the main cause of their origin was natural selection, but he continued to work on year after year to gain yet surer evidence. In 1856 Lyell urged him to publish the results of his researches; Darwin, not satisfied with their completeness, delayed. On June 18th, 1858, he received from Alfred Russel Wallace a paper written in Ternate in the space of three days after reading Malthus' book. In this paper Darwin at once recognized the essence of his own theory. Unwilling to seize the priority of twenty years, which, though rightly his own, might destroy the interest of Wallace's con-tribution, Darwin placed himself in the hands of Lyell and Hooker, who arranged with the Linnaean Society to com-municate on July 1st, 1858, Wallace's paper together with a letter from Darwin to Asa Gray dated 1857, and an abstract of his theory written in 1844.

Darwin then set to work and wrote out in condensed form *The Fight for* the results of his labours, and, on November 24th, 1859, his *Evolution* book was published under the name of *The Origin of Species*.

We have already traced the various converging streams of evolutionary thought—cosmological, anatomical, geological and philosophic, which, blocked by the prejudice in favour of the fixity of species, were yet collecting deeper and deeper behind the dam. Darwin's great torrent of evidence in favour of natural selection broke the barrier with irresistible force, and let loose the fertilizing flood over the whole realm of thought. Now that seventy years have increased our know-ledge of the facts we can see that Darwin and even more his disciples, like the Greek atomists before them, underrated the complexity of the great problem of life. While the general

process of evolution is now evident from the facts of morphology and palaeontology, the details of the origin of species
have even yet not been worked out. Natural selection alone
seems an inadequate explanation. But the spirit of greater
caution, which has come with later years, does not diminish
the historical importance of Darwin's principle. It may
ultimately be proved insufficient: but, at the time, it was the
necessary hypothesis. The idea of natural selection led to a
greater thing than itself—the acceptance of the theory of
organic evolution.

At first the effect seemed to many people to be devastating,
to overwhelm the philosophic and religious landmarks of the
human race. We ought not, however, to condemn without
reflection this widespread attitude of mind. Now that the idea
of evolution has become a familiar factor in our intellectual
outlook, it is difficult to realize how revolutionary it seemed,
and how few were competent to judge the value of the
evidence for it when laid before the world. The evidence
depended on the detailed examination of living creatures and
fossil remains, and was unfamiliar and indeed for the most
part unknown to those who felt compelled either to deny the
validity of the conclusions drawn, or to give up beliefs which
had sustained long generations of their forefathers. Before we
blame them, let us ask ourselves honestly whether, on the face
of things, it is more obvious to believe in a common ancestor
or in a separate act of creation for the frog and the peacock,
the salmon and the humming-bird, the elephant and the
mouse. Except to those few who were able to understand
Darwin's evidence and appreciate the force of his cumulative
argument, the idea of evolution must have seemed far-fetched
and ridiculous.

Even to some naturalists the new ideas were repugnant.
Sir Richard Owen, the great anatomist, wrote a strongly
adverse criticism in the *Edinburgh Review*, and many of his
colleagues agreed with his opinion. But Hooker gave in his
adhesion to Darwin's ideas at once, and he was immediately
followed by Huxley, Asa Gray, Lubbock and W. B. Carpenter,
while Lyell announced his conversion at the Royal Society
dinner in the autumn of 1864.

From the first, Huxley was the protagonist of this band of
evolutionists—"Darwin's bulldog", as he called himself. With

magnificent courage, ability, and clearness of exposition, he
bore the chief brunt of the attack made from all sides on
Darwin's book, and again and again led successful counter-
attacks on his discomfited foes.

Thomas Henry Huxley was born at Ealing in 1825, but he
was descended from families located at Coventry and on the
Welsh Marches, and he had the true fighting temperament of
a border race. He tells us that, to the men of science of that
generation, the publication of the *Origin of Species* had the
effect as of a flash of lightning in the darkness.

"We wanted", he writes, "not to pin our faith to that or any other
speculation, but to get hold of clear and definite conceptions, which
could be brought face to face with facts and have their validity tested.
The *Origin* provided us with the working hypothesis we sought. Moreover, it did the immense service of freeing us forever from the dilemma—
Refuse to accept the Creation hypothesis, and what have you to propose
that can be accepted by any cautious reasoner? In 1857 I had no answer
ready, and I do not think that anyone else had. A year later we re-
proached ourselves with dulness for being perplexed with such an
enquiry. My reflection when I first made myself master of the central
idea of the *Origin*, was, 'How extremely stupid not to have thought of
that!'"

The famous clash between Bishop Wilberforce and Huxley
at the Oxford meeting of the British Association in 1860 has
often been described.[1] Wilberforce had obtained a First-Class
in the Oxford Mathematical Schools in his youth, and therefore,
being regarded by his University as a master of all branches
of natural knowledge, had been selected to uphold the cause
of orthodoxy. The bishop, with no real understanding of the
problem, endeavoured to kill the notion of evolution with
ridicule, and was effectively answered in argument and
severely rebuked for his ignorant interference by Huxley,
while the embryological evidence for evolution was explained
by Sir John Lubbock, afterwards Lord Avebury.

When it was found that neither argument nor ridicule could
prevent the spread of Darwin's theory, his opponents took the
usual next step and denied its originality. But those best able
to judge held a different opinion. Two years after the Oxford
meeting, Huxley wrote to Sir Charles Lyell:

If Darwin is right about natural selection, the discovery of this *vera
causa* sets him to my mind in a different region altogether from all his

[1] *Life of Charles Darwin*, vol. II, p. 320; Leonard Huxley, *Life and Letters
of Thomas Henry Huxley*, vol. I, p. 180.

predecessors. I should no more call his doctrine a modification of Lamarck's than I should call the Newtonian theory of the celestial motions a modification of the Ptolemaic system. Ptolemy imagined a mode of explaining those motions. Newton proved their necessity from the laws and a force demonstrably in operation. If he is only right, Darwin will, I think, take his place with such men as Harvey, and, even if he is wrong, his sobriety and accuracy of thought will put him on a different level from Lamarck.

Huxley indeed pointed out a defect in the evidence. The idea that species are due to a summation of variations ignores the fact that the products of crossing different though allied species are frequently in some degree sterile. If species have a common origin, it is difficult to see why this sterility should arise, and no clear case is known where a certainly sterile hybrid has been bred from fertile parents derived experimentally from a common origin.

It is at the same point that the validity of the claim of natural selection as the main directing force was most questionable. The survival of the fittest was a plausible account of evolution in broad outline, but failed in application to specific difference. The Darwinian philosophy convinced us that every species must "make good" in nature if it is to survive, but no one could tell how the differences—often very sharply fixed—which we recognise as specific, do in fact enable the species to make good.[1]

But although Huxley pointed out the difficulty no one then felt it to be serious. It was assumed that further work would clear it up, and its full weight only became apparent when, in the twentieth century, scientific breeding experiments were made on the large scale. When the first strangeness had been overcome, the biologists of the time accepted evolution and regarded natural selection as its true and sufficient cause.

Though Virchow, most famous of Continental ethnologists, did not accept Darwin's theory, it was in Germany that the idea of evolution by means of natural selection and the survival of the fittest was seized upon with the greatest avidity. Haeckel and other naturalists, and in their train Teutonic philosophers and political theorists, joined to create that *Darwinismus* which made many of his followers more Darwinian than Darwin.

Meanwhile Darwin's own methods of observation and experiment on variation and heredity fell into abeyance. Men accepted natural selection as the proved and adequate cause

[1] William Bateson, *Address to the American Association*, Toronto, 1922.

of evolution and of the origin of species. Darwinism ceased
to be a tentative scientific theory and became a philosophy, almost a religion. Experimental biology turned to morphology and especially embryology. The hypothesis that the development of the individual follows and illustrates the history of the race, suggested by Meckel and elaborated by Haeckel, endowed embryology with evolutionary meaning, and increased the neglect of the slower and more laborious methods of research.

The naturalist, who studied systematic botany or zoology in the field, and the breeder of new plants and animals in the garden or on the farm, were extending their sound knowledge of species and varieties. To naturalist and breeder species remained distinct, and new varieties were produced not by insensible gradations but by sudden, often large, mutations which bred true from the first. But none of the laboratory morphologists consulted the practical man, or gave enough weight to their empirical knowledge. "The evolutionist of the 'eighties", says Bateson, "was perfectly certain that species were a figment of the systematist's mind, not worthy of enlightened attention." It was only in the 'nineties that men trained in the laboratory, led on the Continent by de Vries and in this country by Bateson, turned again to the study of variation and heredity.

Darwin himself, while believing natural selection to be the main cause of evolution, did not exclude the Lamarckian idea of the inheritance of characters acquired by the long action of use or disuse. Contemporary evidence was not enough to settle the question. But towards the end of the century August Weismann began a new chapter in the subject. Weismann showed that a sharp distinction must be drawn between the body (or soma) and the germ cells which it contains. Somatic cells can only reproduce cells like themselves, but germ cells give rise not only to the germ cells of a new individual, but to all the countless types of cell in his body. Hence the units which make up a germ cell must be enough in number and in differences in kind and arrangement to provide for all the multitude of organisms which are found in nature. Germ cells descend from germ cells in a pure line of germ plasm, but somatic cells always trace their origin to germ cells. Thus the body of each individual is a comparatively unimportant by-product of his parents' germ cells; it dies, leaving no offspring. The main pedigree is that of the germ plasm, which shows an unbroken history from cell to cell.

On this view, the products of the germ cells are very unlikely to be affected by changes impressed on the body. Such an influence would resemble an effect on a man produced by changes in his uncle. The germ cells might be injured by the body containing them, but hardly modified in nature. Hence Weismann was led to examine critically the evidence for the inheritance of acquired characters, and, in every case, rejected it as inadequate. Since that time, observation and experiment have brought to light cases where long continued changes in the environment have possibly produced some effect, but they seem to be exceptional, and are not accepted by all naturalists.

When Weismann announced his results, there was some consternation. Biologists had come to rely on "use and disuse" as explanations of unsolved riddles of adaptation. Evolutionary philosophers, especially Herbert Spencer, had put forward the inheritance of such acquired characters as the chief factor in racial development, while philanthropists, educationalists and politicians had tacitly assumed its truth as the underlying basis of social "progress". Biologists soon came generally to accept the new ideas; but Herbert Spencer to the end of his days engaged in active controversy with Weismann;[1] and political reformers, even unto this present, have ignored principles so contrary to their presuppositions. Yet it is clear that the acceptance of the non-inheritance of acquired characters means that "nature" is more than "nurture", heredity than environment. Improvement in the conditions of life can, and of course will, benefit the individual: it can do nothing, save by the indirect process of natural or artificial selection, to improve the inborn qualities of a race.

The particular types of mechanism suggested by Weismann to explain inheritance were perhaps but ingenious speculations, but they served to direct the researches of many of his followers to an examination of the exact processes by which germ cells are formed and somatic cells developed from them. These new researches began during the nineteenth century, but the most striking results appeared later, and it will be more convenient to deal with the whole subject in Chapter VIII.

[1] G. C. Bourne, *Herbert Spencer and Animal Evolution*, Oxford, 1910.

The end of the century also saw the beginning of another controversy which turned on new knowledge.[1] The upholders of pure Darwinism such as Weismann came to regard natural selection as a cause all-sufficient to explain adaptation and through it evolution. Moreover, the variations on which natural selection worked were assumed to be the small variations, which, for example, are found in a continuous series in the stature of men. Among large enough numbers, it will be possible to find men of heights differing by only the hundredth part of an inch throughout a considerable range on each side of the mean. On such minute variations selection was supposed to work, and, given time, to produce new varieties and new species.

The Fight for Evolution

But before the new century began, some naturalists, notably de Vries and Bateson, using the accumulated experience of breeders, fanciers and horticulturalists as a starting point for experiment, had found these ideas contrary to fact. Large mutations often occur, especially after crossing, and new varieties may be established at once. Then, in 1900, Mendel's forgotten work was rediscovered, and a new chapter opened. It seemed that, even if the selection of small variations could not explain evolution, these new ideas might do so. How far this hope was realized will be discussed in Chapter VIII.

Of all the studies regenerated by Darwin, none derived more benefit than anthropology, the comparative study of mankind. Indeed, it is hardly too much to say that modern anthropology arose from the *Origin of Species*. Huxley's classical study of human skulls was inspired by the Darwinian controversy, and was the beginning of that exact measurement of physical characters on which so much of the science now depends. The ideas of natural selection and evolution underlie all succeeding work.

Anthropology

Yet the ground had been prepared for anthropology in other ways also. The same love of novelty, the same eager curiosity, the same acquisitive collector's instinct, which introduced the plants and animals of other climes into European gardens and museums, brought back the artistic and industrial products of other people and the ceremonial objects of other religions, in all stages of development.

[1] A. Weismann, *The Evolution Theory*, Eng. trans. J. A. and M. R. Thomson, London, 1904; Beatrice Bateson, *William Bateson, Naturalist*, Cambridge, 1928, p. 449.

Anthropology　　When the anthropologists were ready to take the field, much of the necessary material was at hand, already familiar, or partly classified, awaiting only the new gift of reinterpretation to give up another aspect of its inward meaning.

In the *Origin of Species* Darwin did not consider mankind in detail, though he pointed out that his conclusions with regard to species in general had an obvious bearing on the problem. In 1863, after an exhaustive examination of the anatomical evidence, Huxley stated that man in body and brain differed from some apes less than apes differed among themselves.[1] He therefore returned to the Linnaean classification and placed man as the first Family in the Order of Primates. Psychologically the gulf between man and ape is greater, but the vertebrate animals show mental processes corresponding to the human ones, though of less power and complexity. This was brought out by Brehm in his *Thierleben*, and by Darwin in his later works.[2] Wallace, on the other hand, still held that man was to be placed apart, "as not only the head and culminating point of the grand series of organic nature, but as in some degree a new and distinct order of being".[3]

Mankind has been divided into varieties or races chiefly by physical characters, though the idea of a correlation between physical characters and mental traits has been upheld. The colour of the skin has always been used to separate the white, yellow, brown and black races, and it is clear that other characters are linked with colour to give a real racial distinction between these four kinds of men though subdivisions are necessary. Next in importance to colour comes the shape of the skull, which is generally specified by the method due to Retsius. Looking at the skull from above, the longer diameter from front to back is taken as 100. On this scale, the length of the shorter or cross diameter gives what is called the cephalic index. If it is less than 80, the skull is classed as long, and if more than 80, it is called broad.

As an example of these methods and their results, we may take the analysis of the population of Europe.[4] Considered physically, European people differ chiefly in three charac-

[1] T. H. Huxley, *Man's Place in Nature*, London, 1863.
[2] Charles Darwin, *The Descent of Man*; *The Expression of the Emotions in Man and Other Animals*.
[3] A. R. Wallace, *Natural Selection*, p. 324.
[4] W. Z. Ripley, *The Races of Europe*, Boston and London, 1899.

teristics: stature, coloration and skull shape. On the average of large numbers, as we move northwards until we approach the Baltic region, the stature becomes greater and the colouring fairer, while the farther south we go, the shorter and darker becomes the population. In the intermediate Alpine region, stature and colouring are intermediate also. But the shape of the head tells a different tale. While both northern and southern folk are long-skulled, with a cephalic index of 75 to 79, the round-headed people of the hills have broader skulls with an index of 85 to 89.

To explain these facts it is assumed that in Europe there are three primary races: the first is a tall, fair, Northern race, found in its greatest purity round the shores of the Baltic. Secondly there is a short, dark, Southern race living about the Mediterranean coasts and up the Atlantic seaboard. Both of these races have long skulls. But lying between them geographically is a broad-headed Alpine race, intermediate in colour and stature, inhabiting the mountainous regions of Central Europe. From one aspect, the history of Europe is the history of the interaction and migration of these three races.[1]

Similar methods of investigation, using other characters such as the texture of the hair, have been applied to the physical anthropology of other continents, where more primitive folk are to be found.

Since Lyell described what was left of man in the geological record, many discoveries have been made, whereby different races have been distinguished in remote prehistoric times. Much was done in the nineteenth century. It was shown that tens of thousands of years ago the cave-men were decorating their walls with spirited likenesses of the bison and the wild boar. At Neanderthal in 1856, and at Spy in 1886, still older remains came to light, showing the existence of more primitive types of man; and in 1893 Dubois discovered, in the late Pliocene deposits in Java, bones which most authorities hold to be those of a being intermediate in structure between the anthropoid apes and the earliest known forms of man.

Man cannot be descended from any species of ape now existing. But, if not a lineal descendant, he is at least a distant

[1] A. C. Haddon, *The Wanderings of Peoples*, Cambridge, 1911.

w

Anthropology cousin. More variable forms may have preceded all those now extant and have been their common ancestors. It is certain that the process has been more complicated than was thought at first. The separate shoots that rise above the visible plain of history spring from a complex root system buried deeply in the ground of the irrecoverable past.

The application of statistical methods to anthropology may be said to have begun with the work of the Belgian astronomer L. A. J. Quetelet (1796–1874). In 1835 and later years Quetelet showed that the theory of probability could be applied to

Fig. 7.

human problems.[1] He found that the chest measurements of Scottish soldiers or the height of French conscripts vary round the average according to the same laws as are seen in the distribution of bullets round the centre of a target or in the runs of luck at a gaming table. Expressed graphically, as in Fig. 7, the measurements give a curve of variation which, except that it is symmetrical on both sides, resembles that giving the velocities of molecules in a gas (p. 250).

In 1869 Darwin's cousin Francis Galton applied the ideas of heredity which appear in *The Origin of Species* to the inheritance of mental qualities in mankind.[2] He proved by

[1] *Sur l'Homme et le Développement de ses Facultés*, 1835. *Physique Sociale*, 1869. *Anthropométrie*, 1870.
[2] *Hereditary Genius*, London, 1869.

tracing the distribution of marks among the candidates in an examination that the same laws hold as for physical qualities or molecular velocities. Most men have mediocre intellectual powers, and, as we pass towards genius on the one hand or idiocy on the other, the numbers fall off in the familiar way.

A Senior Wrangler obtained on the average about thirty times the number of marks of the lowest honours man, which, in turn, might have exceeded those of the pass men, had they entered for the same examination. Owing to the limits of time allowed, these numbers underestimate the differences in intellect, which are clearly enormous. Galton restricted the word "eminent" to those qualities which only appear in about 250 men in a million, and the word "illustrious" to those appearing in only one in a million or more. At the other end of the scale 250 in a million about includes the hopeless idiots and imbeciles, who depart from the normal one way as much as the eminent do in the other. By studying books of reference, Galton found that eminent men have in the aggregate a far larger number of eminent relatives than have an equal number of men taken at random from the population. For instance, he reckoned that the chance of the son of a judge showing great ability was five hundred times as great as that of a man taken at random. If it be objected that judges have greater opportunities than most men of helping their sons, it may be replied that Galton's figures show it to be nearly as likely that a judge will have an able father as an able son, and even judges have small opportunity of educating or advancing their fathers. By such arguments, Galton fairly met the criticisms made on his work. Little stress can be laid on his exact figures, but the broad results are certain and unmistakable. While prediction cannot be made about individuals, on the average of large numbers the inheritance of ability is certain; the differences of innate ability are enormous; and the democratic idea that all men are born equal is demonstrably false. Darwin's theory of natural selection then led to the recognition that any change in the legal, social or economic environment must favour some strains in a mixed population more than others, and thus modify the average biological quality of the people. Galton had doubts from the first about the inheritance of acquired characters, and, when

Anthropology Weismann's work showed that there was no evidence in its favour that would stand critical examination, Galton's principles were strengthened immensely. It became clear that the influence of environment had been greatly overestimated, that education can but bring into prominence characters already in being, and that the biological qualities of a race can only be improved by favouring the better strains. The reason why breeding is all-important became manifest.

Chapter VII

NINETEENTH-CENTURY SCIENCE AND PHILOSOPHIC THOUGHT

General Tendencies of Scientific Thought—Matter and Force—
The Theory of Energy—Psychology—Biology and Materialism
—Science and Sociology—Evolution and Religion—Evolution
and Philosophy.

I<small>N</small> the seventeenth and eighteenth centuries the influence
of that nationalism which replaced the ecclesiastical uni-
versalism of the Middle Ages began to be apparent. Science,
indeed thought in general, acquired strongly-marked national
characters and was accompanied by an intellectual separation
between the nations, while the several vernacular languages
of Europe superseded Latin as the vehicle for scientific writing.
Journeys of intellectual discovery, such as those of Voltaire
to England in 1726, of Adam Smith to France in 1765, and of
Wordsworth and Coleridge to Germany in 1798, had to be
undertaken before the Newtonian astronomy, the economics
of the "physiocrats", or the philosophy of Kant and Schelling
could become known in countries other than those of their
authors.[1]

General Tendencies of Scientific Thought

In the early years of the nineteenth century the scientific
centre of the world was Paris. In 1793 the Revolutionary
Government had guillotined Lavoisier, Bailly and Cousin,
driven Condorcet to suicide, and suspended the *Académie des
Sciences*. But it soon found that it had to appeal for help to
the former members of that Society: "everything was wanting
for the defence of the country", science became a necessity
to society at large, and in 1795 the *Académie* was reopened as
part of the *Institut*. The mathematics of Laplace, Lagrange
and Monge, the new chemistry initiated by Lavoisier, and the
geometrical crystallography created by the Abbé Haüy, united
to form a brilliant constellation of physical sciences.

The theory of probability, founded by Pascal and Fermat
in the seventeenth century, was developed into a system by
Laplace, and applied not only to estimate the errors of physical

---

[1] J. T. Merz, *History of European Thought in the Nineteenth Century*, 4 vols.
Edinburgh and London, 1896–1914, vol. I, p. 16.

measurement but also to rationalize such human affairs as insurance and the statistics of the problems of government and administration where large numbers are involved. Cuvier carried exact research into comparative anatomy, and, in his position as permanent secretary of the *Académie des Sciences*, did much to keep the scientific spirit up to a high standard in all subjects.

During the eighteenth century it was in France alone that science permeated literature; "no other country has a Fontenelle, a Voltaire, a Buffon"; and in the early nineteenth century this connection between science and literature was maintained on a lofty and dignified plane, largely owing to the constitution of the *Académie* as part of the *Institut*.

If the home of French science is to be found in the *Académie*, that of German lay in the Universities. But long after the methods of exact science were being used in Paris, the German Universities, while eminent in classical and philosophic studies, were teaching a hybrid *Naturphilosophie*, which deduced its conclusions from doubtful philosophic theories, instead of obtaining them by the patient study of natural phenomena. About 1830 this influence died away, partly owing to the mathematics of Gauss and to the chemical work of Liebig, who, trained at Paris under Gay-Lussac, had opened a laboratory at Giessen in 1826. From then onwards, the systematic organization of research has been carried further in Germany than in any other country, and German compendiums and analyses of the world's work have been preeminent. Moreover the wider meaning of the word *Wissenschaft*, which includes all systematic knowledge, whether in what we should call science or in philology, history and philosophy, has done much to keep all these subjects in touch with each other and to give them all a correspondingly wider outlook.

Perhaps the most striking peculiarity of English science has been its individualist spirit, and the frequency with which work of brilliant genius has been done by those of no academic position. This is illustrated by a list of the great men of science of the first half of the nineteenth century, when Oxford and Cambridge, unrivalled as places of liberal education, were not yet awake to the continental spirit of research. Complaints were frequent that the state of science was low in England,[1]

[1] See for example, *Edinburgh Review*, vol. xxvii, 1816, p. 98, and C. Babbage, *Decline of the State of Science in England*, 1830.

and it needed the stimulus of an undergraduate society, formed by Babbage, Herschel and Peacock, to introduce continental mathematics, largely developed though they were from those of Newton, into the University of Cambridge.

But, in the middle of the century, Oxford and Cambridge were reformed, and rapidly became as efficient in modern studies as in the graceful activities which they had inherited from earlier times. Mathematical physics, first of the sciences, found once more a congenial home in Cambridge, and later, under the inspiration of Clerk Maxwell, Lord Rayleigh and J. J. Thomson, the world-famous experimental school of the Cavendish Laboratory grew up. The biological subjects followed, under the leadership of Michael Foster, Langley and Bateson, and Cambridge took its place as the great home of science we know to-day.

Thus, during the second half of the nineteenth century, the intellectual isolation of the nations of Europe, which had lasted through the first half, was again broken down. Facilities of transport increased personal intercourse, scientific periodicals and the proceedings of learned societies brought new results to the cognizance of all those interested, and science became once more international.

On the other hand, the different departments of knowledge became more specialized, and, as national barriers were overthrown, departmental isolation increased. At the beginning of the nineteenth century it was still possible for German Universities to have courses of lectures on *Encyclopädie*, under the impression that unity and completeness of knowledge could be found in one and the same arrangement of study.[1] Philosophy, under the influence of Kant, Fichte and Schleiermacher, still took into account all branches of knowledge, and in its turn still permeated scientific thought.

How science and philosophy for a time lost touch with each other will be described later. The process was doubtless hastened by the simultaneous segregation of science into sciences. The growth of knowledge went on so fast that no man could keep track of it all. Meanwhile laboratories, which hitherto had been the private rooms of individual "natural philosophers", were built and endowed by or for Universities, and brought the experimental method of study not only to

[1] Merz, *loc. cit.* vol. I, p. 37.

those who were advancing knowledge by research, but also to the more elementary student. The opportunities thus provided for the more thorough study of each subject left less time for general surveys, and men of science tended not to see their wood for its trees. In recent years inter-connections between the different sciences are becoming more and more apparent, while mathematics and physics are pointing the way to a new philosophy. But, speaking generally, the fissiparous tendencies lasted till the end of the nineteenth century, save for a few broad generalizations, such as the principle of the conservation of energy, which was seen to hold good in physics, chemistry and biology alike.

In attempting to trace the effect produced on other subjects, and especially on philosophic thought, by the growth of science during the nineteenth century, it must not be forgotten that, as already pointed out, the effect during this period of the advance in mathematics and physics was much less than it had been in the sixteenth, seventeenth and eighteenth centuries. The volume of mathematical and physical research was far greater, and the change in scientific outlook which took place between the years 1800 and 1900 was enormous, yet, from the point of view of philosophy, no such revolutionary physical discoveries were made in that century as those of Copernicus and Newton, which altered so profoundly man's idea of the position and importance in the Universe of his world and himself. In the nineteenth century a like revolutionary result came from biology, when physiology and psychology examined the relations of mind and matter, and again when the theory of evolution was established by Darwin on the basis of natural selection.

During the Renaissance and the Newtonian Epoch, we have seen the links between science and philosophy gradually loosened by the action of men of science in devising a new method of induction and experiment proper to the study of nature. Yet the philosophers tried to maintain a *de jure* suzerainty over the whole field of knowledge, even though *de facto* the sovereignty over a large part of it had passed from them. Till the days of Kant they still framed their systems to include the results of physical science.

But we now come to a time when, chiefly owing to the influence of later Hegelians rather than of Hegel himself, the separation between science and philosophy became much more distinct.

The story is well told by Helmholtz,[1] who, writing in 1862, was near enough to the time fully to appreciate its effects:

It has been made of late a reproach against natural philosophy that it has struck out a path of its own, and has separated itself more and more widely from the other sciences [Wissenschaften] which are united by common philological and historical studies. This opposition has, in fact, been long apparent, and seems to me to have grown up mainly under the influence of the Hegelian philosophy, or, at any rate, to have been brought out into more distinct relief by that philosophy. Certainly, at the end of the last century, when Kantian philosophy reigned supreme, such a schism had never been proclaimed; on the contrary, Kant's philosophy rested on exactly the same ground as the physical sciences, as is evident from his own scientific works, especially from his "Cosmogony", based upon Newton's Law of Gravitation, which afterwards, under the name of Laplace's Nebular Hypothesis, came to be universally recognized. The sole object of Kant's "Critical Philosophy" was to test the sources and the authority of our knowledge, and to fix a definite scope and standard for the researches of philosophy, as compared with other sciences. According to his teaching, a principle discovered *a priori* by pure thought was a rule applicable to the method of pure thought, and nothing further; it could contain no real, positive knowledge. [Hegel's] "Philosophy of Identity"[2] was bolder. It started with the hypothesis that not only spiritual phenomena, but even the actual world—nature, that is, and man—were the result of an act of thought on the part of a creative mind, similar, it was supposed, in kind to the human mind. On this hypothesis it seemed competent for the human mind, even without the guidance of external experience, to think over again the thoughts of the Creator, and to rediscover them by its own inner activity. Such was the view with which the "Philosophy of Identity" set to work to construct *a priori* the results of other sciences. The process might be more or less successful in matters of theology, law, politics, language, art, history, in short in all sciences, the subject-matter of which really grows out of our moral nature, and which are therefore properly classed together under the name of moral sciences.... But even granting that Hegel was more or less successful in constructing, *a priori*, the leading results of the moral sciences, still it was no proof of the correctness of the hypothesis of Identity with which he started. The facts of nature would have been the crucial test....It was at this point that Hegel's philosophy, we venture to say, utterly broke down. His system of nature seemed, at least to natural philosophers, absolutely crazy. Of all the distinguished scientific men who were his contemporaries, not one was found to stand up for his ideas. Accordingly, Hegel himself, convinced of the importance of winning for his philosophy in

[1] H. Helmholtz, *Popular Lectures on Scientific Subjects*, Eng. trans. E. Atkinson, London, 1873, p. 5.

[2] So called because it proclaimed the identity not only of subject and object, but of contradictories, such as existence and non-existence. Tr.

the field of physical science that recognition which had been so freely accorded to it elsewhere, launched out, with unusual vehemence and acrimony, against the natural philosophers, and especially against Sir Isaac Newton, as the first and greatest representative of physical investigation. The philosophers accused the scientific men of narrowness; the scientific men retorted that the philosophers were crazy. And so it came about that men of science began to lay some stress on the banishment of all philosophic influences from their work; while some of them, including men of the greatest acuteness, went so far as to condemn philosophy altogether, not merely as useless, but as mischievous dreaming. Thus, it must be confessed, not only were the illegitimate pretensions of the Hegelian system to subordinate to itself all other studies rejected, but no regard was paid to the rightful claims of philosophy, that is, the criticism of the sources of cognition, and the definition of the functions of the intellect.

For about half a century, especially in Germany, this separation between science and philosophy persisted. The Hegelians despised the experimentalists, somewhat as did the Greek philosophers. The men of science disliked and finally ignored the Hegelians. Even Helmholtz, in deploring this attitude, as is seen above, limited philosophy to its critical function—the elucidation of the theory of knowledge—and denied its claim to attack other more speculative problems, such as the deeper questions of the nature of reality and the meaning of the Universe.

The philosophers, from their side, were equally blind, and used any weapon which came to their hand in their attack on the experimentalists. The poet Goethe had done good work in both animal and vegetable comparative anatomy, where the facts lay on the surface. But where deeper analysis was needed, as in physics, Goethe's method failed. A flash of poetic insight assured him that white light must be simpler and purer than coloured, and that therefore Newton's theory of colour must be wrong.[1] He would not consider the facts brought out by careful experiment or the inferences drawn from them. To him the senses must reveal at once the truth about nature, and the true inwardness of things be made visible by direct aesthetic imagination. He therefore framed a theory of colour in which white light was fundamental—a theory which could not stand the simplest physical analysis, and was supported by nothing but Goethe's abuse of Newton and by the compromising help of the Hegelians. It is not surprising that the men of

[1] Helmholtz, *loc. cit.* p. 33.

science learnt to ignore the writings of the philosophers. But the complete separation could not last long, and science soon began once more to influence the general thought of the time.

In England a new variety of an old controversy arose between Whewell on the one hand, who maintained the *a priori* nature of mathematics, and Herschel and John Stuart Mill on the other, who held that Euclidean axioms, such as that two parallel straight lines produced to infinity can never meet, are inductions from experience.[1] Kant referred the validity of these axioms, as of other scientific concepts, to the nature of our minds, and nowadays the axioms might be regarded as mere definitions of the kind of space we were going to investigate in our geometry. Other axioms can be framed which lead to a geometry of non-Euclidean space. Indeed the work of Lobatchewski, Bolyai, Gauss and Riemann gradually showed that what we call space is a particular case of a general possible manifoldness which may have four or more dimensions. Our minds can frame the axioms and investigate the properties of these other kinds of "space". Experience, it is true, shows that the space we observe is approximately three dimensional and Euclidean, but, examined more accurately by Einstein, it proved to be not exactly so, but to conform, as far as present accuracy goes, to one out of the many other possible kinds of space. Thus the Whewell-Mill controversy, like so many others, has faded away into a solution which contains the essence of both alternatives.

Whewell distinguished the necessary axioms of mathematics from the merely probable hypotheses of natural science, which he recognized as being based on induction from experience, though, following Kant, he held that in every act of knowledge a formal or mental element co-operates with an element derived directly from sensation. Mill's attitude is partly due to the fact that, in his day, empiricists were still opposing, consciously or unconsciously, the old phantom of innate ideas—Platonic revelations from a super-sensual world. The same survival seems to have misled Ueberweg in his polemic against Kant.[2] Nineteenth-century empiricists often failed to see the strength or bearings of the view that experience does

[1] W. Whewell, *Philosophy of the Inductive Sciences*, London, 1840, and *History of the Inductive Sciences*, London, 1837; J. S. Mill, *Logic*, London, 1843.

[2] See F. A. Lange, *Die Geschichte der Materialismus*, Eng. trans. E. C. Thomas, vol. II, 3rd ed. p. 173.

not lead us directly to things as they are, but is only a process by which the appearance of things arises in our minds, and that therefore the picture of nature we construct is partly determined *a priori* by the structure of our minds, as also is the fact that we have experiences at all.

Indeed, during the greater part of the nineteenth century, most men of science, especially biologists, thinking they were keeping clear of metaphysics, accepted uncritically the model of nature put together by science as ultimate reality. Some of the physicists and philosophers were more cautious. Even Herbert Spencer, whose work was based on the science of his day, held that the ultimate concepts of physics—space, time, atoms—involve mental inconsistencies which make it clear that the reality which underlies phenomena is unknowable. Here, he argued, science joins hands with religion, which, stripped of all doubtful elements, is the faith that all things are the manifestation of a Power that transcends our knowledge.

The philosophy of science was also studied in England by G. Boole, who (1854) introduced symbolic language and notation into logic; by W. Stanley Jevons, who, in his *Principles of Science* (1874), gave a high place to intuition in scientific methods of discovery; and by W. K. Clifford (1845–1879), who held that Kant's argument for the universality and necessity of geometrical truths was valid as against Hume's empiricism, but that the researches of Lobatchewski and Riemann proved that, while ideal space might be defined and investigated *a priori*, actual space and its geometry as known to us are products of experience. It is clear that Darwin's theory of natural selection has a bearing on this problem. It will therefore be reconsidered later in this chapter.

But Boole, Jevons and Clifford had little influence among men of science. Even physicists had lost touch so entirely with philosophy that when in 1883 attention was called by Ernst Mach to the philosophical basis of mechanics, his work was ignored by some, slighted as fanciful by others, and over-estimated for originality by the few who studied and appreciated it.[1]

[1] Dr Ernst Mach, *Die Mechanik in ihrer Entwickelung historisch-kritisch dargestellt*, 1st ed. 1883, 4th ed. 1901, Eng. trans. T. J. McCormack, Chicago, 1893, 2nd ed. London, 1902.

In writing his treatise on mechanics he made use of the historical method, then unusual. His criticism of Newton's definition of mass and his account of the fundamental discoveries of dynamical principles have been described in Chapter v.

Taking up the tradition of Locke, Hume and Kant, Mach pointed out that science does but construct a model of what our senses tell us about Nature, and that mechanics, far from being necessarily the ultimate truth about Nature as some believe it to be, is but one aspect from which that model may be regarded. Other aspects, chemical, physiological and so forth, are equally fundamental and important. We have no right to assume a knowledge of absolute space or time, since space and time are but sensations, and the one can only be referred to the frame of the fixed stars, and the other to astronomical movement. Space as known to us is a concept derived from experience, for Riemann and other mathematicians have imagined different kinds of space, or space-like manifolds. "A body is a relatively constant sum of touch and sight sensations." A natural law is "a concise compendious rule" giving the result of past experience as a guide to future sense-perceptions. Most of Mach's ideas may be found in the writings of the older philosophers, but they came quite fresh to the unphilosophic men of science of the late nineteenth century.

From the philosophic point of view perhaps the first important single effect of the new developments in physical science was produced by Lavoisier's demonstration of the persistence of matter through all chemical changes. The idea of matter gained through the sense of touch is one of the earliest concepts given to science by common-sense, and led to the metaphysical concept of substance as that which is extended in space and persistent in time. It has been seen in earlier chapters how, at certain periods in history, the experience of solidity in matter recurrently gave rise to a materialist philosophy. Lavoisier demonstrated scientifically that, through all the apparent changes and disappearances of chemical action, the total mass as measured by weight remained unaltered, and thus he strengthened immensely the common-sense view that matter was an ultimate reality, for persistence in time is one of the common-sense marks of reality.

Matter and Force   But it was the general impression produced by the success of physical science that had the most momentous effect on philosophic thought in the first two-thirds of the nineteenth century. Dalton's atomic theory, the reduction of the phenomena of electricity and magnetism to mathematical laws, the concordance with experiment of the wave theory of light, the revelation by spectrum analysis of the composition of the Sun and stars, the explanation of the constitution of all the host of organic compounds by structural formulae, the production of new compounds and even of new elements, and the method of predicting their existence even before their discovery—all these and other triumphs gave an overwhelming sense of growing power both in the interpretation of nature and in the control of natural forces. It was difficult to remember that one mystery was only cleared up by expressing it in terms of another, and that, in ultimate analysis, the fundamental problems of Reality remained much as they were. And, indeed, this fact was often forgotten as the first sixty or seventy years of the century passed away, and uncritical men came to believe more firmly first in matter and force and then in matter and motion as ultimate explanations.

It will be well to trace more carefully the threads of thought which led to the idea of the dominance of matter and force. Newton himself, in framing his hypothesis of universal gravitational attraction, never accepted gravity as an inherent and ultimate property of matter, or action at a distance as a physical explanation. He says that he has been unable to satisfy himself about the cause of the attraction, and only puts forth a query whether it might not be due to an aethereal medium, which, being denser in free space than near matter, presses gravitating masses towards each other. He lays no stress on this suggestion, but he distinctly regards gravity as needing explanation, and leaves its cause for future consideration.

Nevertheless, during the eighteenth and early nineteenth centuries, it came to be assumed by many philosophers and some physicists that the Newtonian system, an extension of Galileo's idea of force, involved action at a distance, and was to be distinguished in this from the school which traced its pedigree back to Descartes, and sought to explain the interactions of matter by some comprehensible mechanical means.

For instance, while the French physicists Ampère and Cauchy were investigating electric forces mathematically on the Newtonian law of inverse squares, in England Faraday and (later) William Thomson and Clerk Maxwell were studying the effect of the intervening medium, and trying to picture a mechanism by which the electric forces could be transmitted through it.

Similar questions arose in atomic and molecular problems. To the ancients, and indeed to Gassendi and Boyle, the atoms only acted on each other by collision and contact. Atoms with rough surfaces, even with teeth or hooks, were imagined in order to explain cohesion and other properties of matter. But, if atoms can act on each other at a distance, these ideas become unnecessary. The kinetic theory, it is true, is superficially a return to the view that atoms or molecules act on each other by direct collision. But it has to be assumed that, when near, the molecules exert forces on each other, and moreover, since they must be supposed to rebound on collision, they must be taken as elastic, and therefore must have structure and be composed of smaller parts. Even if atoms are in practice indivisible, in imagination they can be divided to infinity, and ultimately we must picture an infinitely small particle, that is a point, which, since it influences other similar points, must be a centre of force. Such reasoning led Boscovitch, an eighteenth-century Jesuit, to regard the atoms themselves as immaterial centres of force, and, in the nineteenth century, logically-minded French physicists such as Ampère and Cauchy saw that the atom of their day had in analysis become an unextended bearer of forces, the idea of solid particles being only retained in deference to the materialist instincts of unphilosophic minds. In 1929 the atom is no longer unextended; even the electron shows signs of a more minute structure, and is being sublimated into a source of radiation or a disembodied wave-system. When we look beyond the electron, we still seem to be left with the alternatives of regarding the ultimate units of matter as unextended centres of force, or of imagining an infinite series of structures, one within another, and each more minute than the last.

But, in spite of Boscovitch, Ampère and Cauchy, with their reduction of the atom to a mere centre of force, Newtonian science, based on particles of matter and the similar ideas applied by Lavoisier to chemistry, led many of those interested in such things to an opposite philosophy, which regarded hard lumps of matter as the sole reality, while the forces between them were accepted as their only mode of action. Helmholtz and other physicists regarded the reduction of a problem to mass and force as an adequate solution. In this they followed Newton. It was a mathematical solution, and as such satisfactory, though not a physical explanation. But those who were not familiar with physics misunderstood them, and thought they regarded a mathematical solution as an ultimate explanation.

In the eighteenth century, philosophic materialism, as explained in Chapter IV, was revived in France; in the nineteenth, it arose anew in Germany.[1] The early protagonists, Moleschott, Büchner and Vögt, based their philosophy definitely on the results of science, and especially on those of physiology and psychology. But the title of Büchner's book, *Kraft und Stoff* (1855), shows that the ideas of force and matter as ultimate realities formed an essential part of the movement. Perhaps the attention thus called to the clear-cut results of natural science had a healthy effect after half a century of somewhat foggy Hegelian idealism, but it is remarkable that this revival of a materialist philosophy arose when among men of science matter had been replaced by the accurately definable quantity mass, and force was just being shown to have been used ambiguously to mean either force or energy. Moreover, these German writers confused their materialism with sensationalism and even with scepticism, and never seemed to understand clearly the problem of knowledge.

The acceptance of the principle of the conservation of matter led to a somewhat crude materialism. The later establishment of the corresponding principle of the conservation of energy, though it could not be pressed into the service of philosophic materialism, was used as evidence for the allied theory of philosophic mechanism and determinism.

In the first place, it helped to throw doubt on the prevalent form of biological vitalism, which held that in living beings there exists a vital force, which controls or even suspends physical and chemical laws, adapts the organism to its environment, and shapes its ends. It was now seen that animals,

---

[1] F. A. Lange, *loc. cit.* vol. II, chaps. II, III.

like machines, can only move and do work when supplied with *The Theory* energy from without—with fuel in the form of food, and with *of Energy* air containing oxygen. If control be exercised by a vital principle, it must be in a more subtle way than had been assumed. It was still possible to imagine an evasion of the second (or statistical) law of thermodynamics by some such action as that of Maxwell's hypothetical daemon, but the first law—the principle of the conservation of energy—was seen to hold good in living as in dead systems.

Secondly, if the amount of energy in the Universe is limited and constant, we are faced with the possible cessation of the Sun's activity, as well as with the problem of the age of the Earth in the past and its life in the future. The old idea that the Sun was a hot body slowly cooling was seen to be inadequate; even if it were made of coal it would burn out and its heat be exhausted in a time all too short. But the new physical principles also showed that immense stores of energy would be converted into heat as the original nebula condensed and its parts fell together to form the Sun. Moreover, a steady contraction of the Sun, if still going on, would continue this evolution of heat, and, it was thought, perhaps give time enough for solar existence. In 1854 Helmholtz calculated that a contraction of one ten-thousandth part of its radius would supply the heat radiated by the Sun for more than 2000 years.

William Thomson, afterwards Lord Kelvin, estimated the age of the Earth by a similar calculation and used it to supplement others based (1) on the heat conducted upward through the crust of the Earth, and (2) on the frictional effect of the tides in lengthening the day. In 1862 he estimated that less than 200 million years ago the Earth was a molten mass, and in 1899 he shortened the limit to something between 20 and 40 million years. By this time, both the geologists and the biologists demanded a much greater time for the Earth and its inhabitants. A pretty quarrel arose, but the bases on which the physical calculations were founded were undermined, first by the discovery of possible new sources of heat in radio-activity, and then by the new atomic and cosmic theories of to-day. In the tremendous temperatures inside the Sun and stars, transmutation of one element into another, and even the direct conversion of matter into energy, are now held to occur, and would supply stores of heat far transcending those contemplated by the older theories. The historians of cosmic and organic evolution can now have as much time as they want.

The actual numbers involved in the nineteenth-century calculations are not important. Whatever be the length of the past life of the Sun and Earth, the principle of the conservation of energy pointed to a beginning and an end, and brought the investigation within the bounds of science.

William Thomson also studied the problem in another way with the help of the second principle of thermodynamics. Mechanical work can only be obtained from heat when heat passes from a hot body to a cold one. This process tends to diminish the difference of temperature, which is also decreased by conduction of heat, friction, and other irreversible processes. The availability of energy in an irreversible system is always becoming less, and its converse—the quantity called by Clausius the entropy—is always tending to a maximum. Thus the energy of an isolated system, and therefore (it was assumed) of the Universe, is slowly passing into heat, uniformly distributed and therefore unavailable as a source of useful work. Eventually, it was thought, the Universe must become motionless and dead.

Thomson's work, like that of Newton, was seized upon by those who confused physical science with mechanical philosophy, and our model of nature with ultimate reality. The "death of the Universe" was thought to be another proof of atheism and philosophic determinism. But, on the alternative theistic theory, if God created the World, there seems to be no good reason why He should not bring it to an end when He has had enough of it; and man's soul, being by this hypothesis spiritual and immortal, can regard with equanimity the supersession of a physical Universe in which it will have ceased long since to be confined. Again, the application of the principles of thermodynamics to cosmic theories, at all events on nineteenth-century evidence, was of doubtful validity. It was unjustifiable to extend to the Universe results inferred from such limited instances, even though they had been successfully used to predict the behaviour of finite isolated or isothermal systems. We now know that the problem is far more complicated than was understood when it was first formulated. Moreover, even if the beginning and the end of the Sun and the Earth as they exist at present were made clear by science, it must be pointed out that the bearing *The Theory* of the result on the metaphysical problem of the origin, *of Energy* meaning and end of the Universe as a whole is very small. The lives of the Sun and Earth, indeed of the whole galaxy of stars, might be traced from the primaeval nebula to the final dead state; we should but have traced a few stages in the evolution of the Cosmos, and should still be as far as ever from solving the mystery of its existence.

The mind of man can be studied in two ways, rationally or *Psychology* empirically. Assuming some metaphysical system of the Universe—say, for instance, that of the Roman Church or that of the German materialists—we can deduce rationally the place of the human mind in that system and its relations thereto. On the other hand, assuming no such system, we can investigate the phenomena of mind by empirical observation and perhaps experiment. This empirical study can be made by two methods, by introspection of our own minds, or by objective observation and experiment on the minds of ourselves or of others. By this last course, psychology becomes a branch of natural science.

At the beginning of the nineteenth century, rational psychology was characteristic of Germany, where in the Universities it was combined with cosmology and theology in a broad study of metaphysics. Empirical psychology had already appeared in England and in Scotland, and followed introspective methods, which held the field for two-thirds of the century, especially in the hands of James Mill and Alexander Bain. In France a beginning had been made in the examination of mind in its outward manifestations as a physiological and pathological problem, and also by an examination of its external signs in language, grammar and logic.[1]

When the methods of science were extended to subjects other than those in which they arose, rational psychology was speedily replaced by empirical in all countries. In this form Herbart used it in Germany in opposition to the prevailing systematic idealist philosophy, though he still based his psychology on metaphysics as well as on experience. On the other hand, especially in the works of Lotze, it was made the basis of a deeper discussion of the materialist hypothesis than could be found in the writings of Vögt, Moleschott and

[1] J. T. Merz, *loc. cit.* vol. III, p. 203.

Büchner. The Germans received with some surprise this empirical "psychology (Seelenlehre) without a soul", i.e. without a preconceived system of metaphysics, for the German mind, from Leibniz onward, has always sought to construct a broad rational theory of the Universe before examining any part of it. But empirical psychology came naturally to the "common-sense" outlook of Englishmen and Scotsmen. As often before, they were well able to follow a line of thought in isolation as far as it proved practically useful, without reference to its apparent logical effect on other subjects. British psychologists for the most part left theology to theologians and metaphysics to metaphysicians, even while their own methods, though empirical, were introspective. When they became experimental, this attitude of course became even easier. French psychology, chiefly in the hands of physiologists and physicians, naturally led the way in scientific experimental methods, and was in no danger from metaphysical systems. And, when psychology, like natural science, became international, the French contribution had perhaps the greatest influence.

The attitude of physical science, including physiology and experimental psychology, is analytic, regarding a problem successively from different aspects—mechanical, chemical or physiological—and, in each, resolving the subjects of study into simple concepts, such as cells, atoms, electrons, and their mutual relations. But biology suggests that each living being is an organic whole, and, even more markedly, each man feels in himself a deep-seated consciousness of unity of being. While science deals with relations which can be verified by any competent observer, each man's mind is fully accessible only to himself. Hence this consciousness of unity cannot be adequately investigated by scientific methods. In physiology and experimental psychology, it is necessary to suppose that animals are subject to and explicable by physical and chemical principles, and that man is a machine, for no progress can be made on any other assumption. But when continental pseudo-logicians argued that this useful working assumption represented reality, and that man was *nothing but* a machine, the British, with their usual common-sense point of view, saw that, though it was in accordance with one set of facts, it did not agree with another, and they were quite content to regard man as a machine in the physiological laboratory, as a being possessing free will and responsibility when they met him in the ordinary affairs of life, and as an immortal soul when they went to church. Each view was found to be a good working hypothesis for its own special purpose, so why not use them all at appropriate times and places? They may be reconciled some day in the light of future knowledge, and meanwhile they all help to get things done. This characteristic British attitude of mind was shown not only in the days of Newton and at the inception of modern psychology, but in many other scientific and philosophic problems of the nineteenth century and afterwards. Though it seems illogical to continental minds, it may still be the true scientific attitude. It takes theories as working hypotheses as long as they produce useful results, and, if they do so, does not shrink from employing simultaneously two theories which, in the then state of knowledge, look mutually inconsistent. If either proves incompatible with facts (or with cherished convictions), it can readily and easily be dropped. At the present time (1929) physics, hitherto the most rational of sciences, is using two fundamental theories apparently quite inconsistent with each other, thus perhaps justifying the British habit of mind.

Alexander Bain (1818–1903) was one of the first to use contemporary scientific knowledge in the empirical examination of mental processes by the introspective method. He followed Locke's theory that the phenomena of the mind can be traced back to sensations, and adopted "the association psychology" of British writers from Hume to James Mill, whereby higher and more complex ideas are supposed to be compounded out of simpler elements by association. Bain strengthened these principles by evidence drawn from physiology, though he did not fully appreciate the bearing that the French researches on morbid psychology had on the theory of the normal action of the mind, and he completed his main work before the days of evolution brought a realization of the contrasted influence of heredity and environment.

Even when psychology looked to natural science for help, there were for a time characteristic national differences in its application. In France and England it was the *methods* of science which were used—observation, hypothesis, deduction of consequences, and comparison of these with further obser-

Psychology vation and (later) experiment. In Germany, though idealist Hegelian metaphysics, which had come to be somewhat discredited, were no longer used as a basis, psychologists still sought to build on a metaphysical system. As natural science was in the ascendant, and Johannes Müller and Liebig were applying physiology and chemistry so successfully to medicine and industry, the psychologists took over scientific concepts, instead of only scientific method. They proceeded "to elevate the supposed elementary notions with which the natural sciences operated and which were in current use, such as matter and force, to the rank of fundamental principles for the mental sciences or even to that of articles of a new creed". This "led to an abstract and contracted view of mental phenomena, to hasty generalizations, and in the end to purely verbal distinctions".[1]

But about this time—the middle of the nineteenth century—the application of physical methods, brought in from different sides, produced a revolution in psychology. Curiously enough, psychophysics can be traced back to Bishop Berkeley, who, in his *New Theory of Vision*, referred our awareness of space and matter ultimately to the sense of touch. Its later development began with Galvani's discovery that the legs of frogs contracted when touched by two different metals. This observation, besides starting the great science of current electricity, led to wild speculations in physiology and psychology. Enthusiasts unqualified for scientific research, misusing Galvani's work and also Mesmer's investigation of the phenomena of hypnotism, falsely called "animal magnetism", degraded the study of the rôle of electricity in physiology till Helmholtz and du Bois Reymond applied scientific methods again a generation later.

We have seen how Gall's work on the localization of sensation in parts of the brain was similarly degraded by popular ignorance into the absurdities of "phrenology", but, in more careful hands, it led to a great increase of knowledge of cerebral action. The special senses were studied from the physical side by Thomas Young, who revised and improved Newton's theory that colour vision depends on three primary colour sensations, and by Helmholtz, who, in his study of physiological acoustics, elucidated the physiological basis of

[1] Merz, *loc. cit.* vol. III, p. 211.

music and speech. Again, in his physiological optics, Helmholtz not only advanced our knowledge of the sensation of sight, but helped also to analyse our perceptions of space, using among other methods the stereoscope invented earlier by Sir Charles Wheatstone.

But it was E. H. Weber, of Leipzig, who began the present science of experimental psychology by his observations on the limits of sensation. For instance, touching different parts of the skin simultaneously with two pins, he measured their distance apart when they can just be felt as giving separate pressures. He also investigated the increase in a stimulus necessary to produce an increase in sensation. Here he discovered a definite mathematical relation—that the stimulus must increase according to its intensity at the beginning of each step, that is, in a geometrical progression.

Among the more philosophically minded, the new outlook had been early recognized by Beneke in his *Psychologie als Naturwissenschaft* (1833), Lotze (1852), who accepted mathematical methods as applicable to some parts of psychology, and Fechner, who first used the term "psychophysics" (1860). The modern school appears plainly in Wundt, of Leipzig, who, besides making measurements himself, as on the sensation of time, collected the different threads of enquiry into a coherent whole. While appreciating to the full the use of the analytic method in the study of special problems, Wundt never lost sight of the fundamental unity of the inner life. Here again the work of Darwin marked an epoch. His study of the expression of the emotions in animals and man opened the way to the modern subject of comparative psychology, which has thrown so much light on the human mind.

The most characteristic contribution of the later nineteenth century to the main psychological problem of the relation of mind and body is the theory of psychophysical parallelism. Its germ can be traced through Descartes, Spinoza and Leibniz to Weber, Lotze, Fechner and Wundt. Physical and psychical phenomena clearly run parallel; they are simultaneous if not connected. The theory regards consciousness as a concomitant epi-phenomenon of the more accessible though complex changes in the nervous system. For the purposes of psychophysics this is enough: we do not need to know whether the epi-phenomena have independent existence. But conscious

Psychology life has the faculty of continuous growth as it becomes manifest in language, literature, science, art and all the social activities —a growth in mental values. Hence psychology has become connected with, and has given new power to, the sciences of language, philology and phonetics, and through them has found a way of penetrating from the outside world to the inner world of thought.

The examination of the central problems of the unity of self-conscious life is at present beyond the methods of exact science. Here we pass into metaphysics. Is the feeling of unity the reflection of a reality, and has the inner mind, soul, call it what we will, an independent existence? On the other hand, is it only a derived complex, built up by the grouping together of sensations, perceptions and memories, as later developments of "association psychology" suppose? Does it control the body, is it a mere epi-phenomenon of the brain or is there some higher unity? Cabanis suggested that the function of the brain in its connection with thought should be studied as the functions of other bodily organs, and this was put in coarse language by Vogt, who said that the brain secretes thought as the liver secretes bile. That materialist outlook is crude and unsatisfying, but it serves to focus the greatest problem which psychology hands over to philosophy.

Biology and Materialism If the discoveries of the principles of the conservation of matter and energy, combined with the atomic theory, were used as the chief basis of materialism, the simultaneous progress of physiology and psychology in the first half of the nineteenth century led to a strengthening of the mechanical philosophy, which, illogically but inevitably, was confused with materialism. Johannes Müller, with his *Handbuch der Physiologie* (1833), and E. H. Weber were the pioneers of scientific method in this subject in Germany. Then came the French influence, especially in the physiology of the brain and nervous system, and the psychology and treatment of mental disease founded on it. Next came the application of statistics to human actions by Quetelet. This extension of science over new domains was seized on by Vogt, Moleschott, Büchner and other German materialists to support their metaphysics. The old arguments used a hundred years before in France were revived and developed with the added weight of the new physics, physiology and psychology behind them. In some continental countries, ecclesiastical conservatism found effective means of suppressing these views, till the struggle for political liberty was combined with that for intellectual freedom, and culminated in the revolutionary outbreaks of 1848.

In the following years the industrial changes, which had already gone far in England, began to extend to the Continent. Science, and especially chemistry, came into closer relation with ordinary life. In practical England, this process had had little effect on religious orthodoxy, but, in logical France and metaphysical Germany, it certainly helped to swell the rising tide of mechanical and materialistic philosophy. Moreover, compared with idealist systems, materialism has a superficial simplicity. Büchner, in his *Kraft und Stoff* (1855), proclaimed that "expositions not intelligible to an educated man are not worth the ink they are printed with", and in Germany the "materialistic controversy" reached sections of the people that it never touched in other countries. As Lange says, "Germany is the only country in the world where the apothecary cannot make up a prescription without being conscious of the relation of his activity to the constitution of the universe".[1]

It is impossible to read the works of the Germans who called themselves materialists in the middle of the nineteenth century without seeing that theirs was no thorough-going, logical materialism like one side of the dualism of Descartes. Moleschott, Vögt and Büchner confuse materialism with naturalism, with sensationalism, even with agnosticism. Indeed, the name seems to cover in turn almost any views which could be opposed to the prevalent German idealism or to ecclesiastical orthodoxy. It was a philosophy of revolt, and used any stick which came to hand. Philosophic materialism, the idea that the only ultimate reality is to be found in lumps of dead matter, cannot explain consciousness or stand for a moment against critical analysis. But many of the systems with which in this Teutonic fog it was confused cannot be refuted out of hand. Hence the prolongation and general inconclusiveness of the discussion.

The great dividing line in this realm of thought, especially in Germany, was the work of Darwin. When the *Origin of Species* became generally known, German philosophers, led

[1] Lange, *loc. cit.* vol. II, p. 263.

by Ernst Haeckel, developed Darwin's teaching into a philosophic creed. On this *Darwinismus* they founded a new form
of monism allied to materialism, and thenceforward in all
countries such controversies ranged themselves round the
concept of evolution.

The general acceptance of the theory of evolution, as based
by Darwin on natural selection, produced profound changes
not only in those sciences directly affected, but also in many
other realms of thought. To a consideration of these changes
we must now turn.

Even in the first half of the nineteenth century science began
to influence many other branches of human activity as well as
philosophy. Its dispassionate methods of enquiry, its effective
combination of observation, logical reasoning and experiment,
were found useful in other subjects. By the middle of the
century this tendency began to be realized. Helmholtz says:

> I do think that our age has learnt many lessons from the physical
> sciences. The absolute, unconditional reverence for facts, and the fidelity
> with which they are collected, a certain distrustfulness of appearances,
> the effort to detect in all cases relations of cause and effect, and the
> tendency to assume their existence, which distinguish our century from
> preceding ones, seem to me to point to such an influence.

When one looks at the history of politics, even in our own
day, one tends to feel that Helmholtz was too optimistic. But
perhaps comparison with former ages may go some way
towards justifying him. Men learnt in the nineteenth century
that the subject of economics, at all events, was suitable in
parts for mathematical treatment, and that it would be the
better throughout for dispassionate and expert study, the
results of which, though sometimes mistaken, can at least be
honest attempts to reach the truth.

In one department, that of statistics, the methods of mathematics and physics were definitely applied to the problems of
insurance and of sociology. As explained in Chapter VI, these
applications were first made to anthropology by Quetelet in
the years from 1835 onwards. He showed how the numbers of
men possessing a certain quality, such as stature, to a definite
degree are grouped round the mean representing the extent
of the quality in the average man, so that the theory of
probability could be applied. He obtained results similar to
those of games of chance or the distribution of molecular

velocities,[1] and represented them on similar diagrams. The subject of social statistics was carried further in England by William Farr (1807–1883), who, from a post in the Office of the Registrar General, did much to improve medical and insurance statistics, and to put the census returns on a sound basis.

During the later years of the century, evolutionary philosophy modified profoundly men's conceptions of human society. It has, in fact, destroyed for ever the idea of finality, whether in the State as it is or in a future Utopia. Political institutions, no less than living beings, must fit their environment. Both are subject to variation, and, for the social weal, they must develop *pari passu*. Institutions successful with one race may fail lamentably with another. Representative Government on the British model may not be applicable to every nation. The demonstration of innate differences and variations in body and mind destroyed for ever the idea that "all men are born equal".

A similar change passed over economics. The formal political economy of the earlier days of the science sought to establish laws of society, eternal, universal, valid for all times, in all places, and for all peoples. Doubt was thrown on this idea of absolute laws by the historical school, which, in many directions, has shown that every state of society has economic laws of its own, and that their application varies with the ever-varying environment.

The changes in political institutions and in economic conditions are not as slow as those in biology. Still, even in them, it is not possible to take short cuts to the next stage, or indeed to know where the next stage will lead us. Survivals of past times are found side by side with rudimentary forms ready for new growth. As morphology discloses in the animal body vestiges of organs useful in past phases of organic evolution, so the study of social institutions reveals traces of the older stages through which they have passed. From these traces, rightly interpreted, their history and origin may often be inferred. And, from a knowledge of history and origin, light is cast on present meaning and true significance, perhaps even on the probabilities of the future.

If man has been brought into being by the same processes

[1] See pp. 250, 306.

of evolution as the animal races, he must be subject still to the same variation and selection. When Francis Galton, working on this idea about 1869, traced the inheritance of physical and mental qualities in mankind, it followed that selection must continue to operate not only in order to maintain the race in the direction that civilized men have agreed to consider upward, but even in order to prevent its deterioration. Galton gave the name Eugenics to the study of the inborn transmissible qualities of mankind and the application of the knowledge so obtained to the welfare of the human race.

In civilized states it is probable that the most powerful agent in natural selection is disease. Those specially liable to any particular weakness tend to die early and leave no offspring, and in this way the hereditary predisposition to the complaint is bred out of the race. But any change in the environment, as explained in Chapter VI, whether produced by law, social custom or economic pressure, must favour some strains more than others in a mixed race, and thus modify the average biological quality of the population. Galton's work threw a new light on social questions: biological knowledge was shown to be applicable to politics, economics and sociology. But his ideas were too much out of harmony with nineteenth-century equalitarian thought to produce a great effect at once; it was only after the end of the century that they won even partial acceptance.

When we pass to the bearing of Darwin's work on theories of politics, we find that no consensus of opinion was reached. The principle of the survival of the fittest was used to revivify aristocratic ideas by Vacher de Bourget, Ammon and Nietzsche. But, on the other hand, it was urged that evil qualities may have an advantage in present conditions; that a secure aristocratic position removes competition and therefore selection; that "equality of opportunity" is of the essence of Darwinian progress. Moreover, socialists pointed to the societies formed by animals for mutual aid, and drew attention to their great survival value, thus finding in the lives of the bee and the ant arguments for a communistic order of society. But such a society leads to a finality of development, and ends by becoming stationary. The bee world has shown no signs of progress during the two thousand years that it has been under observation. It is rigid, utilitarian, self-sufficing—a model of communal life, when human desire and individual initiative have been bred out of the race. Such divergent results show at least one fact—that the application of the principle of natural selection to sociology is so complex a problem that almost any school of thought can obtain from it valid arguments for their own special tenets.

Science and Sociology

Yet it is a curious psychological fact that, whether in studying family history or in speculating about the origin of humanity, man prefers to fancy that he has fallen from the state of ancestors better than himself rather than to believe that he has risen in the social or racial scale. This faith in the value of heredity, like other such prepossessions, probably has more value than the nineteenth century was willing to believe, and should be treated with respect. Men may therefore be forgiven when they provide themselves, if Nature and the College of Arms have omitted to do so, with noble forbears, in much the same way as primitive races postulate a direct descent from the gods, or, if somewhat more modest, claim only a specific divine act of creation to have been exercised in their favour. Even civilized man, confronted with the choice between the Book of Genesis and the *Origin of Species*, at first loudly proclaimed with Disraeli that he was "on the side of the angels".

Yet the evidence of man's affinity with animals was overwhelming, and soon prevailed within the limited circle where rational discussion was possible. As Copernicus and Galileo deposed the Earth from its position at the centre of the Universe, so Darwin took man from his cold pedestal of isolation as a fallen angel, and forced him to recognize his kith and kin in Saint Francis' little brothers, the birds. As Newton proved that terrestrial dynamics hold sway in the heights of heaven and in the depths of space, so Darwin sought to show that the familiar variation and selection, by which man moulds his flocks and herds, may explain the development of species and the origin of man himself from lower beings. The Darwinian hypothesis of natural selection may be unable to explain the conversion of one species into another in the world of to-day. But the broad concept of evolution has been only confirmed by more recent knowledge. Organic nature, like physical nature, can from this point of view be regarded as a whole—a new and mighty revelation to the human mind.

If the influence of Darwin was great on sociology, he produced an even more profound effect on the theory of religion, and on those doctrines in which, at the time, religion was enshrined by theology. The destruction of the crude dogma of separate specific acts of creation, though it now seems to us but the most superficial of the results, was the most obvious, and over it the clash first came.

During the Middle Ages men had freely speculated from time to time on the natural origin of different forms of life.[1] The emphasis laid by the Protestant Reformers on the verbal inspiration of the Bible led to a more literal interpretation, and by the eighteenth century an acceptance of the details of the story of organic creation, as given in the first chapter of Genesis, became necessary to orthodoxy. In the nineteenth it was apparently believed by almost the whole Christian world. Geological study must have suggested doubts about the chronology of Archbishop Ussher, who put the date of creation in the year 4004 B.C., but even such a well-informed man as Philip Goss seriously contended in 1857 that God had put misleading fossils into the rocks to test the faith of mankind. It may be impossible logically to refute this argument, indeed the world may have been created last week, with fossils, memories and records all complete; nevertheless the hypothesis seems improbable.

The discussion which followed the publication of the *Origin of Species* in 1859 first challenged the popular belief in definite acts of creation for each species. Gradually the cumulative evidence for evolution, and for natural selection as, at all events, one factor in its process, penetrated the educated part of each nation. Again, the principle of natural selection seemed to weaken immeasurably the old "argument from design" of the Christian apologists. Adaptation of means to ends in plants and animals received a naturalistic interpretation, which, if not complete in the deepest recesses of the problem, went far towards a superficial solution. No longer was it thought necessary to invoke an intelligent and beneficent Artificer to explain the details of bodily structure or the protective markings on a butterfly's wing. If there was still need of a Creator, it seemed likely that He had turned

---

[1] *Darwin and Modern Science*, Cambridge, 1909; Rev. P. N. Waggett, *Religious Thought*, p. 487.

away and left the great machine to spin unheeded down the
ringing grooves of change.

But gradually it became clear that the destruction of untenable positions was a real service rendered to an unwilling
theology by the revelation of evolution. Soon leading theologians, and later the more timid clergy, came to realize that
creation must be regarded as a continuous process, that life,
essentially one, was much more wonderful and mysterious than
they had thought. To trace the method by which species, with
their characteristic bodily and mental qualities, developed
from earlier forms did little to explain the essential meaning
and origin of life or the phenomena of consciousness, of will,
of the moral and aesthetic emotions. Still less did it touch
the terrible problem of existence—why anything (or nothing)
is. There was still room—indeed the whole Universe—for a
sense of awe and mystery, still room for reverent enquiry, for
faith in things unseen. Instead of the childish story of the
six days, with their separate acts of creation, the real problem
of Being arose, stupendous, overwhelming.

While Huxley, the Duke of Argyll and the bishops were
exciting themselves and the world about Darwin and the Book
of Genesis, changes much more important and fundamental
than those they were discussing were quietly going on. The
idea that some of the orthodox beliefs and practices of our
own day had developed from more primitive cults of the past
had been suggested by isolated thinkers, among others by
Hume and by Herder. But that idea only became an effective
starting point for the comparative study of religions under
the stimulus of Darwin's work. The more recent results of
this study belong to the twentieth century. But, before the
end of the nineteenth, certain striking facts had emerged.
Dr E. B. Tylor, one of the first anthropologists in this field,
published a book on Primitive Culture in 1871. Darwin wrote:

It is wonderful how you trace animism from the lower races up the
religious belief of the highest races. It will make me for the future look
at religion—a belief in the soul, etc.—from a new point of view.

The study of anthropology was soon advanced by others,
working on similar lines. In J. G. Frazer's *Totemism*, published
in 1887, information on totemism and marriage customs was
collected from widespread sources. Totemism is derived from
animism, and involves an elaborate net of custom, woven

round the idea of the totem, or sacred animal, which is connected in a mystic way with the tribe or the individual that
bears its name. Savage life is dangerous, crises are frequent,
and ill-luck, incalculable and mysterious, is of all things to be
guarded against. Customs grow up which are thought to help
in crises and to prevent ill-luck: woe to him who transgresses
them!

In the first edition of *The Golden Bough*, which appeared in
1890, Frazer took as his text the rites at Nemi, near Aricia in
Italy, where, down to classical times, one priest reigned as
Rex Nemorensis till slain by another. Similar customs among
primitive or savage peoples can be traced back to sympathetic
magic, whereby the drama of the year, with death at harvest
and a joyous resurrection at each new spring, is symbolized
by rites and ceremonies, and, it is thought, the continued
fertility of crops and herds can thus be secured to mankind.
Sympathetic magic, mingled with other factors such as fear
of the dead, leads to ideas of superhuman gods or daemons,
and the nature-rites, including those of initiation and communion, are continued with new meanings.

In some such way as this the anthropologists who first used
the concept of evolution found the mind of the savage to work,
and the framework of primitive religion to be formed. The
bearing of their discoveries on the early history of the religions
of civilized races was obvious, but it took some time to become
widely known. It made less noise than the somewhat superficial controversy about special acts of creation, but, in the
twentieth century, its ultimate effects have been and will be
much greater.

Thus, in several ways, the acceptance of the theory of
evolution on the basis of natural selection first disturbed and
then benefited the theological or dogmatic framework of
religion, which is so often confused with religion itself.
Christian thought, save in obscurantist quarters, accepted
the theory of evolution, and is now slowly coming to accept
in general the modern outlook. Forced to reconsider its
premises, it created a new spirit of reverent enquiry and
freedom of thought. In place of the theory of a rigid and
complete body of doctrine, delivered once for all to the Saints,
a theory constantly liable to dislocation through the shocks
of historical discovery, religious men gained the vision of an

evolution of religious ideas, of continuous revelation marked at certain times by supreme outpourings, but never ceasing to interpret the Will of God to mankind. Moreover, by this modern spirit, they have been driven in the study of religion to give proper weight to that observational method which has proved so necessary in science. This has led to the consideration of the variety of religious experience, and to a recognition of the value of mystical insight as an individualist complement both to ritual as a communal act of worship and to authority as the guardian of tradition.

Evolution and Religion

On the practical side of religion—the side of ethics—evolutionary ideas first brought science into close contact with the problem of the basis of morality. If the moral law has been delivered to mankind once for all amid the thunders of Sinai, there is no more to be said. Man has a perfectly valid reason for his ideals of conduct, and has nothing to do but obey, and, as far as in him lies, to make other people obey also.

But, if we are not sure about Sinai, we are driven to feel for other ground on which to plant our drowning feet. This has been sought in two places. Either, with Kant, we must accept the moral law of our consciences as an innate "categorical imperative", to be accepted as an ultimate, undoubted, though inexplicable fact, or alternatively we must look for some naturalistic explanation.

Bentham, Mill and the utilitarians looked for a naturalistic basis in the securing of "the greatest happiness of the greatest number", and thought that, if man's feeling of unity with his fellow-creatures was taught from infancy as religion is taught, with the whole force of education and practice, there need be no doubt about the force of the sanctions for altruistic conduct. Henry Sidgwick's criticism and reconciliation of the opposing intuitional and utilitarian schools led him to see the moral process as the removal of the centre of interest from the moment and the individual, to the longer life and wider range of social welfare.

But utilitarian ethics only came into touch with fundamentals when they were modified by the evolutionary philosophy. The first systematic attempt so to modify them was made by Herbert Spencer, but the more extreme form of evolutionary ethics appeared in the developments of Darwinism in Germany.

w

Evolution and Religion

The main thesis, of course, is that moral instincts are chance variations preserved and deepened by natural selection. Families and races which possess those instincts gain an advantage in solidarity and co-operation over those that have them not. Thus, by inheritance, moral instincts are developed in mankind.

This is merely explanatory. It shows, on the hypothesis of natural selection, how moral instincts, once in being, grow in power. But the struggle for life takes place between individuals as well as between races, and the contrast between the moral law and the selfishness needed for success in that struggle impressed most writers rather than did the social unity indicated by the deeper analysis. They "saw nature red in tooth and claw", and thought that morality stood little chance. Thus Huxley held that the cosmic and moral orders are in perpetual conflict, that goodness or virtue is opposed to those qualities which lead to success in the struggle for existence.

For some time there was no dispute about the content of ethics. Neither intuitionists nor utilitarians nor evolutionists opposed the traditional or Christian morality; they were only concerned with its fate when the dogmatic religious sanction should be removed. On the practical side of ethics there was complete agreement; on the speculative side controversy and confusion.[1]

But, when metaphysical Germany and logical France fully assimilated the idea of natural selection, the lessons of the struggle for life were pressed to their conclusion. If evolutionary philosophy be accepted without reserve, are not the qualities which favour the survival of the fittest the real moral qualities? Nietzsche in particular taught that Christian morality was a slave morality, useless and outgrown, and that the super-man, to whom the world must look for enlightenment and control, would have freed himself completely from such hampering restrictions. Taken up by politicians and militarists, this teaching did much, in combination with the success of the wars of 1866 and 1870, to form the mentality of the German Empire, and to bring about the cataclysm of 1914. In France the influence was more individual than political; but the "struggle-for-life" became a catchword

[1] A. J. Balfour, in *Mind*, vol. III, 1878, p. 67; T. H. Huxley, in *Nineteenth Century*, vol. I, 1877, p. 539.

among those, to be found in all ages, who wanted a finely sounding excuse for ignoring conventional morality.

Evolution and Religion

It is easy to criticize this particular set of ideas. If brute strength and selfishness are the only qualities of survival value, on the evolutionary hypothesis itself there can be no explanation of the moral feeling or conscience, which certainly exists in most men. On the other hand, to explain the development of the moral sense as an outcome of natural selection between groups does not invalidate it, though it may weaken it to some men by changing its basis from an arbitrary precept of revealed religion to a social instinct of survival value, part of the wonderful whole in which our life is set.

The complete theory of the Ethics of Naturalism has been studied critically in England especially by James Ward and W. R. Sorley.[1] Both writers conclude that the efforts of the supporters of naturalism to derive an ethical doctrine from the basis of evolution alone are fruitless, and that an idealist interpretation of the Universe is as necessary for secure ethics as for rational metaphysics.

The influence of Darwin on metaphysics might well be included in this section on religion, for, on the dogmatic side, religion is a metaphysic. Since, however, questions other than religious ones are involved, it will be better to deal with the whole subject under the next heading of evolution and philosophy.

In attempting to estimate the influence that the establishment of the theory of evolution had on philosophic thought, we must remember the history that has been traced in the foregoing pages.

Evolution and Philosophy

As thought has moved on from age to age, mechanical and spiritual theories of the Universe have alternated with each other in recurring pulsations which hitherto seem to have been necessary for a healthy growth of knowledge. With each great advance in science, with each subjection of a new kingdom to the rule of natural law (as the process comes to be regarded), the human mind, by an inevitable exaggeration of the power of the new method, tends to think that it is on the point of reaching a complete mechanical explanation of the Universe. The Greek atomists made a guess at the structure of matter,

[1] James Ward, *Naturalism and Agnosticism*, 1899; W. R. Sorley, *Ethics of Naturalism*, 1885, 1904.

Evolution and Philosophy

a guess which chances to accord with modern views, though, from the scientific point of view, their evidence for it was most exiguous. Not content with applying their theory to the inorganic world, they framed accounts and explanations of life and its phenomena on the idea of a "fortuitous concourse of atoms", all unconscious of the vast complexity of inorganic nature, and the still vaster world of new phenomena which had to be explored before the problem of life, for which they gave a confident solution, could even be approached. Yet the atomists did good work, and did it under the inspiration of a materialist philosophy. But the insufficiency of their evidence was recognized by Plato and Aristotle, who, also on doubtful ground, framed two varieties of idealism, which, adapted successively by Christian theology, were handed on to the Middle Ages as the characteristic thought of ancient Greece.

When the growth of knowledge began afresh at the period of the Renaissance, the natural oscillations of opinion once more became apparent. The triumph of Copernicus, and the amazing success of Newton in interpreting the phenomena of the heavens, led up to an exaggeration of the power of their methods. Laplace thought that a skilful enough mind would be able to calculate the whole of the past and future history of the Universe from a knowledge of the momentary configuration and velocities of the masses composing it. At each step in advance this over-estimation of the possibilities of mechanism became a marked feature in contemporary thought. As each new piece of knowledge was assimilated, the old problems were seen in their essence to be unaltered; the poet, the seer and the mystic again came into their own, and, in new language, and from a higher vantage ground, proclaimed their eternal message to mankind.

Now, speaking broadly, a manifestation of this recurrent phenomenon of a wave of mechanical philosophy was the first main result of Darwin's success. Quite legitimately and without exaggeration, the establishment of the principle of evolution greatly strengthened the feeling of the intelligibility of nature, and gave new confidence to those who based their theory of life on scientific ground. With the new physiology and psychology it was the complement on the biological side of the contemporary tendencies in physics, tendencies which pointed to a complete account of the inorganic world in terms of eternal, unchanging matter, and a limited and strictly constant amount of energy.

The application to living beings of the principles of the conservation of matter and energy led to the exaggerated belief that all the various activities, physical, biological and psychological, of the existing organism would soon be explained as mere modes of motion of molecules, and manifestations of mechanical or chemical energy. The acceptance of the theory of evolution produced the illusion that an insight into the method by which the result had been obtained had given a complete solution of the problem, and that a knowledge of man's origin and history had laid bare the nature of his inward spirit as well as the structure of the human organism regarded from without. It was in Germany that this development of *Darwinismus* was most prevalent.

It is best seen in Haeckel's *Welträtsel*, The Riddle of the Universe.[1] Not only had Darwin shown that the evolution of the bodies of animals and men could be explained, partly at any rate, by natural selection; he had also given evidence to prove that the instincts of animals, like other vital processes, are subject to development under the influence of selection, and that the mental functions of man are allied to them and subject to similar changes. Haeckel founded on Darwin's work a complete and uncompromising monist philosophy. He asserted the unity of organic and inorganic nature. The chemical properties of carbon are the sole cause of living movement, and the simplest form of living protoplasm must arise from inorganic nitrogenous carbon compounds by a process of spontaneous generation (though unluckily there was no direct evidence in favour of this conclusion). Psychical activity is merely a group of vital phenomena which depend solely on material changes in the protoplasm. Every living cell has psychic properties, and the highest faculties of the human mind, evolved from the simple cell-soul of the unicellular Protozoa, is but the sum total of the psychic functions of the cells of the brain.

This view may be compared and contrasted with that of W. K. Clifford, who agreed with Berkeley that mind is the ultimate reality, but held a form of idealist monism in which

[1] Ernst Haeckel, *Die Welträtsel*, 1899, Eng. trans. London, 1900.

consciousness is supposed to be built up from atoms of "mind-stuff".

Haeckel claimed Darwin's support for his own complete system, and incidentally made plain the history of the immediate influence of Darwin on this type of philosophy.[1]

We are now fairly agreed in a monistic conception of nature, that regards the whole universe, including man, as a wonderful unity, governed by unalterable and eternal laws....I have endeavoured to show that this pure monism is firmly established, and that the admission of the all-powerful rule of the same principle of evolution throughout the universe compels us to formulate a single supreme law, the all-embracing "Law of Substance", or the united laws of the constancy of matter and the conservation of energy. We should never have reached this supreme general conception if Charles Darwin—"a monistic philosopher" in the true sense of the word—had not prepared the way by his theory of descent by natural selection, and crowned the great work of his life by the association of this theory with a naturalistic anthropology.

It is probable that Darwin would not have subscribed to the views of his most prominent German disciple. Indeed, with characteristic modesty, he was very reticent about the philosophic import of his work. The problem of descent is more complicated than it appeared to Darwin's ardent followers. Whether a naturalistic solution of the more difficult problem of man's whole nature will ever be reached, it is impossible to say. But it is quite certain that as yet it has not been attained; nor will it be attained till many more alternations towards and away from mechanical philosophy have passed like waves over the human mind. Indeed, the particular wave induced by the coalescence of the theory of evolution with nineteenth-century physics has already gone. The very principle of evolution itself requires us to look forward to an ever-changing stream of thought, which will develop from age to age, while past experience goes to show that the development will not be steady and continuous, but intermittent and oscillatory.

The later German materialists and mechanists rested their case chiefly on biology. Their dogmas were criticized by the Berlin physiologist Emil du Bois-Reymond and his brother Paul,[2] who pointed out that, even if the problems of life were

[1] E. Haeckel, chapter on "Darwin as Anthropologist", in *Darwin and Modern Science*, Cambridge, 1909, p. 151.
[2] E. du Bois-Reymond, *Ueber die Grenzen des Naturerkennens*, Leipzig, 1876; P. du Bois-Reymond, *Ueber die Grundlagen der Erkenntniss in den exacten Wissenschaften*, Tübingen, 1890.

reduced to those of physics and chemistry, the concepts of matter and force were but abstractions from phenomena, and gave no ultimate explanation. They argued that some problems are beyond human knowledge for ever—*ignorabimus*.

This limitation of the power of human faculty may be compared with Huxley's agnosticism, and Spencer's doctrine of the Unknowable. To fix such limits of knowledge was thought dangerous by Karl Pearson. In *The Grammar of Science*[1] he denied the name of knowledge to any result not reached by scientific methods, but asked with Galileo, "Who is willing to set limits to the human intellect?" While of course admitting much as unknown, he refused to accept a hopeless Unknowable for ever beyond the power of science to investigate.

The principle of natural selection was applied to the theory of knowledge by Herbert Spencer and Karl Pearson. Our fundamental notions may be obtained, or at all events developed, by the process of natural selection and inheritance. Notions and axioms best fitted to symbolize and describe the experience gained through the senses will be established in the course of generations, while others will die out. Thus the fundamental concepts of mathematics may be "innate ideas" in the individual, but the data of experience for the race. This is a fascinating theory, though it is not easy to see how an innate appreciation of the axioms of Euclid or of Riemann can have much "survival value" or much advantage in "sexual selection". Possibly it is held to be linked with other, more attractive, qualities.

In one sense, the acceptance of the theory of natural selection is the completion of the philosophic work begun and mapped out by Francis Bacon, who taught that the method of empirical experiment was the sole road to natural knowledge. Darwin proved, as Democritus and Lucretius had guessed, that Nature herself uses the method of empirical experiment, both in the animal and vegetable worlds. She tries all possible variations, and, out of countless trials, succeeds in a few cases in establishing that new and greater harmony between the being and its environment from which evolution proceeds.

If accepted in its fullest sense, natural selection is the negation of all teleology. There is no end in view: merely a

[1] 1st ed. London, 1892.

constant haphazard change both of individuals and of environment, and sometimes a chance agreement between them,
which, for a brief moment, may give some appearance of
finality.

Herbert Spencer's phrase for natural selection, "the survival
of the fittest", standing alone begs the question. What is the
fittest? The answer is: "The fittest is that which best fits the
existing environment". It may be a higher type than that
which preceded it, or it may be a lower. Evolution by natural
selection may lead to advancement, but it is also possible
that it may lead to degeneration. As Lord Balfour has
pointed out, on the full selectivist philosophy the only proof
of fitness is survival—that which is fit survives, and that
which survives is fit. We may seek to break away from the
circle by declaring that, on the whole, evolution has produced a rise in type, that man is higher than his simian
ancestors. But then we are taking upon ourselves to pronounce authoritatively on what is higher and what is lower,
and the thorough-going selectivist may reply that our judgment
is itself formed by natural selection, and thereby is framed to
appreciate and rate as higher that which, in reality, merely
has survival value—that which, in fact, has permitted us to
exist. From the purely naturalistic standpoint there seems no
escape. We have to accept an absolute judgment by some
other standard of what is high and low, good and evil, if we
seek another outlook.

Indeed it may be pointed out that the order in which we
place creation is largely a matter of race and racial religion.
To the Oriental Buddhist, existence is an evil, consciousness
a greater evil. To him, logically, the highest form of life is
a simple cell of protoplasm in the tranquil depths of the ocean's
bed, and all the evolution of the ages is in truth downward
from that calm ideal, which is itself a fall from the inorganic
matter that probably preceded it.

Darwin himself did not regard natural selection as a complete
explanation of the evolutionary process. It says nothing about
the causes of variations or mutations. They may be due to
chance conjunctions of unit elements in the organism, which
by the laws of probability would give the observed distribution
of individuals round the mean or average; they may be due
to other, more recondite, causes. Natural selection does not

produce variations; it only cuts off those that are useless. It throws no light on the deeper problems of life: why life exists at all, and why it seems to press in wherever it can, up to and beyond the limits of subsistence.

When regarded from the aspect of analytical physiology, with its biophysics and biochemistry, man is by definition a machine, working by physical and chemical principles: old and new vitalism are alike inadmissible. But, regarded as a whole, as in natural history, any organism shows a synthetic unity as its characteristic expression of life, and man, carrying further what is seen in other animals, displays a higher unity in his mind and consciousness—a new aspect of life. The theory of evolution carries this synthetic process a step onward, and discloses an underlying unity in the whole organic creation. Life is one manifestation of the cosmic process. Life from a single cell of protoplasm to that infinitely complex structure, fearfully and wonderfully made, which we call man, is linked in all its parts by evolutionary ties. It forms one problem; a problem not to be investigated completely by the analytic method of science, which deals with it in successive aspects, and, in each, tries to reduce it to its simplest terms; a problem which needs also the synoptic view of philosophy, by which we can "see life steadily and see it whole"; a problem the solution of which, could we reach it, would show us also the solution of subordinate problems, and give us a firm basis for ethics, aesthetics and metaphysics, the inner meaning of the Good, the Beautiful and the True. And one clue to the solution is the theory of evolution elucidated by Darwin's principle of natural selection.

Chapter VIII

RECENT DEVELOPMENT IN BIOLOGY AND ANTHROPOLOGY

The Position in Biology—Mendel and Inheritance—The Statistical Study of Inheritance—Recent Views on Evolution—Heredity and Society—Physiology—Psychology—Is Man a Machine?—Physical Anthropology—Social Anthropology.

The Position in Biology Since the end of the nineteenth century great advances have been made in our knowledge of life and its manifestations, but the chief ideas by which those advances have been guided were formulated before 1901. Twentieth-century mathematics and physics, breaking away from the Newtonian scheme, have marked a veritable revolution in thought, and are now influencing philosophy profoundly. Twentieth-century biology is still following the main lines laid down before the century began.

Towards the end of the nineteenth century, naturalists, accepting Darwin's work as final, had almost given up his characteristic method of experiment on breeding and inheritance. Evolution by natural selection was accepted as an established scientific principle—one might almost say as a scientific creed. It was thought that further information on its details could best be obtained from the study of embryology, a belief founded on the hypothesis of Meckel and Haeckel that the history of the individual is the history of the species.

Of course there were exceptions. De Vries was already experimenting on variation, and in 1890 William Bateson (1861–1926) criticized the logical basis of the evidence for Haeckel's so-called "law", and advocated a return to Darwin's own methods.[1] He was thus led to plan and undertake those experiments on variation and heredity which he afterwards pursued so successfully. Of the difficulties which confronted the then prevalent Darwinian ideas about the origin of species, the two following were the most serious:

The first is the difficulty which turns on the magnitude of the variations by which new forms arise. In all the older work on evolution it is

[1] *William Bateson, Naturalist*, Memoir by Beatrice Bateson, Cambridge, 1928, p. 32.

assumed, if the assumption is not always expressly stated, that the variations by which species are built up are *small*. But, if they are small, how can they be sufficiently useful to their possessors to give those individuals an advantage over their fellows? That is known as the difficulty of *small or initial variations*.

The second difficulty is somewhat similar. Granting that variations occur, and granting too that if they could persist and be perpetuated species might be built up of them, how *can* they be perpetuated? When the varying individuals breed with their non-varying fellows, will not these variations be obliterated? This second difficulty is known as that of the *swamping effect of inter-crossing*.[1]

Bateson went on to point out that every breeder of plants or animals knows that while *small* variations from the normal do occur *large* variations also are common. De Vries and Bateson himself had by 1900 done enough scientific work on the subject to prove that large, discontinuous mutations are by no means rare, and that some of them, at all events, are transmitted in a perfect form to offspring. Thus new varieties, if not new species, may be established readily and quickly. There was no evidence about the *cause* of the variations; their existence had to be taken as a crude fact. But, accepting their existence, their discontinuity seemed to diminish the difficulties of Darwinian evolution. And, in this same year, 1900, new (or rather old and long forgotten) facts came to light.

Simultaneously with the later work of Darwin (1865), a series of researches was being carried on in the cloister of Brünn, which, had they come to his notice, might have modified the history of Darwin's hypothesis. Gregor Johann Mendel, a native of Austrian Silesia, an Augustinian monk, and eventually Abbot or Prälat of the Königskloster, not satisfied that Darwin's view of natural selection was sufficient alone to explain the formation of new species, undertook a series of experiments on the hybridization or cross-breeding of peas. He published his results in the volumes of the local scientific society, where they lay buried for forty years. Their rediscovery in 1900 by de Vries, Correns and Tschermak, and their confirmation and extension by these biologists, as well as by William Bateson and other workers, marks the first step in the recent development of heredity as an exact experimental and industrial science.

[1] W. Bateson, *loc. cit.* p. 162. Quoted from *Journal of the Royal Horticultural Society*, 1900.

The Position in Biology

Mendel and Inheritance

Mendel and Inheritance

The essence of Mendel's discovery consists in the disclosure that in heredity certain characters may be treated as indivisible and apparently unalterable units, thus introducing what may perhaps be termed an atomic or quantum conception into biology. An organism either has or has not one of these units; its presence or absence is a sharply contrasted pair of qualities. Thus the tall and dwarf varieties of the common edible pea, when self-fertilized, each breed true to type. When crossed with each other, all the hybrids are tall, and outwardly resemble the tall parent. Tallness is therefore said to be "dominant" over dwarfness, which is called "recessive". But, when these tall hybrids are allowed to fertilize themselves in the usual way, they are found to be different in genetic properties from the parent whom they resemble outwardly. Instead of breeding true, their offspring differ among themselves; three-quarters of them are tall and one-quarter dwarf. The dwarfs in turn all breed true, but of the talls only one-third breed true and produce tall plants, while the remaining two-thirds repeat in the next generation the phenomena of the first hybrids, and again produce pure dwarfs, pure talls and mixed talls.

These relations can be explained if we suppose that the germ cells of the original plants bear tallness or dwarfness as one pair of contrasted characters. When a tall plant is crossed with a dwarf one, all the hybrids, though externally similar to the dominant, tall parent, have germ cells half of which bear tallness and the other half dwarfness in their potential characters. Each germ cell bears one or other quality but not both. Thus when, by the chance conjunction of a male with a female cell from these hybrids, a new individual is formed, it is an even chance whether, as regards the qualities of tallness and dwarfness, we get two like or two unlike cells to meet; and, if the cells be like, it is again an even chance whether they prove both tall or both dwarf. Hence, in the next generation, we get one-quarter pure talls, one-quarter pure dwarfs, while the remaining half are hybrids, which, since tallness is a dominant, resemble the pure talls. Thus, in outward appearance, three-quarters of the seedlings are tall.

In view of recent tendencies in physics, it is of great interest to note this reduction of biological qualities to atomic units, the occurrence and combinations of which are subject to the

mathematical laws of probability. Neither the motion of a
single atom or electron, nor the occurrence of a Mendelian
unit in an individual organism can be foretold. But we can
calculate the probabilities involved, and, on the average of
large numbers, our predictions will be verified.

Mendel and Inheritance

It will be seen that the methods of inheritance are different
in the cases of dominant and recessive characters. While an
individual can only transmit a dominant character to his
descendants if he himself shows it, in certain conditions a
recessive character may appear without warning in a pedigree.
If two individuals mate who carry the recessive character
concealed in their germ cells, though not outwardly visible in
themselves, it will usually appear in about one-quarter of
their offspring. But, in the majority of cases, the conditions
of inheritance are far more complicated than would appear
from the study of two simply contrasted qualities in the green
pea. For instance, qualities may act as dominants or recessives
according to sex; characters may be linked in pairs, so that
one cannot appear without the other, or again they may be
incompatible and never be present together.

Many Mendelian characters have now been traced in plants
and animals; while, as a practical guide in breeding, the
method has been successfully applied to unite certain desirable
qualities, and to exclude others of a harmful tendency. By
working on these lines, plant breeders and animal breeders
have superseded "rule of thumb" methods by a science. For
instance, Biffen has established new and valuable species of
wheat, in which immunity to rust, high cropping power and
certain baking qualities have been brought together in one
and the same species, as the outcome of a long series of experiments based on the Mendelian laws of inheritance.

When Mendel's work was rediscovered in 1900, investigation
into cell structure had revealed the fact that within each cell
nucleus is a definite number of thread-like bodies which have
been called chromosomes.[1] When two germ cells unite, the
fertilized ovum will therefore contain double the number of
chromosomes, two of each kind, one from each parent cell.
When the ovum divides, every chromosome divides likewise,
the two parts going to the two daughter cells. Thus each new

[1] T. H. Morgan and others, *The Mechanism of Mendelian Heredity*, New
York, 1915, especially chap. I.

cell receives one chromosome from each original chromosome. This occurs with each subsequent division, so that every cell of the plant or animal contains a double set of chromosomes, derived equally from the two parents.

The germ cells also have at first the double set of chromosomes, but, at their last stage of transformation into sperm cells or ova, the chromosomes unite in pairs. There is then a different kind of division: the chromosomes do not split, but the members of each pair separate, and each member goes into one of the daughter cells. Thus each mature germ cell receives one or other member of every pair of chromosomes and the number is halved.

The parallelism between these cell phenomena and the facts of Mendelian inheritance was noticed by several people, but the first to put the relation into the definite form which came to be accepted was Sutton. He pointed out that both chromosomes and hereditary factors undergo segregation, and that in each case different pairs of factors or chromosomes segregate independently of the other pairs.

But, since the number of hereditary factors is large in comparison with the number of pairs of chromosomes, it was to be expected that several factors should be associated with one chromosome, and therefore be linked together. In 1906 Bateson and Punnett discovered this phenomenon of linkage in the sweet pea, certain factors for colour and pollen-shape being always inherited together. The bearing of this discovery on the chromosome theory was pointed out in the same year by Lock.

Since 1910 T. H. Morgan and his colleagues in New York have worked out these relations much more fully in the fruit fly, *Drosophila*, and have found an actual numerical correspondence between the number of groups of hereditary qualities and the number of pairs of chromosomes, each being four. Usually the number is larger; in the garden pea it is seven, in wheat eight, in the mouse twenty, in man probably twenty-four.

Even with twenty pairs of chromosomes, there will be over a million possible kinds of germ cells, and two such sets will give a possible number of combinations which is enormously greater. Thus it is easy to understand why no two individuals in a mixed race are identical.

Simultaneously with this Mendelian work, heredity has also been investigated by the statistical study of large numbers. The application to human variation by Quetelet and Galton of the theory of probability with its statistical law of error has been continued in the twentieth century, especially by Karl Pearson and his colleagues in London.

The normal curve of error, or something like it, is usually obtained from the study of large numbers, but certain dangers in its use were illustrated by the work of de Vries on the evening primrose. Fig. 8 represents the variation in length of the fruits of three varieties, the lengths being plotted horizontally and the number of individuals showing particular lengths vertically. The varieties A and C have a characteristic

14 16 18 20 22 24 26 28 30 32 34 36 38 40

Fig. 8.

mean size of fruit and their curves closely resemble the normal. But B shows signs of subdivision into two separate groups at least. Had the seeds of all three varieties been measured together, the three curves would have coalesced into one, approaching the normal shape. It is often impossible to tell from the data whether the material is of one kind or whether, as in this case, two or more groups are involved.

Johannsen found that, if a single bean seed be made the starting point of a family of self-fertilized descendants, the variations, say in weight of seed, of the individuals in this "pure line" conform accurately to the law of error. But such variations are not inherited; if heavier seeds be picked out and grown, the seeds of their offspring are no heavier than the average.

The Statistical Study of Inheritance

Excluding these pure lines with identical ancestry, an ordinary mixed race shows variations due to mixture of ancestral characters, and these ancestral variations are transmitted. Selecting both parents for some quality, say race-horses for speed, we can establish a strain in which the desired quality reaches a value higher than the average. Galton found that the sons of tall parents were on the average taller than the mean height of the race, though not so tall as their fathers. Pearson and others investigated these phenomena more closely. If the average stature of the men of a race be 5 feet 8 inches, a man of 6 feet will exceed the mean by 4 inches. On the average of large numbers sons of fathers 6 feet tall have a height of about 5 feet 10 inches, so that they exceed the mean by 2 inches, by half as much as their fathers. This result is expressed by saying that the coefficient of correlation is one half, or 0·5. If the sons had been equal in stature to the fathers, the coefficient would have been unity, had the sons' average height reverted to that of the race in general, there would have been no relation and the coefficient zero, and had the sons been shorter than the average of the race the coefficient would have been negative. Other qualities in plants and animals show similar relations, and, for any one quality, the coefficient of correlation between parents and offspring is generally between 0·4 and 0·6. These methods of expressing correlation, here illustrated for heredity, together with other allied mathematical processes, are now used in statistical enquiries of many kinds, not only in science, but in the arts and in sociology. For instance, an investigation of the agricultural value of different varieties of one crop, or of different types of manuring, requires either a large number of parallel strips or else a "chess-board" of trial plots, the statistics of the yields being studied by mathematical analysis.

Much controversy at one time went on between the Mendelians and the Biometricians who used these statistical methods. In any complete study of heredity there seems room for both kinds of enquiry.[1]

Recent Views on Evolution

The theory of evolution, as a general account of the process of life on the Earth, has become more and more firmly established as palaeontological evidence has accumulated. For

---

[1] R. H. Lock, *Recent Progress in the Study of Variation, Heredity and Evolution*, London, 1907.

example, there were no Angiosperms—higher plants with protected seeds—in Carboniferous times: new orders and new
species must therefore have arisen somehow on the Earth.

Some biologists still hold that natural selection acting on
small variations is enough when long continued to explain
evolution. Others think that, in Mendelian mutations, which
may certainly give rise to new varieties, we see species in the
making. But others again, and among them some of the
leaders in modern thought, have become doubtful, even
sceptical. For instance, in 1922 Bateson said:

In dim outline evolution is evident enough. From the facts it is a
conclusion which inevitably follows. But that particular and essential
bit of the theory of evolution which is concerned with the origin and
nature of *species* remains utterly mysterious.[1]

Systematists still recognize distinct species, and neither
Darwinian variation nor Mendelian mutation, as used in
genetic experiments, seems to reach to those fundamental,
underlying differences on which species depend. Perhaps in
earlier ages living organisms were more plastic, and now that
they have become fixed are only susceptible of superficial
changes. There is evidence that occasionally a species may
even now enter upon a phase of mutability; this is believed to
have occurred with the evening primrose studied by de Vries.

The problem of the inheritance of acquired characters, considered in Chapter VI, is still a subject of controversy, the cases
adduced in favour of such inheritance not being universally
accepted as convincing. The segregation of germ-cells from
body-cells found in animals does not occur at such an early
stage in plants, and therefore in them the inheritance of acquired characters should be more likely. Among more recent
evidence we may mention some collected by F. O. Bower,
which seems to show that in ferns long-continued differences in
the environment may produce heritable characters.[2]

Another difficulty has arisen. Variations seem to depend
on elements being lost and not gained. Bateson says:

even in *Drosophila*, where hundreds of genetically distinct factors have
been identified, very few new dominants, that is positive additions, have
been seen, and I am assured that none of them are of a class which could
be expected to be viable under natural conditions.... [But] our doubts
are not as to the reality or truth of evolution, but as to the origin of

[1] William Bateson, *loc. cit.* p. 395.
[2] F. O. Bower, *The Ferns*, Cambridge, 1923–28, vol. III, p. 287.

Recent Views
on Evolution

species, a technical, almost domestic, problem. Any day that mystery may be solved. The discoveries of the last twenty-five years enable us for the first time to discuss these problems intelligently and on a basis of fact. That synthesis will follow on analysis, we do not and cannot doubt.[1]

Meanwhile the palaeontologists, especially in America, have been collecting fossil remains of series of organisms in far greater numbers than ever before, ranging through many geological epochs and demonstrating a continuity of succession through different forms of life, which in some cases seem to suggest evolution along definitely directed lines. The problem is much more complex and difficult than was realized fifty years ago. The broad drift of evolution is clear, but we must wait for more knowledge before attempting a new description of its details.

Heredity and
Society

The application to mankind of our knowledge of heredity and variation has been much extended by Mendelian research. Many deficiencies and diseases, such as colour blindness and the congenital cataract studied by Nettleship, have been shown to follow Mendelian rules in their descent. Only one normal character—the brown coloured pigment in the eye—has been definitely proved by the work of C. C. Hurst to be Mendelian, but there are many indications that other hereditary qualities in man, like those in so many plants and animals, are Mendelian units. Indeed the almost exact equality in the numbers of boys and girls born into the world irresistibly suggests that sex itself is such a unit quality. If all female germ cells carry femaleness and half the male cells carry maleness and half femaleness, the phenomena would be explained.

In plants and animals we know that pairs of unit qualities may be linked together so that one cannot be present without the other, or, on the other hand, may repel each other so that the two cannot coexist. In man experiment is impossible, and observation is restricted to the few generations which are all that can usually be examined. There is little doubt that, were our powers of investigation extended, we should find in mankind too a conglomerate of unit qualities, derived from two parents, and related both to each other and to the chemical natures of the different secretions which the ductless glands pour into the blood-stream. Whether these Mendelian

---

[1] William Bateson, *loc. cit.* pp. 395–398.

qualities make up the essential structure of man, or whether they form but a superficial pattern on a deeper, non-Mendelian substructure, remains a subject for future investigation.

Heredity and Society

In 1909 an attempt was made to adapt Galton's ideas to the knowledge which had accumulated since 1869 when his work was published.[1] The importance which he assigned to heredity had been emphasized by the Mendelian researches of Hurst, Nettleship and others, and by the mathematical work of Karl Pearson and his pupils, who had much extended Galton's biometric methods. The evidence which had become available seemed to justify the conclusion that the mixed populations of modern states must contain intermingled strains of different innate qualities, roughly sorted by natural selection in accordance with the classes to which their owners belong, and therefore bearing some sort of general relation to the work they will probably have to do. Environment, training and education, though undoubtedly they may develop and give opportunity for the display of inborn characters, cannot create them. An able man, still more a genius, is born, not made, and the store of ability in a people is limited by nature.

Survival of the fittest is of no use to the race unless the fittest have a preponderating number of children, and this conclusion suggested an investigation of the average size of the family in different classes of the community. A statistical study of records showed that, from 1831 to 1840, families that had possessed hereditary Peerages for at least two preceding generations had an average of 7·1 births to each fertile marriage, but that, in the decade 1881 to 1890, the number had fallen to 3·13. The laymen of sufficient prominence to find a place in the pages of *Who's Who* had an average of 5·2 children to each fertile couple before 1870 and only 3·08 after that date. In clerical families the corresponding figures were 4·99 and 4·2. Men in the Regular Army, who had attained the rank of Captain at least, gave numbers of 4·98 and 2·07. Thus, while there were differences in detail, the broad result emerged that the landed, professional and upper commercial classes had diminished their output of children to less than one half. An almost equal fall was shown by statistics of Friendly

---

[1] W. C. Dampier Whetham and Catherine D. Whetham, *The Family and the Nation*, London, 1909.

Societies, whose members were drawn from the ranks of the skilled artisans. As it needs an average of about four children to each fertile marriage to maintain a population unaltered, it is clear that even in 1909 the most effective sections of the community were falling in numbers both relatively and absolutely. On the other hand, Roman Catholic families, the miners (for special causes), the unskilled labourers, and (much more alarming) the feeble-minded were maintaining the numbers of their children almost unaltered.

How serious the effects of this discrepancy might become was illustrated by a calculation. If a thrifty strain have three children to each fertile marriage and a death-rate of fifteen per 1000, it appeared that, in 100 years, each original 1000 would be represented by only 687 descendants. On the other hand, 1000 of an unthrifty strain, with a birth-rate of thirty-three and a death-rate of twenty per 1000, would in 100 years have 3600 descendants. If the numbers were equal in 1870 when the differential birth-rate began to be apparent, by 1970 the thrifty strain would be but one in six of the total, and by the year 2070 only one in thirty. It would be lost in the unthrifty stocks of predominant fertility.

During the last twenty years two more hopeful signs have appeared. A Mental Deficiency Act has done something (though not enough) to check the torrent of feeble-minded children, and, as F. A. Woods has proved, both in England and America those members of the upper classes whose public record shows that they render service to the community have more children than do the "idle rich", Woods' average figures being 2·44 and 1·95 living children respectively.[1] This result probably indicates a good effect of the power of voluntarily controlling the birth-rate. Those who wish to evade the trouble, expense and responsibility of several children weed themselves out of the race. In 1909[2] the hope was expressed that it would come to be understood that to produce a larger number of children was a duty for healthy, able and conscientious parents, and it is pleasant to see that hope being fulfilled.

Nevertheless, for the time, the outlook remains disquieting. The intellectual work of the world, on which depends con-

[1] *Journal of Heredity* (American Genetic Association), vol. XIX, Washington, D.C., June 1928.
[2] See *The Family and the Nation*, p. 228.

tinued progress, and indeed the maintenance of the general standard of life, is done by a small fraction of the people, drawn for the most part from the classes who have cut down their output of children, though now not to the lowest level. Scholarships and other means of advancing the able from all classes may supply the deficiency for a time, but the amount of ability in the country is limited, and is proportionately less in the lower ranks of society. If it be steadily picked out and raised from those ranks, it will be partially sterilized as it rises by a decreased birth-rate, and will leave behind it the dead level of an unintelligent proletariat. Gradually the strains of ability will be weeded out of the nation, with ever increasing danger to civilization. On the other hand, if the democratic ideal of equality is enforced, able men will have little opportunity to use their powers for the benefit of the nation. Socialist government, in which the State controls most of the means of production, worked well in the pre-war aristocratic and bureaucratic German Empire, but it would probably break down in a democratic nation. Socialism and democracy, in spite of their association in current political phraseology, are probably in practice incompatible with each other.

The differential birth-rate is not the only selective action going on; we can trace many others. Probably a tendency to disease is still effective in destroying those liable, and thus favouring those stocks which are immune. Legislation, passed with quite other objects in view, often produces selective effects: death-duties are rapidly destroying the old landed families, on which the country has been wont to rely for unpaid work in the counties, and underpaid work in the Church, the Army and the Navy. Dean Inge has shown that recent legislation will tend towards the extinction of the intellectual middle classes. The birth-rate among textile operatives is low owing to the habit of employing women in the textile mills, while that among miners, where paid employment is limited to men, remained high, at all events till the depression of 1925. We must give up the nineteenth-century idea of the nation as a number of individuals of equal potential capacity, only waiting for education and opportunity, and look on it as an interwoven network of strains of innate hereditary qualities, differing profoundly in character and value, and appearing and disappearing chiefly in accordance with natural or artificial selection. Almost any action, social, economic or legislative, favours some of these strains at the expense of others, and alters the average biological character of the nation.

These general ideas were given the weighty support of that eminent naturalist William Bateson in papers published in 1912 and 1919.[1] The old birth-rate combined with the new death-rate would have hardly left standing room on the earth in a few hundred years. Restriction of births is therefore necessary, but it is important to restrict the bad rather than the good strains in a nation. Moreover, competition is not only between individuals but between communities. There are inferior races as there are inferior families. Bateson says:

> Philosophers have declared that men are born equal. The naturalist knows that statement to be untrue. Whether we measure the bodily or the intellectual powers of men, we find that the inequality is extreme. Moreover we know that the progress of civilization has resulted solely from the work of exceptional men. The rest merely copy and labour. By civilization I mean, here as always, not necessarily a social ideal, but progress in man's control over Nature. As between individuals, so between nations, there is similar inequality. When even in Europe we observe that there are teeming populations which have scarcely made any significant contribution to art, learning or science throughout their history, we perfectly appreciate that fact. We know how to deal also with the exceptions which believers in equality may adduce. If I see a red mangold in a field of "Prizewinners", I know that its colour came from a red variety, such as Golden Tankard or Golden Globe, and that the plant is probably only a first cross.

Bateson then gives instances of the rare illustrious men who appear among the inferior races, and shows that, in these cases at all events, one or other of their parents were members of foreign nations. He concludes:

> There are proletariat races as there are proletariat families, and their redemption does not lie in statesmanship. The unequal distribution of illustrious men among the nations is a biological fact. France, Great Britain, Italy, Germany, and some smaller groups, have since the revival of learning contributed many men of the magnitude we have now in mind. Some have excelled more in special arts or sciences, as for instance, in painting, music, literature, astronomy, chemistry and physics, biology or engineering, but in a wide view of these manifold excellences there is no obvious disparity to be noted between those nations.... The inferiority of the proletariat nations becomes still more manifest.

[1] William Bateson, *loc. cit.* p. 359.

The hope for the future lies in the sense of responsibility of the better stocks in the race. If they maintain and increase their output of children, as the work of F. A. Woods indicates they are beginning to do, the nations of the world can reverse the bad selection of the last fifty years, and gradually improve their average of health, beauty and ability. *Heredity and Society*

The most marked feature of twentieth-century physiology is the extension of the application of the methods of physics and chemistry to physiological problems. Indeed, it can almost be said that physiology has been resolved into biophysics and biochemistry. *Physiology*[1]

The physics and chemistry of colloids are of supreme importance in biology, for the protoplasm which forms the contents of living cells consists of colloids, the nucleus being more solid than the remainder. Colloids have also become prominent in agricultural science, for soil, formerly conceived of as hard particles worn down from rocks and mixed with decaying animal and vegetable matter, is now recognized to be a complex structure of organic and inorganic colloids, in which micro-organisms play an essential part. The ground beneath our feet is living not dead; the function of the soil and its multitude of inhabitants is to break up the raw materials it contains, or which it gains from without, and to supply them in forms available as food for the plants that grow upon it.

The distinction between crystalloids and colloids was recognized by Graham in 1850, and it became clear that at all events one cause of the difference in properties was the large size of colloid particles compared with the molecules of crystallizable bodies. The solution of a crystalloid like sugar or common salt is a homogeneous liquid, but the solution of a colloid is a two-phase system, with a definite surface of separation between the phases, and area enough to show the phenomena of surface tension.

Some colloid particles are so large that they are visible in a microscope. The curious and irregular oscillatory motion of such particles was noticed by Robert Brown in 1828, and in 1908 Perrin produced evidence to show that this Brownian movement was due to the bombardment of neighbouring molecules. If this be so, the particles should acquire the same

[1] Sir W. M. Bayliss, *Principles of General Physiology*, 4th ed. London, 1924.

Physiology kinetic energy as the molecules, and, from the distribution and motion of the particles, three separate methods have given a numerical agreement with the consequences of Perrin's hypothesis.

The investigation of the properties of smaller colloid particles was facilitated by the invention of the "ultra-microscope" by Siedentopf and Zsigmondy in 1903. The wavelength of visible light lies between 400 and $700\mu\mu$ (thousandths of a millimetre), and particles smaller than this cannot be seen clearly. But, if a beam of intense light be directed on to them, it will be scattered, and, if an observer looks at the particles through a microscope with its axis at right angles to the beam, they will appear as separate bright discs in Brownian movement, if they are about the size of a wave-length, and will show as a general haze if they are much smaller.

The theory of colloids was considerably advanced by a study of their electrical properties. They move one way or the other in an electric field of force, and this shows that they carry positive or negative electric charges, probably owing to a preferential adsorption of ions. Sir W. B. Hardy found that, when the surrounding liquid was changed slowly, so that from being faintly acid it became faintly alkaline, the charge on certain colloids was reversed. At the "iso-electric" point, where the charge was neutralized, the system became unstable, and the colloid was precipitated from its solution.

Therefore, it appeared, the electric charge on the particles played some important part in their solution. As an example known to all, we may refer to the fact that, when milk turns sour, the casein in it "curdles", that is, coagulates. It was known to Faraday that salts coagulate solutions of colloidal gold, and this phenomenon was investigated by Graham. Schultze noticed in 1882 that the coagulative power depended on the valency of the ions of the salt, and in 1895 Linder and Picton found the average coagulative powers of uni-valent, di-valent and tri-valent ions to be proportional to 1 : 35 : 1023. In 1900 Hardy proved that the active ion was the one of sign opposite to that on the colloid particles. In 1899 the present writer investigated the subject by means of the theory of probability, on the assumption that a minimum number of unit electric charges had to be brought simultaneously into a certain space to neutralize the opposite charges on a number of colloid particles and allow them to coalesce. The electric charge carried by an ion is proportional to its chemical valency; therefore it will need the conjunction of two tri-valent ions, three di-valent ions or six uni-valent ions to give the same charge. Mathematical calculation shows that the coagulative powers should be as $1 : x : x^2$, where x is some unknown number depending on the system. Putting $x = 32$, we get $1 : 32 : 1024$ to compare with the observed values given above. This is only an approximate theory, for it ignores the stabilizing influence of the opposite ion and other disturbing factors. But the method used seems capable of extension to other similar phenomena, indeed to chemical combination itself, while similar considerations of probability are now used in chemical thermodynamics and have become the basis of quantum physics.

The state of aggregation of the colloids in clay controls the physical nature of heavy soils, which only become porous and fertile when the plastic particles are coagulated. Again, since protoplasm is of colloidal structure, the electrical and other properties of colloids are of great interest in biology. For instance, the importance of the valency relation in physiology may be illustrated by one example discovered by Mines in 1912: the heart of the dog-fish is ten thousand times more sensitive to the action of various tri-valent ions than to a di-valent ion such as magnesium. Since coagulation of the colloids would usually kill the tissues which contain them, it is fortunate that they can be protected from the action of electrolytes. Faraday knew that the precipitating effect of "salt" on colloidal gold could be prevented by adding a trace of "jelly". Many such protective colloids which themselves form emulsions have since been investigated by Mines (1912) and other physiologists. The emulsoid seems to form a film over the solid particles of the coagulable colloid or suspensoid, and thus to preserve it from contact with the active ions.

As water is purified by repeated distillation, its electrical conductivity sinks towards a limiting value corresponding to a concentration of hydrogen (H+) and hydroxyl (OH−) ions of about 10^{-7} gram-molecules per litre.[1] If this water be acidified, the hydrogen-ion concentration of course rises, and,

---

[1] For convenience the hydrogen-ion concentration is usually written as P_H and expressed in negative logarithmic terms. Thus, since the hydrogen-ion concentration of pure water is 10^{-7}, its P_H is 7.

Physiology as a measure of the acidity of a medium, this quantity is in constant use, not only in general physical chemistry, but especially in soil-science and in physiology. For example, in physical chemistry the rate of "inversion" of cane sugar—its conversion into dextrose and laevulose—depends on the hydrogen-ion concentration. In agriculture, the acidity of soils is a measure of their need for treatment with lime. In physiology, the maximum range of hydrogen-ion concentration in human blood compatible with life appears to lie between $10^{-7.8}$ and $10^{-7.0}$, and the normal limits are $10^{-7.5}$ and $10^{-7.3}$. The change from the normal reaction to the most acid allowable is only such as occurs when one part of hydrochloric acid is added to 50 million of water.

The animal body contains elaborate mechanisms which preserve the exact adjustments necessary for life. For instance, Haldane and Priestley (1905) showed that the respiratory nervous centres are very sensitive to small increases of carbon dioxide in the blood, so that the action of breathing is hastened and the excess of carbon dioxide removed. Later work proved that the controlling factor is the hydrogen-ion concentration of the blood as affected by the dissolved carbonic acid. There are also direct chemical controls. Various substances present in the blood and tissues, such as bicarbonates, phosphates, amino-acids and proteins, react with acids to give neutral salts. Thus they shield the tissues from the action of acids and preserve approximate neutrality; for this reason they are known as "buffers".

The study of the problems of nutrition was notably advanced during the first quarter of the twentieth century, especially when it was found that a diet amply sufficient to supply all energy requirements might fail to maintain growth. The classical experiments are those of Sir Frederick Gowland Hopkins in 1912. Hopkins showed that young rats, fed on chemically pure food, ceased to grow, but that growth began again when minute quantities of fresh milk were added. Fresh milk therefore contains what Hopkins called "accessory food factors", which are necessary for growth and health. Later work has distinguished several different kinds of these bodies, which are usually known as vitamins. Vitamins A and D are found chiefly in animal fats, such as butter and cod-liver oil,

and in green plants, the distribution of the two being somewhat different. Vitamin A protects generally from infection
and also from a form of eye-disease. It has recently been
distinguished from D, which is necessary for the proper
calcification of bones in the growing animal. A remarkable
result appeared when it was proved that ultra-violet light, if
allowed to act either on the child or on the food it ate, produced the same effect as vitamin D in preventing the disease
of rickets. By extraction from active food-stuffs, the chemical
substance responsible for this effect was isolated in 1927
by several independent workers, and its conversion into the
vitamin under the influence of ultra-violet light is now (1929)
being studied. It is a complex alcohol known as ergosterol,
and it is already being manufactured from yeast and irra-
diated to provide a form of "bottled sunlight". Vitamin B is
found in the outer layers of various grains, in yeast, etc., and
it protects from the disease of the nervous system known as
beri-beri, which occurs in Eastern populations living to a
large extent on polished rice. Vitamin C is present in fresh
green plant tissues, and in certain fruits, especially the lemon,
and is necessary to prevent scurvy. Recent work in America
indicates the existence of a fifth vitamin connected with the
maintenance of fertility, and there is reason to suppose that
others may yet be identified. In all cases a very small quantity
is enough to exert the characteristic effect.

The secretory organs have been proved to possess a far
greater importance in the animal economy than was formerly
realized. Besides those with obvious secretions such as the
salivary glands, there are others which pour their products
into the blood, and thereby supply different parts of the
body with substances necessary for their health and growth.

The mechanism and function of these glands of internal
secretion for long remained mysterious. In 1902 Bayliss and
Starling found that pancreatic secretion, previously thought
to be caused by a nervous reflex, is induced by a chemical
substance formed by the action of acid on the intestine and
carried through the blood to the pancreas. This substance,
which they named secretin, is normally produced in the course
of digestion, when the acid contents of the stomach enter
the intestine and need the action of the pancreatic juice. The

discovery of secretin called attention to other similar internal secretions, each of which is produced in one organ and carried by the blood to others, where its effect is manifested. Hardy suggested for these substances the general name of hormones (ὁρμάω, I rouse to activity), and this word, adopted by Bayliss and Starling, has become current in physiological literature.

Early in 1922 Banting and Best obtained from the pancreas of the sheep an extract which, injected into dogs rendered diabetic by removal of the pancreas, caused a regular reduction of the abnormally high concentration of sugar in the blood, by restoring the power of using the sugar. The extract is a hormone, which has been named insulin. It is now prepared on a large scale, and successfully used in alleviation of human diabetes.

The secretion of the thyroid gland is necessary for both bodily and mental health. If absent in the young, growth slows down, and the variety of idiocy known as cretinism results, while the patient assumes the physical appearance seen in the Mongol races. Deficiency of thyroid occurring in the adult causes the state known as myxoedema. These conditions can be cured by treatment with thyroid extract, as was described in Chapter VI. On the other hand, excess of the hormone causes Graves' disease, exophthalmic goitre. The active principle of the gland, known as thyroxin, was isolated by Kendall in 1919, and its chemical constitution was determined by Harington (1926), who also synthesized it in the laboratory. Thyroxin contains a large amount of iodine, and it has been found that a diet deficient in iodine may produce myxoedema, while the simple administration of salts of iodine may sometimes have the same effect as giving thyroid extract. The need in the animal economy of iodine and other mineral constituents of food has also been demonstrated by experiments on the feeding of cattle and other farm animals.

Some of the effects of the removal of the sexual glands have been known for centuries, but the subject has only been accurately studied in recent years. This work may be said to have begun in 1910 with the experiments of Steinach, who showed that qualities absent from castrated frogs could be developed by the injection of the substance of the testes of other frogs. Later experiments have shown that grafting the glands into mutilated or senile animals results, temporarily at all events, in a return of vigour.

Other examples of the action of internal secretions might be given. The small pituitary gland when over-active produces gigantism and a distortion of the features known as acromegaly, while want of pituitary secretion appears to cause dwarfism. Adrenalin, a hormone found in the suprarenal bodies, is discharged into the blood in conditions, such as fright, anaesthesia, etc., which stimulate certain nerves called the splanchnic nerves. Conversely, injection of adrenalin produces the physical symptoms which accompany emotion or fear. This hormone was isolated and its chemical constitution determined in 1901 by the Japanese Takamine.

One of the most important branches of physiology is the study of the nervous system. In an organism, as in a nation, efficiency and progress depend on common action among the units, and the nerves are the organs of communication between the units, and thus the chief factors in physiological synthesis. In this field, the modern pioneer work has been done by Sir Charles Sherrington in the years from 1906 onwards. Dr Adrian has given me the following paragraphs:

In most complex animals the nerve cells and their delicate protoplasmic extensions form a central mass which communicates with other parts of the body by the peripheral nerve fibres. These are the channels by which messages pass from the sense organs (or receptors) to the central nervous system, and from it to the muscles and glands. The activity of the nerve fibres is accompanied by small changes of electric potential at their surface, and the investigation of these changes (aided in recent years by the introduction of valve amplification) has shown what kind of messages the fibres transmit. Both sensory and motor messages consist of a series of brief "impulses" differing little from one another but spaced close together or far apart according to the intensity of the stimulus. But this tells us little of what goes on in the central nervous system, and the outstanding problem is to discover how the incoming messages are coordinated there and the outgoing built up in such a way that the animal responds as a whole with the appropriate movements.

To solve this completely would mean accounting for the entire behaviour of an animal in physiological terms, but Sherrington has shown that a great deal of the "integrative action" of the nervous system can be made intelligible by the study of the simple reflexes and their interaction. For example, an orderly movement is only possible if the contraction of one group of muscles is accompanied by the relaxation of muscles antagonistic to it, and this is brought about by a dual effect of the incoming message which excites certain nerve cells and depresses or "inhibits" others. Again the time relations of the inhibitory and excitatory states have been shown to account for the smooth precision with which one reflex may succeed another. This work, initiated by Sherring-

Physiology ton, has focussed attention on the reflex as a key to the knowledge of nervous organization and (with Pavlov's work) has been responsible for the mechanistic trend in recent psychological theory.

The highest part of the central nervous system, the brain, is developed in connection with the "distance receptors", as Sherrington calls them, the senses of sight and hearing, which put the animal into touch with distant objects. Mental functions have their seat in a part of the brain called the cerebrum, and especially in its cortex. By stimulation of limited regions of the cortex, localized movements of the limbs, etc. are produced; the effects of electrical stimuli were first investigated by Fritsch and Hitzig in 1870, and the areas of the cortex were mapped out and its reactions studied later, especially by Horsley, Sherrington, Graham Brown and Head.

Another part of the brain, the cerebellum, has been shown to be concerned with balance, posture and movement, and the complicated co-ordinations needed for them. It acts in response to stimuli received from the muscles of the body and from the labyrinth of the ear.

The involuntary nervous system, which controls the unconscious bodily functions, was first investigated thoroughly by Gaskell (1886–1889) and Langley (1891 *et seq.*), who showed that, though it possesses a certain degree of subsidiary independent action, it is essentially an outflow from the cerebro-spinal system and under its general control.

Pavlov (1910) pointed out that it may be unnecessary to introduce psychological ideas, which is usually done as soon as the higher nervous functions are studied. The certain and unconditioned reflexes of the simpler functions pass into more complex reflexes conditioned by other factors, but the method of observing stimulation and resultant action may still be applied. If one phenomenon, which has been associated regularly with food, is accompanied for some time with another, the new phenomenon alone may produce the reflex action proper to food: the dinner-bell may cause one's mouth to water. This method does not touch the problem of the ultimate nature of the intervening consciousness, but it has led to the development of a school of psychology called behaviourism, which, like physiology, ignores consciousness.

Psychology The application of experiment to psychology, initiated by Weber and others in the nineteenth century, enabled later workers to develop a type of psychology which could definitely be classed among the natural sciences.[1] The acuteness of sight, taste, smell and feeling can be measured by mechanical devices. More complex tests of the same kind can estimate memory, attention, association, reasoning and other faculties; while another set of tests deals with fatigue, reaction to stimulus, and co-ordination between hand and eye. As an example we may instance the experiments of Miss Kellor of Chicago on the effects of emotion on respiration, as a result of which she found that negresses are less affected than white women. In all such investigations, psychology is treated by the objective and analytic method of natural science.

While pure physiologists studied the physics and chemistry of muscular contraction, of glandular secretion, of the conduction of nervous impulses and their connection with the central nervous system, those interested in psychology worked at the mental aspect of these same physical manifestations. For instance, the investigations of Sir Henry Head on such affections as aphasia are of far more than merely medical interest. A large number of new psychological facts were obtained by neurologists during the War of 1914–1918 from the study of the mental effects of localized injuries.

The associationist school of Herbart, the Mills and Bain, regarded the Self or Ego not as a pre-existing source of psychological representations, as did the older orthodox view, but as pieced together by the association of discrete ideas. The physiology of the "conditioned reflexes", initiated by Pavlov, carried this line of thought further, and led naturally to the psychology of behaviourism developed by J. B. Watson in 1914 and the following years. The fundamental ideas were outlined in 1894 and 1900 by Lloyd Morgan, a British psychologist who founded the American school of animal psychology.

These investigators broke away from the prevalent interpretation of the actions of animals in terms of supposed consciousness, and set to work to observe their behaviour, and later on that of men, objectively as the facts of physics and chemistry are observed. No one from outside can detect a being's consciousness, sensation, perception or will; they must be ignored in the study of stimulus and response. If his cornea

[1] C. S. Myers and F. C. Bartlett, *Text-Book of Experimental Psychology*, Parts 1 and 2, Cambridge, 1925.

be touched, a man blinks, but the observer knows nothing about the intervening feeling of irritation.

In a new-born babe the number of unlearned responses is small, comprising only such fundamental actions as breathing, crying, etc. Fear is only excited by loud sounds or a sudden failure in support. But the child soon learns also to fear any conditions which accompany these things a few times, whether there is any real connection or not. Thus conditioned reflexes are built up. Once established, they can only be removed by a slow process of "unconditioning", whereby the automatic association is broken.

According to Watson, thought is a secondary product, which is slowly gained through the habit of language, as skill in tennis or golf is acquired by muscular activity. A child talks to himself as a reflex action from external stimuli; mental imagery builds itself round the words, and gradually he finds it better to stop talking aloud. But always a stimulus is supposed to produce rudimentary or suppressed speech. We talk and then we think—if indeed we think at all.

That there is some truth in this theory no one who listens to tea-table chatter or to political debate can deny, and, from the point of view of psychology, there is much to be learned from it. But its philosophic import should not be over-valued. As a man is regarded as a machine by the definitions of mechanics, so to the behaviourist he is merely a nexus of stimuli and responses, because behaviourism, by its own definitions and axioms, is merely the study of the relations between stimuli and responses. In so far as behaviourism is a success, it gives evidence that its assumptions will lead to results in accordance with facts, but, as in other similar cases, the evidence of the ultimate reality of those assumptions, for what it is worth, is metaphysical and not scientific.

Modern psychology is acquiring a practical application in the problems of industry. Industrial operations have to be performed by human beings subject to emotions, prejudices and impulses, and, for the most part, very little swayed by reason or "enlightened self-interest". It is the function of the industrial psychologist to study such factors, as well as simpler ones such as bodily fatigue, and to so adjust manufacturing operations that work shall cause as little weariness and as little repugnance as may be.

Each person has a natural rhythm of his own, and a definite *Psychology* rate of periodic movement in activity; it is necessary to take such individual peculiarities into account if the best results are to be obtained. The manual processes in factories have been studied closely, especially in America, and modifications introduced which have simplified the workman's movements or made them more rhythmical, thus saving him fatigue and increasing his rate of output.

Similarly, educational psychology is learning to make an observational and experimental study of the child's mind. Tests of mental activity and alertness have been devised, and some indications gained as to means of detecting special aptitudes likely to be of use in deciding on the child's future.

Psychology is also becoming increasingly important in medicine. Hitherto attempts to find material changes in the brain to correspond with the changes which take place in the mind have met with little success, and physiological and pathological tests may detect nothing abnormal even in the complete disorganization of the ideas and emotions which occurs in insanity. There is little doubt that physical changes do occur with every change of mood or thought, but, until we know about them, we must describe the mind and its disorders in psychological terms. Modern psycho-pathology covers a much wider field than its name would imply, for the study of the abnormal helps to reveal the normal. Its development is largely due to the widespread interest created by the work of Freud, who introduced the idea of a strict determinism into modern psychology, explaining everything, from our most trivial mistakes to our most cherished beliefs, as due to the operation of powerful instinctive forces, which mature with the body and may be the cause of mental ill-health if their development is checked or distorted.

Another application of psychology, which may or may not give results of scientific value, is the so-called psychical research. Among the phenomena of "spiritualism" are doubtless many due to self-deception and even conscious and deliberate fraud. But, in the view of some competent observers, when deception and fraud are eliminated, there remains an unexplained residue which is worthy of scientific investigation. Special aptitudes, and experience of both hysteria and the art of the conjuror, are needed in those who set out to examine

Psychology these phenomena. Much careful work is described in the publications of the Society for Psychical Research, but no consensus of competent opinion has yet been obtained either in favour of or against a spiritualistic interpretation. Till more knowledge properly attested by critical methods has been accumulated, judgment must be held in suspense.

Is Man a Machine? In the history of biology, vitalism and mechanism have alternated with each other for the last three hundred years. In Descartes' dualism, man's body, in contradistinction to his soul, was held to be purely mechanical, and indeed materialistic. The French Encyclopaedists of the middle and end of the eighteenth century went further, and, basing their philosophy on Newtonian dynamics, held that man, body and soul, was but a machine. This point of view was criticized not only by orthodox theologians, but by other writers more scientifically effective. At the end of the eighteenth century, vitalism was once more in the ascendant, largely owing to the influence of Bichat. Nineteenth-century physiology, with Claude Bernard as its protagonist, together with the theory of evolution by natural selection, led to a reaction in the direction of determinism, specially in the school of German philosophic materialists and also among biologists—Haeckel and others.

The more recent history of the controversy has been summarized by Nordenskiöld[1] and by Joseph Needham.[2] Experimental physiologists and psychologists, working on the implicit assumption that the laws of mechanics, physics and chemistry were applicable to living matter, have continually increased the field within which mechanism seems an adequate explanation of vital phenomena. But some biologists, sensible of the wide areas over which ignorance still reigns, or impressed with the apparent purposefulness of living organisms, have returned to the view that the facts can only be explained by regarding living things as organic wholes.

Among these observers we may specially mention von Uexküll (1922), who held that living organisms were peculiar in that they are units in time as well as in space, J. S. Haldane (1913), who stressed the tendency of animals to maintain constancy amid changes in their external and internal environments, and Driesch, who thought that early embryonic develop-

---

[1] *Loc. cit.* p. 603 et seq.
[2] Joseph Needham, *Man a Machine*, London, 1927.

ment can only be explained by a non-material guiding force. Others, such as J. A. Thomson, E. S. Russell and W. McBride, instanced one or more among the multifarious phenomena of life as impossible of explanation in mechanical terms.

Among the philosophers, E. Rignano has insisted that the essence of living matter is teleological—a purposiveness, a striving for a goal, which controls the growth and functions of the body and of the mind in a way quite beyond the power of the blind forces of mechanics and chemistry.[1] He argues, for instance, that

the living substance...selects from the very complex mixture of chemical substances dissolved in the nutritive liquid exactly those compounds or radicals capable of reconstructing it in the same specificity as before. And as *selection*, this process has a marked purposive aspect.

Now many of the arguments of the neo-vitalists rest on gaps in our present knowledge of biophysics and biochemistry. To rely on such temporary ignorance is dangerous. Some of the arguments have already been refuted by recent research. Others, like Rignano's given above, might have been refuted at the time they were used. It would have been only necessary to point out that besides the compounds "capable of reconstructing it" the living substance is quite ready to absorb toxic bodies which poison it.

Lotze argued that the function of mechanism in the world is absolutely universal and yet quite subordinate. The mechanistic view is the only one which supplies working hypotheses for the experimentalist to use. It is only "a point of view", but within its own limits it is supreme. Physical science regards nature from the aspect of number and measurement, and the mechanistic thread of thought is woven into its essential structure by the mental loom which forms it. The teleological aspect is, and must be, foreign to science, though it may be part of the spiritual aspect of reality, of the meaning of the whole process.

Another answer is given by Lawrence Henderson, who points out that the environment bears as much the mark of teleology as does the organism.[2] Life, at all events as we know it, is only possible because of the exceptional chemical properties of carbon, hydrogen and oxygen, and the physical

[1] E. Rignano, *Man not a Machine*, London, 1926.
[2] *The Fitness of the Environment*. Quoted by Needham, *loc. cit.*

24-2

properties of water. Also it can only appear within the narrow range of conditions found in a world like our own where temperature, moisture and similar circumstances are suitable. Thus organic teleology is merged in universal teleology.

In spite of the great and growing success of biophysicists and biochemists in interpreting the phenomena of life in terms of physical and chemical conceptions, there may be an error in mechanism as a philosophy. From Descartes onwards, mechanists assumed that physical science reveals reality, whereas it is only an abstraction, looking at reality from one point of view. Hence, as a complete representation of reality, mechanism is periodically seen to fail, and naturally leads to vitalism—the idea that a spirit or soul, temporarily or permanently connected with the body, controls or even suspends physical laws to some appointed end.

The error of the vitalists seems to be that they have tried to apply the idea of purpose to the limited scientific problems of physiology, which by their nature can only be attacked by the analytical methods of physical science, whereas purpose, if purpose there be, can only work in the organism as a whole, and perhaps only be revealed by a metaphysical study of reality, to which the whole of existence is relevant.[1]

Yet it must be pointed out that the recent changes in physics, which began in 1925, seemed, by the year 1929, likely to weaken the argument from mechanical determinism itself. Philosophy has been wont to draw its strongest evidence for scientific determinism from physics, where it was thought that there was a closed circuit of mathematical necessity. But as will be explained later, the new wave-mechanics seem to suggest that there is a principle of indeterminacy at the base of the ultimate units or electrons, which makes an exact measure of *both* position and velocity for ever impossible. If this surprising development be confirmed, the strongest scientific argument for philosophic determinism will break down. But it is too soon to dogmatize.

As the continued study of fossil records strengthened our confidence in the accuracy of the broad theory of the evolution of plants and animals, so the palaeontological discoveries made in the early years of the twentieth century confirmed the truth of the general conclusions of Lyell, Darwin and

[1] J. S. Haldane, *The Sciences and Philosophy*, London, 1929.

Huxley about man's place in nature. Moreover, much new evidence came to light about the origin of the anthropoid apes and of the different varieties of man himself. It was gradually recognized that apes and men were probably differentiated from each other as early as the middle of Miocene times, while physiological evidence of their present close connection was given by new information about the similarity of their blood.

In 1901 C. W. Andrews discovered in the Egyptian Fayum fossils probably representing ancestors of existing mammals, and his prediction that early forms of anthropoid apes would also be found there was verified by Schlosser in 1911. In the foothills of the Himalayas, Pilgrim found fossil apes with peculiarities of structure which suggested that they were the ancestors of the *hominidae*. In 1912 Dawson and Woodward discovered at Piltdown in Sussex man-like remains embedded in early Pleistocene deposits and associated with crude flint implements.

Knowledge of Neanderthal man, whose bones were first discovered in the valley of that name in 1856, has been increased by the finding of similar remains in other places. They suggest a being with a large flattened head, prominent eyebrow ridges, a coarse face, and a brain which, though large, was deficient in the frontal region. Neanderthal man represented a species preceding and more brutal than that called *homo sapiens*, which includes all present races.

The Neanderthal men were followed in Europe by the tall, long-skulled Cro-Magnon race, a true variety of *homo sapiens*. The flint implements of these people are of much better type, and their paintings on the walls of caves show considerable artistic power. Other races, contemporary or succeeding, can be distinguished, and have been given names—Solutrian, Magdalenian, and so on. Then came the Neolithic peoples, who, in their wanderings, brought to Western Europe the great world-civilization of Egypt and Mesopotamia.

At the beginning of the twentieth century it was generally believed in England and France that civilizations resembling each other could arise quite independently among different races in separate parts of the world, and this belief produced a curious blindness to illuminating points of similarity. On the other hand, an important German school initiated by Ratzel (1886), and supported later by the work of Schmidt

Physical Anthropology (1910) and Graebner (1911), traced the origin of similar artistic cultures to the intermingling of peoples. This point of view was reached independently by W. H. R. Rivers, in his classical study of relationships, social organization and language in the islands of the Pacific. Rivers, whose early death was a serious loss to anthropology, called attention in 1911[1] to the German work, and since then this theory has been adopted by observers of other arts, particularly by Elliott Smith in his study of embalming. Indeed, the widespread custom of erecting monoliths and other stone structures, orientated in relation to the Sun or stars, and rude copies of Egyptian models, is alone almost enough to show a common origin, not of race, but of civilization.

Social Anthropology If physical anthropology in the twentieth century has followed in the main the lines laid down by Darwin and Huxley, social anthropology has struck out new roads. This is due, firstly, to a more intimate knowledge of the psychology of primitive peoples obtained by men like Rivers from long sojourn among them; secondly, to the study of Greek religion made by such authors as Jane Harrison and F. M. Cornford; and, thirdly, to the exhaustive collection of worldwide data made by J. G. Frazer. Rivers' work was important, not only for the facts of primitive life which he collected, but also for a revolution in method introduced by him. He found that the general terms in which older enquirers put their questions were quite unintelligible to a primitive mind. It is useless to ask, let us say, whether or why a man may marry his deceased wife's sister. One must first ask: "Can you marry that woman?" and then: "What relation are you to her and she to you?"; general rules must be slowly put together from single examples. From his researches in Oceania, Rivers concluded that a vague sense of awe and mystery, generally called *mana*, is probably a more primitive source of magic and religion than the animism described by Tylor.

The prolonged study of primitive forms of religion, still or lately extant in savage lands, has led to a complete change of outlook.[2] The old view, both among believers and sceptics, was that religion was a body of doctrine, theology if the

[1] *Presidential Address, Section H, British Association*, 1911.
[2] For example, see "Darwin and Modern Science," Cambridge, 1909, *The Study of Religions*, by Jane Ellen Harrison, p. 494.

religion is our own, or mythology if it is that of other people. *Social*
Ritual, when considered at all, was thought to be merely a *Anthropology*
form in which beliefs, already defined and fixed, were publicly
expressed, while, for the most part, that "inward spiritual
grace" which, from one point of view, constitutes the essence
of religion, was ignored or confused with doctrine. Further,
the dogmas of the faith formed a complete and unalterable
body of doctrine revealed once for all to mankind, and safe-
guarded by an infallible Book or an infallible Church. Man's
only duty was to accept its creeds and obey its precepts.

Miss Harrison says:[1]

Religion always contains two factors. First a theoretical factor, what
a man thinks about the unseen—his theology, or, if we prefer so to call
it, his mythology. Second, what he does in relation to the unseen—his
ritual. These factors rarely if ever occur in complete separation; they are
blended in very varying proportions. Religion we have seen was in the
last century regarded mainly in its theoretical aspect as a doctrine.
Greek religion for example meant to most educated persons Greek
mythology. Yet even a cursory examination shows that neither Greek
nor Roman had any creed or dogma, any hard and fast formulation of
belief. In the Greek Mysteries[2] only we find what we should call a
Confiteor; and this is not a confession of faith, but an avowal of rites
performed. When the religion of primitive peoples came to be examined,
it was speedily seen that, though vague beliefs necessarily abound,
definite creeds are practically non-existent. Ritual is dominant and
imperative.

This predominance and priority of ritual over definite creed was
first forced upon our notice by the study of savages, but it promptly
and happily joined hands with modern psychology. Popular belief says,
I think, therefore I act; modern scientific psychology says, I act (or
rather, react to outside stimulus) and so I come to think. Thus there is
set going a recurrent series: act and thought become in their turn stimuli
to fresh acts and thoughts.

The real "heathen in his blindness" does not "bow down
to wood and stone". He is busy practising magic. He does
not ask a god to send sun or rain: he dances a sun-dance, or
croaks like a frog to bring the rain he has learnt to associate
with that noise. In many totemistic beliefs he is closely
related to some animal, which becomes endowed with sanctity.
Sometimes the animal becomes *taboo* and may not be touched;
sometimes by eating its flesh the savage acquires its courage

[1] "Darwin and Modern Science," *loc. cit.* p. 498.
[2] For details see J. E. Harrison, *Prolegomena to the Study of Greek Religions*,
Cambridge, 1903, p. 155.

or its strength. Rhythmic dancing, with or without the help of alcohol, leads to ecstacy, which seems to give freedom to the will, and a sense of power transcending ordinary limits. The savage does not pray, he wills.

The relations of magic to religion and to science are still subjects of controversy. Magic attempts to compel outward things to obey man's will. Religion in primitive form tries to influence outward things by the help of God or gods. Science, with clearer insight than is possessed by magic, humbly studies nature's laws, and by obeying them gains that control of nature which magic falsely imagines itself to have acquired. Whatever be the exact relation between the three, magic seems to be the primitive matrix out of which both religion and science emerged.

Having thus, in his desire to work his will, developed a ritual, the savage uses it, in conjunction with his primitive ideas, to frame a mythology. He has not our distinction of subjective and objective: everything he experiences—sensation, thought, dream, or even a memory—is real and objective, though it may have different degrees of reality.

Herbert Spencer argued that when a savage dreamed a dream of his dead father he sought to account for it, and so invented a spirit-world. But primitive man has not Spencer's sophisticated rationality. The dream is real to him; not so real, perhaps, as his mother who is still alive, but yet real. He does *not* seek to account for it, he accepts it as true, and his father as in some sense still living. He feels a life-power within himself: he cannot touch it, but it is real, and his father who is dead must have had it too. When his father died it ceased to inhabit his body, but it comes back in dreams: it is a breath, an image, a shade, a ghost. It is a mixture of life-essence and separable phantom.[1]

Tylor[2] has shown how the efforts of a savage to classify common objects, and thus to arrive at the idea of a class, lead to the belief that a species is a family of beings, with a tribal god to protect them and a name which, in some mystic way, contains their common essence. Number, too, to the savage is part of the super-sensuous world, and essentially mysterious

---

[1] Körperseele or Psyche, see Wundt, *Völkerpsychologie*, Leipzig, 1900, vol. II, p. 1; Jane Harrison, *loc. cit.* p. 501.

[2] *Primitive Culture*, London, 1903, vol. II, 4th ed. p. 245.

and religious. "We can touch and see seven apples, but seven itself, that wonderful thing that shifts from object to object, giving it its sevenness...is a fit denison of the upper world."

With this confused, super-sensuous region of dream and phantom, of name, image and number, is mingled the mystical experience of ritual, magic and rhythmic dance. The elements act and react, and out of the mixture of feeling and action the savage perhaps develops some idea of a god.

The most striking collection of data in social anthropology is to be found in J. G. Frazer's great book, *The Golden Bough*. The first edition of two volumes published in 1890 was followed by a second edition in 1900, and eventually the two volumes have been expanded into twelve. In this monumental work Frazer describes primitive custom, ritual and belief, with examples culled from archaeological inscriptions, ancient and mediaeval historians, modern travellers, missionaries, ethnologists and anthropologists—sources of varying value. Whereas some authorities hold that magic is the common origin of religion and science, Frazer believes that they come in sequence. When the direct control over nature sought by magic is found to fail, man turns to gods to give it to him, trying to influence them by worship and prayer; when these too prove vain, and man begins to recognize a uniformity in nature, he comes to the threshold of science.

To a primitive mind, our sharp distinction between the natural and the supernatural is unknown. The control over his thoughts, which man feels himself to possess, is extended by the savage till he thinks he can control things also. The shadowy beings which appear in his dreams of his dead parents rise into shadowy gods, who must be able to control things too, perhaps even more effectively than he can. In the excitement of wine or the dance he feels his powers expand; his soul has become inspired by these gods. Other men may be more inspired; his kings and priests themselves become gods. Sympathetic magic, which attempts to produce natural phenomena by imitating them or their effects, leads on to the many symbolic rituals of primitive religion. Most widespread of all is the drama of the year: seed-time, growth, destruction at harvest and resurrection of life in the spring, are symbolized in countless forms through many ages and in many lands. Man first performed ceremonies and cast spells to make the

Social Anthropology

rain to fall, the sun to shine, and plants and animals to multiply. Then he saw that some deeper, more mysterious cause must be at work, and imagined that growth and decay must be effects of the waxing and waning strength of divine beings.

Such gods and their rites were specially celebrated in the lands which border the Eastern Mediterranean, under such names as Osiris, Tammuz, Adonis and Attis. Tammuz of the Babylonians and Syrians became the Adonis of the Greeks. Tammuz appears as the spouse of Ishtar, the great mother goddess of fertility, and Adonis is the lover of Astarte or Aphrodite. Their union is necessary for the fertility of the Earth, and is celebrated by rites and mysteries in their temples. Similarly, Attis was the son of Cybele, the Great Mother, Mother of the Gods, who had her chief home in Phrygia, and was brought to Rome in 204 B.C.

With varieties in detail, the ceremonies of these cults bore a general resemblance to each other. Every year the death of the god, perhaps symbolized by the slaying of a human or animal victim, was mourned, and his resurrection acclaimed, sometimes on the following day, sometimes at a different season of the year. In some cults, the birth of the new year, of the Sun, or of a virgin-born god representing the Sun, was celebrated at the winter solstice.

More complex are the stories of the Egyptian Isis and Osiris as told by Plutarch and Herodotus, though the underlying ideas and symbolism seem to have been much the same. In Hellenistic times the chief Egyptian deities were Isis, Anubis, the god who conducted souls to the realm of immortal life, and Serapis, who was "deliberately created by Ptolemy I... the only god ever successfully made by a modern man". Serapis was Osiris combined with Greek elements meant to unite Greeks and Egyptians in a common worship. The Egyptians would have none of him; but he became the Greek god of Alexandria, he and his consort Isis being represented on earth by the royal Ptolemaic pair.[1]

Again, the mystery religion of Mithras, an old Persian deity, bore strong resemblances to that of Cybele on the one hand and to Christianity on the other, a similarity which the early Christian Fathers could only regard as a wile of the devil. The Mithraic religion was a formidable rival to Christianity,

---

[1] W. W. Tarn, *Hellenistic Civilization*, London, 1927, p. 294.

combining as it did a solemn ritual with aspirations after moral purity and a hope of immortality. Indeed, the issue of the conflict between the two faiths for the conquest of the Roman world seems to have hung for a time in the balance.

Other mystery religions, resembling that of Mithras, helped it to fill the place left by the decay of belief in classical mythology, a decay which marked the centuries just before and after the birth of Christ. These religions all sought mystic union with the divine through rites of initiation and communion, clearly derived from those of more primitive cults. After a full discussion of innumerable instances of ceremonies of communion, and their connection with totemism and nature-rites among primitive peoples in many lands, Sir James Frazer writes:

> It is now easy to understand why a savage should desire to partake of the flesh of an animal or man whom he regards as divine. By eating the body of the god he shares in the god's attributes and powers. And when the god is a corn-god, the corn is his proper body; when he is a wine-god, the juice of the grape is his blood; and so, by eating the bread and drinking the wine, the worshipper partakes of the real body and blood of his god. Thus the drinking of wine in the rites of a vine-god like Dionysos is not an act of revelry, it is a solemn sacrament.[1]

Though beliefs change, the ancient ritual persists, and is sublimated in the sacraments of higher religions. Then comes the critical mind, either of a Roman philosopher or of a Protestant Reformer. Cicero says:

> When we call corn Ceres and wine Bacchus, we use a common figure of speech, but do we imagine that anyone is so foolish as to believe the thing he feeds upon is a god?

The mistake of the critical mind is in thinking it possible that man's ritual and beliefs should depend on reason alone, when his instincts are the inheritance of a million years of animistic ancestors. In its practice, the Roman Church has never made this mistake, though in theory it has based its philosophy, both in the late Middle Ages and in the nineteenth century, on the rationalism of Saint Thomas Aquinas.

Besides the formal religions and philosophies of the first Christian century, there was a deep and pervading undercurrent of these more primitive heathen rituals and beliefs

---

[1] *The Golden Bough*, 3rd ed. Part v; *Spirits of the Corn and Wild*, vol. ii, p. 167 ff. For a short account of the subject see "Primitive Sacramentalism", by H. J. D. Astley, *Modern Churchman*, vol. xvi, 1926, p. 294.

mingled with the sacrificial ideas which are found both in
these beliefs and in some of the Hebrew rites set forth in the
Old Testament. In trying to understand the mental atmosphere of the time which saw the early development of
Christianity, we must not ignore this under-current of primitive
and Eastern ideas.

Frazer's opinion of the Oriental elements with which Christianity became entangled is shown by what follows:[1]

> The ecstatic frenzies, which were mistaken for divine inspiration, the
> mangling of the body, the theory of a new birth and the remission of sins
> through the shedding of blood, have all their origin in savagery, and
> they naturally appealed to peoples in whom the savage instincts were
> still strong.... The religion of the Great Mother, with its curious blending
> of crude savagery with spiritual aspirations, was only one of a multitude
> of similar Oriental faiths which in the later days of paganism spread
> over the Roman Empire, and by saturating the European peoples with
> alien ideals of life gradually undermined the whole fabric of ancient
> civilization. Greek and Roman society was built on the conception of
> the subordination of the individual to the community, of the citizen to
> the state; it set the safety of the commonwealth as the supreme aim of
> conduct, above the safety of the individual whether in this world or in
> a world to come.... All this was changed by the spread of Oriental
> religions which inculcated the communion of the soul with God and its
> eternal salvation as the only objects worth living for, objects in com-
> parison with which the prosperity and even the existence of the state
> sank into insignificance.... This obsession lasted for a thousand years.
> The revival of Roman law, of the Aristotelian philosophy, of ancient art
> and literature at the close of the Middle Ages, marked the return of
> Europe to native ideals of life and conduct, to saner, manlier views of
> the world. The long halt in the march of civilization was over. The tide
> of Oriental invasion had turned at last.

Those who take a different view may reasonably point out
that this passage begs the question at issue. If the underlying
assumption of the mystic happens to be true, the communion
of human souls with God *is* more important than states or
nationalities. But, whatever may be each man's choice between
these opposite ideals of life, the opinion of one who, like
Frazer, has done so much to advance this branch of knowledge,
must needs command attention and respect.

The deeper and more important question of the bearing of
modern historical and anthropological research on the problem
of the origin and meaning of Christianity itself still remains a
matter of discussion, in which inherited and acquired pre-

---

[1] *Loc. cit.* pp. 356 *et seq.*

conceptions, one way or the other, very often condition the action of reason. It is clear that many of the doctrines of traditional Christianity can be paralleled closely by similar beliefs in the religions that preceded and accompanied its rise, and that many Christian rites are the equivalents of corresponding heathen mysteries. Some hold that such similarities indicate that Christianity is to be classed with the mystery religions of the first century. Others point out that the consequences of recent anthropology may be exaggerated. New light has certainly been thrown on the connection of the mystery religions with earlier and more primitive cults, but the existence and nature of the mystery religions themselves have always been familiar to historians and theologians. Similarity in form does not necessarily connote identity in origin and meaning.

Whether we take an orthodox or an unorthodox view of Christianity, we must admit that modern anthropology has helped us better to understand the connections between psychology and fundamental religion—the direct consciousness of unseen divine power—on the one hand, and between primitive beliefs and more developed forms of theology on the other.

Social Anthropology

Chapter IX

THE NEW ERA IN PHYSICS

The New Physics—Cathode Rays and Electrons—Positive or
Atomic Rays—Radio-Activity—X-Rays and Atomic Numbers
—Table of Elements—The Quantum Theory—The Structure of
the Atom—Bohr's Theory—Quantum Mechanics—Relativity
—Relativity and Gravitation—Astro-Physics: The Stellar Universe—The Nature of Stars—Stellar Evolution—Relativity and
the Universe.

The New
Physics[1]
PHYSICAL science continued to follow the course of development traced in Chapter VI until the last decade of the nineteenth century. It seemed as though the main framework
had been put together once for all, and that little remained to
be done but to measure physical constants to the increased
accuracy represented by another decimal place, and to carry
farther those investigations which had seemed at intervals
to be on the point of solving the problem of the structure of
matter in terms of the luminiferous aether.

The new physics may be said to have begun in 1895 with
the discovery of X-rays by Professor Wilhelm Konrad Röntgen
of Munich (1845–1923). Before that date many experiments
had been made on electric discharge through gases, especially
by Faraday, Hittorf, Geissler, Goldstein, Crookes, and later
by J. J. Thomson, now Sir Joseph Thomson, Master of Trinity
College, Cambridge. But these experiments seemed of importance only to those with exceptional insight, and it was
Röntgen's work which first focussed on them the chief attention of physicists.

Great discoveries are made accidentally less often than
the populace likes to think. Nevertheless it was an accident,
bound indeed sometime to occur, yet none the less an accident,
that put Röntgen on the track of X-rays. Photographic plates,
though protected from light, were found to become fogged and
spoilt when kept in the neighbourhood of highly exhausted
glass tubes or bulbs through which electric discharges were
passing. It appeared that rays of some kind which could

---

[1] For a general account, the successive editions (1904–1924) of the author's
book *The Recent Development of Physical Science* may be consulted.

penetrate the coverings of the plates were emitted by the discharge tubes.

Röntgen found that a screen covered with a phosphorescent substance, such as potassium-platino-cyanide, became luminous near such a tube, and that a thick slab of metal cast a heavy shadow when interposed between the tube and the phosphorescent screen, while light substances such as thin aluminium or wood, though opaque to light, with these new rays cast shadows hardly visible. The absorption of the rays seemed roughly proportional to the thickness and density of the absorbent, and the rays became more penetrating the higher the exhaustion of the gas in the vacuum tube. Rays of an appropriate "hardness" were found to throw a shadow of the bones within the living flesh on a phosphorescent or photographic plate, and, when the right technique had been elaborated, this fact proved invaluable in surgery.

From the point of view of pure science, a discovery of more importance was made by J. J. Thomson and others as soon as the existence of X-rays was announced.[1] When the rays pass through a gas, they make it a conductor of electricity. In this field of investigation the ionic theory of liquid electrolytes, founded by Faraday and developed chiefly by Kohlrausch, Van't Hoff and Arrhenius,[2] had already suggested a similar mechanism for conduction in gases, and a corresponding theory of gaseous ions now proved even more successful.

When X-rays were passed through a gas and then cut off, the conductivity of the gas was found to persist for a time but gradually to die away. Thomson and Rutherford also discovered that when a gas, made conducting by X-rays, was passed through glass-wool, or between two oppositely electrified plates, the conductivity disappeared, indicating that it was due to charged particles which were discharged by contact with the glass-wool or one of the electrified plates. Rutherford found that, in a conducting gas, the current was first proportional to the applied electromotive force, but, as that force was raised, the current increased more slowly, and finally reached a maximum or saturation value. From such experiments it became clear that, while ions were part of the ordinary

[1] Camb. Phil. Soc. See *University Reporter*, February 4th, 1896.
[2] See chap. v, pp. 266–268.

and permanent constitution of a liquid electrolyte, they are
only formed in gases when X-rays or other ionizing agencies
are acting. Left to themselves, the ions gradually re-combine
and disappear. The large surface of glass-wool absorbs the
ions, or helps them to re-combine, and, when subject to a
high electromotive force, the ions are swept away to the
electrodes as fast as they are formed, and accordingly no
further increase in electromotive force can increase the
current.

Röntgen's discovery led also to another field of research—
that of radio-activity. X-rays produce marked effects on
phosphorescent substances, and it was natural to enquire if
these or any other natural bodies produce X-rays in turn. In
this search, the first success fell to Henri Becquerel, who, in
February 1896, found that the double sulphate of potassium
and uranium, and later that uranium itself and all its compounds, emit rays which affect a photographic plate through
black paper and other substances opaque to light.

The next year, 1897, was marked by the great discovery
of ultra-atomic corpuscles, particles far lighter than the
atoms of any chemical element. The new era in physics had
begun.

As a glass tube with platinum electrodes is gradually
evacuated with an air-pump, an electric discharge through it
undergoes many changes in character, and finally produces
phosphorescent effects on the glass walls of the tube or on other
solid bodies within it, which then become the source of X-rays.
In 1869, Hittorf showed that obstacles, placed between the
negative electrode or cathode and the glass, throw a shadow
thereon. Goldstein, who confirmed this result in 1876, and
introduced the name *Kathodenstrahlen*, or cathode rays, regarded them as aethereal waves of the same nature as light.
On the other hand Varley and Crookes gave evidence, such
as the deflection of the rays in a magnetic field, to show that
they were electrified particles shot out from the cathode
and producing phosphorescence by bombardment. In 1890
Schuster measured the ratio of the charge to the mass of these
hypothetical particles by observing the deflection in a magnetic
field, and estimated the ratio to be about 500 times the value

---

[1] J. J. Thomson, *Conduction of Electricity through Gases*, Cambridge, 1903
and 1906. J. S. E. Townsend, *Electricity in Gases*, Oxford, 1915.

for the hydrogen ion in liquids.[1] Assuming that the particles were of atomic dimensions, he inferred that the charge on gaseous ions was much greater than that on liquid ions. Hertz, in 1892, found that cathode rays would penetrate thin gold leaf or aluminium, which seemed difficult to reconcile with the idea that the particles were streams of ordinary atoms or molecules. In 1895 Perrin showed that they gave a negative electric charge to an insulated conductor when deflected on to it. The problem of their nature was eventually solved during the year 1897, when the velocity and the ratio of the charge e to the mass m of the particles were determined satisfactorily by several physicists.[2] In January Wiechert published work which showed that the velocity of some of the rays was about one-tenth that of light, and that e/m was 2000 to 4000 times as great as the value for the hydrogen atom in liquid electrolytes. He measured the velocity in terms of the time of oscillation of a condenser, and then e/m by the magnetic deflection. In July there appeared an account of experiments by Kaufmann, in which the energy of the particles was deduced from the potential difference between the electrodes, and again the magnetic deflection observed. Finally, in October, J. J. Thomson found that in high vacua the cathode rays could be deflected by an electric field as well as by a magnetic field, and measured both these deflections.[3]

Fig. 9 shows the apparatus used by Thomson in the last named historic experiments. A highly exhausted glass tube contained metallic electrodes—a cathode C and an anode A pierced by a slit. Some of the cathode rays from C traversed the slit, and were still further cut down by a second slit in B. The narrow pencil of rays thus obtained fell on a fluorescent screen or a photographic plate at the other end of the tube, passing

Cathode Rays and Electrons

---

[1] A moving electrified particle is equivalent to a current, and will consequently be deflected by a magnet (see p. 237). If a magnetic field of intensity H be applied, the mechanical force on the particle is Hev. The force acts at right angles to the magnetic field and in the direction of motion of the particle at each instant. This is what is wanted to produce circular motion (see p. 167), the force Hev representing the centripetal force mv^2/r. Thus $r = mv/eH$. In the experiment, only a small segment of a circle is described, and the deflection from a straight path will be $S_m = l^2/2r = l^2He/2vm$.

[2] For the detailed history of these epoch-making researches, see Townsend, *loc. cit.* pp. 453 *et seq.*

[3] *Phil. Mag.* vol. XLIV, 1897, p. 293.

between two insulated plates D and E on the way. These plates could be connected with the opposite poles of a high tension electric battery, and an electric field was thus set up between them. The whole apparatus was fixed between the poles of a powerful electro-magnet, so that a magnetic field also could be applied to the rays.

On the assumption that the rays consist of flights of negatively electrified particles, a simple calculation shows that the electric deflections like the magnetic depend on v, the velocity of the particles in the rays, and on e/m, the ratio of their electric charge to their mass.[1] Hence two measurements —those of the electric and magnetic deflections—give values for both v and e/m.

Thomson found that, while the velocity of the particles varied about a value of one-tenth the speed of light, the

Fig. 9.

quantity e/m was the same whatever was the pressure, or the nature of the gas or of the electrode. In liquid electrolytes,[2] e/m is greatest for the hydrogen ion, for which its value is about 10,000 or 10^4. In gases Thomson found $e/m = 7 \cdot 7 \times 10^6$, that is 770 times as great as e/m for the liquid hydrogen ion, while, in December 1897, Kaufmann gave the much more accurate value of $1 \cdot 77 \times 10^7$. These results might mean that, in cathode ray particles in gases, either the charge was much greater than in the hydrogen atom as Schuster held, or the mass was much less. Thomson provisionally took the view that the particles were smaller than atoms. He gave them the Newtonian name of corpuscles, and suggested that they were

---

[1] If a uniform electric field of intensity f acts at right angles to the direction of motion of a particle of mass m and charge e, the acceleration a is fe/m and the displacement in the direction of the electric force is $S_e = \frac{1}{2}at^2 = \frac{1}{2}\dfrac{fe}{m}t^2$. During the time t, the particle traverses with its original velocity v a distance $l = vt$. Hence t^2 is l^2/v^2, and the displacement at right angles to the original motion is $S_e = fel^2/2mv^2$.

[2] See chap. v, p. 236.

the long-sought common constituents of different elements.
But there was as yet no clear evidence that the electric charge
on the corpuscles was not greater than that on electrolytic
univalent ions, so that the mass could not be calculated. This
question of the electric charge was clearly the next problem
to be attacked.

In 1898 and 1899 Thomson measured the charge on the
ions produced in gases by X-rays. He used a method discovered by C. T. R. Wilson, who in 1897 had shown that ions,
like dust particles, act as cloud nuclei for the condensation of
drops of water in moist air. The size of the drops can be
estimated by the rate at which the clouds fall against the
resistance of the air. The total volume of water condensed
gives the number of the drops, and the electric current produced by a known electromotive force gives the total charge
carried. Shortly afterwards Townsend measured the rates of
diffusion of ions through gases, and from the result calculated
the charge. The proof was complete in 1899 when Thomson
measured both e by the cloud method and e/m by magnetic
deflection for the same particles—those obtained when ultra-
violet light falls on a zinc plate. In all these measurements
the value obtained agreed with the charge on a univalent
liquid ion within the limits of the experimental error—indeed,
in more recent experiments by Millikan, the two figures
agreed within less than a fourth of one per cent.

Therefore it became certain that it is not the electric charge
which is greater than the charge on the liquid hydrogen ion,
but the mass which is smaller. Corpuscles are parts of atoms,
and are the same whatever the nature of the substance. From
Thomson's original experiments it appeared that each corpuscle possessed a mass equal to about the 1/770th part of
that of a hydrogen atom. But a better result might have
been obtained from the measurements of e/m by Kaufmann
described above. Since that date many new determinations of
the electronic charge and thus of e/m have been made,
especially by Millikan, who in 1910 improved Wilson's cloud
method, and in 1911 measured the velocity of a minute drop
of oil falling through ionized air. As the drop caught an
ion, the velocity could be seen to change suddenly. In this
way the charge on an ion was estimated as 4.775×10^{-10}
electrostatic units, which indicates that the mass of the

corpuscle or electron is the 1830th part of that of the hydrogen atom.[1] The mass of a single hydrogen atom, as calculated from the kinetic theory of gases, is about $1 \cdot 66 \times 10^{-24}$ gramme. It follows that the mass of a single corpuscle is about 9×10^{-28} gramme.

This great discovery has solved at last the problem—old as the Greeks—whether different kinds of matter have a common basis. It also gave a meaning to electrification. Thomson thus expressed his own views at the time:

I regard the atom as containing a large number of smaller bodies which I will call corpuscles; these corpuscles are equal to each other; the mass of a corpuscle is the mass of the negative ion in a gas at low pressure, i.e. about 3×10^{-28} of a gramme. In the normal atom, this assemblage of corpuscles forms a system which is electrically neutral. Though the individual corpuscles behave like negative ions, yet when they are assembled in a neutral atom the negative effect is balanced by something which causes the space through which the corpuscles are spread to act as if it had a charge of positive electricity equal in amount to the sum of the negative charges on the corpuscles. Electrification of a gas I regard as due to the splitting up of some of the atoms of the gas, resulting in the detachment of a corpuscle from some of the atoms. The detached corpuscles behave like negative ions, each carrying a constant negative charge, which we shall call for brevity the unit charge, while the part of the atom left behind behaves like a positive ion with the unit positive charge, and a mass large compared with that of the negative ion. On this view, electrification essentially involves the splitting up of the atom, a part of the mass of the atom getting free and becoming detached from the original atom.[2]

These new developments are connected with a somewhat older line of research. On Maxwell's theory, light, being a system of electromagnetic waves, must be emitted by vibrating electric systems.[3] As spectra are characteristic of elements and not of their compounds, the vibrators must be atoms or parts of atoms. On these lines an electric theory of matter was being built up by Lorentz in the years just preceding Thomson's discovery. It involved the expectation that a magnetic field would affect the appearance of spectra, and this expectation was realized by Zeeman, who, in 1896, observed a broadening of the lines in the sodium spectrum when the source of light was placed in the magnetic field of a powerful electro-magnet.

[1] R. A. Millikan, *Trans. American Electrochemical Society*, xxi, p. 185, 1912. Also Townsend, *loc. cit.* p. 244.
[2] *Phil. Mag.* ser. 5, vol. lxviii (1899), p. 565.
[3] See chap. v, p. 262.

With still stronger fields he succeeded later in resolving single
spectral lines into two or more components. Measurement of
these separations supplied data which, by Lorentz's theory,
gave a new value for e/m, the ratio of the electric charge to
the mass of the vibrating particle. It appeared to be of the
order of 10^7 electromagnetic units, and more exact determinations have led to a figure of about $1·77 \times 10^7$, in good agreement with the value obtained from observations on cathode
rays and otherwise.

Cathode Rays and Electrons

Lorentz used Johnstone Stoney's name of "electrons" for
these vibrating electric particles, and the discovery and
measurement of the Zeeman effect showed that they were
identical with Thomson's corpuscles. They may be taken as
isolated units of negative electricity. As suggested by Larmor,
the electrons must possess, by virtue of their electric energy,
an inertia which is equivalent to mass. Lorentz's theory thus
becomes an electronic theory of matter, and coalesces completely with the view which follows from Thomson's discovery.
But, while Thomson explained electricity in terms of matter,
Lorentz expressed matter in terms of electricity.

It is well to point out that one tacit assumption was made
which was not justified by later work. It was naturally
assumed that the corpuscles or electrons in the atom move
in accordance with Newtonian dynamics, and, even at first,
the atom was likened to a solar system in miniature, electrons
revolving within it as planets swing round the Sun. It is
clear now (1929) that the idea of planetary orbits does not
necessarily follow from the facts.

It was soon found that corpuscles or electrons could be
obtained in many other ways: for instance, they are emitted
by substances at high temperatures, and by metals under the
influence of ultra-violet light. These effects were investigated
by Elster and Geitel, O. W. Richardson, Ladenburg and
others, and since then the heat effect has become of practical
importance in the thermionic valves used in wireless telegraphy and telephony.

Cathode rays, as described, proceed from the negative
electrode (or cathode) in a vacuum tube through which an
electric discharge is passed. The corresponding positive rays
from the anode were detected in 1886 by Goldstein. They can
be examined by boring holes through a cathode placed directly

Positive or Atomic Rays

Positive or
Atomic Rays

opposite the anode. When the discharge passes, luminous rays which have traversed the holes are seen beyond the cathode. The magnetic and electric deflection of these *Kanalstrahlen* were first measured by Wien in 1898, and soon afterwards by Thomson. The value of e/m showed that the rays consist of positive particles which possess masses comparable with those of ordinary atoms and molecules.

The investigation was carried farther by Thomson in 1910 and 1911. By using a large apparatus very highly exhausted, and fixing a long narrow tube through the cathode, he obtained a very small pencil of rays, the position of which could be recorded on a photographic plate inside the apparatus. The magnetic and electric forces were so arranged that the deflections produced were at right angles to each other. The magnetic deflection is inversely proportional to the velocity of the particles and the electric deflection to the square of the velocity. Thus, if identical particles of differing velocities are found in the rays, a parabolic curve will be photographed on the plate. The lines which actually appear depend on the nature of the residual gas in the apparatus. In hydrogen, the fundamental line gives a value of 10^4 for e/m or 10^{-4} for m/e, the same as the value for the hydrogen ion in liquid electrolytes. A second line has double this value for m/e, and indicates a hydrogen molecule with twice the mass of the atom carrying a single electric charge. Other elements give more complex systems of many parabolic lines. The ratio of m/e for any element to its value for the hydrogen atom was called by Thomson the "electric atomic weight".

In examining the element neon (atomic weight 20·2) Thomson found two lines, indicating weights of 20 and 22 respectively. This suggested that neon, as ordinarily prepared, might consist of a mixture of two elements, identical in chemical properties, but of different atomic weights. Such elements are indicated and explained by certain radio-active phenomena, and were called by Soddy "isotopes" (ἴσο-τόπος, i.e. occupying the same place in the chemical table).

Thomson's experiments were taken up and carried farther by F. W. Aston,[1] who, with an improved apparatus, obtained regular "mass spectra" of different elements. The isotopic nature of neon was confirmed, and chlorine, with an atomic

[1] F. W. Aston, *Isotopes*, London, 1922 and 1924.

weight of 35·46 which had long puzzled chemists, was shown to consist of a mixture of atoms with weights 35 and 37. Aston obtained similar results with other elements. If the atomic weight of oxygen be taken arbitrarily as 16, the atomic weights of all other elements which have been examined are now known to be very nearly whole numbers, the greatest divergence being that of hydrogen, which, instead of being unity, is 1·008. Small differences from whole numbers depend on the close packing of positive and negative units in the nucleus of the atom and will be considered more fully later. *Positive or Atomic Rays*

Thus Aston cleared up another ancient problem. The work of Newlands and Mendeléeff showed that the different properties of elements were connected in some way with successive increments in atomic weight, and suggested inevitably that the weights themselves should lie in a simple ascending series. Prout's hypothesis, that they are all multiples of that of hydrogen, has now been proved to be true, the slight discrepancy being both explicable by and of surpassing interest in the modern theory of the atom.

Becquerel's original observation of the radio-active properties of uranium was soon followed by the discovery that, like X-rays, uranium rays produced electric conductivity in air and other gases. Compounds of thorium, too, were found to possess similar properties. In the year 1900, M. and Mme Curie made a systematic search for these effects in chemical elements and compounds and in natural products. They found that pitchblende, and several other minerals which contain uranium, were more active than the element itself. The constituents of pitchblende were separated chemically, the radioactivity itself being used as a guide, and salts of three very active substances, which were named radium, polonium and actinium, were isolated by different observers, the most active of those substances being radium, which was separated by the Curies working with Bémont. The quantity of radium in pitchblende is extremely small, many tons of the mineral yielding, after long and tedious labour, only a small fraction of a gramme of a salt of radium. *Radio-activity*[1]

In 1899 Professor Rutherford of Montreal, now Sir Ernest Rutherford of Cambridge, discovered that the radiation from

[1] E. Rutherford, *Radio-activity*, Cambridge, 1904 and 1905. J. Chadwick, *Radio-activity*, London, 1921.

uranium consists of two parts. One part was unable to pass through more than about the fiftieth of a millimetre of aluminium foil, while the other part would pass through about half a millimetre before its intensity was reduced by one-half. The first named, which Rutherford called α rays, produce the most marked electric effects, while the more penetrating, or β rays, are those which affect a photographic plate through opaque screens. At a later date a third type of still more penetrating radiation, known as γ rays, was detected. These last rays can traverse plates of lead a centimetre thick, and still produce photographs and discharge electroscopes. In proportion to its general activity, radium evolves all three types of radiation much more freely than uranium, and is best employed for their investigation.

The moderately penetrating, or β rays, can be deflected easily by a magnet; and Becquerel, who deflected them by an electric field as well, conclusively proved that they were projected particles charged with electricity. Further investigation showed that the β rays behave in all respects like cathode rays, although they possess velocities greater than those of any cathode rays hitherto examined, velocities which have different values varying from 60 to 95 per cent. of the velocity of light. The β rays, then, are negative corpuscles or electrons.

Magnetic and electric fields which are strong enough to deflect considerably the β rays produce no effect on the easily absorbed α rays. Although it had become very probable by about the year 1900 that the α rays were positively charged particles with masses greater than those of the particles which constitute the negative β rays, it was not till some time afterwards that their magnetic and electric deviations were demonstrated experimentally, and shown to be in the direction opposite to that observed with β rays. Rutherford's experiments on α particles in 1906 gave for the ratio e/m of the charge to the mass a value of $5 \cdot 1 \times 10^3$. The value of e/m for the hydrogen ion in liquid electrolytes is about 10^4. Since there is evidence (given later) to show that the α particles consist of helium, it follows that they are helium atoms (atomic weight 4) carrying double the univalent ionic charge. Their velocity is about one-tenth of that of light.

The very penetrating or γ rays cannot be deflected by magnetic or electric forces. They are different in kind from the other types, and, like the X-rays, consist of waves of the same nature as light though of much shorter wavelengths, which have been measured by A. H. Compton and by C. D. Ellis and Fräulein Meitner. Further, it seems that, like some X-rays, they consist of a series of monochromatic constituents characteristic of the emitting body.

In the year 1900 Sir William Crookes found that, if uranium were precipitated from solution by means of ammonium carbonate, and the precipitate were dissolved in an excess of the reagent, a small quantity of insoluble residue remained. This residue, to which Crookes gave the name of uranium-X, was found to be intensely active when examined photographically, while the re-dissolved uranium was photographically inert. Similar results were obtained by Becquerel, who found that, when put aside for a year, the active residue had lost its activity, while the inactive uranium had regained its original radiating properties.

In 1902 Rutherford and Soddy discovered a corresponding effect with thorium, which, they found, could be deprived of part of its activity by precipitation with ammonia. The filtrate, when evaporated, yielded a residue which is very radio-active. After a month's interval, however, this activity had disappeared, while that of the thorium had regained its initial value. The active residue, thorium-X, was seen to be a distinct chemical substance, for it is only separated completely by ammonia. Other reagents which precipitate thorium do not separate it from thorium-X. On these grounds it was concluded that the X compounds are separate bodies, which are produced continuously from the parent substances, and lose their activity with time.

In 1899 Rutherford had discovered that the radiation from thorium was very capricious, being affected especially by slight currents of air passing over the surface of the active material. He traced this effect to the emission of a substance which behaved like a heavy gas having temporary radioactive properties. This emanation, as it was called, is to be distinguished clearly from the radiations previously described, which travel in straight lines with high velocities. The emanation diffuses slowly through the atmosphere, as would the vapour of a volatile liquid. It acts as an independent source of straight line radiations, but suffers a decay of activity with

Radio-activity time. Similar emanations are evolved by radium and actinium, but not by uranium or polonium.

The amount of emanation evolved by radio-active substances is extremely small. A minute bubble was obtained in 1904 by Ramsay and Soddy from some decigrammes of radium bromide, but, in ordinary cases, the amount is much too small to affect the pressure in an exhausted vessel, or to be detected otherwise than by its property of radio-activity. It is usually obtained mixed with a large quantity of air, and can only be transferred from one vessel to another with the air.

M. and Mme Curie noticed in 1899 that if a rod be exposed to the emanation of radium, it will itself acquire radio-active properties. The same result was obtained with thorium by Rutherford in the same year and details investigated. When withdrawn from the vessel containing the emanation, and placed in a testing cylinder, the rod is found to ionize the gas. If a platinum wire which has become active by exposure to thorium emanation be washed with nitric acid, it is unaffected. With sulphuric or hydrochloric acid, however, it loses nearly all its activity, while the acid, when evaporated, gives a radio-active residue. This result indicates that the activity on the wire is due to the deposit of some new type of radio-active matter, which has definite reactions with different chemical reagents. In the light of the conclusions by that time arrived at, it was natural to interpret this new matter as a product of the disintegration of the emanation from which it is formed.

The rate of decay of the activity of thorium-X was investigated by Rutherford and Soddy in 1902, and the important discovery was made that the rate during each short interval of time is proportional to the amount of activity at the beginning of that interval. Similar phenomena appear with uranium-X.[1] The process is illustrated in Fig. 10. It shows the same law as does the decrease in the amount of a chemical compound which is dissociating molecule by molecule into simpler products. When a chemical change is brought about by the interaction of two or more molecules, different laws hold good.

---

[1] If I be the intensity of radio-activity $-dI/dt = \lambda I$. Putting I_0 for the original activity and integrating, we get $\log_e (I/I_0) = -\lambda t$, or $I/I_0 = e^{-\lambda t}$, the logarithmic or exponential law of a mono-molecular chemical reaction.

In 1903 Curie and Laborde drew attention to the remarkable *Radio-activity* fact that compounds of radium constantly emit heat. They calculated from their experiments that one gramme of pure radium would yield about 100 gramme-calories of heat per hour. Later work showed that one gramme of radium in equilibrium with its products gives 135 calories per hour. The rate at which this energy is emitted is unchanged by exposing the radium salt to high temperatures, or to the low temperature of liquid air, and certainly is not diminished even at the temperature of liquid hydrogen.

Fig. 10.

The emission of heat was correlated by Rutherford with the radio-activity. Radium freed from its stored emanation recovers its radio-activity as measured electrically at the same rate as its power of evolving heat, and the separated emanation shows variations in the heat developed corresponding with those observed in its radio-activity. The electric effects of the radio-activity are chiefly due to the α rays, and the heat effect also is chiefly dependent upon the emission of α rays. In the above-named total of 135 calories per hour, only 5 calories are due to β and 6 calories to γ radiation. The heat effect of the α and β rays is clearly due to the kinetic energy of the projected particles.

The demonstration of the continual development of heat by compounds of radium led to many attempts to explain the source of this apparently unfailing supply of energy, and focussed attention on the problem of radio-activity itself.

The facts to be explained may be summarized thus: (1) whenever there is radio-activity there is chemical change, new bodies appearing; (2) the chemical change is a dissociation of single particles and not a combination; (3) the activity is proportional to the mass of the radio-active element whether free or combined, so that the dissociating particles must be atoms and not molecules; (4) the amount of energy liberated is many thousand times more than that associated with the most violent chemical reaction known.

As a result of their experiments on the emanations and the deposited activity produced thereby, in 1903 Rutherford and Soddy explained all known facts by the theory that radio-activity is due to an explosive disintegration of the elementary atoms. Here and there one atom out of many millions suddenly explodes; an α particle, or a β particle and a γ ray, are ejected, and a different atom is left behind. If an α particle has been thrown out, this new element will be less in atomic weight by the four units of a helium atom.

As an illustration, we may well trace the pedigree of the radium family. The earliest known ancestor is uranium, a heavy element which has an atomic weight of 238 and an atomic number of 92, which, as explained later, is the number of electrons in the outer part of the atom. The descendants of uranium are shown in the table below.

Uranium emits an α particle, a helium atom of mass 4 and charge $+ 2$. Uranium X_1 remains behind: its weight is $238 - 4 = 234$, and its atomic number $92 - 2 = 90$. Its radio-activity gives β and γ rays only; the β particle being of negligible mass and carrying a negative charge. Hence the body into which it passes, known as Uranium X_2, has one negative charge less, that is, one positive charge more, than Uranium X_1 and consequently an atomic number of 91. Its atomic weight, 234, is practically unaltered. Its radio-activity also consists of β and γ rays; hence its child, Uranium II, has an atomic number of 92 and, again, the same weight of 234.

And so we go on as shown in the table. When an α ray is emitted, the product has an atomic weight less by four units and an atomic number less by two. When a β ray comes off, the weight is practically unchanged, but the number is raised by unity.

	Atomic number	Atomic weight	Time of half decay	Radio-activity	Radio-activity
Uranium I	92	238	5×10^9 years	α	
↓					
Uranium X₁	90	234	24·5 days	β, γ	
↓					
Uranium X₂	91	234	1·17 minutes	β, γ	
↓					
Uranium II	92	234	2×10^6 years (?)	α	
↓					
Ionium	90	230	2×10^5 years (?)	α	
↓					
Radium	88	226	1590 years	α	
↓					
Radium Emanation...	86	222	3·82 days	α	
↓					
Radium A	84	218	3·05 minutes	α	
↓					
Radium B	82	214	26·8 minutes	β, γ	
↓					
Radium C	83	214	19·7 minutes	α, β, γ	
↓					
Radium D	82	210	25 years	β, γ	
↓					
Radium E	83	210	5 days	β, γ	
↓					
Radium F (Polonium)	84	210	136 days	α	
↓					
Lead	82	206	Inactive		

The last known descendant of the family is lead, and its atomic weight has been found by Richards and Hönigschmit to be 206, while the atomic weight of ordinary lead is 207. Similarly it can be shown that the end product of the thorium series is also lead, and its atomic weight has been found by Soddy to be 208. Again, Aston has found for actinium lead the normal value 207. These three types of lead possess identical chemical properties and are to be regarded as isotopes. They seem to represent the only isotopes in nature found in the isolated condition.

The atomic theory was established by the chemical work of Dalton, but for a hundred years it was impossible to point to any demonstration of the existence of single atoms; they could be treated only statistically by millions. But radio-activity now makes it possible to trace the effect of single α particles. This was first done by Crookes, who observed with a magnifying lens scintillations on a fluorescent screen of zinc sulphide exposed to a speck of radium bromide, and other methods of detection are now available.

A gas at a pressure of a few millimetres of mercury, when acted on by an electric field just weaker than that needed to cause a spark, is in a very sensitive state. An α particle, owing to its immense velocity, will produce many thousand ions by collision with the molecules of gas. These ions, being subject to the strong electric field, are set in rapid motion, and thereupon produce other ions by collision. Hence the total effect of a single α particle is multiplied, and the needle of a sensitive electrometer may be made to give a throw of 20 millimetres or more on the scale. By using a very thin film of active matter, Rutherford reduced the throws to three or four a minute, and counted the number of α particles projected. The life of radium may thus be estimated. The calculation shows that a mass of radium would diminish by one half in about 1600 years.

Another method is due to C. T. R. Wilson. When shot through air saturated with water-vapour, α particles produce ions, which act as nuclei of condensation. Cloud-tracks are thus formed in the air, showing the path of each α particle, and these cloud-tracks may be photographed.

Rutherford's work on radio-activity at length demonstrated the possibility of the transmutation of matter, the dream of the mediaeval alchemist. Till lately, no human means had been discovered of hastening, still less of controlling, these changes. They depend on chance happenings within the atom, and their frequency conforms to the well-known laws of probability. But Rutherford discovered in 1919 that a bombardment by α rays will induce atomic transformations in certain elements such as nitrogen. Nitrogen has an atomic weight of 14; its atom is made up of three helium nuclei weighing 12, and two odd hydrogen nuclei. When struck by an α particle, the nitrogen nucleus is shattered, and, of its constituents, hydrogen nuclei are shot out with great velocity. Here, then, we catch a glimpse of the possibility of inducing at will a breakdown of the atom, a transmutation in one direction. But it is easier to destroy than to build up: it does not follow that we shall ever be able to construct the heavier and more complex atoms from the lighter and simpler. Indeed, modern astronomical evidence is showing that the probable course of the evolution of matter is in one direction, and involves the breaking up of complex atoms into simpler atoms and radiant energy. We may hasten this disintegration in an *Radio-activity* odd atom or two, but we are not likely to find ourselves able to reverse the cosmic process.

The X-rays discovered by Röntgen are not refracted like *X-Rays and* ordinary light, and very little trace of regular reflection or of *Atomic* polarization can be detected. But, on the other hand, they *Numbers*[1] are not deflected by magnetic or electric forces like cathode rays, or α and β particles. For some time their nature was a subject of discussion, but in 1912 Laue made the suggestion that, if X-rays were aethereal waves of very short wavelength, the regular arrangement of atoms in a crystal might be found to diffract X-rays as a surface ruled with large numbers of parallel scratches is used as a grating to diffract ordinary light. Laue worked out the complex mathematical theory, and Friedrich and Kipping successfully tested his theory experimentally. X-rays were thus shown to be electromagnetic waves, shorter than the waves of light, and this discovery opened a new field for research into the structure of crystals, a field which has been explored chiefly by Sir William Bragg and his son W. L. Bragg. Taking first rock-salt, a simple cubic type of crystal, they showed by these diffraction phenomena that the distance between the planes of atoms parallel to the natural faces of rock-salt was $2 \cdot 81 \times 10^{-8}$ centimetre, and that the characteristic X-rays emitted when a target of palladium was bombarded with cathode rays had a wavelength of $0 \cdot 576 \times 10^{-8}$ centimetre, only the one ten-thousandth part of the wave-length of sodium light. Radiation is now known from the long waves used in wireless telegraphy to the short waves of X-rays and γ rays, a range of frequency of about 60 octaves. Of these, only about one octave consists of visible light.

The diffraction spectra of X-rays produced by crystals used as gratings was shown by the work of Sir William Bragg, of Moseley and C. G. Darwin, and of G. W. C. Kaye, to consist of a mixture of diffuse radiation of all wave-lengths within certain limits, and of more intense radiation of definite frequency superimposed as spectral "lines" upon it. This characteristic line radiation is a diffraction phenomenon similar to the line spectra obtained with visible light, and with

[1] Sir William and W. L. Bragg, *X-Rays and Crystal Structure*, London, 1915, 5th ed. 1925. G. W. C. Kaye, *X-Rays*, London, 1914, 4th ed. 1923.

it a very important discovery was made in 1913 and 1914 by a young Oxford man, H. G. J. Moseley,[1] who was killed soon afterwards in the War—an incalculable loss to physical science.

When the target bombarded by cathode rays was changed from one metal to another, and the spectrum of the resultant X-rays was examined by using a crystal of potassium ferro-cyanide as a grating, Moseley found that the frequency of vibration of the characteristic lines in the spectrum undergoes a simple change. The square root of the number n, expressing the number of vibrations per second corresponding to the strongest line in the X-ray spectrum, increases by the same amount on passing from element to element in the periodic table. If $n^{\frac{1}{2}}$ be multiplied by a constant, so as to bring this regular increase to unity, we get a series of atomic numbers, ranging regularly for all solid elements examined, from aluminium 13 to gold 79. Filling in the other known elements, we find that, from hydrogen 1 to uranium 92, there are only two or three places left for undiscovered elements.

Table of
Elements

Atomic Number	Element	Symbol	Atomic Weight	Atomic Number	Element	Symbol	Atomic Weight
1.	Hydrogen	H	1·008	29.	Copper	Cu	63·57
2.	Helium	He	4·00	30.	Zinc	Zn	65·37
3.	Lithium	Li	6·94	31.	Gallium	Ga	69·9
4.	Beryllium	Be	9·1	32.	Germanium	Ge	72·5
5.	Boron	B	11·0	33.	Arsenic	As	74·96
6.	Carbon	C	12·005	34.	Selenium	Se	79·2
7.	Nitrogen	N	14·01	35.	Bromine	Br	79·92
8.	Oxygen	O	16·00	36.	Krypton	Kr	82·92
9.	Fluorine	F	19·0	37.	Rubidium	Rb	85·45
10.	Neon	Ne	20·2	38.	Strontium	Sr	87·63
11.	Sodium	Na	23·00	39.	Yttrium	Y	88·7
12.	Magnesium	Mg	24·32	40.	Zirconium	Zr	90·6
13.	Aluminium	Al	27·1	41.	Niobium	Nb	93·5
14.	Silicon	Si	28·3	42.	Molybdenum	Mo	96·0
15.	Phosphorus	P	31·04	43.	—	—	—
16.	Sulphur	S	32·06	44.	Ruthenium	Ru	101·7
17.	Chlorine	Cl	35·46	45.	Rhodium	Rh	102·9
18.	Argon	A	39·88	46.	Palladium	Pd	106·7
19.	Potassium	K	39·10	47.	Silver	Ag	107·88
20.	Calcium	Ca	40·07	48.	Cadmium	Cd	112·40
21.	Scandium	Sc	44·1	49.	Indium	In	114·8
22.	Titanium	Ti	48·1	50.	Tin	Sn	118·7
23.	Vanadium	V	51·0	51.	Antimony	Sb	120·2
24.	Chromium	Cr	52·0	52.	Tellurium	Te	127·5
25.	Manganese	Mn	54·93	53.	Iodine	I	126·92
26.	Iron	Fe	55·84	54.	Xenon	Xe	130·2
27.	Cobalt	Co	58·97	55.	Caesium	Cs	132·81
28.	Nickel	Ni	58·68	56.	Barium	Ba	137·37

[1] *Phil. Mag.* 1913, 1914, ser. 6, vol. XXVI, pp. 210, 1024, and vol. XXVII, p. 703.

Atomic Number	Element	Symbol	Atomic Weight	Atomic Number	Element	Symbol	Atomic Weight
57.	Lanthanum	La	139·0	76.	Osmium	Os	190·9
58.	Cerium	Ce	140·25	77.	Iridium	Ir	193·1
59.	Praseodymium	Pr	140·9	78.	Platinum	Pt	195·2
60.	Neodymium	Nd	144·3	79.	Gold	Au	197·2
61.	—	—	—	80.	Mercury	Hg	200·6
62.	Samarium	Sm	150·4	81.	Thallium	Tl	204·0
63.	Europium	Eu	152·0	82.	Lead	Pb	207·2
64.	Gadolinium	Gd	157·3	83.	Bismuth	Bi	208·0
65.	Terbium	Tb	159·2	84.	Polonium	Po	210·0
66.	Dysprosium	Ds	162·5	85.	—	—	—
67.	Holmium	Ho	163·5	86.	Radon (Radium emanation)		222·0
68.	Erbium	Er	167·7				
69.	Thulium	Tm	168·5	87.	—	—	—
70.	Ytterbium	Yb	173·5	88.	Radium	Ra	226·0
71.	Lutecium	Lu	175·0	89.	Actinium	Ac	—
72.	Hafnium	Hf	—	90.	Thorium	Th	232·0
73.	Tantalum	Ta	181·5	91.	Proto-actinium	Pa	—
74.	Tungsten	W	184·0	92.	Uranium	U	238·2
75.	—	—	—				

The Quantum Theory[1]

In 1923 Compton found that, when X-rays are scattered by matter, the frequency of the waves becomes less. He explained this effect by the theory of a photon unit of radiation, comparable with the electron and proton units of matter or electric change. The movement of an electron in an atomic orbit would naturally involve the radiation of energy, and, on Newton's dynamics, the orbit would contract, with a consequent quickening of the period of rotation and of the frequency of the waves emitted. Atoms at all stages of this process would exist, and therefore in all spectra radiation of every frequency should be found, instead of the radiation of only a few definite and unchanging frequencies such as that seen in the line spectra of many chemical elements.

Even in the continuous spectrum of an incandescent solid the energy is not evenly distributed but is greatest between certain frequencies, and this range of maximum radiation moves up the spectrum from red to violet as the temperature rises. It is difficult to see how this could be explained on the older theory of atomic or electronic radiation. Indeed, mathematical investigation indicates that oscillators of high frequency should radiate more energy than those of low frequency, so that visible light should always give more heat than the invisible

[1] For a summary, see J. H. Jeans, *Report on Radiation and the Quantum Theory*, 2nd ed. London, 1924.

infra-red rays, and ultra-violet rays more than light. All this is contrary to well-known fact.

To meet these difficulties, Planck in 1901 devised a "Quantum Theory",[1] according to which radiation is not continuous, but, like matter, can be dealt with only in individual units or atoms. The emission and absorption of these units will depend on the principles of probability which, as described in former chapters, have been so much used in other branches of physics and physical chemistry. The units of energy radiated are not all the same size, but are of sizes proportional to the frequency of the oscillation. Hence high-frequency ultra-violet oscillations can only radiate when they have a large amount of energy available, and therefore the chance of many units being available and radiated is very small, as is likewise the total energy emitted. The low-frequency oscillations, on the other hand, emit small units, and therefore the probability is great that many units will be available and radiated; but, since each unit is very small, the total amount of energy is small also. For some special range of intermediate frequency, where the unit is of medium size, the chances will be favourable, the number radiated may be fairly large, and the total energy a maximum.

To explain the facts, Planck's quantum of energy ϵ must be supposed proportional to the frequency, that is, inversely proportional to the period of vibration. Hence we see that

$$\epsilon = h\nu = \frac{h}{T},$$

where ν is the frequency, T the period and h a constant. Hence Planck's constant h is ϵT, the product of energy and time, the quantity which is called Action. This constant unit of action is, of course, independent of the frequency, indeed of everything variable. It is a true natural unit, analogous to the natural unit of matter and electricity found in the electron.

A theory made specially to suit one definite set of facts can be adjusted to fit those facts, and, however good the fit and fashionable the cut, the evidence for the theory being universally applicable is not perhaps very strong. But, if an entirely different set of phenomena can be explained by the same theory, especially if no rational account of them has

---

[1] *Annalen der Physik*, vol. IV, p. 553, 1901.

been given otherwise, the value of the evidence is greatly strengthened, and we begin to feel confident that we may rely on the theory to co-ordinate still more relations.

Planck's theory was introduced to meet the facts of radiation. As it involved a breach with orthodox dynamics, it was rightly viewed with caution, if not scepticism. But, when it was applied by Einstein,[1] by Nernst and Lindemann,[1] and even more successfully by Debye,[2] to explain the phenomena of specific heat, the probability of its extended usefulness was very much increased.

The ordinary kinetic theory suggests that monatomic molecules in solids should have an atomic heat of three times the gas constant, or about six calories per degree, and that this quantity should be independent of temperature. Metals contain monatomic molecules; at ordinary temperatures their atomic heats are roughly constant and equal to 6. But at lower temperatures the value diminishes.

This was first successfully explained by Einstein, who pointed out that, if energy could only be absorbed in definite units or quanta, the rate of absorption would depend on the size of the unit, and therefore on the frequency of vibration and thus on the temperature. Debye calculated from the quantum theory a formula, which gave results agreeing with observation— markedly so in the case of carbon, which, even at ordinary temperatures, has a variable atomic heat, much below the value for metals.

On this quantum theory, light at the moments of emission and absorption is neither the steady aethereal wave of Fresnel nor the continuous electro-magnetic undulation of Clerk Maxwell and Hertz. It seems to consist of a stream of minute gushes of energy which may almost be regarded as atoms of light, equivalent to, though different in kind from, Newton's corpuscles. The reconciliation of this conception with the phenomena of interference was left as a difficulty to be dealt with in the future. If a ray of light be divided, and the two parts taken over paths which differ in length, interference bands are seen where the two parts of the ray finally meet, even though the difference in path may be many thousand wave-lengths. Again, the diffraction pattern seen with the image of a star in a large telescope indicates that the light

---

[1] *Solvay Congress*, Brussels, 1912, pp. 254, 407.
[2] *Annalen der Physik*, vol. xxxix, 1912, p. 789.

from each atom fills the whole object-glass. These facts were taken as proving that light advances in steady trains of waves uniform for a distance of many thousand wave-lengths and extending transversely over a space enough to fill a telescope.

But, if light from the same star falls on a film of potassium, it will eject electrons each with the energy of the quantum which corresponds to the particular light. Here the light acts not as a wave but as a bullet with its energy localized. As distance is increased, the number of bullets hitting a given area is less, but they still strike with the same momentum. Another doubt was cast on the older theory by conclusions drawn from the phenomena of the ionization of gases by X-rays. If the wave-front were uniform, its effect on all molecules in its path would be the same, whereas in reality perhaps only one molecule in a million is ionized. There are reasons which make it improbable that this is due to a very few molecules being unstable, and among others J. J. Thomson argued that such facts indicate that X-rays and light travel not in broad wave-fronts but as waves along localized filaments of aether—Faraday's tubes of force.

Then came the quantum theory, again suggesting that light was discontinuous in another way. Thomson tried to explain all the facts and to reconcile conflicting views by imagining light to consist of particles, each made of a closed ring of electric force and accompanied by a train of waves. Prince Lucien de Broglie has used more recent conceptions to frame a theory in which the properties of waves and particles are combined in a new form of wave-mechanics. A moving particle behaves as a group of waves, of which the velocity v and the wave-length λ are related to the speed v and corresponding mass m of the particle by the equation $\lambda = h/mv$, where h is Planck's constant. The wave-velocity is c^2/v, where c is the velocity of light and v that of both the particle and the wave-group. It is impossible not to notice the similarity of these modern theories of light with the combined corpuscles and waves imagined by Newton.

The modern theory of the atom began in the year 1897 with the discovery of the negatively electrified corpuscle

[1] N. Bohr, *The Theory of Spectra and Atomic Constitution*, Cambridge, 2nd ed. 1924. A. Sommerfeld, *Atombau und Spektrallinien*, 4th ed. 1924. E. N. da C. Andrade, *The Structure of the Atom*, London, 1923, 3rd ed. 1927. B. Russell, *The A.B.C. of Atoms*, London, 1923.

common to all elements, and its identification with the electron.
That discovery also made it clear that the electrical properties
of atoms were to be explained in terms of an excess or defect
in the normal number of electrons, and their optical properties to be explained in terms of electronic vibration.

An earlier observation made by Lenard, who showed that
cathode rays could pass out of the vacuum tube through
an aluminium window, enabled him to prove in 1903, by experiments on absorption, that swift cathode rays could pass
through thousands of atoms. On the semi-materialist ideas
then prevalent, it followed that the greater part of the volume
of an atom must be empty space, the solid matter being
estimated to be only about 10^{-9} (or one thousand millionth)
of the whole. Lenard imagined the "solid matter" to
consist of a number of doublets of positive and negative
electricity scattered about in the empty space within the atom.

This way of providing the necessary positive charge did
not prove satisfactory, and a more systematic attempt to
describe atomic mechanism was made by J. J. Thomson.

He suggested that the atom consists of a sphere of uniform
positive electricity in which negative electrons are revolving.
Following up an investigation by Alfred Mayer on the equilibrium of floating magnets, Thomson showed that a ring of
rotating electrons will be stable till the number exceeds a
definite limit. Two rings will then be formed, and so on. Thus
periodic likenesses in structure are produced by the addition
of electrons, and the recurrence of the physical and chemical
properties of the elements in Mendeléeff's Periodic Table
might perhaps be explained.

But in 1911 experiments on the scattering of α rays when
they strike matter led Rutherford to another view of the
proximate nature of the atom. The cloud tracks of α particles
are usually straight, but occasionally a sharp change in direction is seen. The forces exerted by negative electrons on an
α particle must be too small to produce such scattering, but
the effect is explained if it be supposed that an atom, a complex
body of open structure, has a positive charge concentrated in
a minute nucleus, with negative electrons revolving round
it in space. Since a normal atom is electrically neutral, the
positive charge in the nucleus must be equal as well as opposite
to that on all the electrons together, and, since the mass of

the electrons is small compared with that of an atom, nearly all the mass must be concentrated in the nucleus.

With the general ideas current when this theory was formulated, the atom resembles the solar system, a heavy nucleus or Sun forming the centre, with lighter planetary electrons circling round. Nagaoka had investigated the stability of a similar system in 1904, but Rutherford was the first to bring experimental evidence to support the idea. Lenard's work on absorption of cathode rays and other later experiments showed that, if the atom were supposed to resemble a miniature solar system in which electrons take the place of the planets, the empty spaces in the atom must be proportionately as large as the empty spaces in the sky. In this theory of planetary electrons, the preconceptions implanted in our minds by Newtonian physics perhaps led us farther than the facts warranted, but the atom, nevertheless, as far as penetration by cathode rays and radio-active particles is concerned, is certainly a very open structure.

A moving electric charge carries a field of electro-magnetic force with it; and this, since it has energy, must possess inertia. Hence an electric charge has something which behaves like mass, which, indeed, cannot be distinguished from mass, and may be the essence of the underlying substance in that which we call matter. If a small sphere be drawn round the charge to represent the electron, the electro-magnetic mass exists outside it and can be calculated. J. J. Thomson showed by mathematical analysis that, unless the charge is moving with very great speed, the electric mass is $2e^2/3r$, where e is the charge and r the radius. Thus, on the assumption that all the electro-magnetic energy is outside the electron, the radius can be calculated from the known values of the mass and the charge; for an electron it is somewhere about 10^{-13} of a centimetre. By making the radius r small, that is by concentrating the charge, the effective mass is increased. The nucleus of hydrogen, which is the positive unit corresponding to the electron as the negative unit, is generally called a "proton". Its mass, which is practically the mass of the atom, is 1800 times the mass of a negative electron. Therefore, if all the mass is assumed to be electrical and the nucleus to be a sphere surrounding a point charge of positive electricity, the radius of the nucleus will be only the 1800th part of the radius of an electron, that is, it will be of the order of 5×10^{-17} cm. It must be emphasized that these estimates of size depend on an arbitrary assumption as to the distribution of the electric charge. They are now (1929) of very doubtful value. *The Structure of the Atom*

Whatever be the meaning of "size" in this connection, and whether or no the planetary theory survives, we must regard a hydrogen atom as consisting of a unit positive nucleus or proton, with a single negative electron somewhere outside it. The helium nucleus is made of four protons with two electrons binding them together. Since the atomic weight of hydrogen is 1·008, and the atomic mass of helium as measured by Aston is 4·002, the formation of this complex nucleus involves a destruction of mass of $(4 \times 1·008) - 4·002$ or about ·03 and an equivalent emission of energy. The radio-active disintegration of heavy atoms, such as those of uranium, gives an output of energy, and it has therefore been assumed that all atoms contain a store of energy available when they break up. But the reasoning here given shows that the resolution of helium into hydrogen would involve an absorption of energy—work would have to be done to break up the helium nucleus. It seems then that light atomic nuclei give out energy when they are formed, and heavy nuclei when they break up. This may explain why heavy atoms are radio-active, and why no atom heavier than uranium is known: it would probably be unstable.[1] As α rays are flights of helium atoms, it is probable that helium atoms are some of the bricks of which the nuclei of other heavier atoms are built. The helium atoms themselves, each made up of four protons or hydrogen nuclei, are too firmly knit to be separated even in the adventurous life of an α particle. Thus it is probable that other atoms are made of a complex nucleus containing a number of positive units, probably helium nuclei with, in some cases, hydrogen protons, bound together by a certain smaller number of negative electrons, thus leaving a net positive charge on the nucleus of N, Moseley's atomic number. Other electrons exist outside this centre, and, for neutral atoms, N also represents the total number of these outer electrons, since the total negative charge on those electrons must neutralize the equal net positive charge in the nucleus.

Since atoms can be ionized, and given one, two, three or

[1] E. Rutherford, *Proc. Roy. Soc.* A, 123, p. 373, 1929.

possibly four unit charges in accordance with their chemical
valency, a small number of electrons can be added to or sub-
tracted from an atom with no fundamental change in its
nature. We may suppose these electrons to be placed in outer
rings, while others are in inner rings, and yet others form an
essential and, in general, a stable part of the nucleus.

As already explained, most radio-active transformations
are associated with the ejection of an α particle, which is a
helium atom of mass four, carrying two units of positive
electricity. Such transformations must therefore involve a
catastrophic change in the nucleus. The residue will be four
units lighter, and two negative electrons must be discarded to
re-establish neutrality: a new atom, a new element, will result.

Bohr's Theory
The application of Planck's quantum theory to the problem
of atomic structure was first made in 1913 by Niels Bohr of
Copenhagen, while working in Rutherford's laboratory at
Manchester. He based his work on the theory of planetary
electrons then generally accepted by physicists.

It was already known that regularities appear in the complex spectrum of hydrogen if we consider, not the usual wave-
lengths of its luminous lines, but the number of waves in a
centimetre. It had been found that these so-called vibration
numbers can all be expressed as the difference between two
terms. The first term, known from its discoverer as Rydberg's
constant, is 109,678 waves per centimetre.[1]

Now these relations are quite empirical. They were obtained
by guessing at arithmetical rules till one was found to fit the
results of experiment. But Bohr was able to explain them on
the quantum theory. He pointed out that if "action" is
absorbed in units, only a certain number of all the orbits in

---

[1] The other terms are obtained from Rydberg's constant by dividing it by
four (2×2), nine (3×3), sixteen (4×4), and so on. If we subtract these terms
from the constant R, we get vibration numbers

$$R - \frac{R}{4} = \frac{3R}{4}, \quad R - \frac{R}{9} = \frac{8R}{9}, \text{ etc.}$$

and these numbers are found to correspond with the vibration numbers of
hydrogen lines in the ultra-violet part of the spectrum.

If we begin again with the first derived term, one-fourth of 109,678 or 27,420,
and subtract from it the higher derived terms, we get another series of numbers

$$\frac{R}{4} - \frac{R}{9} = \frac{5R}{36}, \quad \frac{R}{4} - \frac{R}{16} = \frac{3R}{16}, \text{ etc.}$$

These numbers are found to correspond with the visible lines of hydrogen
known as Balmer's series. Yet another group derived from one-ninth of R was
found in the infra-red by Paschen.

which an electron might revolve will be possible. In the smallest orbit the action would be one unit or h, in the next orbit $2h$, and so on.

Bohr supposed that the one electron of the hydrogen atom has four possible stable orbits, corresponding to increasing units of action, as illustrated in Fig. 11, where the circles represent the four stable orbits and the radii the six possible jumps from one orbit to another. At this point Bohr left Newtonian dynamics. It is remarkable that the law of inverse squares can be applied to electrons which are supposed to be circulating in orbits round the nucleus of atoms, but the orbits themselves show quite new relations. A planet might revolve round the Sun in any one of an infinite number of orbits, the actual path being adjusted to its velocity. An electron, on the other hand, Bohr supposed, can only move in one of a few paths. If it leaves one path, it must jump instantaneously to another, apparently without passing over the intervening space. This assumption leads to theoretical results in exact conformity with the empirical rules established by experiment for the vibration numbers.[1] Furthermore, it is possible to calculate the absolute value of the constant R as 109,800 waves per centimetre, a remarkable agreement with the latest observed value of Rydberg's constant given above. Bohr's theory at this stage showed every promise of a long and successful career.

The various types of radiation can be referred to different parts of the atomic structure. X-ray spectra are, for the most part, independent of the temperature or the state of chemical

---

[1] Mathematical investigation shows that the energy of motion in the second orbit is a quarter of that in the first, in the third orbit it is one-ninth, and in the fourth one-sixteenth. As an electron falls in from an outer to an inner orbit or level, it loses energy of position and gains energy of motion. The total loss of energy may be shown to be equal to the gain in energy of motion. Hence if ϵ be the energy of motion in the innermost level, the loss in passing from the second level to the first is $\epsilon - \epsilon/4$ or $3\epsilon/4$, and in passing from the third to the second $8\epsilon/9$. Leaping over one orbit, the electron will give another series of numbers; thus passing straight from the third orbit to the first, it gives $1/4 - 1/9$ or $5\epsilon/36$.

In leaping from one orbit or energy-level to the next, the electron absorbs or radiates energy $h\nu$, where h is Planck's unit of action and ν the frequency of vibration. Since the energies lost are $3\epsilon/4$, $8\epsilon/9$, etc. and h is constant, the frequencies ν_1, ν_2, etc. must be in the ratios $3/4$, $8/9$, etc. in accordance with the known lines of the ultra-violet spectrum, while another series, corresponding with leaps to alternate orbits, gives frequencies beginning with $5/36$, agreeing with Balmer's series.

combination of an atom, on both of which the details of optical spectra depend. Radio-activity, as explained above, is due to an explosive disruption of the nucleus. The evidence now given goes to show that X-rays proceed from the inner layers of the electrons outside the nucleus, while light comes from the outermost electrons, which are more easily detached and are concerned in cohesion and in chemical action.

Chemical combination might well be explained if one or more electrons were common to the combining atoms. The difficulties in representing such unions on the theory of electrons whirling round a nucleus led, in the years 1916 to

Fig. 11.

1921, to attempts to construct a statical model of the atom, especially by Kossel and by Lewis and Langmuir. Such models successfully explained valency and other chemical properties, but artificial assumptions had to be made to coax an account of spectra out of them. The physicist, at all events, at that time preferred Bohr's dynamic atom.

Whatever atomic model be accepted, we meet strong evidence for the fundamental idea of different energy-levels in the facts of ionization potential. In 1902 Lenard first showed that an electron must possess a certain minimum energy before it would produce ionization as it passed through a gas. The energy is measured by the electric potential in volts through which the electron must fall to acquire its velocity, and more recent experiments, such as those of Franck and

Hertz on mercury vapour (1916–1925), show that sharp maxima of ionization occur at multiples of a definite voltage. Simultaneous changes in the spectrum of the gas are observed. For instance, Franck and Hertz showed that the electrons with the velocity produced by 4·9 volts caused low-pressure mercury vapour to emit a spectrum of a single line, which may be supposed to correspond with the leap back to normal from the first outer level in Bohr's atom. Since then a large number of critical potentials have been found for lines or groups of lines which suddenly appear, in agreement with the predictions which can be made on Bohr's theory. The effect on spectra of temperature and of pressure were investigated by Saha, H. N. Russell, R. H. Fowler, E. A. Milne and others, who have applied these new conceptions by means of thermodynamic methods. Their results have proved of the greatest importance in astro-physics, and have opened a new chapter in the measurement of stellar temperatures.

The circular orbits shown in Fig. 11 give only an elementary model of a hydrogen atom. Both Bohr and Sommerfeld showed that the same series spectra would be produced by elliptic orbits, and described more complex atomic systems, though the mathematical difficulties were great, since the motion of even three mutually attracting bodies cannot be expressed in finite terms.

The literature on the subject of Bohr's atom is voluminous, and much progress was made. The general concordance of the results with the coarser structure of spectra gave much confidence that the theory was proceeding on the right lines. Nevertheless, while it accounted for the line spectrum of hydrogen and of ionized helium, it failed with the finer detail of the spectra of neutral helium and with all the tremendous complexity of heavier atoms. The concordance between the number of spectrum lines and the number of possible jumps of electrons from one level to another ceased to hold good. By 1925 it was becoming clear that Bohr's theory of the atom, so successful for a time, was breaking down.

Bohr's atomic model, with its circling planetary electrons, goes farther from the observed facts than it is safe to venture. We can only examine atoms from outside, keeping note of what goes in and what comes out, radiation or radio-active particles. Bohr has described one mechanism which will produce some, at all events, of the atomic properties. But it is possible that other types of mechanism might work equally well. If we could see only the outside of a clock, we might imagine a train of wheels which would move the hands as they are observed to move, but somebody else might describe another set of wheels quite as effective as ours, and no one could decide between us. Again, the great science of thermo-dynamics, which deals only with the changes in heat and energy of a system, makes no use of pictures of intimate mechanism such as are given by atomic conceptions.

In 1925 Heisenberg framed a new theory of quantum mechanics based only on what can be observed, that is, on the radiation absorbed and emitted by the atom.[1] We cannot assign to an electron a position in space at a given time, or follow it in its orbit, and consequently we have no right to assume that Bohr's planetary orbits exist. The fundamental observable magnitudes are the frequencies and amplitudes of the emitted radiation, and the energy levels of the atomic system; it is on these data that the mathematical formulation of the new theory depends. The theory has already been rapidly developed by Heisenberg, Born and Jordan and, from another point of view, by Dirac, and shown to lead to the Balmer formula for the hydrogen spectrum and the observed effects on that spectrum of electric and magnetic fields.

In 1926 Schrödinger attacked the problem from another angle.[2] Following up the work of de Broglie on phase-waves and light-quanta, Schrödinger was led to a theory mathematically equivalent to that of Heisenberg from the view that "material points consist of, or are nothing but, wave systems".[3] The medium carrying the waves is supposed to be

---

[1] *Zeitschrift für Physik*, 33. 12, 1925, p. 879, and 35. 8–9, 1926, p. 557. For abstracts, see H. S. Allen, *The Quantum*, London, 1928; A. S. Eddington, *The Nature of the Physical World*, Cambridge, 1928, p. 206.

[2] *Annalen der Physik*, 79 (1926), pp. 361 and 734.

[3] The mathematics of Heisenberg and Schrödinger lead to similar equations By Hamiltonian principles they arrive at a formula

$$qp - pq = ih/2\pi,$$

where h is the quantum of action and i the square root of -1. p and q are called co-ordinates and momenta, though the words are used in unusual senses. For Born and Jordan p is a matrix—an infinite number of quantities arranged in symmetrical array. For Dirac p has no numerical significance, though at the end numbers appear from the equations. For Schrödinger the momentum p is an operator, a signal to carry out a mathematical operation on what follows. Whatever physical meaning is given to it, the above equation, as Eddington says, seems to lie at, or nearly at, the root of everything in the physical world (*loc. cit.* p. 207).

dispersive, as transparent matter is to light, or as the Heaviside layer, high up in the atmosphere, is to wireless waves. Thus the shorter the period the faster the speed, and it becomes possible for waves of two frequencies to be present together.

As in water, the velocity of an individual wave is not the same as the velocity of a group of waves or a storm. Schrödinger found that the mathematical equations which give the motion of a wave-group with two given frequencies are the same as the usual equations of motion of a particle with corresponding kinetic and potential energies. Thus wave-groups or storms manifest themselves to us as particles, and the frequencies manifest themselves as energies. This leads at once to the constant relation between frequency and energy which first appeared in Planck's constant h.

Two waves with vibrations too quick to be visible may by their interference produce "beats" which appear as light, just as two sounds of nearly equal pitch produce beats of much lower pitch than either. In a hydrogen atom with one proton and one electron, waves will exist in accordance with the equation, and Schrödinger found that solutions of the equations are only possible for definite frequencies, which correspond to the observed spectral lines. In more complex atoms, where Bohr's theory broke down, Schrödinger again gets the right number of frequencies to explain the phenomena of the spectra.

When one of Schrödinger's wave-groups is small, there is no doubt where to locate the electron which is its manifestation. But, as the group expands, the electron can be placed anywhere within it. There is a certain indeterminacy of position. In 1927 these principles were extended by Heisenberg and then by Bohr. They found that, the more accurately they attempted to specify the position of a particle, the less accurately could the velocity or momentum be determined, and vice versa. The necessary uncertainty in our knowledge of position multiplied by the uncertainty in our knowledge of momentum was, approximately at any rate, found to be equal to the quantum constant h. The idea of simultaneous certainty of the two seems to correspond to nothing in nature. Eddington called this result the principle of indeterminacy and assigns to it an importance equal to that of the principle

Quantum Mechanics of relativity.[1] It is now more usually called the principle of uncertainty.

The new quantum mechanics produced a revolution in physical science, already used to revolutions. The mathematical formulations of Heisenberg, of Schrödinger, and of some other exponents, are equivalent to each other, and, if we remain content with mathematical equations, we may feel considerable confidence in the theory. But the ideas from which the equations have been derived, and the interpretations which some have given to them, are fundamentally different. We can hardly expect these ideas and interpretations to last long, though the mathematics which express them are a permanent gain.

Classical mechanics are seen to be a limiting case of quantum mechanics. The failure of classical mechanics to deal with atomic structure is due to the wave-length being comparable with the dimensions of the atom, just as the straight rays of geometrical optics fail when the breadth of the ray or the size of obstacles in its path becomes comparable with the wave-length. There seems some possibility of thus connecting quantum mechanics with classical dynamic theory, with Maxwell's electro-magnetic equations, and with gravitational relativity. Should such a wide co-ordination of knowledge come to pass, the theory will take its place as one of the great historic generalizations of natural science.

Schrödinger's theory must be considered in relation to experiments on electrons which prove that, as de Broglie's theory indicates, a moving electron is accompanied by a series of waves. The Thomsonian corpuscle was first envisaged as a structureless material particle, and then as an electron, a simple unit of negative electricity, whatever that meant. But in 1923 Davisson and Kunsman, and in 1927 Davisson and Germer, working in America, reflected slowly moving electrons from the surfaces of crystals, and found them to possess some of the diffractive properties of wave systems.[2] Later in 1927, G. P. Thomson, Sir J. J. Thomson's son, made experiments which consisted in passing a narrow ray of electrons through an exceedingly thin sheet of metal—thinner than the finest gold leaf. A stream of particles would produce a blurred patch

---

[1] A. S. Eddington, *loc. cit.* p. 220.
[2] *Physical Review*, 22, p. 243, 1923; and *Nature*, 119, p. 558, 1927.

on a photographic plate beyond the sheet, but waves comparable in length with the thickness of the sheet would give a series of bright and dark rings like the diffusion patterns obtained when light passes through thin glass plates or soap films. Such rings were actually obtained, and indicate that a moving electron is accompanied by a train of waves, the wave-length being, like those of fairly penetrating X-rays,[1] only about the millionth part of the wave-length of visible light.

Theory indicates that, if the electron be accompanied by a train of waves, it must be vibrating in unison with the waves. It follows that the electron must have a structure, and thus, even experimentally, it ceases to be the ultimate unit either of matter or of electricity. A vista is opened into even more minute parts. Mathematical investigation shows that the energy of the electron is proportional to the frequency of the waves, and that the product of the momentum of the electron and the wave-length is constant. Since in the atom there are only certain wave-lengths and frequencies, its electronic momentum can only have certain values, and must increase not continuously but by jumps. This indication of discontinuity leads us back to the quantum theory.

The interpretation given of G. P. Thomson's experiments involved a dual-nature for the electron—a particle (or electric charge) and a train of waves. Schrödinger, as we have seen, goes farther, and resolves the electron itself into a wave system. Thus, a quarter of a century after the atom was resolved into electrons, the electron has been resolved into an unknown source of radiation or a disembodied wave-system. The last trace of the old, hard, massy particle has disappeared, and the ultimate conceptions of physics seem to be reduced to mathematical equations. Experimental physicists, especially if they be Englishmen, never feel comfortable with such abstractions, and already attempts are being made to devise atomic models which represent in mechanical or electrical terms the meaning of these equations. It is possible that, as J. J. Thomson suggests, the electron as a particle and a train of waves can only fit into an atom in whole wave-lengths.[2] This may explain the restriction to one of a few orbits or

---

[1] G. P. Thomson, *Proc. Roy. Soc.* A, 117, p. 600, 1928. See also Sir J. J. Thomson, *Beyond the Electron*, Cambridge, 1928.

[2] *The Listener*, Jan. 29, 1930, p. 211.

Quantum
Mechanics

energy levels, and enable us to return for a time to classical dynamics. But, as Newton saw, the ultimate basis which underlies mechanics cannot be mechanical.

Relativity[1]

The discovery that light needed time for its propagation was made by the Danish astronomer Olaus Römer in 1676. Römer found that the intervals between the successive eclipses of one of the satellites of the planet Jupiter were longer when the Earth was receding from Jupiter and shorter when the Earth was approaching. He estimated the velocity of light as 192,000 miles a second.

Fifty years later, James Bradley, the Astronomer Royal, got a concordant result from the aberration of the light from the fixed stars. As seen from a distant star in the plane of the Earth's orbit, the Earth would seem to oscillate from side to side once a year, moving in opposite directions in successive six months. The rays shot from the star to hit the Earth must always be aimed a little in front of it, as we shoot in front of a driven partridge or a rocketting pheasant, and so, if the star now shoots to the right of the Earth's true position, in six months it must aim to the left. This means that the rays by which the star is seen from the Earth at different times are not parallel to each other, but that the star appears to move backwards and forwards in space as the years revolve. From this apparent movement, the ratio of the velocity of light to the velocity of the Earth in its orbit may obviously be calculated.

The first determination of the velocity of light over short distances on the Earth was made in 1849 by Fizeau, who passed a beam of light through one of the gaps in a toothed wheel, and reflected it back on its path by a mirror three or four miles away. When the wheel was at rest, the return beam passed back through the same gap and was visible on the other side, but, when the wheel was rotated rapidly, a speed could be found at which the return way was blocked by the next tooth. The time occupied by the wheel in spinning through this small part of a revolution is clearly the time required for light to travel to the distant mirror and back again.

---

[1] A. Einstein, *Vier Vorlesungen über Relativitätstheorie*, Braunschweig, 1922; *The Meaning of Relativity*, London, 1922. A. S. Eddington, *Space, Time and Gravitation*, Cambridge, 1920; *The Mathematical Theory of Relativity*, Cambridge, 1923 and 1924.

A better method is that devised by L. Foucault. A beam of light from a slit S is made very slightly convergent and then reflected from the plane mirror R to a focus on a concave mirror M. It returns along its path and, if the mirror R is at rest, forms an image of the slit on the slit itself. The mirror R is then rotated rapidly at a known speed. It moves through a small angle while the light travels from R to M and back again, and therefore the return path RS' is not coincident with RS, but will be turned through twice the angle of rotation of the mirror R. The distance between S and S' is then measured and the time occupied by the light in travelling from R to M and back again is calculated.

Fig. 12.

The best modern results for the velocity of light give a value of 186,326 miles or $2 \cdot 2986 \times 10^{10}$ cm. a second *in vacuo*, or 3×10^{10} cm. per sec. to within less than one part in a thousand.

If there be anything in the nature of a luminiferous aether, its effect on light travelling through it should apparently make possible the determination of its motion. If the Earth moves through the aether without disturbing it, the Earth and the aether will be in relative motion. In that case, light should be found to travel faster when it moves with the aether than when it moves against it, and on the whole faster when it travels to and fro across the aether stream than when it passes first in the direction of the stream and then against it. It is quicker to swim from one side of a river and back again, than to swim an equal distance up and down stream.

That is the essence of the famous experiment made by Michelson and Morley in 1887. They mounted their apparatus on a stone floating in mercury to prevent vibration. A beam of light SA is partly reflected and partly transmitted at the glass A (Fig. 13). The two parts are reflected by mirrors at B and D. If $AB = AD$, the paths are equal in length and interference effects will be seen in a telescope by an eye at E. Let us imagine that the Earth is moving in the direction SAD but not carrying the aether with it, so that the aether is moving through the laboratory as the wind through a grove of trees.

This will introduce a difference in the time of transmission over the paths *ABA* and *ADA*, and the interference fringes will not occupy the same place as they would if the aether were relatively at rest. Next let the apparatus be floated round through a right angle. *AB* is now in the direction of motion and *AD* across it. The interference fringes should now move in the opposite direction, the whole displacement being twice that suggested above.

But Michelson and Morley could observe no measurable displacement of the interference fringes, and concluded that

Fig. 13.

there is no appreciable relative motion of the Earth and the aether. A repetition of their experiment showed that, on their assumptions, the relative motion is certainly less than the tenth part of the Earth's velocity in its orbit. The Earth seems to drag the aether with it.

But in calculating the velocity of light from aberration, it is assumed that the aether is undisturbed by the motion of the Earth through it. Moreover, Lodge in 1893 could find no change in the velocity of light between two heavy steel plates spinning at (or beyond) the highest safe speed. Hence masses of this size do not drag the neighbouring aether with them. Thus both the theory of aberration and the deductions from

Lodge's experiment seem quite inconsistent with Michelson's *Relativity* and Morley's result.

Whenever we get a discrepancy of this kind, if we are to hold our belief in the uniformity of nature, we may conclude that something must be wrong either in our experiments or in our conceptions of the causes at work, and it is probable that an interesting and necessary revolution in ideas is under our eyes if we can but see it.

The first useful suggestion was made by G. F. FitzGerald, and developed by Larmor and Lorentz. If matter be electrical in essence, or, indeed, if it be bound together by electric forces, it may contract in the direction of the motion as it moves through an electromagnetic aether. Such a contraction would not otherwise be observed, firstly because it would be too small, and secondly because any scales we used to measure it would themselves be subject to the same contraction, so that, in the direction of motion, the unit of length would be shorter. Thus Michelson's and Morley's apparatus as it rotated might change in dimensions in such a manner as to compensate for the displacement of the interference fringes produced by the Earth's movement through the aether.

It is easy to calculate the contraction necessary. A body would contract in the direction of the aether stream in the ratio $(1 - v^2/c^2)^{\frac{1}{2}}$, where v is the relative velocity of the body and the aether, and c the constant velocity of light.

The velocity of the Earth in its orbit is 1/10,000 the velocity of light. If, at some time of the year, this be its velocity through the aether, Michelson's and Morley's apparatus would contract by one part in 200 million when turned through a right angle, and that minute change would explain their result.

There the subject rested for some years. Whatever the cause, every attempt to measure the velocity of light, whether with or against a supposed aether stream, led to the same result, no change in the measured velocity could be detected.

In 1905 an entirely new direction was given to thought on this subject by Professor A. Einstein, who pointed out that the ideas of absolute space and time were figments of the imagination—metaphysical concepts not derived directly from the observations and experiments of physics. The only space we can experience is that measured in terms of a standard unit of length, defined as the distance between two scratches

Relativity on a bar, and the only time is that measured by some clock set by astronomical events. If changes such as the FitzGerald contraction take place in our standards, they will be quite inappreciable to us who move with them and suffer corresponding changes, but they might be measurable by an observer who was moving differently. Time and space, therefore, are not absolute, but merely relative to the observer.

From this point of view, no explanation is needed of the fact that the velocity of light, as measured by any apparatus and in any circumstances, is always the same. That result must be accepted as the first discovered law of the new physics. Time and space are thus shown to be such that light always travels relatively to any observer with the same measured velocity.

This measured velocity is constant, but neither space nor time nor mass measured separately show the constancy we are accustomed to expect. Michelson's and Morley's apparatus, tested by our constant standard, the speed of light, shows no change in linear dimensions as it rotates. But that is because we are moving with it. If however we could measure accurately enough the length of a bullet as it flew past us, we should find that it appeared shorter than when at rest, and, if its speed approached that of light, it would seem still shorter.

This experiment is not practicable: but it is easy to show, on the principle of relativity, that the mass of the bullet will appear to an observer at rest to be increased, and increased in the same ratio as the length is shortened. If m_0 be the mass at slow speeds, that at a high velocity v is $m_0/\sqrt{1 - v^2/c^2}$, where c is the velocity of light. Hence, at the velocity of light, mass would become infinite. The change in mass may be examined experimentally. Among the marvels of modern science is the measurement of the mass of projectiles which are moving past us with speeds of the same order as that of light. The β particles, shot forth by exploding radio-active atoms, can be directed through electric and magnetic fields of force, and their velocity and their mass can thus be determined, just as the velocity and mass of a cathode ray particle have been determined. If the mass of a β particle moving at moderate speeds be called unity, the following table gives in the second column the mass (calculated on the principle of relativity) of other β particles, the velocity of which approaches that of light, and in the third column their mass as measured by *Relativity* Kauffman experimentally.

Velocity of corpuscle in cm. per second	Ratio of mass to the mass of a slowly moving corpuscle	
	Calculated	Observed
$2\cdot36 \times 10^{10}$	1·65	1·5
$2\cdot48 \times 10^{10}$	1·83	1·66
$2\cdot59 \times 10^{10}$	2·04	2·0
$2\cdot72 \times 10^{10}$	2·43	2·42
$2\cdot85 \times 10^{10}$	3·09	3·1

These β particles are negative electrons, and, when moving, are equivalent to an electric current. Hence they create an electromagnetic field of force, which possesses both energy and inertia. The increase of mass with velocity was also calculated on these lines by J. J. Thomson and by G. F. C. Searle with the same result. Therefore the increase of mass, like Fitz-Gerald's contraction, is in accordance with electromagnetic theory.

Again, on the principle of relativity, mass and energy are equivalent, a mass m, when expressed as energy, being mc^2, where c is the velocity of light. This too is in conformity with Maxwell's theory of electromagnetic waves, which possess momentum equal to E/c where E is their energy. Momentum being mc, we get again that $E = mc^2$.

It is clear at once that these principles lead to remarkable and unexpected results. If we could travel in an airplane (or an aether-plane) with a speed comparable with that of light, our length in the direction of motion as measured by an observer on the earth would appear to be contracted, our mass would seem greater, and our time scale slower than usual. But we ourselves should be unconscious of these changes. Our foot rule might have shrunk, but, as we and all our surroundings would have shrunk also, we should not perceive the change. Our pound weight might have a greater mass, but so should we. Our clocks might go slower, but the atoms of our brains would move more slowly also, and again we should not know.

But, since motion is only relative, the observer on the Earth is moving relatively to us at the same rate as we are to him. Hence we should find on measuring them that his scales of length, mass and time had changed to us as ours had to him.

Relativity   He would seem to us to have suffered an unseemly contraction in the direction of motion, to have a mass out of proportion to his size, and to be ludicrously slow in mind and body. And all the while he would be thinking the same thoughts about us. We both should be unconscious of our own imperfections, but we each should see clearly the sad changes in the other.

It is impossible to say that either of these observers is wrong. Indeed both are right. Length, mass and time are not absolute quantities. Their true physical values are what the measurements indicate. The fact that they are not the same to everybody shows that they can only be defined relatively to one specified observer. The ideas of absolute length, of absolute space, and of an absolute and even flow of time, are metaphysical concepts, which go far beyond what is indicated or justified by observation or experiment.

Nevertheless, as Bergson has pointed out, philosophically it is probable that the only time that is lived, the time that measures what goes on in a system to one moving with it, or in it, is of special, indeed, of unique, importance. But physically space and time, considered individually, are relative quantities depending on the position of the observer. It was, however, pointed out in 1908 by Minkowski that the changes in space and time compensate each other, so that a combination of the two is, even in this new world, the same for all observers. The space of which we are accustomed to think has three dimensions—length, breadth and thickness, and, taught by Minkowski, we must look on time as a fourth dimension in this combination of space and time, one second corresponding to the 186,000 miles which light travels in that time. Just as the distance between two points in the continuous space of Euclidean geometry is the same however measured, so, in the new continuum of space-time, two events may be said to be separated by an "interval", involving both space and time, which has a true absolute value whoever measures it. We feel that here we have found something firm in a shifting world, and we are led to search for other quantities that remain absolute in the realm of relativity. Of quantities already known to us, we find that there still remain as absolutes: number; thermodynamic entropy; and also action, that product of energy and time which gives us the quantum.

In the old world of independent space and time, men had

been accustomed to think of the whole of three-dimensional *Relativity*
space as passing from moment to moment simultaneously,
the past of the world being as it were separated from the
future by the dividing plane of the present, which stretched
everywhere at the same moment through space. But when,
in 1676, Römer discovered that light travelled with a finite
velocity, it must have been realized that the stars, visible
simultaneously at one moment, were really seen as they existed
at times in the past depending on their distances—simul-
taneity had disappeared. The absolute "now" of former
beliefs had become a merely relative "seen-now".

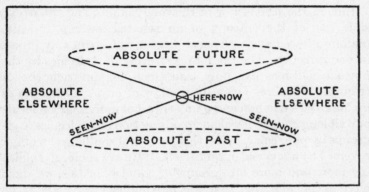

Fig. 14.

The recent developments in science have increased this
relativity. If a traveller, moving with the velocity of light,
takes a trip among the stars and returns to Earth after one of
our years, to us, as we watch his flight, his mass will seem
infinite and the movements of his brain infinitesimally slow.
While we feel a year older, to him no time seems to have
elapsed; he is still in the "now" of our last year. Thus the
analogy of a plane, the same for all men at all places, separating
past and future, must be given up. From the point which
Eddington calls "here-now", lines of "seen-now" must be
drawn through space, making an angle with the axis of time
of which the tangent is equal to the velocity of light.[1] Anywhere within the three-dimensional surface thus generated,
a surface analogous to a double cone or hour-glass in two

[1] A. S. Eddington, *The Nature of the Physical World*, Cambridge, 1928. I am
indebted to Professor Eddington for permission to use the diagram.

dimensions, we get an absolute past or an absolute future. Outside it, things can co-exist simultaneously at what must seem to any one observer different times. The neutral wedge, which separates past and future, can be called the absolute present or the absolute elsewhere, according as we regard it in terms of time or of space.

The passage of time from past to future, which we interpret intuitively in terms of consciousness, has no counterpart in reversible physics. The equations of motion of ordinary dynamical systems, whether terrestrial or astronomic, can be read either way; we cannot tell from Newton's formulae in which direction a planet revolves round the sun.

But, in the second law of thermodynamics and the irreversible rise of the entropy of an isolated system towards a maximum, we have a physical process which can only proceed in one direction. The random scattering of molecules by their mutual collisions can only lead them to approach the distribution velocities given by the law of error. Unless we call up Maxwell's daemon and gain control of individual molecules, or wait long enough for chance conjunctions of molecules to give groups by pure coincidence, this process of shuffling can only be reversed by a reversal in time itself. If we saw molecules collecting more and more into groups of equal velocities, we should have to conclude that time was moving backward. The second law of thermodynamics, the principle of the increase in entropy, describes the one, all important process of nature which corresponds with the remorseless march of time in the human mind.

In 1894 G. F. FitzGerald of Dublin wrote: "Gravity is probably due to a change in structure of the aether, produced by the presence of matter".[1] This sentence, in the language of the older physics, expresses the result of applying a general form of relativity to gravitation, which was done by Einstein in 1915. He proved that the properties of space, and especially the phenomena of the propagation of light, show that Minkowski's space-time continuum resembles Riemann's space and not Euclid's, except in infinitely small regions.[2]

In this space-time, there are natural paths, like the straight paths in three-dimensional space along which we are accus-

---

[1] *Scientific Writings*, p. 313.
[2] The distance between two points depends on the co-ordinate differences *dx dy*. If the form of the dependence is

$$ds^2 = g_{11} \cdot dx^2 + 2g_{12} \cdot dx\,dy + g_{22} \cdot dy^2,$$

tomed to imagine bodies moving when not acted on by a force. Since a projectile falls to the Earth and the planets circle round the Sun, we see that near matter these paths must be curved, and consequently near matter there must be something analogous to a curvature of space-time. Another body entering this curved region tends to move towards or round the matter in a definite path. Indeed, as long as we think in terms of mass and not electricity, the only meaning of matter nowadays is a region in space-time where this curvature occurs. If we prevent the second body from moving freely, holding it up perhaps by the bombardment of the molecules of a chair or of the surface of the ground, we exert force on it, which seems to the body to be due to its own "weight".

This effect is well shown by a lift. When the lift starts upwards, it is subject to an acceleration which appears to the occupants as a temporary increase of their weight, an increase which may indeed be measured like ordinary weight by a spring balance. The effect of the acceleration is identical with the effect of a temporary increase in the so-called gravitational field, and it is impossible to distinguish between these two causes by any experiment known to us.

But if a lift were allowed to fall freely, the occupants would not be conscious of motion. If one of them released an apple held in his hand, it would not fall faster than the lift, but would remain poised by the observer. This principle of equivalence, which first turned the subject towards gravitation, was set forth by Einstein in 1911, and the great mathematical difficulties were overcome during the next few years.[1]

it is a Riemannian metric. A special case of this is given by

$$ds^2 = dx^2 + dy^2.$$

the theorem of Pythagoras, when the continuum is Euclidean.

The quantities g_{11}, g_{12}, g_{22} determine not only the metric of the continuum but also the gravitational field. By investigating the simplest mathematical forms to which these quantities can be subjected, Einstein discovered the new laws of gravity.

[1] See above, footnotes to pp. 192 and 220, Lagrange, Laplace and Hamilton. Einstein developed general equations which reduced to those of Laplace in the special case where neither matter nor energy is present at the point considered and to those of Poisson when the energy is entirely in the form of matter.

A small particle moving in a statical field, in general relativity has its motion determined by the Lagrangian differential equation

$$\frac{d}{dt}\left(\frac{\delta L}{\delta \dot{x}_r}\right) - \frac{dL}{dx_r} = 0,$$

though L is not here, as in classical dynamics, a simple difference of terms of kinetic and potential energy.

It then became clear that Newton's hypothesis of a gravitational attraction may be unnecessary. The movement of a body towards the Earth, or round it in an orbit, may merely be the tracing of its natural path in a curved region of space-time.

Calculation shows that the consequences of this theory are nearly the same as Newton's—quite the same to the usual order of accuracy of observation. Yet, in one or two phenomena, it is just possible to devise a crucial experiment. Of these the most famous is the deflection of a ray of light by the Sun, which, on Einstein's principle, is twice what the Newtonian theory would indicate. The only way in which these minute deflections can be observed is to photograph during an eclipse of the Sun the image of a star which appears just outside the Sun's disc. This was done during the eclipse of 1919 by Eddington at Principe in the Gulf of Guinea and by Crommelin in Brazil. Compared with stars further away from the Sun, it was found that the image of the nearer star was displaced, and displaced to the amount required by Einstein.

Secondly, the discrepancy of 42 seconds of arc per century in the orbit of Mercury, left over by the Newtonian theory, was at once explained by Einstein, who calculated a change of 43 seconds of arc.

Thirdly, on the principle of relativity, an atom should vibrate more slowly in a gravitational field. Hence, on the average, the lines in the spectrum of the Sun, where gravity is more intense, should be displaced towards the red compared with the lines in corresponding terrestrial spectra. The shift to be expected is barely perceptible, but the balance of experimental evidence now goes to show that it exists. It should be larger in the spectra of dense stars, and, its truth being assumed, it has been recently used to measure the density of such stars.

Thus it seems that, as an exact account, Newton's theory must give place to Einstein's. In two directions—in the quantum theory and in the theory of relativity—recent physics seem to be breaking away from the fundamental conceptions by which they have been guided successfully since the days of Galileo. The new thought needs new vehicles for its expression. In some ways, it is clear, the dynamics of Newton, which ushered in two glorious centuries of modern science, are proving inadequate to the tasks imposed by present knowledge. Even matter, the concept of which underlies classical dynamics, has now vanished. The essential idea of a substance, as something extended in space and persistent in time, is now meaningless, since neither space nor time is either absolute or real. A substance has become a mere series of events, connected in some unknown and perhaps causal way, taking place in space-time. Relativity thus reinforces the results which follow from the latest theory of the atom. Newton's dynamics still suffice to predict physical happenings to a high degree of accuracy, and to solve the practical problems of the astronomer, the physicist and the engineer. But, as ultimate physical concepts, his theories pass with an honoured name into history.

Relativity and Gravitation

Perhaps the best way of deriving the laws of nature from the general principle of relativity is by the minimum principle applied by Hilbert in 1915. Hero of Alexandria discovered that reflected light travels by the path which makes the total distance traversed a minimum. This was extended by Fermat in the seventeenth century into a general principle of least time. A hundred years later, Maupertuis, Euler and Lagrange developed the dynamical principle of least action, and in 1834 Hamilton showed that all gravitational, dynamical and electrical laws could be represented as minimum problems. Hilbert proved that, on the principle of relativity, gravitation acts so as to make the total curvature of space-time a minimum[1] or, as E. T. Whittaker puts it, "gravitation simply represents a continual effort of the universe to straighten itself out".[2]

The general theory of relativity at once abolished the idea of a mechanical force due to gravitational attraction: gravity became a metric property of space-time. But, electrified or magnetic bodies had still to be regarded as acted on by forces. Attempts have been made by Weyl and others to bring them into line, but without complete success. But in 1929 Einstein announced that he had devised a new Unitary Field Theory which, taking space to be something between the space of

[1] All physical happenings, gravitational, electrical. etc. are determined by a scalar world function $\mathfrak{H}$, being such as to annul the variation of the integral
$$\iiint \mathfrak{H}\, dx_0\, dx_1\, dx_2\, dx_3.$$
[2] *British Association Report*, 1927, Address to Section A, p. 23.

*Relativity and
Gravitation*

Euclid and that of Riemann, makes electromagnetism also a metric property of space-time.[1] If this work is confirmed, field physics will be reduced to a single form.

Another co-ordination of different concepts was announced by Eddington in 1928.[2] The electronic charge e appears in the wave-equation for two electrons in the combination $hc/2\pi e^2$, where h is the quantum of action, and c the velocity of light. On the principles of quanta and relativity, Eddington calculates the numerical value of this combination as 136. Millikan's latest value for e gives for the same quantity the figure 137·1. The discrepancy is greater than probable experimental errors, but the approximation is of great interest. Indeed, in 1930 it is becoming increasingly clear that all these modern concepts may soon be brought together in a new physical synthesis.

*Astro-Physics:
The Stellar
Universe[3]*

Kepler's observations on the Sun and planets gave a model of the solar system, but the scale of the model is not known till some one distance is measured in terrestrial units. This has been done with modern accuracy in several ways: (1) The "aberration" of the light of a distant star when the Earth moves across the path of the light and six months later moves in the opposite direction, was discovered by Bradley in 1728. It was then used to prove that light travelled with a finite velocity, but, since the velocity of light can now be measured in other ways, aberration can conversely be used to give the Earth's velocity, and therefore the size of its orbit. (2) When the planet Venus passes between the Earth and the Sun, its time of transit at two stations on the Earth gives a means of measuring the distance of the Sun by trigonometry. (3) The distance of the small planet Eros when it passed near the Earth in 1900 was measured by triangulation.

The three methods agree in giving the following dimensions to the solar system. The distance from the Earth to the Sun is 92·8 million miles, a distance which light, moving at 186,000 miles a second, traverses in 8·3 minutes. The Sun's diameter is 865,000 miles, its mass 332,000 times that of the Earth, and its mean density 1·4 grams per cubic centimetre compared with 5·5 for the Earth. The most distant planet, Neptune,

---

[1] A. Einstein, two articles in *The Times* of February 3rd and 5th, 1929.

[2] A. S. Eddington, *Proc. Roy. Soc.* A, vol. cxxii (1928), p. 358.

[3] F. J. M. Stratton, *Astronomical Physics*, London, 1925. Sir J. H. Jeans, *Astronomy and Cosmogony*, Cambridge, 1928. A. S. Eddington, *Stars and Atoms*, Oxford, 1927. T. C. Chamberlin, *The Two Solar Families*, Chicago, 1928.

moves round the Sun in 165 years in an orbit the diameter of which is 5600 million miles. This diameter may be taken as the size of the solar system.

Beyond its outer confines lies a great gulf of space. By careful observation, the nearest stars may be seen to move against the background of those more distant, as the Earth passes in six months from one side of its orbit to the other. Another six months brings them back again, save for any small shift due to the real movements of the stars themselves. Corrected for this latter change and for the aberration of light, a star's six-months' parallax gives its distance by triangulation, since we know the diameter of the Earth's orbit.

An observation of the parallax of a fixed star was made by Henderson at the Cape of Good Hope in 1832, and accurate measurements by Bessel and by Struve followed in 1838. The nearest star, a faint speck called Proxima Centauri, is thus found to be 24 million million ($2\cdot4 \times 10^{12}$) miles away from us—a distance traversed by light in 4·1 years, and four thousand times the diameter of Neptune's orbit. Sirius, the bright dog-star, is 5×10^{12} miles or 8·6 light-years away. The distances of about 2000 stars have thus been determined with high accuracy, but at present this method of measurement is only applicable within a distance of about ten light-years.

On a clear night, the eye may see a few thousand stars. Others become visible as we use telescopes more and more powerful, but the number revealed does not increase in proportion to the power of the instrument, and therefore it may be concluded that the total number is not infinite. The 100-inch reflector of the Mount Wilson Observatory in America, the largest telescope existing in 1928, shows a number estimated at 100 million, and it would seem that in our stellar system the total is some number which has been variously estimated from 1500 million to 30,000 million.

Stars were classified by Hipparchus in six "magnitudes" according to their brightness, and the scale is now continued to include faint stars beyond the twentieth magnitude, whose brightness is only about the one hundred millionth part of that of stars of the first magnitude. This scale depends, of course, on the apparent brightness of the stars as seen from the Earth. For those stars whose distances are known, we can calculate the apparent magnitude which the star would have if moved to a standard distance, and this we call its absolute magnitude.

When classed according to their absolute magnitudes, we find stars of all values, but, as pointed out by Hertzsprung and confirmed by H. N. Russell, there are more in the higher and lower than in the intervening magnitudes. Those in the more populous groups have been called "Giant" and "Dwarf" stars respectively. They will be dealt with more fully later.

Stars of the same spectral type whose distances are known show a regular connection between absolute magnitude and the relative intensity of certain spectral lines. Hence a careful examination of these critical lines gives a value for the absolute magnitudes of other stars at unknown distances. Then, from their apparent magnitude, their distances may be estimated, even when it is too great to be measured by parallax. This calculation gives one of several indirect methods of estimating stellar distances.

Many stars which look single to the naked eye are seen through a telescope to be double. The individual stars in some of these pairs may be far from each other, and only seem near because they are almost in the same line of sight. But the number of double stars is much too great for such chance conjunctions to explain them all. In most cases there must be some connection between the two. William Herschel began observing double stars in 1782, and by 1793 he was able to trace enough of the paths of some binaries, to prove that they describe elliptic orbits about the common centre of gravity in one focus. He thus showed that double stars move in accordance with the laws of gravity demonstrated by Newton for our solar system.

For a few double stars, both the distances and the orbits have been determined, and from these results the masses have been calculated. They are generally found to range from about half to about three times the mass of the Sun, in agreement with other evidence which shows that the difference in mass between different stars is not very great, though the differences in size and density are enormous.

Some double stars are too near each other to be separated by a telescope, but can be resolved spectroscopically. If their orbits are seen edge-on, and the line joining the two stars is perpendicular to the line of sight, one star will be approaching us and one receding. Hence by Doppler's principle the lines in one spectrum will be shifted towards the blue and those in the other towards the red, and, in the actual spectrum of the double star, the lines will be doubled. When the stars are one behind the other, they will be moving nearly across the line of sight and no doubling will appear. By observing these changes in the spectra, the period of revolution and the velocities may be estimated, and the ratio of the masses calculated. Hence, if visual as well as spectroscopic measurements are possible, the individual masses can be determined.

It was in 1889 that E. C. Pickering first detected a double star spectroscopically. He announced that the doubling of some of the lines in the spectrum of ζ Ursa Majoris indicated that it was a binary star with a period of 104 days. Since then many hundreds of spectroscopic binaries have been discovered, chiefly by astronomers working in the clear air and with the great telescopes and spectroscopes of American and Canadian observatories.

The light of many stars varies in strength from time to time. When it varies irregularly, the changes may possibly be due to recurrent outrushes of incandescent gas, but very often the period of change is quite regular, and the cause of variation may be referred to the eclipse of the bright star by an invisible companion, which cuts off some or all of the light at intervals as the two stars revolve round each other. Sometimes this interpretation can be confirmed spectroscopically, the spectral lines being displaced periodically when the bright star is approaching or receding radially from the Earth. From a curve of variation of light with time, combined with spectrum measurements, a very complete description of the system can often be obtained, as, for instance, with the stars named Algol and β Lyrae.

The number of double stars is immense, and still more complex systems, multiple stars, can be recognized and examined by the same methods. For example, the well-known "Pole Star" has been found spectroscopically to comprise two stars revolving round each other in four days, a third star with a period of twelve years, and a fourth star revolving in some such time as twenty thousand years.

Other regular variables, such as δ Cephei, cannot easily be explained by eclipses. They flash out to several times their minimum brightness at intervals of hours or days. When of short period these "Cepheid" stars show a definite relation between the period of variation and the luminosity or absolute magnitude, a relation discovered by Miss Leavitt of Harvard in 1912. The value of this discovery was seen at once by Hertzsprung and by Shapley, then of Mount Wilson. The phenomenon is so regular that measurement of the period of other similar stars at unknown distances can be used as a means of estimating their absolute magnitudes. An observation of the apparent magnitude of the star then gives the distance—another method applicable to stars too far away to show any parallax.

Stars are most numerous in a band of varying width, called the Galaxy or Milky Way, which stretches round the heavens in a great circle. In places the numbers are so great that star-clouds appear, only to be resolved into individual stars by good telescopes, while interspersed are irregular nebulae which cannot be resolved. The great plane, which cuts the Milky Way as nearly as may be in the middle of the band of stars, is called the galactic plane. It may be looked upon as a plane of symmetry in the stellar system. Towards it the stars seem to crowd, especially the hotter stars and also those fainter stars, which, on the average, are farther away.

This indicates that our stellar system is flattened in the galactic plane. It seems to form a vast lens-shaped collection of stars. We are within it, but not at the centre. We see more stars in the Milky Way, chiefly because, when looking at it, we are looking towards the edge of the lens, where the depth of star-strewed space is much greater than elsewhere.

Besides star-clouds and irregular nebulae, there are also known about a hundred globular clusters of stars which are most numerous just outside the central zone of the Milky Way. They contain Cepheid variables, and, from the period of variability and by other indirect methods, the distances of the clusters from us have been estimated by Shapley to range from 20,000 to 200,000 light-years.

It appears then that the stellar system has a longest diameter which it would take light at least 300,000 years to traverse. Our Sun lies about 60,000 light-years from the centre of the whole system, somewhat to the north of the central plane. Observation over many years of the apparent movements of the stars shows that the Sun is travelling towards the constellation called Hercules with a speed of about 13 miles a second, and that, taking this drift as a line of reference, there are two main streams of stars moving through space.

The most stupendous objects in the sky are the great spiral nebulae, which are probably star-systems in the making. Evidence for this view will be given later. These nebulae are colossal in size: though made of tenuous gas, one of them may contain enough matter to make a thousand million Suns. Their numbers are enormous: Dr Hubble, of Mount Wilson Observatory, California, estimates that about two million are visible in the large 100-inch telescope of that Observatory. The distances of some are gigantic: estimates of 500,000 to 140 million light-years have been made, and it is probable that they are far beyond the confines of our stellar system. Space seems to contain an immense number of galaxies, "island Universes" as Shapley calls them, of which our own is but one.

A system of classification of stars depending on their spectra was begun in Rome by Father Secchi about 1867 and was much improved and extended at Harvard Observatory in America. Even the visual colours of stars differ, and, since photography is more sensitive to the violet end of the spectrum, photographic magnitudes are not the same as those estimated by eye, the differences between them giving a scale of colour. These differences are further exemplified in the spectra. A series of spectral lines can be found, passing into each other by insensible gradations, but showing definite characteristics which were distinguished at Harvard by the letters O, B, A, F, G, K, M, N, R, a list in which the bluer stars come first.

The spectra of type O give a faint continuous background on which bright lines appear. In some spectra the hydrogen and helium lines are strong. Type B spectra show dark lines with helium very prominent. Type A show hydrogen, and also calcium and other metals, which increase in importance in type F. Type G includes our Sun; the spectra show dark lines on a bright ground, and the stars are yellow in colour. In type K, bands due to hydrocarbons appear for the first time. Type M stars give broad absorption bands, especially those of titanium oxide. Type N spectra show broad absorption lines due to carbon monoxide and cyanogen, and the stars are red in colour. Type R stars also show the absorption bands found in N, though the colour is not so red.

Astro-Physics: The Stellar Universe

The Nature of Stars

The Nature of Stars

These observations on spectra were used to estimate the effective temperatures of different types of stars. If a black body, which may be regarded as a perfect radiator, is gradually heated, the character as well as the intensity of the radiation changes. For each temperature there is a characteristic curve between radiant energy and wave-length, showing a maximum at some particular wave-length. As the temperature rises, the position of this maximum shifts towards the blue end of the spectrum, and thus indicates the temperature. The distribution of energy has been investigated in several ways, both photographically and by studying variations in the character of the radiation. Furthermore, the effect of temperature and ionization on spectra can be examined in the laboratory within the ranges under our control. The appearance of certain absorption lines in stellar spectra have thus been used to estimate the temperatures of the absorbing atoms by Saha (1920) and by R. H. Fowler and E. A. Milne (1923).

The various methods of estimating stellar temperatures agree well. For stars just visible they are about 1650°, while in the hottest stars known they reach some 23,000° C. These temperatures are of course those of the radiating layer; the inside parts of a star must be much hotter, with temperatures rising to many million degrees.

When considering their absolute magnitudes we saw that stars mostly fell into two groups, "giants" and "dwarfs", one with much greater luminosity than the other, though intermediate stars are not unknown. Now it is remarkable that this division into groups is only clear in the cooler stars of types K onwards, with temperatures not above 4000° C. In the hotter stars the division is less marked, and in type B it has quite disappeared; these stars are all "giants" with luminosities from 40 to 1600 times that of our Sun.

These facts were thought to point to a definite conclusion, namely, that all stars go through a course of evolution roughly identical. Each star was thought to begin as a comparatively cool body, gradually to rise in temperature, to attain a maximum depending on its size, and then to pass down the same temperature scale as it became cool again.

While ascending in this scale, a star emits a very large amount of light, which means that it must be of enormous size.

Therefore it was classed as a "giant" star. As it cools, its atmosphere passes through the same range of temperature in the reverse order, and so it goes through the same spectral types in its descent as in its rise, though certain differences in detail are observed. But now the absolute magnitude of the star, that is its luminosity, is much less, a fact which, since the temperature is the same as in its rise, shows that it is much smaller. The star has become a "dwarf".

This process of stellar evolution, traced by Russell, was in accordance with the dynamics of a mass of gravitating gas, as worked out by Lane and Ritter. If the mass be large enough, gravity will cause it to contract. It will give out heat and grow hotter. But, as it shrinks, the rate of contraction must decrease. At a certain critical density, the heat developed by this colossal mass of glowing vapour becomes less than that radiated, and the mass begins to cool. As we saw in Chapter VIII when considering the age of the Sun, this process cannot explain all the heat evolved, but it was thought possible that other sources of energy, such as atomic disintegration, might depend on temperature and go through a similar history.

This theory of stellar evolution has been modified by more recent research, which has applied to astro-physics our new knowledge of atomic structure. Man from his strategic position mid-way between an atom and a star,[1] has learnt to study each in the light of information obtained from the other.

Knowing the size and average density of the Sun or any star and assuming that the whole mass is gaseous, it is possible to calculate mathematically the rate of increase of pressure with depth beneath the surface, and this has been done by Eddington. At any given level, the pressure above is supported by the elasticity of the gas below, supplemented by the pressure of its radiation. By the kinetic theory, the elasticity is due to impacts of the gaseous particles the velocities of which depend on the temperature. Thus the temperature inside a star can be determined. To support the enormous pressure within the Sun and other similar stars, the temperature must be about 40 or 50 million degrees centigrade. If the star were much larger, Eddington suggested that the pressure of radiation inside it might become so great that the star would become

---

[1] As Eddington has pointed out, about 10^{27} atoms go to build a man's body, and 10^{28} times as many make an average star.

unstable, and fly to pieces. Thus may be fixed a natural upper limit to the size of stars.

A region, even a large region, inside a star is practically a constant-temperature enclosure, and the total radiation will therefore vary as the fourth power of the absolute ·temperature. Furthermore, as the temperature rises, the radiation of maximum energy will pass up the spectrum into waves of shorter and shorter lengths, in accordance with known laws. When the temperature runs to millions of degrees, the maximum energy is far beyond the visible spectrum, and consists of X-rays or radiation of even shorter wave-length. Such radiation would be converted into longer waves as it continually collided and interacted with atoms on its way towards the outer layers of the star; it would eventually emerge as light and heat. But it is a remarkable fact that extremely penetrating rays have been detected by McLennan, Millikan, Kolhörster and others, rays which, though minute in quantity, seem to be always passing through our atmosphere and coming from space. As Jeans says: "In a sense this radiation is the most fundamental physical phenomenon of the whole universe, most regions of space containing more of it than of visible light or heat. Our bodies are traversed by it night and day...it breaks up several million atoms in each of our bodies every second. It may be essential to life or it may be killing us".[1] It is probable that this penetrating radiation is emitted by the mutual annihilation of protons and electrons in places such as the nebulae or the excessively tenuous cloud which seems to fill open space, where the resultant energy has not to fight its way through the superincumbent mass of a star.

We know that X-rays and the even more penetrating γ rays, are a very effective ionizing agency. It therefore follows that the atoms within a star will be highly ionized, that is stripped of their outer electrons; an idea propounded by Jeans in 1917 and worked at by many others. The volume filled by an ordinary atom, the volume within which other complete atoms cannot penetrate, is the volume occupied by the orbits of these outer electrons. When the outer electrons are stripped off, the

[1] Sir J. H. Jeans, *Eos or the Wider Aspects of Cosmogony*, London, 1928, p. 46; also *The Universe Around Us*, New York and Cambridge, 1929, p. 134.

effective volume of the atom becomes much smaller, becomes, in fact, the volume of the nucleus and its closely attendant rings of electrons, with orbits considerably smaller than those of the outer electrons. The result is that, inside the stars, atoms are very much smaller and therefore interfere with each other far less than they do in our laboratories; even at high densities stellar matter acts as a "perfect" gas, conforming to Boyle's law.

Assuming that a star is gaseous, it is possible to calculate mathematically the relation between the mass of a star and the amount of light and heat which leaks out—that is, how bright it will be. In 1924 Eddington calculated that the greater the mass of a star the more it should radiate. He deduced a theoretical relation, and, by adjusting a numerical factor, brought the relation into accordance with facts. It even held for some stars which are so dense that in 1924 they were assumed to be liquid or solid, so that the theory was thought not to be applicable. But Eddington holds that even the Sun, denser than water, and other stars, denser than iron, are in effect gaseous; that their atoms, stripped of outer electrons, are small, and for most of their time outside each other's reach.

Moreover a new discovery has increased the range of possible densities. Sirius, the brightest star in the sky, was found by Bessel in 1844 to describe an elliptic orbit, and an invisible companion star was invented for Sirius to move round, with a mass about 4/5th of that of the Sun. Eighteen years later this star was seen by Alvan Clark; in modern telescopes it is easily visible, and is found to give out 1/360th of the Sun's light. It was assumed to be a dying star, only just red-hot; but in 1914 Adams saw from Mount Wilson that it was not red-hot but white-hot. Its small total emission of light must therefore be due to a very small size; it cannot be much larger than the Earth. This large mass and small size together indicate a density of about a ton to the cubic inch—an amazing result, which at the time seemed quite incredible.

But later on new evidence appeared. Einstein's theory requires that the frequency of emitted radiation should depend on the mass and the size, so that spectral lines should be shifted towards the red by an amount proportional to the mass divided by the radius. Adams succeeded in measuring the spectrum of the Companion of Sirius, and again got indications of the same high density, two thousand times greater than that of platinum. A few other stars have now been found to have similar or higher densities. In these stars, Jeans holds, the matter must have ceased to be gaseous and resemble a liquid. The atoms probably consist of nuclei only, stripped bare of even the innermost rings of electrons. More normal stars like Sirius and the Sun probably consist of atoms with one ring of electrons left round the nucleus. An explanation is thus found in the theory of atomic structure for the fact that stars fall into distinct groups, each group containing stars within certain limits of size. Terrestrial atoms would be completely broken up at such temperatures, and, to retain these different sizes, the atoms in the unknown depths of the stars must be heavier than those known to us on the Earth, while lighter atoms like our own float to the surface and form the radiating layer.

The ages of stars can be estimated in three ways. (1) The orbits of binary stars should begin as circles and be slowly deformed by the forces of passing stars. The probable frequency of such influences can be calculated, and so, from the actual shapes, the probable age can be deduced. (2) Groups of bright stars moving through space gradually lose their smaller constituents, and the time required to produce the observed scattering can be calculated. (3) Like molecules in a gas, the energies of motion of stars must tend to an equality, and those stars near the Sun have been found by Seares to have nearly reached this stage. From kinetic theory we can calculate the time needed to produce this equality. The three methods agreed in indicating some five to ten millions of millions of years as the probable average age of stars in our stellar system.

To provide for such lives as these, enormous supplies of radiant energy are needed, far more than gravitational contraction or even radioactivity will explain. Einstein's theory naturally led to the view that the source might be found in the mutual annihilation of positive protons and negative electrons, an idea suggested by Jeans in 1904 as an explanation of radio-active energy.[1] This theory has now been worked out in detail. It is certain that stars lose mass. Radiation causes pressure of known amount, and therefore possesses a

[1] *Nature*, LXX, p. 101, 1904.

calculable momentum or mass-velocity. The Sun is radiating fifty horse-power from each square inch of surface, which means that the Sun as a whole is losing mass at the rate of 360,000 million tons a day, and the mutual cancellation of protons and electrons suggests a mechanism by which this loss may occur. The Sun must have lost mass more quickly when it was larger and younger, and thus an upper limit can be fixed for its age, a limit of somewhere about eight million million years. This agrees well with the independent estimates for the stars.

Having estimated the age of stars, it is natural to ask how they are born. Even in the largest telescope, a star has no visible dimensions—the nearest is too far away. But areas of luminosity, called nebulae, have long been known. One, the great nebula in the constellation Andromeda, being visible to the naked eye, was observed before the invention of the telescope, and another, situated in Orion, was discovered by Huygens in 1656.

There are three chief classes of nebulae:

(1) Irregularly shaped nebulae such as that in Orion.

(2) Planetary nebulae, smaller bodies of regular shape.

(3) Spiral nebulae, like great whirlpools of light.

The greatest number of nebulae are of spiral form. As already stated, it seems that about two million are visible in modern telescopes. Their spectra are continuous, with superposed absorption lines—spectra which resemble those of stars of classes F to K, including our Sun. Some nebulae are masses of dispersed glowing vapour, others contain definite-formed stars. The nebulae also show evidence of rapid rotation. Those which we see edge-on can be examined spectroscopically, and some of those which are at right angles to us, when photographed year after year, show measurable rotation, indicating a rate of one revolution in some millions of years. This may seem slow, but very high linear velocities have been observed, so that the long period of rotation is due to colossal size rather than to slow movement.

If we assume that different nebulae rotate with velocities of the same order, a comparison of the radial speed of edge-on nebulae measured spectroscopically with the annual angular rotation of nebulae with planes across the line of sight gives an estimate of distance. Cepheid variables are to be seen in the arms of spiral nebulae, and their period of variation in brightness may be assumed to be connected with their absolute brightness in the usual way; a measurement of the apparent brightness then gives another estimate of the distance. From this evidence, values have been obtained ranging from hundreds of thousands to millions of light-years. Most spiral nebulae, therefore, are very far away, and lie outside our system of stars.

The nebular theory of stellar evolution was first suggested by Kant and then again by Laplace at the end of the eighteenth century, in an attempt to explain the origin of the solar system. Laplace began with the idea of a gaseous nebula, which filled the space comprised in Neptune's orbit, and possessed a motion of rotation. Under its own gravitation, the nebula contracted, and therefore, since the angular momentum was constant, it moved with increasing velocity. At various stages as it shrank it left behind rings of matter, which condensed into the planets and their satellites, revolving round the central mass which formed the Sun.

Now there are several difficulties in this interpretation. F. R. Moulton showed in 1900 that the breaking of a ring into a globe was unlikely, and T. C. Chamberlin gave evidence that for a mass of gas of the required dimensions, gravity would not overcome the diffusive effects of molecular velocities and radiation pressure. Again, Jeans has shown that planetary condensations would not be formed.

But the spiral nebulae are bodies a million times larger than that imagined by Laplace, and on this scale the whole course of development is different. Gravitation is now more effective than both gas pressure and radiation pressure, and the nebula, instead of scattering, contracts and spins faster as Laplace supposed. The explanation fails for the comparatively small solar system, but succeeds for a gigantic stellar galaxy.

Jeans has proved mathematically that a mass of gravitating gas, set in rotation perhaps by the tidal action of other masses, will gradually assume the form of a double convex lens. As it spins faster, the edge must eventually become unstable, and break up into two arms. Local condensations will occur in the arms, each of the appropriate size to form a star within the somewhat narrow limits of size we find stars to possess. This theoretical prediction has been confirmed by Hubble, who, from observation, classified nebulae in the different groups foretold by Jeans. In spiral nebulae, then, we see new stellar systems in the making far in the depths of space beyond our own system of stars.

Will one tiny globule on the arm of a spiral nebula form a solar system such as ours? Jeans' mathematics indicate that it is not probable. If the rotation of the globule be fast enough to cause disruption, it seems that a double star with the two partners waltzing round each other should result. Thus double stars probably show one normal course of stellar life, an alternative to that of solitary single stars.

But Moulton, Chamberlin and Jeans have given speculative accounts of the origin of the solar system. If, at an early period, two gaseous stars came near each other, tidal waves would appear. If the stars approached within a certain critical distance, such a wave would shoot out a long arm of matter, which might break up into bodies of appropriate size and character to form the Earth and other planets. But this would happen rarely, and Jeans calculates that planetary systems such as ours may only accompany one star in about a hundred thousand.

The new theory of stellar evolution can now be described. Stars are flung into space from the arms of spiral nebulae as masses of vapour of approximately equal size. They radiate and therefore lose mass, and, as they radiate faster when large, their masses gradually approach nearer to equality.

The youngest stars are heaviest and generate most energy, irrespective of temperature and pressure. This would not be so if they were made entirely of terrestrial atoms, which radiate more as the temperature and pressure rise. Such evidence again indicates that the bulk of the energy for radiation comes from types of intensely active matter unknown to us, which vanish as the star ages, probably by the coalescence of positive protons and negative electrons, their consequent annihilation as matter and their conversion into gushes of electromagnetic radiation. The energy thus liberated is enormous: as stated in the section on Relativity, that given by the annihilation of a mass m will be mc^2, where c is the velocity of light, 3×10^{10} cm. per second, so that if a gram of matter passes into radiation, its energy will be equal to 9×10^{20} ergs. The energy produced by the annihilation of a good-sized drop of oil would drive a large ship across the Atlantic Ocean.

This recent theory of astrophysics recalls Newton's query 30 in his book on *Opticks*: "Are not gross bodies and light convertible into one another...the changing of bodies into light, and light into bodies, is very conformable to the course of Nature, which seems delighted with transmutations".

Stars are passing away into radiation, and the fate of the matter of the Universe is either to pass directly into the radiation of space or to become such inert, non-active stuff as that of which our world is chiefly made. Terrestrial matter consists of 92 elements, 90 of which are known, ranging from hydrogen with an atomic number of 1 to uranium 92. If other elements exist, they must have higher atomic numbers, and be more complex even than uranium. They would probably be intensely radioactive and therefore unstable, and perhaps have already passed out of existence. It was formerly thought that spectroscopic evidence indicated an evolution of matter from simple to complex, from hydrogen in an older star to calcium in a younger. But this evidence is now interpreted otherwise, merely as showing that the conditions of the stars favour the appearance of hydrogen or calcium in their atmospheres, and the emission of radiation from them. Stellar evolution is now thought by some astronomers to be accompanied by a breaking down of complex atoms, most of which are transformed directly into radiation, a small fraction of the whole passing into the inert ash which, though but a bye-product of cosmic change, is the substance of our bodies and our world. Uranium and radium are perhaps an intermediate type of matter between the last traces of such active primeval atoms left on the Earth and the non-active elements.

Life seems only possible in conditions which closely resemble our own, and such conditions are rare if not unique. There may be other planets like the Earth, but, compared with the immense number of the stars, it is probable that they are few.

Kelvin's principle of dissipation of energy indicated a final state of things in which matter and energy would be uniformly distributed and no more motion possible. Modern thought has modified the process, but arrived at a similar conclusion. The final state towards which the Universe seems to be tending, is the passing of active stellar atoms into the radiation of space and into a little inert matter in extinct Suns or frozen Earths. The radiation derived from the annihilation of all the matter in the Universe would only raise the temperature of space by a few degrees. Jeans calculates that space would only become saturated with radiation and re-precipitate matter if the temperature rose to $7 \cdot 5 \times 10^{12}$ degrees. The probability against any atoms of active matter surviving, or of radiation concentrating in any region by chance till matter re-precipitates, is fantastically great. Yet however long we should have to wait for such a chance to occur, eternity is longer, and it has been suggested by J. B. S. Haldane, and also, Professor Eddington tells me, in conversation by Professor Sterne of Hamburg, that such chance concentrations may produce a re-creation of a Universe after our own has vanished away—perhaps may have created ours after aeons of diffused radiation. I must add that both Sir James Jeans and Professor Eddington have told me that they are not convinced by this argument. Other happenings are so much more probable, that they would interfere with and prevent this excessively unlikely contingency.

It seems impossible that we should ever reach definite evidence about such problems. But history teaches us to be cautious; our present outlook in astro-physics has only been opened during the last few years, and what we know is little compared with what there is yet to learn.

The new outlook on nature given by the theory of relativity must, as it unfolds, affect profoundly our views about the physical Universe. The replacement of the idea of attractive force as an explanation of gravitation by the theory of natural tracks, which appear to us curved in gravitational fields, not only leads to slightly different results in the exact experiments already described, but must change completely our ideas about the confines of the Universe.

With Euclidean space and Newtonian time, we naturally thought of existence as infinite. Space stretched indefinitely beyond the farthest stars, and time, both before and after us, flowed on uniform and eternal.

But, if our new space-time continuum be curved owing to the presence of matter, we enter on another range of thought. Time may still run from everlasting to everlasting in a never ending series of moments, but the curvature of space means a Universe finite in its space dimensions. If we travel long enough with a ray of light we shall meet a limit, or perhaps return to our starting point. Dr Hubble estimates that the whole of space is about a thousand million times as large as the part which is visible in the big telescope at Mount Wilson, which discloses some two million nebulae outside our stellar system. This indicates that light would take something like 10^{11}, that is a hundred thousand million, years to travel round the Universe. Einstein described a three-dimensional space curved in a way which, in two dimensions, we should call cylindrical. Time is like the axis of the cylinder. De Sitter imagined a spherical space-time. If we travel outwards, and trace ever wider spheres, we come to one of maximum size. Here time observed from the Earth seems to stand still. As Eddington says: "Like the Mad Hatter's tea-party, it is always six o'clock and nothing whatever can happen however long we wait". But if we could get to this Conservative paradise we should find nevertheless that time as experienced on the spot was still running on, though in another direction—whatever that may mean.

One slight indication of such a slowing down of time as observed from the Earth has been pointed out by de Sitter. Some of the spiral nebulae are the most remote bodies known to us. Their spectral lines are displaced compared with the same lines in terrestrial spectra, and, in a large preponderance of cases at least, the displacements are towards the red. This has been usually interpreted as being due to very great velocities of recession—greater than any others observed in celestial bodies. But it is just possible that we are here observing the slowing down of atomic vibration as seen from the Earth, a change in the rate of Nature's clock, a variation in the scale of time.

Chapter X

SCIENTIFIC PHILOSOPHY AND
ITS OUTLOOK

Philosophy in the Twentieth Century—Logic and Mathe-
matics—Induction—The Laws of Nature—The Theory of
Knowledge—Mathematics and Nature—The Evanescence of
Matter—Free-Will and Determinism—The Concept of Organ-
ism—Physics, Consciousness and Entropy—Cosmogony—
Science, Philosophy and Religion.

THE various threads of philosophic thought, which in *Philosophy in*
Chapter VII were traced through the nineteenth century, must *the Twentieth*
now be followed into the twentieth. *Century*

The philosophy bequeathed by the French Encyclopaedists was based on Newtonian science, and, as already
explained, was combined later on with *Darwinismus* to form
German materialism. But, before that time, Kant, Hegel
and their followers had developed an alternative system of
idealism, which, although predominant among academic
philosophers, repelled men of science, who, for the most part,
ignored philosophy for a hundred years.

The Papal Encyclical of 1879, whereby Leo XIII re-
established the Wisdom of Saint Thomas Aquinas as the
official philosophy of the Church of Rome, led to a revival of
Thomism in Catholic schools of thought. Attempts were made
to interpret mediaeval Scholasticism in terms of modern
knowledge, or as much of such knowledge as could be accepted
by orthodox theologians.[1] The results can be said perhaps to
have made terms between Scholasticism and some branches of
science, rather than to have accepted the scientific spirit in its
entirety. Consequently they lie off the main road of enquiry
which we are following, and we must turn to other developments.

At the beginning of the twentieth century, the majority of
men of science held unconsciously a naïve materialism, or, if
they thought at all about such problems, inclined to the
phenomenalism of Mach and Karl Pearson, or the evolutionary
monism of Haeckel or of W. K. Clifford.

---

[1] *A Manual of Modern Scholastic Philosophy*, chiefly by Cardinal Mercier,
Eng. trans. 2nd. ed. 2 vols. London, 1917.

Evolution, which in the modest mind of Darwin was
only a scientific theory, perhaps partially explained by the
hypothesis of natural selection, had become a philosophy,
indeed to some men almost a creed. The real lesson which
evolutionary biology teaches to general thought is that continuous change must be expected in all things, and that
selection of some sort may stop the change proceeding far in
directions unsuited to the environment. We have already
seen how that lesson was learned by one department of thought
after another, and how it widened and deepened them all.
But such a legitimate effect of a scientific development stops
very far short of exalting it into a philosophic system, the
basis and meaning of reality. Biology and palaeontology
indicate an evolution during a few million years from a simple
ancestry to many differentiated and complex species, but the
evolutionary philosophers from Herbert Spencer onwards
assumed that this progress was a universal law of being. Hence
evolutionism, though linked at first with materialist determinism, became for a time an optimist philosophy. Even if
death were the end of each man, he could feel that he was one
link in a chain leading to continual improvement in organic
nature, perhaps also in cosmic structure.

In more recent years, evolutionary philosophy has shown
new tendencies, especially in a desire to use biology as a road
of escape from that mechanical view of things which is apparently imposed by physics. Bergson went even further, and
tried to sweep away not only physics but also logic with its
fixed principles.[1] To him life is a universal stream of becoming,
in which divisions are illusory, and reality can be lived but
not reasoned about. He accepts a doctrine of final causes, but
causes which, unlike those of the old, predetermined finalism,
are moulded anew as creative evolution proceeds.

Hence Bergson exalts instinct and intuition as against
reason, which he holds was developed by natural selection as
a mere practical advantage in the struggle for life. Such an
argument seems to apply even more strongly to instinct,
which is, as a matter of fact, strongest in those primitive and
practical needs which have most survival value. Reason, and
the fertile combination of intuition and reason by which
advances in knowledge are made, seem chiefly useful at a

[1] *Evolution Créatrice*, Paris, 1907; Eng. trans. London, 1911.

later stage and for purposes of no clear significance in natural selection. For instance, they are certainly necessary for science, even for the construction of the theory of natural selection which Bergson invoked, and for philosophy, even that of the variety of creative evolution which he formulated.

Philosophy in the Twentieth Century

William James's pragmatism shows another form of evolutionary philosophy, in which the sole test of truth in a belief is whether it is useful. Pragmatism evades both scientific and religious agnosticism. It meets the difficulty about the validity of induction by pointing out that we must assume induction to be valid in order that we ourselves should survive. Unless we use our past observation as a guide to the future, disaster will overtake us. On the full theory of natural selection, since religion is so widespread, it is probable that some religious beliefs have survival value and are therefore, according to pragmatic definition, "true". Perhaps it is fair to remark that a pragmatist who adjusted his beliefs to give survival value through the reigns of Henry VIII, Edward VI, Mary and Elizabeth would have had his ideas of "truth" effectively enlarged. It may be, as William James held, that many beliefs, both in science and in everyday life, are only true in this same sense—that they work in practice. But others can clearly be put to another test, that of direct observation or experiment, and thus a criterion unrecognized by strict pragmatism can be brought to bear.

Although evolutionism worked down from science and philosophy till it became a popular guide to history, sociology and politics, yet all the time most academic philosophers maintained some form of the classical tradition, still derived ultimately from Plato through German idealism, either Kantian or Hegelian. Hegel imagined that a knowledge of the real world could be obtained *a priori* by logic, and in England this opinion was modernized by Bradley, whose book, *Appearance and Reality*, was published in 1893. According to Bradley, the world of appearance, expressed by science in terms of time and space, is self-contradictory and therefore illusory; the world of reality must be logically self-consistent, and therefore ultimately reduces to a timeless and boundless Absolute. Such ideas echo down the ages from Parmenides, Zeno and Plato.

About 1900 a reaction against this Hegelian mode of thought

became clear even among philosophers. On one side logicians like Husserl found fallacies in Hegel, and denied Bradley's belief that relations and plurality, time and space, are self-contradictory. In this their work linked up with that of mathematicians who came to similar conclusions. On the other side, those who revolted against the constraint of reason, or the classical formalism of a logical world, accepted Bergson's exaltation of intuition or instinct, or followed William James either into pragmatism or into radical empiricism, in which ideas about reality are founded on experience alone. The last line of thought and that of the mathematicians have clearly the closest affinity with the scientific outlook, and from them arose a new development to weld physical science and philosophy together once more.

The ideas adopted by Mach in his analysis of experience[1] reappear in James's radical empiricism. Combined with new views in logic, in the theory of knowledge and in the principles of mathematics,[2] they led to a mode of thought which is sometimes called new realism. This philosophy, largely developed at Harvard, gives up the idea of a comprehensive system, based on some theory of the Universe as a whole, as science gave up that idea when breaking away from Scholasticism in the seventeenth century; it fits knowledge together piecemeal when investigating general problems, as science does when studying special ones, and formulates hypotheses where observational or experimental evidence is not yet available. In its theory of knowledge, it abandons the belief that reality necessarily depends in some way on our thoughts: in this it departs from idealism. But it goes beyond Mach's pure phenomenalism, and holds that science is concerned in some way with persisting realities, not merely with sensations and mental concepts. In logic, according to the new realism, the intrinsic character of one thing does not enable us to deduce its relations to other things. In both logic and theory of knowledge, therefore, the new philosophy is thrown back on an analytic method. But the greatest effect was produced by its connection with the principles of mathematics. Russell says:

Ever since Zeno the Eleatic, philosophers of an idealistic caste have sought to throw discredit on mathematics by manufacturing contra-

---

[1] E. Mach, *Die Analyse der Empfindungen*, Jena, 1886; 6th ed. 1911.
[2] Bertrand Russell, *Sceptical Essays*, London, 1928, pp. 54–79.

dictions which were designed to show that mathematicians had not arrived at real metaphysical truth, and that the philosophers were able to supply a better brand. There is a great deal of this in Kant, and still more in Hegel. During the nineteenth century the mathematicians destroyed this part of Kant's philosophy. Lobatchevski, by inventing non-Euclidean geometry, undermined the mathematical argument of Kant's transcendental aesthetic. Weierstrass proved that continuity does not involve infinitesimals; Georg Cantor invented a theory of continuity and a theory of infinity which did away with all the old paradoxes upon which philosophers had battened. Frege showed that arithmetic follows from logic, which Kant had denied. All these results were obtained by ordinary mathematical methods, and were as in-dubitable as the multiplication table. Philosophers met the situation by not reading the authors concerned. Only the new philosophy assimilated the new results, and thereby won an easy argumentative victory over the partisans of continued ignorance.[1]

Now the full details of this revolution in philosophic thought can be appreciated only by those able to follow the very technical and difficult mathematics involved. But the general result is plain. Philosophy can no longer stand on its own base; it is once more linked with other knowledge. But whereas in the Middle Ages and in many of the philosophic systems of modern times other subjects were deduced from and fitted into a preconceived philosophic scheme of the Universe, the new realism has taught philosophy now, as in the days of Newton, to take account of mathematics and science before building its own temple. Moreover, it must build that temple stone by stone, and not try to bring it down as a complete finished whole from cloud-cuckoo-land.

The new realism uses mathematical logic as its means of construction, and is thus able to trace the philosophic meaning of fresh knowledge in science in a way impossible before. Consequently, although the new method arose chiefly from developments in mathematics, its most important data are now obtained from physics—from relativity, the quantum theory and wave-mechanics. An attempt will now be made to give in non-technical terms some account of this latest of all the philosophies which have been founded on science.

Logic is the general science of inference, and so includes all types of reasoning, though, owing to historical accident, it

---

[1] *Sceptical Essays*, p. 71. For fuller treatment see *Our Knowledge of the External World*, Chapters v and vi. London, 1914; 2nd ed. 1926.

[2] See T. Case, art. "Logic", in *Encyclopaedia Britannica*, 11th ed.; and Bertrand Russell, *Our Knowledge of the External World*.

Logic and
Mathematics

began as the theory of deduction. The great Greek discovery of deductive geometry led Aristotle, in founding logic, to lay too much stress on deductive inference generally. Francis Bacon, on the other hand, in a natural reaction produced by his vision of the possibilities of the new experimental method, insisted on the unique importance of induction. Nevertheless, he distinguished three kinds of inference—from particular to particular, from particular to general, and from general to particular. Mill pointed out that true scientific method involved both induction and deduction, and thus combined the work of Aristotle with that of Bacon.

Metaphysics may be considered as the study of being in general—of things which are or may be apprehended by the mind. Psychology is the study of mind in general, including its operations, one of which is inference or reasoning. Thus by classification logic is a department of psychology, though its importance, and the possibility of studying it in separation from other branches of psychology, have made it practically an independent subject.

Till recently, much of formal logic was little more than an account of the technical terms and syllogistic rules bequeathed by Aristotle and the mediaeval Schoolmen. Luckily, informal methods of reasoning grew up among practical men of science. In their combination of induction and deduction, these methods began with Galileo, and even in deduction developed into processes not contemplated by the syllogism, while logicians still kept to the old ways.

In 1920 it was pointed out by N. R. Campbell that, to a man of science, even the logistic syllogism seems to depend on induction.[1] Take, for instance, the familiar case—all men are mortal; Socrates is a man; therefore Socrates is mortal. By observation and experiment we find that certain bodily and mental properties are uniformly associated; this law is expressed in the concept "man." That concept is also found to be associated with the property of mortality, and we state another law that the association is universal. It is a fair inference that the law will hold for the individual, and Socrates prove to be mortal. But the argument as thus put involves induction. Of course the pure logician will say that the premises are supposed to be given, and that logic is only

[1] N. R. Campbell, *Physics, The Elements*, Cambridge, 1920, p. 235.

concerned with deductions from them. Campbell thinks that
if reasoning be really without any inductive element, it
carries no conviction to a scientific mind.

*Logic and
Mathematics*

Traditional logic holds that every proposition must necessarily consist in ascribing a predicate to a subject, and this
assumption led philosophers like Hegel and Bradley to some
of their characteristic conclusions, such as that there can be
only one real subject, the Absolute, for if there were two, the
proposition that there were two would not ascribe a predicate
to either. Thus the separate objects of sense, it is argued, are
illusory, and merge in a single Absolute. This assumption of
the logical universality of the subject-predicate form led also
to the refusal to admit the reality of relations, and to the
attempt to reduce them to properties of the apparently
related terms. Thus the objects of science (which is chiefly
the study of relations), like the objects of sense, became
illusory.

Perhaps a symmetrical relation, such as equality or inequality between two things, may be regarded as an expression
of properties, but with an asymmetrical relation, where, for
instance, one thing is greater than or before another, the
attempt breaks down. It appears then that we must admit
the reality of relations, and thus this purely logical ground for
supposing the world illusory vanishes.

Probably such verbal arguments will carry little weight,
one way or another, to those used to the more concrete reasoning of science. But they lead up to the mathematical evidence
which we must now try to describe.

Modern mathematical logic began in 1854 with Boole, who
invented a mathematical symbolism for deducing consequences
from premises. Then Peano and Frege showed by mathematical
analysis that many propositions regarded by traditional logic
as of the same form, such as "this man is mortal" and "all
men are mortal" were fundamentally different. The old confusion had obscured the relation of things to their qualities,
of concrete existence to abstract concepts and of the world of
sense to that of Platonic ideas.

Mathematical logic enables the enquirer to deal easily with
abstract conceptions; and suggests new hypotheses which
otherwise would be overlooked. It has led to a theory of
physical concepts, and also to a new theory of number,

discovered by Frege in 1884 and independently by Russell some twenty years later. Russell says:[1]

> Most philosophers have thought that the physical and the mental between them exhausted the world of being. Some have argued that the objects of mathematics were obviously not subjective, and therefore must be physical and empirical; others have argued that they were obviously not physical, and therefore must be subjective and mental. Both sides were right in what they denied, and wrong in what they asserted; Frege has the merit of accepting both denials, and finding a third assertion by recognising the world of logic, which is neither mental nor physical.

Frege distinguishes things merely objective, such as the Earth's axis, from those that are also actual and spacial, like the Earth itself. In this sense number, and indeed all mathematics and logic, are neither spacial and physical nor subjective, but are non-sensible and objective. This leads to the conclusion that we must regard numbers as classes—the number 2 as the class of all couples, the number 3 as the class of all triads, and so on. As Russell defines it: "the number of terms in a given class is the class of all classes that are similar to the given class". This is found to satisfy the formulae of arithmetic, and applies to 0 and to 1 and to infinite numbers, all of which present difficulties to other theories. It does not matter if classes are fictitious and do not exist; the definition works equally well if for "class" is substituted the hypothesis of anything having the defining property of the class. Then, though numbers become unreal, they remain equally effective logical forms.

One of the grounds on which some philosophers have questioned the reality of the sensible world is the supposed self-contradiction and therefore the impossibility of infinity and continuity. No conclusive empirical evidence can be adduced in favour of infinity or continuity in the physical world, but for mathematical reasoning they are necessary, and the supposed contradictions are now known to be illusory.

The problem of continuity is essentially the same as that of infinity, for a continuous series must have an infinite number of terms. The question arose with Pythagoras, who discovered that the square on the hypothenuse of a right-angled triangle is equal to the sum of the squares on the sides, and, if the sides are equal, the square on the diagonal is double the square on

[1] *Our Knowledge of the External World*, p. 205.

either side. But the Pythagoreans soon proved that the square of one whole number cannot be double that of another, so that, measuring in whole numbers, the length of the side and the length of the diagonal are incommensurable. The Pythagoreans, who believed that the essence of the world was number, are said to have made this discovery with dismay and to have tried to keep it secret. Geometry was reconstructed on the basis adopted by Euclid, which did not involve arithmetic and thus evaded the difficulty.

Cartesian geometry returned to arithmetical methods, and was soon developed by the use of "irrational" numbers, which give the ratios of incommensurable lengths. These numbers were found to conform with the rules of arithmetic and came to be used with complete confidence long before satisfactory definitions of them were given in recent years and the problem of incommensurables solved.

We can also indicate, in a general way, how modern mathematicians have produced a theory of infinity, which has cleared up the difficulties that, from Zeno onwards, have given philosophers so much to talk about. The problem is essentially mathematical, and, until mathematical processes were sufficiently advanced, could not be attacked or even formulated successfully.

Infinite series and infinite numbers appeared at an early stage in modern mathematics. Some of their properties appeared unfamiliar, but, instead of concluding that the ideas of infinity were illusory, mathematicians continued to employ them, and, in the sequel, found a logical basis for their methods.

The difficulties about infinity are partly misunderstandings about the meanings of words, caused by the confusion of the mathematical infinities with the somewhat vague ideas of infinity imagined by non-mathematical philosophers—ideas which are irrelevant to mathematical problems. Etymologically, "infinite" means having no ends, but some infinite series (e.g. the series of past moments terminating now, or the infinite number of points in a finite line) have ends, and some other infinite series have not, while some collections are infinite without being serial.

Other difficulties are due to the attempt to apply to infinite numbers certain properties of finite numbers, such as the property of being countable. Infinite series may be known by the qualities of their own class, though their terms cannot be enumerated. Again, an infinite number is not increased by adding to it or even doubling it, or lessened by subtracting from or dividing it. If all numbers 1, 2, 3, ..., etc. be written in one row and all even numbers 2, 4, 6 ..., etc. in a second row beneath the first, the number of figures in the two rows is the same, yet the second row results from taking away the infinite number of odd numbers from the infinite collection of all numbers. The whole apparently is not greater than the part. Such contradictions led philosophers to deny the existence of infinite numbers. But the word "greater" is ambiguous. Here it means "containing a greater number of terms", and in this sense the whole can be equal to its part without self-contradiction.

The modern theory of infinity was developed by Georg Cantor in 1882-3. He showed that there is an infinite number of different infinite numbers, and that in general the idea of greater and less can be applied to them. In some cases, where this apparently fails, new questions arise. For instance, the number of mathematical points is the same in a long line as in a short one; but here greater and less are not purely arithmetical; they involve new geometrical conceptions.

The difficulties of philosophers have largely arisen from assuming that the properties of finite numbers could be assigned to those that are infinite. Zeno's arguments might be valid if finite times and spaces consisted of a finite number of instants and points. We can escape from his paradoxes either (1) by denying the reality of time and space; or (2) by denying that space and time consist of points and instants at all; or (3) by maintaining that if space and time consist of points and instants, the number of them is infinite. Zeno and many of his followers chose the first mode of escape; others like Bergson the second.

But on other grounds the existence of infinite numbers and series, and infinite collections in which no terms are consecutive, must be admitted. For instance, we can arrange a series of fractions less than unity, in the order 1/2, 1/4, 1/8, etc., but between any two of them there are others, e.g. 7/16, 3/8. No two fractions in the series are consecutive, but the total number of them is infinite. Yet beyond the sum of them all is unity, so that we must admit the existence of numbers beyond the sum of an infinite series. Much of what Zeno says of points in a line applies to this collection of fractions. We cannot deny that there are fractions, so that, effectively to escape Zeno's paradoxes, we must find some tenable theory of infinite numbers. *Logic and Mathematics*

Beyond all the numbers which can be reached by counting are the infinite numbers of mathematics. No succession of steps from one number to the next will reach them. They exist in classes, which can only be defined in mathematical terms and examined by mathematical processes. But all those competent to judge are satisfied that mathematical logic and the mathematical theory of infinity have been developed on right lines. The old logical arguments for the illusory nature of the objects of sense and the laws of science have been proved invalid; the problem remains open and must therefore be attacked by other methods. In spite of the teaching of so many idealist philosophers, it is impossible to deduce the nature of the external world by *a priori* mental processes. The observational and inductive methods of science are necessary.

The part of logic that deals with the process by which general laws are discovered from particular phenomena—the process of induction—is of special importance for experimental science. It was studied, as we have seen in former chapters, by many philosophers, among whom Aristotle and Francis Bacon were perhaps the most famous. *Induction*

Bacon, in his exaltation of experiment, held that, by an almost mechanical process, general laws can be established with complete certainty. The sceptical Hume pointed out that if an induction is used to obtain new knowledge, i.e. if it is to fulfil its proper purpose, it may sometimes lead to erroneous results, so that the laws obtained by its means are merely more or less probable, but cannot claim certainty. But, in spite of Hume, most men of science and some philosophers still regarded induction as a road to absolute truth. Even Mill held this belief, founding induction on a "law of causality", which he regarded as proved by the enumeration of large numbers of instances in which events can be shown to have causes. Whewell pointed out that experience alone might prove generality but not universality. Nevertheless, he held that universality could be reached by the additional use of

Induction   necessary truths, such as the rules of arithmetic and the axioms and deductions of geometry. This was of course before the days of non-Euclidean space.[1] In spite of Whewell's caution, it is probable that Mill expressed the general belief of his time. As Henri Poincaré writes[2]:

> Pour un observateur superficiel, la verité scientifique est hors des atteintes du doute; la logique de la science est infaillible et, si les savants se trompent quelquefois, c'est pour avoir méconnue les règles.

The function of science is to trace relations between phenomena, or rather between the concepts in which phenomena are expressed. But when, for instance, we have discovered that an increase of pressure in a gas produces a decrease in volume, we can equally well say that a decrease in volume produces an increase in pressure.[3] Whichever variable is thought of first seems to the mind to act as cause. Here the ambiguity of the ideas of cause and effect is clear; it is when the element of time is involved—when one of the related events follows the other—that the mind instinctively identifies *post hoc* with *propter hoc*. But then it is impossible to isolate the real cause of an event from a long train of antecedent circumstances— all necessary for its happening. Moreover, relativity has shown that an event in the "here-now" can only cause events in the absolute future and be caused by events in the absolute past; the events in the neutral zones of Fig. 14 (see p. 423 above) can have no causal connection with a "here-now" event, because the influence would have to be transmitted with a speed faster than light.[4] Again, if the principle of causation is to be used to establish the validity of induction as a guide to absolute truth, it cannot logically itself be established by a process of induction. Thus the basis of Mill's argument is discredited.

Indeed, while the *method* of induction is easy to describe, its logical *validity* is difficult to establish. Its method is certainly not Baconian. Whewell pointed out that induction depends for its success on having the right idea to start with.

---

[1] It is possible that Whewell was right about arithmetic; the relations of integral numbers still seem to involve absolute truth. Perhaps, as Kronecker says: "Die ganzen Zahlen hat Gott gemacht; alles anderes ist Menchenwerk".

[2] H. Poincaré, *La Science et l'Hypothèse*, Paris, p. 1.

[3] W. C. D. Dampier-Whetham, *The Recent Development of Physical Science*, 1st ed. London, 1904, p. 29.

[4] A. S. Eddington, *The Nature of the Physical World*, Cambridge, 1928, p. 295.

Insight, imagination, and perhaps genius, are required firstly *Induction*
to pick out the best fundamental concepts and to classify the
phenomena in a way that makes induction possible,[1] and then
to frame a tentative "law" as a working hypothesis which
can be tested by further observation and experiment.

Let us take some examples. Aristotle's ideas of substance
and qualities, natural places, etc. were useless as concepts for
dynamics, and only led, if they led anywhere, to false conclusions, such as that heavier things fall faster. No advance
was possible till Galileo and Newton, discarding the whole
Aristotelian scheme, picked out from the chaos as new fundamental concepts distance or length, time and mass, and thus
were able to think in terms of matter and motion.

With distance and time to work with, and their derivative
velocity, Galileo, after one failure, guessed the right relation
between the velocity of a falling body and the time of fall,
deduced its mathematical consequences and verified them
experimentally. Adding the concept of mass, implicit in
Galileo's work, Newton formulated the laws of motion, and
deduced from them the science of dynamics, abundantly verified by observation and experiment.

The importance of right concepts is clear, and right definition
of those concepts when formed. Thus Poincaré holds that our
measurement of time from noon to noon, instead of, for
example, from sunrise to sunrise, was chosen unconsciously
because it, and it alone, made Newtonian dynamics possible.[2]
Those who dispute this, for instance Whitehead and Ritchie,
do so by accepting consciousness as arbiter, and our direct
sense of the equality of times as the basis of measurement.[3]

Having chosen the right fundamental concepts, it is probable that relations between some of them soon appear, as to
Galileo. The relations, or logical deductions from them, can
be tested experimentally, and some of them will be confirmed.
Thus simple laws are established, and the new subject begins
to take shape. Each new relation proved suggests new
experiments, and the growth in experimental knowledge
needs and suggests new hypothetical relations. Insight and

---

[1] H. Poincaré, *loc. cit.*; N. R. Campbell, *loc. cit.*; A. D. Ritchie, *Scientific Method*, London, 1923, p. 62.

[2] *La Valeur de la Science*, Chap. ii.

[3] A. N. Whitehead, *Concept of Nature*, pp. 121 *et seq.*; A. D. Ritchie, *Scientific Method*, London, 1923, p. 140.

Induction   imagination are needed to formulate probable hypotheses; logical and sometimes mathematical power is needed to deduce their consequences; patience, perseverance and experimental skill are needed to test their validity. In fact, as N. R. Campbell says, induction is an art and science the noblest of arts.

In the light of the recent work in physiology and psychology, as set forth in Chapter VIII, some people, such as those who hold "behaviourist" views, think that the fundamental process which underlies induction, is closely allied to the "conditional reflex" of psychology. A child touches fire and is hurt; he avoids fire for the future. If the fire was in a fireplace, he may equally avoid fireplaces also, even when empty. In the first case his induction was right, in the second wrong, though logically each was an unjustified generalization from one special case. Similar results are found to occur in animals; but, whether in animals or men, they are at first merely instinctive; the theory of the process, its expression in words, comes much later, and may be what the Freudians call a "rationalization"—an invention of reasons, good or bad, to prove that what we have acquired a habit of doing is rational. Some think that these simple cases may throw light on, even explain, the more complex inductions which science needs. These ideas are in a sense an extension of "behaviourism" in psychology, and will probably stand or fall with those somewhat mechanical views of mental processes generally.

And now let us consider the validity of the process of induction. The mathematical theory of probability has been applied in recent years to the problem, especially by J. M. Keynes.[1] Keynes' chief question is: Can induction be based on a mere number of instances, as held by Mill?

Keynes comes to the conclusion that the probability of an induction does increase with the number of instances, not for the simple reason given by Mill, but because the more numerous the instances are, the more likely it is that no third variable is present throughout, so that it becomes increasingly probable that the instances have nothing in common but the characteristics under consideration. For this strengthening in the validity of the induction, it is necessary also that each new instance should be independent, that is, must not necessarily follow from the former instances. An induction may approach

[1] J. M. Keynes, *Treatise on Probability*, London, 1921.

certainty with an increasing number of instances, but for this *Induction* to hold we must first prove or assume that the intrinsic probability of the generalization we are seeking to establish is not itself infinitely small.

In examining this assumption, Keynes is led to the view that the qualities of objects, like certain Mendelian units, cohere in groups, so that the number of possible independent variables is much less than the total number of qualities. This principle is needed also to establish laws by the use of statistics, indeed for all scientific knowledge, except that given by pure mathematics. Thus, according to Keynes, we need to assume a finite probability that an object has only a finite number of independent qualities, or, according to Nicod, a number less than some assigned finite number.[1]

Induction has also been treated by the methods of probability by C. D. Broad, who has tried to show that unless some realist belief is held—some such assumption made as that scientific "laws" are concerned with persistent objects underlying perceptions and concepts—"it is impossible to justify the confidence which we feel in the results of 'well-established' inductions".[2] The thorough-going empiricist or phenomenalist might perhaps reply that such confidence, though useful as a guide to what is probable in future, has often proved to be mistaken.

If an induction is successful, it gives us a working hypo- *The Laws* thesis, which, if confirmed by observation or experiment, *of Nature* becomes an accepted theory and finally takes rank as a natural law.

The exaggeration of the philosophic importance of the Laws of Nature, an exaggeration for which the French Encyclopaedists of the eighteenth century were largely responsible, lasted till about the end of the nineteenth. Then, chiefly under the influence of Mach, the pendulum of scientific thought swung heavily in the other direction, and natural laws became mere short-hand statements of experience, of routines of sensation.

Modern views lie between these two extremes. For instance, in 1920 N. R. Campbell, in a critical analysis of the meaning of hypotheses, laws and theories, gave reasons for believing

[1] Bertrand Russell, *An Outline of Philosophy*, London, 1927, p. 284.
[2] C. D. Broad, *Scientific Thought*, London, 1923, p. 403.

The Laws of Nature

that, in spite of the common slightly contemptuous contrast of theories with facts, an empirical law, which rests on "facts" alone, does not inspire much confidence, but that confidence follows the explanation of the law by an accepted theory.[1] Such a law may be more than a mere routine of sensation.

According to Campbell, laws are of two kinds: (1) uniform associations of properties such as those connoted by the concepts "man" or silver; and (2) relations, often mathematical in form, between concepts.[2] Mill and his followers only deal with the second kind of law. "They occupy long treatises in explaining how we discover the law that sparks cause explosions in gases, but do not think the inquiry how we discover the laws that there are sparks, explosions and gases (the knowledge of which is assumed in their discussions) worth a moment's attention; and yet these laws are almost infinitely more important for science."[3] Those who have not themselves spent their lives doing scientific work have little sense of the relative importance of different laws.

Again, the critical examination of the process of induction, from the work of Hume to that of Keynes, has shown that inductive science, though often unconscious of its limitations, can only draw conclusions which are more or less probable. Sometimes the probability in favour of a generalization is enormous, but the infinite probability of certainty is never reached. A few years ago, the exact accuracy of Newton's law of gravity and the permanence of the chemical elements were thought to be quite certain, and, in fact, the probability in favour of those principles was so great that we all should have been willing to bet our last shillings at long odds on their truth. Yet Einstein and Rutherford have proved that we were wrong, and our money would have gone to that rash gambler who had the apparent (nay real) folly to take our bets.

Thus experience confirms modern theories, and goes to show that the generalizations or laws established by induction, even when universally accepted as true, should be regarded only as probabilities. Since much of the evidence for philosophic determinism rests on a belief in the universal validity

[1] N. R. Campbell, *Physics, The Elements*, p. 153.
[2] *Ibid*. p. 43.   [3] *Ibid*. p. 101.

of natural laws, this question is of importance. Indeed, the *The Laws* word "law" used in this connection is misleading, and has *of Nature* had an unfortunate effect. It imparted a kind of moral obligation, which bade the phenomena "obey the law" and led to the notion that, when we have traced a law, we have discovered an ultimate cause.

In view of the firm position held twenty-five years ago by the laws or generalizations known as the persistence of matter and the conservation of energy, and the change in outlook which has since taken place, the following quotation from a book by the present writer, first published in 1904, may perhaps be of interest:[1]

While fully recognizing the importance of these generalizations from the physical point of view, we must be careful how we give them any metaphysical significance. Under certain limiting conditions, other physical quantities besides mass and energy may be conserved. Thus in pure mechanics we recognize the conservation of momentum—a name for the mathematical quantity obtained by multiplying together the measures of mass and velocity. Again, in reversible systems, where physical or chemical changes may occur in either direction with equal freedom, thermodynamics indicates the conservation of another quantity, named by Clausius entropy. Momentum and entropy are only conserved under restricted conditions; in physical systems the momentum of visible masses is often destroyed, while in irreversible processes entropy always tends to increase.

Mass and energy may seem to be conserved in the conditions known to us, and we are justified in extending the principle of their conservation to all cases where those conditions apply. It does not follow, however, that conditions unknown to us may not exist, in which mass and energy might disappear or come into existence. A wave, travelling over the surface of the sea, seems to persist. It keeps its form unchanged and the quantity of water in it remains unaltered. We might talk about the conservation of waves, and, perhaps, in so doing, be as near the truth as when we talk of the persistence of the ultimate particles of matter. But the persistence of waves is an apparent phenomenon. The form of the wave indeed truly persists, but the matter in it is always changing— changing in such a way that successive portions of matter take, one after another, an identical form. Indications are not wanting that only in some such sense as this is mass persistent.

Moreover, as the author used to teach many years ago in his lectures on Heat and Thermodynamics, there is yet another reason which makes it dangerous to assign too much philosophic importance to these principles of persistence. When

[1] *Recent Development of Physical Science*, 1st ed. London, 1904, p. 39; 5th ed. 1924.

The Laws
of Nature

the mind is groping in a welter of unclassified phenomena and trying to find a basis for order, such concepts as mass and energy naturally present themselves *because* they are constant quantities, and remain unchanged throughout a series of processes. The mind picks them out of the confusion as convenient physical concepts on which to build a scheme of knowledge, and thus they enter into the structure of our physical theories. Then comes the experimentalist, Lavoisier or Joule, and, with great ingenuity and labour, rediscovers their constancy, and establishes the law of the persistence of matter or the conservation of energy.

These ideas, somewhat unusual twenty-five years ago, are now very generally accepted. The present forms of some of them have already been described, and new evidence for others will appear in the following pages.

Campbell says that science starts by selecting for consideration those judgments concerning which universal agreement can be obtained and those regions where order can be discovered, though, at every stage of the reasoning to which they are submitted, a personal or relative element is introduced which brings in the possibility of error, but leads to the highest achievements in science as in art.[1]

Eddington has analysed the result which relativity must have on the meaning of our model of nature and its laws.[2] We express its structure in terms of *relations* and of things to be related or *relata*, and its possible configuration in a number of co-ordinates. To get from the equations containing these co-ordinates a model of the physical world adapted to our minds, we find the best mathematical operation is that invented by Hamilton. Eddington says it "is virtually the symbol for the creation of an active world out of a formless background". There seems nothing in the basal relations which calls for this particular operation, but, by following it, we construct things which satisfy the law of conservation. These things are selected by the mind, which ever seeks what is permanent—hence arise the concepts of substance, energy, waves.

In this way we do not touch atoms, electrons or quanta;

[1] *Physics, The Elements*, p. 22.
[2] A. S. Eddington, *The Nature of the Physical World*, Cambridge, 1928, p. 295.

but, as regards field physics, the structure is fairly complete. *The Laws*
The field laws, conservation of energy, mass, momentum and *of Nature*
electric charge, the law of gravitation and the electromagnetic
equations, describe the phenomena in virtue of the way they
have been formulated. They are truisms or identities. Thus
Eddington justifies by deeper and more general analysis the
contention put forward many years ago by the present writer
in the special cases of the conservation of mass and energy.

Eddington divides natural laws into three classes.

(1) Identical laws—those like the conservation of mass or
energy which are mathematical identities owing to the way
they have been built up.

(2) Statistical laws—those which describe the behaviour
of crowds, whether of atoms or of men. Much of our sense of
mechanical necessity has arisen because till recently we have
dealt with atoms only statistically in vast numbers. The uniformity of nature is a uniformity of averages. The mind has
commanded a model of nature to satisfy these laws.

(3) Transcendental laws—those which are not obvious
identities, implied in our scheme of model-making. They are
concerned with the individual behaviour of atoms, electrons,
and quanta. They do not necessarily lead to things that are
permanent, but to things like action, forced on our attention, but somewhat repugnant, because unintelligible to our
minds.

Eddington suggests that perhaps what seem to us the
brutal crudity and unintelligibility of concepts like action
are signs that we have touched reality at last. If so, we are
almost brought back in science to the theological dictum of
Tertullian—*Credo quia impossibile.*

Logic, traditional and mathematical, leads to a study of *The Theory*
induction and of the validity of the natural laws established *of Knowledge*
by its means. Now, in the light of the information thus gained,
we must turn to examine the general theory of knowledge. In
Chapter VII we saw how Mach and Karl Pearson once more
brought the problem of knowledge to the notice of men of
science, and attempted to convert the prevalent crude realism
into sensationalism or phenomenalism, a belief that knowledge is made up of sensations and complexes of sensations,
that science gives only a conceptual model of phenomena and
enables us only to trace a routine of sensations.

This was of course little more than a revival of the ideas of Locke, Hume and Mill, but it came as a new discovery to many. Men of science, ignoring the philosophers, had for the most part taken the naïve view of common-sense realism about the meaning of their work, but some of them listened to physicists and mathematicians like Mach and Pearson, and, at the end of the nineteenth, and in the early years of the twentieth century, phenomenalism began to have a certain vogue.

Yet not everyone carried it as far as Mach. For instance, in 1904 the present writer pointed out that, while science by its own methods cannot escape from phenomenalism, yet metaphysics can fairly use the results of science as a valid argument for a form of realism.[1]

Science itself can only carry out its observations and make its measurements from impressions on our ordinary senses:

> Though, for instance, the galvanometer seems at first to supply us with a new electrical sense, on further thought we see that it merely translates the unknown into a language our sense of sight can appreciate, as a spot of light moves over a scale.[2]

In modern phraseology, physical science can only deal with what are, or are equivalent to, pointer-readings, and the connections it traces, either experimentally or by mathematical deduction, are those between one pointer-reading and another.

The division of science into subjects is quite arbitrary; the different subjects are, as it were, sections cut through our conceptual model of nature—or rather, perhaps, plane diagrams from which our idea of a solid model is derived. One phenomenon may be regarded in different ways. A stick to the schoolboy is a long elastic rod; to the botanist it is a bundle of fibres and cell walls; to the chemist a collection of complex molecules; to the physicist, a swarm of electrons. A nerve-impulse may be considered in a physical, a physiological or a psychological aspect, and none is more real than another. The idea that a mechanical explanation of every phenomenon is both possible and fundamental arose from the facts that mechanics happened to be the earliest of the physical sciences, and that its concepts, methods and conclusions are fairly intelligible to the ordinary man. Yet

[1] *Recent Development of Physical Science*, 1st ed. pp. 12 *et seq.*
[2] *Ibid.* p. 14.

mechanics is no more fundamental than other sciences, indeed, even in 1904, matter was being resolved into electricity.

Thus the work of inductive science is to put together a conceptual model of nature, and science, by its own methods, cannot touch the problem of metaphysical reality. But the possibility of constructing a consistent model of phenomena is strong metaphysical evidence that an equally consistent reality underlies the phenomena, though, in its essence, it may be very different from our model of it, for, by the limitations of our faculties and the nature of our minds, the model must be conventional and not realistic. Though the age-long attempts to prove by verbal logic that the objects of sense and the pictures of science are illusory have been shown to be fallacious, the crude realism, which believed that science, or even common-sense, saw things as they actually are, is clearly untenable. But, as Campbell holds, the scientific idea of reality is different from the metaphysical, and, for science, its own concepts are real enough.

The controversy between realism and phenomenalism as formerly carried on involved some confusion between a perception and its object, as is shown by G. E. Moore in his *Refutation of Idealism*.[1] Moore insists on the truism that, when one perceives, one perceives something, and that what one does perceive cannot be the same as the perception of it. He also shows that this truism refutes most of the then current arguments for idealism. As Broad puts it: "What we perceive exists and has the qualities that it is perceived to have.... The worst that can be said of it, is that it is not also *real*, i.e. that it does not exist when it is not the object of someone's perception, not that it does not exist at all".[2] The thing that one perceives may be a stick, which physicists, by regarding strictly from the analytical point of view, have resolved into electrons or wave-groups; but these physical concepts are not one's perception of the stick. The long, elastic rod certainly exists while the schoolboy perceives it. Thus Moore and Broad lead us away by another road from the idealism of Hegel and the phenomenalism of Mach, not, it is true, back to the naïve realism of common-sense and nineteenth-century science, but to a more sophisticated form of realism, which

[1] *Philosophical Studies*, London, 1922, p. 1.
[2] *Perception, Physics and Reality*, Cambridge, 1914, p. 3.

The Theory of Knowledge accepts the existence of the objects perceived by the senses as they are perceived, and yet is consistent with the philosophy built on modern mathematics and physics.

Bertrand Russell and A. N. Whitehead published their great work *Principia Mathematica* during the years 1910 to 1914, and in later books they developed further the view of nature which follows. Perhaps that view may be summarized in some such very shortened form as this. Our knowledge of the physical world is only an abstraction. We can construct a model of that world, and trace the relations between its parts. By these methods we cannot reveal the intrinsic nature of reality; but we can infer that something exists independently of our thoughts about it, and that, in some unknown way, the relations between its parts correspond with those of our model.

This new realism traces its origins to Locke, who first appealed to psychology, and began enquiries into philosophic problems of limited scope. Modern realists also no longer start by assuming complete systems of philosophy and deducing from them special applications. Using mathematics, physics, biology, psychology, ethics—whatever comes to hand —they study isolated problems, and only slowly fit together their results as does inductive science. Thus in philosophy, as in science, the only test of validity is self-consistency.

Mathematics and Nature To complete our account of recent contributions to the theory of knowledge as applied to science, we have to deal not only with induction, but with mathematical deduction also. How is it that mathematics has obtained its ideal abstractions of points, planes, particles and momentary configurations from the rough facts of mensuration and the mechanical arts, in which no such ideal things occur, and how can it apply the knowledge won by analysis from the abstractions to the elucidation of that rough world again, as it does with such success in mathematical physics?

This and other problems in the philosophy of natural science have been much advanced by A. N. Whitehead, especially by his "principle of extensive abstraction".[1] Some account of this work is here given, but those who are not interested in the principles of mathematics can omit this section with no loss of continuity in the book.

---

[1] *Principles of Natural Knowledge. Concept of Nature.* For simplified account see Broad, *Scientific Thought*, pp. 39 *et seq.*

Science is not concerned with the inner nature of any of the terms used, but only with their mutual relations. It follows that any set of terms with a set of mutual relations is equivalent to any other set of terms with the same mutual relations. Irrational quantities like $\sqrt{2}$ and $\sqrt{3}$ can be treated in mathematics as numbers, because they obey the same laws of addition and multiplication that integral numbers obey. Therefore, for these purposes they *are* numbers. *Mathematics and Nature*

Again, $\sqrt{2}$ and $\sqrt{3}$ are usually defined as the limits of the series of rationals whose squares are less than 2 or less than 3. But we cannot prove that these series have limits, and the definitions might stand for nothing at all. On the other hand, if we define $\sqrt{2}$ and $\sqrt{3}$, not as the limits of series, but as these series themselves, we get quantities which contain unexpected internal structure, but yet certainly exist, and can be shown to bear to each other and to other mathematical quantities the same relations as do $\sqrt{2}$ and $\sqrt{3}$ as usually defined. The new definitions can therefore be substituted for the old ones.

Whitehead showed that the principles first discovered for irrational mathematical quantities could be applied also to geometry and physics. For instance, there is an old difficulty about points. For some purposes it would be useful to define a point as the limit of a series of smaller and smaller concentric spheres, one inside the other. But volumes, however small, are always volumes, and this definition conflicts with that needed for other purposes, which describes a point as having position but no magnitude.

If we define a point, not as the limit of a series of volumes, but as that series itself, the point so defined being what would usually be called the centre of the system, we get quantities which may be shown to bear to each other the same relations that points do when defined in *either* of the two older ways. Thus the discrepancy of definition is evaded, and the complex internal structure which these new points possess does not matter, because science is concerned not with inner structure, but with outer mutual relations.

In this way Whitehead showed the connection between what can be perceived but cannot be used mathematically, such as actual volumes, rods or particles, and what can be dealt with mathematically but cannot be perceived, such as points without volume and lines with no breadth, in terms of which geometry and physics must be expressed.

Such considerations remind us of the long-established methods of thermodynamics, in which the internal structure and changes of a system are treated as irrelevant, and indeed are so. Account is only taken of the heat and other forms of energy which enter and leave the system. Molecular theory gives one description of the inner nature of the system, but thermodynamics has nothing to say for or against that description. If another theory could be devised to give the same external relations, for thermodynamics it would do just as well. A good example is seen in the theory of solution.[1]

Van 't Hoff proved thermodynamically that the osmotic pressure of solutions must have the same value and obey the same physical laws as the ordinary pressure of gases, whereupon many physical chemists assumed that van 't Hoff's theory required that the cause of the pressure should be the same, namely, the bombardment of molecules. The thermodynamic relation was of course consistent with any " cause "—with chemical affinity or with molecular bombardment.

In the most recently opened field of physical research, to take another example, the mathematics of Heisenberg are equivalent to those of Schrödinger, although the former approaches atomic structure from the electrons and energy-levels of Bohr while discarding his electronic orbits, and the latter has formulated them on the fundamental ideas of wave-mechanics. Here two views of the inner nature of atoms are expressed in similar mathematical equations, and, for the ultimate purposes of science, are identical, though they arise from different physical conceptions.

The philosophic lesson which these results inculcate is that, while we must accept provisionally and with caution the mental models which are made from time to time to represent the *relata*, the quantities between which physical relations hold, we can use freely and feel growing confidence in the ever-increasing knowledge of those relations which science gives us. That knowledge is an affair of probability, but the odds in favour of much of it are very high, and, for the most part, rising rapidly. It is quite good enough to act upon; the truth of the relations does not depend on the reality of the *relata*.

[1] See above, p. 268, and *Theory of Solution*, p. 166.

Towards the close of the nineteenth century, Newton's hard, massy particles, which, as nineteenth-century atoms, bore to Clerk Maxwell the stamp of manufactured goods, had shown signs of failure to account for the facts. Kelvin's vortex atoms and Larmor's centres of aethereal strain, were attempts to express in more fundamental terms what had hitherto been regarded as ultimate scientific concepts.

The Evanescence of Matter

Maxwell's proof that light is electro-magnetic radiation foreshadowed the end of the elastic solid theory of a luminiferous aether, and the identification of J. J. Thomson's corpuscles with the electrons of Lorentz and Larmor similarly turned matter into electricity. Indubitably the world became less intelligible. Men had thought that they knew what was meant by massive atoms and transverse waves in the aether of space: they had to confess that they knew little about the intrinsic nature of electricity or the meaning of electro-magnetic vibrations.

During the next stage, electrons and protons were used with increasing success in new physical theories. We grew so accustomed to handling them in thought that they became familiar ideas, till Bohr and Sommerfeld almost persuaded us that their wonderful atomic models represented physical, though not of course metaphysical, reality. Before they had quite done so, their theory broke down, while Heisenberg's work showed how much unverified assumption underlay the idea of planetary electrons, and that we had been carrying over into atomic physics the preconceptions of Newtonian astronomy. All that we really know about atoms concerns what goes into them or what comes out. Electrons are to us mere sources and absorbers of radiation, and we can only detect and study them at their moments of discontinuous emission of energy. For us they *are* radiation, and that is all about it. From another angle, de Broglie and Schrödinger also resolved them into systems of waves by a process mathematically equivalent to that of Heisenberg.

We must not, however, forget the lessons of history. Thermodynamics dispensed with atomic conceptions, and Ostwald finally proposed to discard such conceptions in favour of energetics shortly before the new physics began to use atomic ideas in an extreme form. It is possible that we may some day get new evidence on the problem of the structure

of the atom. But there are indications that the limit of
physical models of nature has been reached. For the time, at
any rate, the new quantum mechanics hold the field, and we
have to leave our explanation of the phenomena in the form of
mathematical equations.

On the old idea of substance, matter was resolved into
molecules and atoms, and then atoms were analysed into
protons and electrons. These in turn have now been dissolved
into sources of radiation or into wave-groups: into a mere set
of events which proceed outward from a centre. About what
exists at the centre, or about the medium which carries the
waves (if indeed wave-equations connote waves in a medium),
we know nothing. Moreover, there seems a fundamental
limit to the accuracy of possible knowledge about these wave-
systems which constitute electrons. If, from the equations,
we calculate the exact position of an electron, its velocity
becomes uncertain. If we calculate its exact velocity, we
cannot specify its position accurately. This uncertainty is
connected with the relation between the size of the electron
and the wave-length of the light by which it might be observed.
With long wave-lengths, no exact definition can be obtained.
When the wave-length is decreased enough to give definition,
the radiation knocks the electron out of its position. There
seems here an ultimate impossibility of exact knowledge, a
fundamental indeterminacy behind which we cannot go. It
looks as though the final limits of human knowledge were near.

Similar results have been reached by way of the doctrine
of Relativity. To the philosopher of old, matter was in essence
something extended in space which persisted through time.
But space and time are now relative to the observer, and there
is no one cosmic space or cosmic time. Instead of persistent
lumps of matter or electrons in a three-dimensional space, we
have a series of "events" in a four-dimensional space-time,
events, some of which seem to be connected so as to present
an air of persistence as does a wave on the sea or a musical
note. Forces at a distance, especially gravitational forces, and
the need of "explaining" them, have alike gone. There are
only differential relations which connect together neighbouring
events in space-time. Physical reality is reduced to a set of
Hamiltonian equations. The old materialism is dead, and even
the electrons, which for a time replaced particles of matter,

have become but disembodied ghosts, mere wave-forms. They are not even waves in our familiar space, or in Maxwell's aether, but in a four-dimensional space-time, which our minds cannot picture in comprehensible terms.

The Evanescence of Matter

Moreover, even as disembodied ghosts, their careers are short. The only known cause which will explain the vast output of radiant energy from the Sun and other stars is the mutual annihilation of protons and electrons. The matter of our Earth may consist of dead ashes that will not burn, but in stars and inter-stellar spaces protons and electrons might coalesce and destroy each other, and most of the substance of the Universe be passing into radiation. Thus matter, which seemed so familiar, resistant and eternal to nineteenth-century materialists, has become incredibly complex; it is scattered as minute electrons in the vast empty spaces of atoms, or as wave-groups which somehow pervade the whole of them, and, moreover, is vanishing into radiation, even from our Sun alone at the rate of 250 million tons a minute.

The problem whether or no man is a machine was discussed from the modern biological point of view in Chapter VIII. Some biologists still hold that the activities of life are not completely explicable in terms of mechanics, physics and chemistry, but show a co-ordination or integration of functions special to the living organism. The mechanists retort by pointing out that one region after another of physiology and psychology is annexed by bio-physics and bio-chemistry, and that there seems no limit to this process. Yet a third opinion accepts physical and chemical mechanism as a necessary assumption for scientific advance in knowledge, but either merges neo-vitalist teleology in a wider, universal teleology, or takes a subjectionist view of the problem, regarding physics, biology and psychology as different aspects from which the whole being of man must be viewed according to the immediate question at issue.

Free-Will and Determinism

From the historical standpoint, we have seen vitalism and mechanism alternating with each other, even from the days of the Greek philosophers. But, though no conclusion has been reached, we have now more evidence than ever before on the true nature of the problem; if we cannot solve it, we may at least formulate it more clearly.

As Ritchie says,[1] life is curiously conditioned by its physical environment, and yet in some respects is independent of the environment and unlike anything not living. The first thing a reasonable man must do is to be content with a very little knowledge and a very great deal of ignorance:

> It is natural for anybody of a sanguine temperament who is impressed by the dependence of life on physical circumstances...to think that he is only a short way from the solution of every problem. He thinks he is delivering a final assault on the very citadel of Life itself; then, when the heat of the combat is over and he can look round at what he has accomplished, he finds that it is only an insignificant and almost undefended out-work that he has taken, and the citadel is as far off as ever.

Nevertheless, as Ritchie goes on to explain, "the important point is that the 'mechanical' method gives us some knowledge and in fact gives us nearly all we have". For successful research in physiology, perhaps even in psychology, it is necessary to assume that the next problems can be attacked by mechanical, physical or chemical methods, though that assumption need not prejudice our view of the whole philosophic, or even of the biological question. The neo-vitalist can still claim that the processes of life are controlled so as to secure the maintenance or reproduction of the normal state for each organism in a way beyond the power of physics or chemistry. Others, such as Professor J. S. Haldane, can still argue that, while mechanism is inadequate as a complete explanation, the control emphasized by the vitalist is a consequence of a mechanical environment. Thus mechanism and vitalism both fail. But the inner nature of reality involves an integration or co-ordination, especially manifested in living beings.[2] The idea of adaptation, used so fruitfully by Claude Bernard and his followers, may prove as fundamental in physiology as are the principles of conservation of matter and energy in physical chemistry.[3]

Turning from biology to physical science, we find a quite new light recently thrown on the old problem of determinism. Philosophic determinism, which was re-built in modern times on Newton's work, and was so strong in eighteenth and nineteenth century thought, gains less support from physics nowadays. The old laws of science, about which so much was

[1] *Scientific Method*, p. 177.
[2] J. S. Haldane, *The Sciences and Philosophy*, London, 1929.
[3] C. Lovatt Evans, *Brit. Assoc. Rep.* 1928, p. 163.

said, prove to be either truisms inserted by ourselves into our model of nature, or statements of probability; the most a man of science can do, even in that part of his subject which deals either with large-scale or with statistical phenomena, is to bet long odds on his predictions being verified, while he cannot foretell the action of single atoms or quanta.

Accepting the well-known laws as expressions of probable tendencies, they are found to be concerned, not with individual molecules, atoms or electrons, but with statistical averages only. If we heat a gas through one degree, we know by how much the average energy of large numbers of molecules will be increased. But the energy of any one molecule depends on chance collisions, which at present are not calculable. We can predict how many atoms in a milligram of radium will disintegrate in a minute, and it is very probable that our prediction will be verified within narrow limits of error. But we cannot tell when any one individual atom will explode. We know how many electrons will emit a quantum of energy at a given temperature, but not when any one electron will fall into a new orbit and therefore radiate. It is possible that at some future time a new theory of mechanics may be developed, and individual molecules, atoms and electrons become determinate. But as yet there is no sign of such a theory.

Indeed, present tendencies point the other way. The principle of indeterminacy seems to introduce a new kind of incalculability into nature. The uncertainties hitherto described might possibly be due to ignorance, and might pass into determinism again as knowledge increased. It is dangerous to build on them a philosophy of free-will. But, as Eddington has pointed out, the work of Schrödinger and Bohr indicates that there is an uncertainty in the nature of things. The alternative uncertainties that, if we try to calculate the position of an electron, its velocity becomes incalculable, and if we wish to determine its velocity its position becomes indeterminate, seem to indicate that, in ultimate analysis, scientific determinism breaks down.

It is impossible to miss the analogy of the first kind of these uncertainties with those which beset the study of living organisms. We can predict, within narrow limits, how many infants will die in England in a year, or the expectation of life for a man of a given age. But we cannot foretell whether one

particular baby will live or die, or when a certain insurance
policy will fall in. Here too, increased knowledge and skill
may conceivably give us new powers of prophecy some day,
but again, there is no sign of it yet.

It must not be forgotten that, for effective freedom of will,
nature must be orderly. No condition is so servile as that of him
who is subject to a capricious and incalculable tyrant. To be
masters of our lives, we must be able to steer our course over
well-charted seas, as well as have power to control the rudder.
According to present knowledge, mankind may be statistically
the slaves of fate, but for the individual the mechanism to
which he is subject may be orderly though determinable,
and there may still be room for free-will. It is possible that
future investigation may show that this result is premature
and inconsistent with wider knowledge, just as further work
in quantum mechanics may determine the lives of individual
atoms. The next stage in the evolution of science may be
another swing towards a mechanical philosophy. But, for the
time, at all events, the analogy from physics, for what it is
worth, points in the other direction.

This problem is closely connected with the old controversy
about mind and matter. Till the seventeenth century it was
universally assumed that man's soul was material, of the same
nature as a gas. But Descartes drew the distinction between
mind and matter which has lasted till our own day, and has
assumed the form of psycho-physical parallelism. To avoid
Descartes' dualism, two ways seemed open. The materialists
took matter as the sole reality, and held mind to be an
illusion. The idealists or mentalists believed with Berkeley
that mind was real and matter an illusion. In the work of
phenomenalists such as Hume and Mach, a new view appears
—that the concepts of mind and matter are different ways of
looking at our picture of nature, or, as perhaps we may better
say, different plane diagrams from which science constructs a
solid model of nature. These ideas have been developed into
what is called "neutral monism" by many recent philosophers
from William James to Bertrand Russell. According to this
theory, mind and matter are both composed of something
more primitive, which is neither mental nor material.

While we know nothing of the intrinsic nature of the reality
(if any) for which our model of the physical world stands, we

do know something about the intrinsic nature of the mental world, and, as far as direct knowledge goes, the mental world is the more real. Physics cannot show that the intrinsic nature of the physical world differs from that of the mental world: mental and physical events may well form one causal whole.

That they are connected is certain. Neurology and experimental psychology show the joint physical and mental concomitants of nervous action; bio-chemistry has proved that secretion from the ductless glands may change the mental character of a man. Adrenalin when injected produces the physical symptoms of fear, though we have Mr Russell's experimental testimony that the mental emotion of fear does not necessarily accompany those symptoms.[1] But these obvious connections between the mental and physical worlds do not disclose the ultimate nature of either.

In comparing the two we recognize that physics, at all events, can only give us a knowledge of relations and conceptual *relata* for them to connect, and such knowledge can only be acquired by and exist in mind. In this sense, mind is certainly more real than matter, and may be more real than mechanism, since determinate mechanism seems now only to hold good in those macroscopic phenomena which depend on the statistical average action of multitudes of units, and to fail when the ultra-microscopic detail of individual atoms, electrons and quanta are considered.

When light from a star reaches our eyes, it is the end of a long train of events which can be traced by physics. But the sensation of sight is the only event in the whole series about which we can say anything not purely abstract and mathematical. A blind man might know all physics, but never the sensation of seeing. A knowledge that things are pleasant or unpleasant is not physics. Hence it is clear that there is knowledge which is not included in physical science—a knowledge of our own mental sensations.

And of these sensations one of the most vivid and most persistent is that of volition and free-will. Hitherto the strongest argument against its validity has been the mechanical determinism which seemed to some to follow inevitably from physical science. But Eddington holds that if philosophic

[1] *Outline of Philosophy*, London, no date, p. 226.

determinism is still to be defended, it must now be on meta-physical evidence. Its advocates can no longer call science to witness in its favour. Scientific determinism has broken down, and broken down in the very citadel of its power—the inner structure of the atom.[1]

It is not yet time for men of science to investigate possible modes of action by which conscious will might control matter. But philosophers may well speculate on such questions. Eddington points out that volition might control the un-determined quantum jumps of a few atoms, possibly of a single atom, and thus by a nervous impulse switch the material world from one course to another. This he regards as improb-able, and he prefers to suggest that the mind may act by changing the conditions of probability of a crowd of undeter-mined atoms. He says:

> I do not wish to minimize the seriousness of admitting this difference between living and dead matter. But I think that the difficulty has been eased a little, if it has not been removed. To leave the atom constituted as it was, but to interfere with the probability of its undetermined be-haviour, does not seem quite so drastic an interference with natural law as other modes of mental interference that have been suggested.

The suggestions of Eddington must be treated with all respect. But it is, of course, obvious that the problem of the mechanism of the connection between mind and brain is one of surpassing difficulty, and it would be rash to pin one's faith to any guess, however shrewd, at its solution. For the time, it may be better to leave this problem in its earlier form. Experience comprises many aspects: physical science is one of them; psychology is another; and psychology must recognize as part of its data aesthetic, moral and religious emotion.

Science makes abstractions from the world of phenomena, and formulates concepts which contain in themselves logical implications. Thus, between the concept and all possible valid deductions there is an unbreakable chain. Scientific deter-minism, therefore, is due to the fact that science is a process of abstraction.[2] Mechanics, for example, frames abstract concepts—space, time, matter—from the ideas called up by sensations, and on them builds up a logical, deterministic scheme from which there can only emerge abstractions of the

---

[1] Eddington, *loc. cit.*
[2] Compare R. G. Collingwood, *Speculum Mentis*, Oxford, 1924, p. 166, and Whitehead, *loc. cit.*

same nature as those put in. From the point of view of *Free-Will and* mechanics, nature is inevitably mechanical, and, from the *Determinism* point of view of any abstract and logical science, it is deterministic. But there are other points of view, which exact science cannot reach.

Again, the question is bound up with that of causation. If causation is held to be *a priori*, a necessity of thought, its validity does not depend on science, and science is not responsible for its consequences. If, on the other hand, causation is held to be proved empirically, its law has only been verified in certain cases. Though in other cases there is no positive evidence against it, neither is there proof of its universality, and we are not justified in concluding that it must necessarily control human volitions which are very different from the phenomena in which it has perhaps been proved to hold.[1]

Much of the repugnance felt to determinism, according to Russell, is due to inadequate analysis, which leads to confusion between the impersonal causation, which is all science suggests, and the idea of human volition. We should hate to feel that we were compelled to act by an alien power against our will; but as our will, even on the determinist theory, is in agreement with the causes of our actions, this can never happen. As Russell says:[2] "Freedom, in short, in any valuable sense, demands only that our volitions shall be, as they are, the result of our own desires, not of an outside force compelling us to will what we would rather not will....Free-will, therefore, is true in the only form which is important". Another development of philosophic thought which involves this same question must now be considered.

The usual method of natural science is that of analysis in *The Concept* a search for simplicity. Psychologists try to analyse and *of Organism* express their results in terms of physiological causes, physiologists in those of physics and chemistry. Physicists in turn dissect matter into atoms and electrons, and there they have now been brought up against the failure of all mechanical models, and a principle, apparently fundamental, of uncertainty. Perhaps they may once more form a successful model of the atom, but in the end the construction of models must

[1] See Bertrand Russell, *Our Knowledge of the External World*, p. 236.
[2] *Ibid.*, p. 239.

The Concept
of Organism

prove impossible, and ultimate physical concepts be left in terms of mathematical equations.

But physics is not the only science, and science itself is not the only mode of experience. Biology, it is true, comprises analytic physiology, which reduces what it can to chemical and physical terms, but it deals also with natural history, in which living organisms are viewed as wholes. Psychology is concerned not only with the experimental analysis of sensations and feelings, but with the inner consciousness of mind and of integral personality. The synthetic method of approach to reality may be as valid as the analytic. Such reasons have led Whitehead to insist that a further stage of provisional realism is required, in which the scientific scheme is recast and founded upon the ultimate concept of organism.[1]

The seventeenth century discovered that the world could be represented with amazing success as a series of instantaneous configurations of matter, which determined their own changes and thus formed a logically closed circle, a complete mechanistic system. Idealistic minds from Berkeley to Bergson have revolted against this system, and, not understanding the real issue, usually got the worst of the controversy. There is an error, but not where it has generally been imagined to be. It is really the error that has been pointed out so often in this book, the error of mistaking for concrete reality the abstractions inherently necessary for science, the error which Whitehead calls the Fallacy of Misplaced Concreteness. Abstractions are necessary for analysis, but they involve the ignoring of the rest of nature and of experience, from which the abstractions are made. Thus they give an incomplete picture even of science, and a still more incomplete one of the whole of existence. The doctrine of deterministic mechanism only applies to very abstract entities, the product of logical analysis. The concrete enduring entities of the world are complete organisms, so that the structure of the whole influences the character of the parts. An atom may behave differently when it forms part of a man; its conditions are determined by the nature of the man as an organism. Mental states enter into the structure of the total organism, and thus modify the plans of the subordinate parts right down to the electrons. An electron blindly runs, but within the body it blindly runs as

[1] A. N. Whitehead, *Science and the Modern World*, Cambridge, 1927, p. 80.

conditioned by the whole plan of the body, including the *The Concept* mental state. We may strengthen this argument by pointing *of Organism* out that an electron within an atom is conditioned by the structure of the atom as a whole, and is very different from an electron outside travelling through "empty" space. Thus Whitehead replaces scientific determinism by an alternative doctrine of organism. He approaches the problem from the side opposite to that taken by Eddington, who, as we have seen, attacks determinism from a basis of atoms, electrons and quanta—the ultimate products of physical analysis. Whitehead argues that analysis, by its essence, is misleading in philosophic questions, and founds his doctrine on the synthetic concept of the complete organism. His ultimate appeal is to naïve experience, which tells us "that we are *within* a world of colours, sounds and other sense objects, related in space and time to enduring objects such as stones, trees and human bodies. We seem to be ourselves elements of this world in the same sense as are the other things which we perceive". Thus by the light of the new realism, which he himself has done much to formulate, Whitehead takes much the same view as Moore and Broad, and seems to restore to us a scientific theory of the world of beauty and moral values, a theory which Burtt holds was taken from us by Galileo. For Whitehead, the ultimate unit of natural occurrence is the event, and, as with Bergson, the essence of reality is *becoming*, that is, it is a continual and active process, a creative evolution.

In discussing the meaning of exact science, Eddington *Physics,* emphasizes the point that it is concerned only with the readings *Consciousness* of some physical instrument. In calculating, for instance, the *and Entropy* time taken by a body to slide down a hill, we put into our calculation pointer readings like the mass of the body, the slope of the hill and the acceleration of gravity, and we get out another pointer reading—the position of a hand on the dial of our watch. Using this method, physics has constructed a logically closed circle of knowledge, which contains only physical concepts connected with each other. In old terms matter and its configuration determined the forces, and the forces determined the future configuration. In modern terms the series runs: potential, interval, scale, matter, stress, potential... and so on for ever. The only way of escape from the circle is to recognize the undoubted fact that the concordance of the logical scheme with the actual world can only be tested by the action of the mind. Physics alone might trace a disturbance in its closed circle till it became the motion of matter in a brain, and might observe that motion objectively from without. But, if the brain disturbance is translated into consciousness, we touch reality. "There is no question about consciousness being real or not; consciousness is self-knowing, and the epithet real adds nothing to that."

Here we are brought back to the problem of the nature of the self or *ego*, considered in Chapters VII and VIII. Is the self an entity existing before and independently of experience, as in the older philosophies, or is it a composite, secondary structure, put together by the very action of sensations, perceptions and other mental activities, as some modern psychologists hold? The question cannot be answered by general agreement, but perhaps it need not be answered. However formed, the self is conscious, and in Eddington's sense is self-knowing and therefore real.

The ordinary equations of reversible physics say nothing about the direction in which motion takes place; the planets might go round the Sun the other way as far as formal dynamics can tell us. Again, it is only our consciousness which, in a reversible world, could enable us to distinguish between past and future. In the physical world, however, there is one criterion not involving consciousness. The physical world is non-reversible, and the second law of thermodynamics tells us that, in an irreversible system, the energy is continually becoming less available as time goes on, the entropy increasing. Is it possible that it is irreversible processes going on in our brains which produce in our minds the sense of the passage of time?

This increase of entropy is analogous to shuffling a pack of cards, originally in order of numbers and suits, by a mechanical shuffler. The shuffling can never be undone, save by conscious sorting, or by the indescribably remote chance of the cards happening to fall into their original order again. If the number of cards were much larger, the process of shuffling would need a long time. The stage of shuffling reached would then be a measure of the time, and, since the process is irreversible, it would also serve as a pointer giving its direction. If, on examination, the shuffling is found to be becoming more perfect, time is going forward; if the cards are of themselves getting into order, we must be tracing time backward.

And so, in the physical world, entropy, as Eddington says, is time's arrow. If temperature inequalities are decreasing, energy becoming dissipated and less available, entropy increasing, the process of time is positive: we are moving towards the future. If, in our equations, we find that entropy is diminishing and energy becoming more available, we should know that we were tracing a process backward from its end towards its beginning.

Physics, Consciousness and Entropy

The kinetic theory of gases enables us to translate into molecular terms the process by which entropy increases. If we began with two vessels with an equal number of molecules in each, one vessel being hot and the other cold, the average energy and velocity of the molecules in the first would be greater than in the second. If the vessels were put into communication, molecular collisions would equalize the average molecular energies, till the distribution of velocities was that of the law discovered by Maxwell and Boltzmann. This represents the final state, and can only be undone by conscious action, such as that imagined to be carried on by Maxwell's daemon, or by the almost incredibly unlikely chance that all fast-moving molecules should happen to be in one vessel together. In infinite time, however, this unlikely chance might possibly occasionally occur, unless, as indeed is more likely, something else less improbable happened first to upset the whole system.

Once the Earth has been dethroned from its central position in space and the stars have been recognized as distant Suns, a mere increase in our estimates of size is of little real human importance. Moreover, the problems of cosmogony are those of science and not those of philosophy. Yet the mind is naturally impressed by the immense advances in knowledge which have been made in astro-physics, and it may be worth while here to recapitulate some of the results which have been reached.

Cosmogony

Our galaxy contains some thousands of millions of stars, and light would take perhaps 300,000 years to flash between those farthest from each other. Across the vast gulfs of space that lie beyond our stellar system are millions of spiral nebulae— new galaxies of stars in the making, some so distant that their light travels for about 140 million years to reach our eyes.

Yet space, boundless to Newton, now seems to be finite, curved by the presence of scattered matter. If light travels outwards for some thousands of millions of years, it may return to its starting point.

Men became men perhaps half a million years ago. The age of the Earth may be some thousands of millions of years. The Sun and stars with internal temperatures of 40–50 million degrees, may have radiated energy for 5–10 millions of millions of years.

The ninety chemical elements found on earth might be destroyed by the heat within the stars. Unknown, more radio-active atoms may there exist, and by their disintegration, or by the mutual clash of protons and electrons, matter may pass into radiation, and supply the energy for stellar lives. Terrestrial atoms, of which the Earth and our bodies are made, may be but dead, inert ash, a bye-product of this cosmic process.

The nebular hypothesis has been shown to be competent to explain the formation of gigantic galaxies of stars, though it fails to account for the birth of our modest solar system. For the origin of our system we must look to some rare occurrence, such as tidal waves on two bodies which chance to pass near each other when in the liquid state. Thus the conditions necessary for life as we know it may be rare if not unique in the present Universe. Life, it seems, may be regarded either as a negligible accident in a bye-product of the cosmic process, or as the supreme manifestation of the high effort of creative evolution, for which the Earth alone, in the chances of time and space, has given a fitting home. Science can frame these alternative appreciations of the position, but, in its present state at all events, it cannot decide between them.

And what of the future of the Universe? Kelvin's principle of dissipation of energy, Clausius' increase of entropy towards a maximum, suggested a final, dead state of equilibrium, in which heat is uniformly diffused, and matter for ever at rest. Recent views modify the details, but leave the result unchanged. Active matter passes into radiation which will finally wander through a space far too vast to become saturated with radiation and precipitate matter again. Jeans calculates that the chance against a single active atom surviving is $10^{420,000,000,000}$ to one. The Universe is running down into uniformly distributed radiation.

But, if it is still running down, it must at some definite time, have been wound up; it cannot have been going for ever, or it would have reached the final state of equilibrium. Jeans says:

Everything points with overwhelming force to a definite event, or series of events, of creation at some time or times, not infinitely remote. The universe cannot have originated by chance out of its present ingredients, and neither can it have been always the same as now. For in either of these events no atoms would be left save such as are incapable of dissolving into radiation; there would be neither sunlight nor starlight but only a cool glow of radiation uniformly diffused through space. This is, indeed, so far as present-day science can see, the final end towards which all creation moves, and at which it must at long last arrive.[1]

To some minds, the final death of the Universe is an intolerable thought. It is perhaps unlikely that the Universe will be kept alive to please them, but (of natural means) there seems one possible way out of its final destruction, suggested by Haldane and Sterne. If infinite time is available, all unlikely things may happen. Chance concentrations of molecules might reverse the action of random shuffling, and undo the work of the second law of thermodynamics. Chance concentrations of radiant energy might saturate a part of space, and new matter, perhaps one of our spiral nebulae, crystallize out. Are we and all our myriad stars perchance one of such accidental happenings?

However fantastically great Jeans' probability against it, infinity is greater. However long it is necessary to wait for a chance to happen, eternity is longer. It is possible that one of the incredible chances which may happen in infinite time, a new "fortuitous concourse of atoms", may explain the *modus operandi* of past creation, and again bring about a new beginning when the present Universe has passed, apparently for ever, into a "cool glow of radiation".

We cannot say that this is probable, for we are treading on or beyond the limits of knowledge. Indeed, as with a swarm of molecules, it is more likely that some other chance would intervene, and prevent such an improbable contingency from coming to pass. All such suggestions are but random speculation.

[1] Sir J. H. Jeans, *Eos, or the Wider Aspects of Cosmogony*, London, 1928, p. 55.

The history of science in its relations with philosophy and religion cannot but be helpful when we attempt to describe present conditions and to survey the future outlook. Indeed, it is doubtful whether an attempt to do so could be of much value without a preliminary historical study. Those working at specific scientific problems have perhaps no need for history, but those who try to understand the deeper meaning of science itself, and its connection with other subjects of human thought and activity, must know something of the story of its development.

The triumphs of science are clear to all men. Its practical applications in engineering, industry, medicine, affect more and more the lives of modern nations. Its misuse in machines of destruction threatens civilization with catastrophe should the world be foolish and wicked enough to allow another great war. Pure science is continually improving and extending our model of nature from the microcosm of the atom to the macrocosm of the visible Universe of spiral nebulae and galaxies of stars. The relations between the older parts of the model are ever becoming better known, and new parts are continually being added, added indeed so fast that there is no time for the adventurous builders to fit them into, or even on to, the older structure. When the pace slackens a little, the next generation, like the last, can co-ordinate and complete the work; the present generation is in too great a hurry to waste time in doing so.

The men of the Middle Ages sought as the goal of philosophy and religion the attainment of a complete rational harmony of the understanding, and, for the most part, felt that they had reached it in the Scholastic synthesis of Thomas Aquinas. The physics of Galileo and Newton upset this consistent scheme of knowledge; science took the attitude of a common-sense realism based on mechanics, and was used to support a mechanical, deterministic philosophy, while for daily life men still held an unshaken belief that they were self-determining organisms controlled by their own free-will. Many attempts to reconcile these conflicting views having failed, men were forced either to choose the one and despise the other, or to accept both provisionally, while waiting for further enlightenment.

Then, as we have seen in these pages, philosophers came to

understand that science could only disclose certain aspects of reality, could only draw plane diagrams, sketches for a model of nature, and that it was by its own definitions, axioms and underlying assumptions that science was necessarily mechanical and deterministic. *Science, Philosophy and Religion*

All this time science, though it had broken away from the synthesis of Scholasticism, was at least consistent with itself, indeed, as the pieces of the puzzle were fitted together, self-consistency had come to be regarded as the only test of validity. But now, temporarily perhaps but none the less clearly, the inconsistency which science introduced into the world of general thought has invaded, not indeed the superstructure, but the ultimate physical concepts underlying science itself.

Physical research, in this year 1929, is in a peculiar state, or let us say, in a state unfamiliar since the seventeenth century. Its classical setting, in the dynamics of Newton and the electromagnetism of Clerk Maxwell, is still used and is still yielding results of great value. Yet in the most striking discoveries of to-day—those in the theory of atomic structure—the classical laws have broken down, and we are forced to accept the ideas of relativity and quanta. As Sir William Bragg says, we use the classical theory on Mondays, Wednesdays and Fridays, and the quantum theory on Tuesdays, Thursdays and Saturdays. For the time, at all events, consistency has gone by the board, and we take either set of ideas to get results, according to the subject in hand. This discrepancy probably always appears to some extent when a great intellectual revolution is being made, as for example when the ideas of Aristotle and Galileo strove for the mastery, but the present instance seems to illustrate the tendency in an extreme form. It may possibly even allow us to hold a third set of ideas on Sundays, for which Bragg omitted to provide a theory.

Science must admit the psychological validity of religious experience. The mystical and direct apprehension of God is clearly to some men as real as their consciousness of personality or their perception of the external world. It is this sense of communion with the Divine, and the awe and worship which it evokes, that constitute religion—to most a vision seen only at moments of exaltation, but to the Saints an experience as normal, all-pervading and perpetual as the breath of life. It is not necessary, indeed it is impossible, to

486 SCIENTIFIC PHILOSOPHY AND

Science, Philosophy and Religion

define what is meant by God; those who know Him will want no definition.

Weak humanity needs imagery in which to clothe its vision, creates ritual, accepts dogma, theology, mythology if you will. Such systems may be true or false, but religion itself does not stand or fall with any set of doctrines. They are exposed to historical, philosophic or scientific criticism, and have often fared badly in the encounter. But true religion is a deeper thing—founded on the impregnable rock of direct experience. Some may be colour-blind, but others see the bright hues of sunrise. Some may have no religious sense, but others live and move and have their being in the transcendent glory of God.

For most men dogma of some kind is necessary for religious life, and it is useless to ignore the fact, or try to establish new religions without a doctrinal framework. But, in the realm of doctrinal theology, from time to time a clash has come with science, history or anthropology. The trouble is that "religion always mistakes what it says for what it means. And rationalism, so to speak, runs about after it pointing out that what it says is untrue".[1] Yet, even here, there is a slow approach going on between the different modes of thought. Christian theology had to relinquish the belief in an immediate Second Coming, which seemed essential to the Apostolic Age. In later days, it had to accept the Copernican system, and abandon a whole presentation of dogma founded on a fixed and central Earth, with the Gates of Heaven just above the sky and the Abyss of Hell close beneath the ground. It had to accept evolution at the hands of Darwin, and to consent to trace the pedigree of men from apes instead of angels. When it realizes the implications of modern anthropology, it may have to abandon other beliefs, which to some timid souls seem as necessary now as the doctrines of a central Earth and special acts of creation seemed to our forefathers.

It is unfortunate that theology opposes each change when first it comes. As Whitehead says:[2]

Religion will not regain its old power until it can face change in the same spirit as does science. Its principles may be eternal, but the expression of those principles requires continual development....Religious

[1] R. G. Collingwood, *Speculum Mentis*, p. 148.
[2] A. N. Whitehead, *Science and the Modern World*, Cambridge, 1927, pp. 234, 236.

thought developes into an increasing accuracy of expression, disengaged from adventitious imagery, and the interaction between religion and science is one great factor in promoting this development.

Science has been slower to move towards theology—indeed, for long it seemed to force philosophy into mechanical determinism. Moreover, nineteenth-century determinism, taking the prevalent ideas of the inevitable "progress" of mankind, showed a somewhat shallow optimism; but its twentieth-century counterpart is frankly pessimistic. Bertrand Russell says:[1]

> That man is the product of causes which had no prevision of the end they were achieving; that his origin, his growth, his hopes and fears, his loves and his beliefs, are but the outcome of accidental collocations of atoms; that no fire, no heroism, no intensity of thought and feeling can preserve an individual life beyond the grave; that all the labours of all the ages, all the devotion, all the inspiration, all the noonday brightness of human genius are destined to extinction in the vast death of the solar system, and that the whole temple of man's achievement must inevitably be buried beneath the debris of a universe in ruins—all these things, if not quite beyond dispute, are yet so nearly certain that no philosophy which rejects them can hope to stand.

On the other hand, this pessimistic determinism increases the importance of religion to those who still admit its validity. It would, of course, be easy to quote from any number of orthodox theologians. But, as we are only concerned with the effects of scientific thought, let us turn to another great philosophic mathematician. Whitehead writes:[2]

> The fact of the religious vision, and its history of persistent expansion, is our one ground for optimism. Apart from it, human life is a flash of occasional enjoyments lighting up a mass of pain and misery, a bagatelle of transient experience.

Again, to some philosophers, such as Eddington, it seems that a better understanding of the theory of knowledge and recent developments in fundamental physics have weakened the support given by science to philosophic determinism.

However that may be, men are coming to see more clearly both the power and the limits of science. Science may (save perhaps in atomic theory and quantum mechanics) be in itself deterministic. But that is because it is by its nature concerned with regularities in nature, and can only work where it finds them. In these pages we have often found reason to suggest

---

[1] *Mysticism and Logic*, p. 47. [2] Whitehead, *loc. cit.* p. 238.

that the concepts of science are but models and not reality. Let us quote Eddington once more:

> The symbolic nature of the entities of physics is generally recognized; and the scheme of physics is now formulated in such a way as to make it almost self-evident that it is a partial aspect of something wider.... The problem of the scientific world is part of a broader problem—the problem of all experience....We all know that there are regions of the human spirit untrammelled by the world of physics. In the mystic sense of the creation around us, in the expression of art, in a yearning towards God, the soul grows upward and finds the fulfilment of something implanted in its nature....Whether in the intellectual pursuits of science or in the mystical pursuits of the spirit, the light beckons áhead and the purpose surging in our nature responds. Can we not leave it at that? Is it really necessary to drag in the comfortable word "reality"?

Our scientific model of nature is so successful that we gain increasing confidence in believing that reality is something like it. But it remains a model, and a model which can only be examined in sections, cut to suit our own minds. Man, regarded mechanically, is naturally a machine, but, regarded spiritually, he may still be a rational mind and a living soul. Science, recognizing its true meaning, no longer tries to bind the spirit of man in fetters of Law, but leaves him free to approach the Divine in whatever way his soul demands.

To trace the reactions of modern knowledge on systems of theology, and on the Churches which hold them as Creeds, is a problem far less fundamental than that involved in the deep questions of reality and religion with which we have been concerned. To deal with such practical and active controversies is perhaps outside the proper scope of this book. Yet it has been impossible to avoid them when considering past times, and perhaps something may be said without offence in regard to the present and the future, though it may be impossible to avoid all bias due to personal opinion.

The vast extension, both of scientific knowledge and of scientific modes of thought, which, though helpful to essential religion, are antagonistic to the mental attitude of some religious people, has doubtless done much to increase the drift away from the organized Christian Churches—a drift characteristic of the present age. A growing number of both the critically minded and the careless ignore the Churches, leaving in them those who, for one reason or another, accept the familiar doctrines, literally and with a whole heart fervently.

*Science,
Philosophy
and Religion*

Meanwhile, the unintelligent and uninstructed, who form the majority in any section of the community, obtain more and more power, both ecclesiastical and civil, with increasing measures of self-government and popular representation.[1] The process of segregation becomes cumulative, men with different views drift farther and farther apart, even in Anglo-Saxon countries, where hitherto lines of division have been less sharp than in lands where Roman Catholicism is predominant. Those who try to reconcile theological thought with modern knowledge are attacked from both sides. "What have modern knowledge and criticism to do with the faith once delivered to the Saints?" cries a prominent Anglo-Catholic. "How can men who understand parts of their creed in a symbolic sense dare to profess and call themselves Christians?" asks both the "fundamentalist" and the crude unbeliever. Hence "modernists" who attempt reconciliation find it a difficult and thankless task.

But there is yet another way of combining necessary freedom of thought with a recognition of man's religious needs. It is possible to accept the fundamentals both of science, and of religion, as enshrined in the form natural to each man, and wait patiently for time to resolve discrepancies. This attitude, held consciously or sub-consciously by more people than is generally realized, can be defended on logical and on historical grounds. From recent anthropology and psychology it appears that rite and ritual are prior to and more essential than dogma, and are themselves of more spiritual value. On this theory, if a Church have a dignified and worthy liturgy, there is no need to trouble overmuch about the exact doctrines which that liturgy enshrines. Slowly, and lagging somewhat behind, they adapt themselves to the changing outlook of each succeeding age. There is abundant justification in history for a waiting attitude towards the divergencies between other branches of learning and even the most liberal theology—a waiting attitude so characteristic of English ways of thought. Meanwhile, as regards the liturgy itself, we may well follow the authoritative advice "to keep the mean between the two extremes, of too much stiffness in refusing, and of too much

[1] For the effect in Holland of a more democratic form of Church Government in favouring "fundamentalism" at the expense of "modernism", see Kirksopp Lake, *The Religion of Yesterday and Tomorrow*, 1925, p. 63.

easiness in admitting any variation from it". Indeed, from this point of view, our people are fortunate among the nations: the Church of England gives that historic order and dignified ritual, that established place in the structure of the State, necessary to keep religion in organic contact with the whole of life. By its very constitution it is unable to enforce uniformity, and must still find room within its fold for the Catholic, the Protestant, the Modernist and the religiously minded Agnostic. Some may regard this comprehensiveness as a weakness; but to others it seems a supreme safeguard of religious liberty.

The prospect, both in science and religion, is not without signs of danger. Outbreaks of "fundamentalism" in America, such as that which tried to suppress the teaching of evolution in the schools, and the recrudescence of artificial mediaevalism in England, are matched on the other side by religious persecutions in Russia. Freedom of thought may yet again be destroyed. The "anti-vivisection" movement is not solely due to ignorance and a mistaken sense that all experiment on animals involves cruelty. It displays from time to time a distinct hatred of science for its own sake—indeed, the balanced, dispassionate, scientific mind is still repellent to the many who cannot hold their judgment in suspense while as yet there is no valid evidence on which a judgment can be formed. Such dangers may grow if the world becomes more democratic—more swayed by emotion than by reason.

Even excluding ignorance and prejudice, there is an honest and intelligible divergence of view. To the scholar or the theologian, the man of science sometimes seems to be busy about little facts and trivial problems in an entirely superficial way. On the other hand, to the philosopher or the man of science, if they ignore the underlying verities and look only to literal interpretations, it seems that, as Hume said, "popular theology has a positive appetite for absurdity". Here again the historical method enables us to get beneath surface trivialities, see the deep secrets of nature that may lie hid in the movements of the needle of a galvanometer or the markings on a butterfly's wing, and trace the gropings of man's soul after true religion in the exclusiveness of the Catholic or the incredible beliefs of the "fundamentalist". *Tout comprendre, c'est tout pardonner.*

In spite of ignorance, folly and passion, the scientific *Science,*
method has won field after field since the days of Galileo. *Philosophy*
From mechanics it passed to physics, from physics to biology, *and Religion*
from biology to psychology, where it is slowly adapting itself
to unfamiliar ground. There seems no limit to research, for,
as has been well and truly said, the more the sphere of knowledge grows, the larger becomes the surface of contact with
the unknown.

Physicists, dealing with ultimate concepts, have always
been more conscious of this outer darkness. Biologists have
tended to think that, when a phenomenon is described in
physical terms, in matter, force, energy, or whatever be the
concepts in use at the time, an ultimate explanation has been
found. Physicists know that the difficulties of interpretation
are then but beginning. Biologists are right to reduce their
problems to physics where this is possible. But biology has
a fundamental unit of its own. Whitehead has shown the
philosophic importance both in physics and biology of the
concept of organism, which was used in old days in natural
history, and in more recent times in the study of evolution.
The organism is the biological unit; but, since the organism
is conditioned by physical and chemical laws, we must continue
to examine it analytically also, and, where possible, express
its activities in physical terms.

Meanwhile, physical science, though now more fully conscious than ever of the mystery underlying its ultimate concepts, is becoming even surer of its power over its proper
kingdom. Sometimes, it strikes out into new regions in the
ardent spirit of youth seeking adventure, with no time as yet
to reduce the fresh-won territory to order. Then a great synthesis of knowledge, such as that which seems coming now,
reconciles different ideas and gives unity instead of confusion.
And so physical science continually widens our knowledge of
the phenomena of the natural world, and of the relations
between the concepts, final or proximate, that we use to
interpret the phenomena. On its new lands it builds more
temples for the human mind. But also it has dug so deep that,
before the eyes of this generation, it seems to have exposed its
foundations, and to have reached the unknown ground beneath, which necessarily is of a nature different from that of
the superstructure. As Newton said, "The Business of Natural

*Science,
Philosophy
and Religion*

Philosophy is to argue from Phenomena...and to deduce causes from effects, till we come to the very first Cause, which certainly is not mechanical". In electrons, wave-groups and quanta of action we reach ideas which certainly are not mechanical. We are loth to give up the familiar conceptual mechanism which, for two hundred and fifty years, has interpreted the structure of the natural world with such marvellous success. Within its own realm science will continue to use that mechanism to expand man's power over nature, and to gain a yet wider survey of and insight into the wonderful complexity of the inter-relations of natural phenomena. Possibly the present difficulties will be overcome, and physicists formulate a new atomic model which for a time will satisfy our minds. But, now or later, intelligible mechanism will fail, and we shall be left face to face with the awful mystery which is reality.

Index

The references to sections are printed in italics